NOBEL PRIZE WINNERS

PUBLISHED BY ALFRED A. KNOPF

VERNER VON HEIDENSTAM [1916]

KNUT HAMSUN [1920]

LADISLAS REYMONT [1924]

SIGRID UNDSET [1928]

THOMAS MANN [1929]

IVAN BUNIN [1933]

F. E. SILLANPÄÄ [1939]

JOHANNES V. JENSEN [1944]

THE CITATION

ON THE AWARD OF THE NOBEL PRIZE TO

JOHANNES V. JENSEN

"FOR HIS EPIC NOVEL

THE LONG JOURNEY "

"THE SWEDISH ACADEMY *has conferred the* 1944 *Nobel Prize for Literature upon* JOHANNES V. JENSEN *because of the exceptional vigor and fertility of his poetic imagination, combined with an all-embracing intellectuality and bold creative expression.*"

The Long Journey

dup.

JOHANNES V. JENSEN

FIRE AND ICE

THE CIMBRIANS

CHRISTOPHER COLUMBUS

TRANSLATED FROM THE DANISH BY
A. G. CHATER
WITH AN INTRODUCTION BY
FRANCIS HACKETT
NOBEL PRIZE EDITION

ALFRED A. KNOPF : 1945   NEW YORK

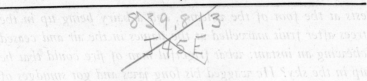

THE PLOT

TO THE NORTH-EAST OF SEALAND THE LONG PROMONTORY *of Kullen thrusts out from Skoane into the open sea, where the Sound passes into the Cattegats a broken rocky outline which has a strange look to one accustomed to the lowlands, taking his thoughts back to other epochs. It is an ancient line, which seems to resemble an upturned face with vague, eternal features, the face of Time.*

The Sealander of a thousand and two thousand years ago saw the same profile; at the foot of Kullen old fishing sites of the Stone Age have been found; the existence of our earliest ancestors was bounded by the same horizons as ours to-day. Kullen as we see it has been crushed into shape by the ice.

But before the Ice Age, in an earlier period of the earth's history, when the northern zone still possessed its warm forests, there were mountains in Skoane, volcanos, whose eruptions have left traces like the streaks of ashes in the brick-earth of the island of Mors, which is an old sea-bed of the Tertiary Age. Infinitesimal marine creatures deposited their shells, the imperceptible accumulation of thousands of years, until they formed strata as high as hills; the sea has disappeared and its bed is stratified — so long ago is it since that hour-glass ran out. But still those streaks bear witness with the clarity of a petrified instant to the ancient volcanic eruptions: veiled halos round the sun and mighty opal sunsets with an atmosphere full of dust, inconceivably long ago. The dust fell on the sub-tropical for-

ests at the foot of the volcano, and a hairy being up in the trees after fruit marvelled at the flames in the air and ceased chewing an instant: what frightful man of fire could that be up in the sky? He wagged his long jaws and got smudges of dust on his nose, for there is a fine layer of dust on fruit, leaves and everything, he gets it on his fingers and it grates between his teeth. This is Man, and the tree beneath him stands in the Garden of Eden.

Kullen as it is now is like the empty site of a vanished building, the root of a mountain. When great summer clouds pile themselves dome-like over the Sound and up over Sweden, they form the outline and the peaks of a mountain-chain which once loomed here as high as they. In the light midsummer nights, when a thunderstorm beleaguers the sky and the lightnings flash out from a world of clouds like the ghosts of fires in heaven, one seems to see an immense cone astride over half the horizon with its summit crowned by lightning and with a pillar of smoke reaching up towards the moon — this is Gunung Api, the Source of Fire, the Father of Fear — but also of loving-kindness, for at his foot the man of the woods received the gift of fire and became human, with every possibility in germ, and terror in the depths of his soul.

Here in warm forests but in a northern latitude Mankind began its long journey. And the memory of an existence in perpetual summer lives again in the innermost consciousness of all later generations, like a buried heritage of the soul, which grows with the soul and passes into ideas — imagined worlds more and more beautiful as the human extends its sway within the once unconscious creature of the woods; and from an inherited memory arise the legends of the Garden of Paradise, the Tree of Life, Happy Isles somewhere or other in the ocean *which, still spared the debasement of the world, are a refuge for the Blest; finally the idea of spheres in Heaven itself, where fallen humanity will recover its happiness — all obscure memories, transfigured in the light of desire, of the Lost Country, growing and shrinking with the swing of the seasons between winter, which drives out hope, and the brief northern summer, which kindles it again and calls up visions of promise deep down in the soul.*

In winter, when thick banks of cloud heavy with snow shut out one side of the sky, with the sun low down on the other like a distant refracting disc of ice, we are reminded of the Ice Sheet which once lay right across Northern Europe, gaping towards the south with cliffs hundreds of feet high and miles wide and with deserts of ice on its back which extended to the Pole; nothing passed there but freezing hurricanes; but in the wet, slushy lowland below the edge of the ice-sheet the reindeer splashed with broad hoofs and the mammoth felt its way among the rocks with pounding feet; the roving man, long-haired and benumbed, sought refuge in caves, or hollows in the foot of the ice-sheet from which rivers rushed forth; squadrons of calving icebergs floated out into the Western Ocean.

When at last the ice was melted and had retreated towards the Pole it had ground the mountains of Skoane off the face of the earth, right down to their roots, and had deposited them as shingle in the Baltic; centuries of torrential rain — the Deluge — furrowed the tundra, and to the cold land that was exposed when the mills of the ice had ceased, man returned and began to learn in the school of adversity the elements of a new kind of life — though the memory of life's carefree dawn was never lost as a race inheritance.

So great are the contrasts that have formed man's nature. But not all were thus formed. The Ice Age marked the division; it was the cause of the parting of mankind on its journey into two distinct roads, since one body remained in the North and took up the struggle with harsh conditions, became transformed, grew in humanity inwardly and upwards; while the rest turned aside from adversity and fled instead of growing; they lost themselves to the southward, followed the warm climate and continued to be the naked jungle folk they were in the beginning; even to-day their descendants live in their primitive state in the tropics.

The old warm forests of Northern Europe were razed by the ice, like the volcanos of Skoane; but man retained the fire, the hearth. In time the Northerners had new forests to dwell in, the cool leafy forests of the North; in their shade and in constant mists our ancestors grew up. A firmly rooted but profoundly restless folk; time after time, in prehistoric and historic days, the forgotten tradition of the Lost Country, still persistent in their blood, drives the Northerners from their wintry dwelling-places towards the South and brings them to prosperity in warmer climates. But as Northerners they are lost in their new home; they become absorbed in other peoples and lose the germinating power of their nature, which is bound by their destiny to the North and to a beneficent yearning to leave it. This is the history of the Migrations, of the Vikings, of the Normans. A primitive instinct finds vent in voyages: the forests change into the Ship.

Old Northern forest myths soon condensed to a universal image, the world-tree Ygdrasil. The childhood of the race and all that it absorbed in its native land, together with the craving for an outlook upon the wide world, the spirit of the race, seeks a form in Old Northern poetry and may be summed up, with a leap through time, in the old fragmentary saga of Norn Guest, who was himself imagined as a gatherer and hoarder of the ages.

In him as a figure the Northern spirit yearns beyond the North. He outlives his generation and seeks it in the Land of the Dead. North and South, which since the Lost Country have been sundered worlds, begin to come together again. Cimbrians and Teutons move southwards in Norn Guest's footsteps, and the first clash takes place between Northern "barbarians" and the nations of Antiquity. Later, when Christianity begins to penetrate to the North, it meets the people streaming southward; the Christian belief in immortality directly revives the memory of the Lost Country: from this union of South and North springs the most beautiful myth of the Middle Ages — the Virgin Mary, Goddess of Spring, the soul of the Northerner and the art of the Ancients in one, blossoming into its highest consummation at the Renaissance.

The ash Ygdrasil spreads beyond itself. In the Middle Ages it rises into a greater image, which combines with religious symbols and finds its expression in Gothic art: the Cathedral. A migration checked for the time leads to expansion in the domain of the soul; thus the aspiration of the Northerner gathers and transforms memories of the youth of the race and Christian symbols into a work of art, as the snail builds up its shell from its body: the Forest and the Ship become the Church.

With the voyages of discovery the primeval dreams force themselves to the front again, seeking their embodiment not in Heaven, in another life, but, with a certain impatience, in reality, on earth, in distant lands: the Church changes back into a ship.

Columbus seeks the Kingdom of Heaven and finds the savages of Guanahani. The Northern soul in its complete development here for the first time meets again its origin, primitive man; the Lost Country is confronted with the Tropics. The symbol is lost; but in place of it mankind enters the New World. The Ship is once more Forest, earth. The ring is complete.

It is an imaginary ring; perhaps it has come about of itself as a shadow of the curve within which an individual human life begins and returns to its starting-point. Unless we have a form we cannot survey things that are dispersed in time and place without any known plan. Outside our circle the world may be viewed in many other ways, more accurately and more completely. Here at any rate one fixed point has been chosen from which the upward march of humanity is viewed. Within the circle as it is laid out, with the building that has been raised upon it — a work of art in its way, this too, I suppose, which does its best to shape the materials at its disposal; and with the life of a work of art, which lasts only until the mind has created new ones — within this circle "The Long Journey" is to be read.

JOHANNES V. JENSEN

DENMARK, under great strain in 1944, was heartened when Johannes V. Jensen won the Nobel prize. It is not too much to call it a national event, and many Danes were quick to say, "he should have had it twenty years ago."

Serious author though he is, his very name is pervasive up and down Denmark. It rings like an honest coin the minute it is sounded, so alert and responsive are Danes to "Johannes V.", whether they be seamen or teachers, bankers, laundry women, novelists, house painters. What he says in a poem or in a newspaper goes into national currency. His most famous book, the one in this volume, sold an unbelievable number of copies before the war — four million would be a similar sale in this country, and that would mean about twenty million readers. By no means everyone thinks equally well of him, or has read every one of his sixty books. But Johannes V. Jensen is Denmark's greatest living author today.

Local pride and glory, however, are not world currency. The Nobel award to a Scandinavian may always be ascribed to piety, no matter how belated it may be. To be accepted at home, for reasons of local orientation, local sympathy, does not endow a Nobel prize author with a world public. Johannes V. Jensen's importance in world literature, moreover, has to be achieved through a translation.

And this importance, in the case of a Dane, has little political backing.

When I asked Danes about him, six years ago, his unique quality seemed vague. Was he a great novelist? Not primarily. A philosopher? In a certain sense. A biologist? An anthropologist? Not of any school. A radical or a conservative? No exact response. Even the content of "The Long Journey" somehow defied definition. And they warned me his Danish was beautiful and original but elusive.

When I met him, a slender, reddish blond, rather smallish man, he was at first singularly inexpressive. Like many of his unsentimental kind from Jutland, he has a way of being silent that is a power in itself. Silence seems to fall on him like a doom. It occupies him, as being unoccupied seems to occupy an unoccupied house. It is not a disdainful silence, but it is final. It is as if he had never communicated, and he stays gravely silent, like an image carved in a hard wood.

But when he breaks it, the act is significant, as if he were breaking bread with you. I met him in a large group, at dinner, and he had instantly seen which was "the Irishman." By the shape of my head I could be nothing else. When we talked together afterwards, he was far from loquacious, but he was expressive and warm like a steady fire in the hearth. He speaks from his centre. The whole man is in what he says. A smile lights up, like a tongue of flame, crisp and animated. And behind whatever he says, in the play of his irony or the weight of his wisdom, there is the force not of his will but of a long and beautiful integration. One feels in him the deep dignity of an independence.

The first time I met Johannes V., paired off with him after dinner, I had to ask him something portentous, so I asked him about Ibsen. He smiled. "Ibsen did not know Asia." Later I read one of Johannes V.'s own stories about a coolie in Singapore. Primitive hunger was in it, modern fears minimized, old fears intensified, and long before the war it had stark struggle and geological ages behind it. A citizen of the whole world was living it — but also a Dane, a free man, not encumbered by a political need to embrace an empire and yet free to embrace a world.

That was "the long journey" that a Dane had travelled. I mentioned the people that I had seen going to work in Hamburg a few days before, their faces grim with determination, in contrast with the levity in Paris. "They're still at it," he nodded about the French, and he could see where it was leading, six years before the war. For where others had taken social revolution as a fundamental theme, and still others the Freudian revolution, toward both of which Ibsen might be felt to have tended, Johannes V. Jensen went to the edge of time itself for the span of his journey, and carried it to the other side of the Chicago he had known. "The Long Journey" is a Bible of evolution, and it was in terms of that evolution, not in terms of politics, that he judged the impending struggle.

"Ask yourself," requests William Howells in his survey of "Mankind So Far," "ask yourself how you have always thought of Adam and Eve. In your mind's eye, tutored by Michelangelo or Dürer, they were doubtless white. But if you seriously try to picture to yourself how the actual parents of all living men might have looked, you will see what we are up against."

But that is what Johannes V. Jensen went up against, a generation ago. When he looked down the dinner table to see the Kelt, it was with the anthropological eye. He lives as part of a drama that began before the Ice Age, and of all living men he is, unless I am much mistaken, the one who has had the clearest notion of our "actual parents," and of the nostalgia we still have for the Garden of Paradise.

What an imagination! The Old Man of the Tribe is at once abominably alien and closely related. The All-Father he has known personally. Johannes V. Jensen has dwelt in trees, has lost the divine fire, has himself captured it from flint, has killed the bear and slept enclosed in its warm entrails, has invented the wheel and tamed the wild horse. He has, long before Sjaelland took shape, lived in the thunders and lightnings of the sub-tropics, known the mammoth in the ice, loved Eve in a cave. For him there is no incrimination of our ancestors, setting out on the long journey. He was one with them. The loquacity of monkeys, the opacity of the superstitious, may cause him to flicker with a smile, but from the Ark to the voyage of the *Beagle* is an adventure that stimulates in him not merely the thinker but the seer and the poet. The walls of cities do not exclude him from the adventure. They burn with it. At the very moment that fire is captured, Carl has a vision. "A long dripping, yellowish blue spark flew from the stone. *Now* —

"In that flash it is as though Carl's soul expands so mightily that he knows and is part of all the light reveals, though it is a world incomprehensible to him. It is night and winter, but everywhere is a blaze of light and thousands of human beings pass close beside him. Well yes — he is on a street corner in Chicago, and the magic spark drips from the overhead wires of the trolley-cars." He beholds the mystery and the magic of it, as A. E. beheld it in a Dublin tram.

These flashes of imagination blaze and drip from Jensen. He does not glorify the tailless apes who riot and revel, "with a great deal of lofty self-assertion and trampling on the rights of all other creatures." The conquest of circumstance, concrete and tenacious, has intense romance for him, but so has the budding of tenderness. Riot and revelry come after immense expenditure of effort, then "everything" is allowed. But he spares man nothing. Adversity teaches him to face and do the impossible. And if life is inexorably cruel, there is no delight of the senses in the rush of sound and sight, no fragrance or sweetness, no ecstasy of the stars, no vein in the mountain's heart or jewel in the waves, that he does not bestow on his experiencer. His theme is no favored race, but he feels that the Northerner elects to wage the battle that has most edge in it, and his mastery over brute nature is the keenest.

At Göteborg there is a fine modern concert hall that is lined with wood, as though it were an inverted ship, and when Johannes V. Jensen gazed at it, it might have been one of those early structures he describes in "The Long Journey." His aesthetic has that sort of native quality. It even has it when he sees a girl like the vestal Cimbrian whom he leads to the Greek sculptor by the Tiber. At any moment, in a Copenhagen house, this quiet and sober Jyllander may see a goddess and proclaim her. People live for him who keep step with the march of aeons, but where this might be pedantry in an investigator he lifts it out of dry classification into individuality, and into a feeling for the individual.

What does he think of America? We crossed on the *Drottningholm* with him in early March, 1939, when he and his wife came for a fresh look at it. A smashing hurricane in his company was just the thing, and yet, as he divided his interest squarely between the *New York Times* and the *New York Daily News*, or swirled in the lobby of the Taft, he was still the imperturbable veteran, up at the prow, flairing the wind for himself, desiring the full flood of events and the inundation of people. She was like a golden daughter of the saga he has written, now become matron, and he a trim, tired captain of many stormy passages. They went circling the country by day coach and bus, seeing it as the next stage in the long journey.

For, while Denmark is the theatre of his second volume, in the way that Finland is the inspiration of Sibelius, what arrests Johannes V.'s imagination is the venture in which we all participate. The planet is his, and if it is oysters and mussels that he cracks or pries open, on Gilleleje strand, the fire he lights is from the sun. Anywhere, under the sun, he is alive to man's venture. In America he sees a continent vast enough for man's spirit. The surge of its hope is in him. He participates with the Red Man, the Negro, the White. As he grows older, he goes beneath the skin, into the universal blood stream, not in dithyramb but probing, understanding.

It is a small detail, but it struck me forcibly that the very first thing he noted in Central Park were the markings from the ice age. When he saw the soil in Georgia, it reminded him of landscapes at the other side of the ocean, and Arizona was linked with Africa. These to him are hieroglyphics of his Carl — and of Charles's Wain; of Cain and Abel, of Adam.

But while he includes so much, no one who reads "The Long Journey" can fail to see the novelist and storyteller. For the youth of the world he has caught the youth of mankind itself. He has, by sheer power of imagination, made us one with the origin of species. He has not done it by a specious cleverness. He has not the pace of advertising copy, or the empty echo that comes with imitating ancient literature. Every episode grows out of the inevitable plight that nature forced on primitive man, and so well has Johannes V. Jensen infused himself into man's history that he has correctly inferred the existence of certain facts which science has since vindicated. Once the reader lends himself to the persuasive journey, so forbiddingly remote and so pressingly present, the art of it, even in another tongue, makes it indelible.

To dazzle a child with a glittering object and to make the child reach for it — that is one way of winning attention. But Johannes V. Jensen has a better way. He is himself dazzled. That which man has suffered, in his conquest of nature, and in spite of his own nature, in order to survive, has inspired this modern testament. Local in many intimate pages, it is really the most universal of themes, and of infinite resource and variety. The ocean bathes it. The stars dwell in it. The steppes resound to its wild horses. It roars with its jungles, and the fire of hell is capped by its ice. Denmark is just a tassel on it.

And yet, out of shrewd, hard apprenticeship to adversity, no one can know better than a Dane what this long journey has cost, and what its murderous quarrels amount to. The Danish people have made the book their own because of its beauty and its truth. They understand how steeped in wisdom it is, so they give it to their children, because they love their children, and want them to play the man and outwit the beast.

Is there something not dreamt of, in this philosophy of Johannes V. Jensen? Yes, there is. Its decency and fair play are a pragmatic faith, where foul behavior by a masterful race is not less pragmatic. Where does Jensen's ironic smile come from, and his power of indignation? Not all his worship derives from primitive fear and wonder. He has heard other music.

FRANCIS HACKETT

CONTENTS

THE CIMBRIANS

BOOK ONE: NORNA GEST

BOOK TWO: THE CIMBRIANS

PART I: IN JUTLAND

BOOK THREE: THE RAID

CHRISTOPHER COLUMBUS

BOOK ONE: THE CATHEDRAL

BOOK TWO: THE CARAVEL

BOOK THREE: THE PHANTOM SHIP

CHRISTOPHER COLUMBUS

Book One: The Cathedral

Book Two: The Caravel

Book Three: The Phantom Ship

Fire & Ice

BOOK ONE: FIRE

I

GUNUNG API

AMID the forests rose a mountain spouting fire, with its scarred black head reaching above the clouds and with palms growing at its foot; this was in the warm ages when summer was still eternal, before the Ice came.

In the daytime the volcano sent a pillar of smoke up into the sky, vast masses of vapour which blended with the highest cloud-summits, miles up; but at night it smouldered like a huge bloody throat gaping over the earth, and from time to time it flung flames and glowing rocks up towards the moon. This was Gunung Api, the great Thunderer, the Father of Earthquake and of Fire.

For long ages he stood there in airy solitude, chewing the fire within him, with now and then a quaking and a subterranean rumbling as though the mountain had a quiet joke all to itself. Very seldom did Gunung Api reveal himself; he surrounded his privacy with a world of cloud, wrapped himself in vapours and slumbered.

On starry nights Gunung Api might cast the gloom from his countenance and blow off ashes into the abyss of space, cooling his crater and his lava breast in the ether; and then a mighty cone was outlined against the night with its base spread over half the horizon and its summit aspiring to the zenith; this was Gunung Api baring himself to the firmament and giving it a view of his size. And the stars spread out their bright hosts before him; the Milky Way turned hovering beneath the topmost roof of the nocturnal heaven, the moon rose round, its pale disc sailing through the night; the Pleiades aired their dewy web on high; slowly the whole heaven revolved, showing its radiance from every side.

Then Gunung Api would send out sulphurous clouds and illumine himself with lightnings in all his immense nakedness, uncovering his long steep shaft, scored and blackened as he was from head to foot; and the lightnings would show up the rough clefts in his body, the primeval forest beneath him, hundreds of leagues of lowland on every side with a mighty river winding through it all, and in the distance the ocean; all this lay below him and was altogether puny; verily he was no mean wart upon the earth!

But the stars kept silence and blinked, all of them together, as though a keen cold wind were circling through space.

Gunung Api surrounded his head with electric storms like a crown of many colours, and the heavens answered again in a ghostly hush with the northern lights. Thus Gunung Api and the firmament would take each other's measure in the noble silence of the night. Such Powers apply themselves to contemplation alone, without waste of words.

But at last the stars pale — and was not that a laugh from Gunung Api? — there is a rumble miles below the surface, and Gunung Api opens a rift in his side and puffs out his gaiety in steam. A shower of sparks shoots out of his crater; Gunung Api cannot quite suppress a sort of cough, and it shakes his foundations a little — oh, yes, the stars! he has every respect for them; they are of course innumerable, but small!

In a little while the dawn takes fire, the sky swings up from the east with an almighty flush, the young herald of the day refreshed by sleep; and long beams of light spread fanwise over half the heavens; a great event is approaching, dawn is here, the daylight mounts, the sky bursts into flame, and out of the east leaps the Sun.

But Gunung Api has already turned his back on the battlefield, he is busy gathering mists about him; one thing at a time. The day for those who like it, but Gunung Api for his part has buried himself in a cloud-burst; he flashes savagely through the murky air and lets go a landslide, shaking pumice-stones and streams of muddy water from his flanks.

And then Gunung Api keeps quiet, as long as it suits him, with his mantle of cloud up over his brows, asleep.

II

THE FOREST OF CHANGE

WHENEVER Gunung Api dozed for a while the forest crawled far up over his breast, and when he awoke again it was there with trees a thousand years old, harbouring all manner of beasts; Gunung Api yawned and spilled over a stream of lava, sent a wave of his fiery breath down into the valleys; and then everything died. The birds burst into flame in the air as they flew and turned to spots of fire which went out and sank to earth as scraps of cinder; lakes and tarns boiled up, fizzed off in steam and sailed towards the sky as balls of cloud, leaving charred fish lying on their black, smoking beds; for miles around the whole forest was at once fire and flame and the next moment nothing but a heap of red-hot ashes. A shower of stones followed the fire; day vanished in primeval darkness. And when Gunung Api's eruption was over and he was once more cooling his sooty cone in the starlight, a desolate waste of sulphur and tufa lay as before for miles around his foot where the forest had crept up.

Gunung Api is dreaming. The lava sinks from his crater down to the ancient lakes of fire imprisoned in the depths. Here a confined and fluid mass is in motion, torrid memories of a flaming ocean of fire which once freely encircled the globe. Alas, times were not what they had been! At first the fire had only had to contend with a few scattered lumps of slag, solidified islands in the flaming ocean; but they had grown into continents, and the continents adhered the whole way round, until the fire was shut in. And when some of the glow had left the earth's crust, immense floods of rain fell and formed the seas upon the earth; once more there were billows, as in the days of the fiery ocean, but what a difference! Gunung Api's fire delights in chasing back to the sky in the form of steam all the water it can reach, but that is not much. When the seas had descended out of the air, the blue sky appeared; this was the morning of life upon the earth. And when the seas had cooled, there came life in them; out crept the creature, the earth fermented and formed mould. Herbs wantoned with the sun and with the rain, the enemy of fire; of this was born the forest. This came about slowly, in ages unnumbered, and during all that time the fire had been shut in, only finding vent now and then through Gunung Api's mouth, when it laid waste as far as it could reach. But its range was not as great as it fain would have had it. This clammy wet life multiplied upon the earth, assuming one form after another; the forest spread, the earth showed green — well, there it was!

But what if fire one day regained its freedom? What if the earth split open — yes, split, became fluid again, melted, breathed fire, turned again to a billowing ocean of fire as in the beginning of the ages, chased water out into space, dissolved white-hot in its own conflagration, reposed in itself for eternities, once more a dazzling universe of fire! Ho! O!

A light cloud of fire rises from Gunung Api and settles in a ring on the mountain's head, like the sacred halo upon the brow of one who dreams; Gunung Api is dreaming.

Meanwhile the forest has begun again from the beginning at the foot of the mountain. First it sends out lichen and moss over the rocks, then its other modest outposts, herbs and shrubs, until a thicket is formed and the trees begin once more to shoot up on high and grow strong. Birds and beasts return with the forest. Thus Gunung Api and the forest carry on their duel.

But down on the lowlands beyond the range of the volcano the primeval forest spread over a whole continent from sea to sea, compact league after league and without bounds, one tree with its branches locked in the next. Great lakes there were in the forest, and rivers made their way through it, but the trees came right down to the brink, wading out on prop roots as far as they could find bottom; deep in the forest were glades, far-reaching steppes even, swamps, tablelands, pastures — but beyond them again were dense immeasurable woods; it was one forest over the whole earth.

Such were the almighty forests on the earth before the Ice Age, in Europe, through Asia and Siberia, arctic America and Greenland; boundless on every side, over every country, round three continents and the whole northern hemisphere the forests extended, entirely untouched, left to themselves and subject to no law but wind and weather, their own growth and the mercy of sky and earth. So far might an animal roam; and so long might it be on the way, each new brood advancing through thousands of generations, that the last descendants would come through the forest as quite different animals from those that had begun the journey.

It was the forest of change. It grew from year to year but changed in its growth through the ages. It had adopted the primitive forms and was reaching out towards other new, unknown futures. The simple plants of vanished ages found a place here and developed according to their nature, the soul of a warmer time; dark conifers stood in the heat fermenting with fecundity and sweating resin; their thick juices were distilled from baking sunshine, tepid rain and the volcanic soil and smelt of a younger earth, but the forest had room for them. The plants of a yet earlier time, those that formed the vast steamy forests of the carboniferous age, could not hold their own, they had had their time; and yet the fern and the horse-tail grew in the forest; the forms that were extinct as trees still kept their place as plants.

Camphor and cinnamon trees, palms and plantains, and breadfruit trees grew in the northern forests; they stood there bathed in sunshine and alive, with their tops full of incense and their roots down in the warm ferment of the swamp; they have since withdrawn southward to the tropics, but at that time conditions in the forest were elastic enough to include them too.

With special efforts the forest provides for the future — a new life within itself which is to form new forests: the foliage trees. A slender, delicate tree appears, young as yet and tentative, but destined to become the oak. Other nascent trees, with a strange coolness and habits which the old evergreen trees had never thought of, flock together in little groves and form troops, making themselves at home where they find a place: the young ash, the rowan-tree, the lime; they have a fine sense of something new in the air, and the air will one day make them strong, when even the mighty camphor-tree will have to give up and go. It is the *Seasons* that are beginning quite imperceptibly to influence the forest. The elements affect it, sun, wind and rain, and less stable things than these, but not a whim of the weather is lost upon the forest; in the sun it grows green, before the wind it bows down, in the rain it stands still and drinks — forest so long as it lasts, and nothing is to be depended upon, but through one hazard and another it does last and the forest remains standing. But it does not remain the same.

In itself it only persists through change. An impulse that passes from one form into another dominates the forest, this it is that makes it forest. What else has made the trees into trees than growth in a higher sense, in the family and beyond the individual? The trees get their stems from growing in company. For originally they were all herbs in proximity to the earth, but by the power of the forest, by standing many together and stretching up to reach past each other to the light — the source of life above just as much as the earth from which they draw their nourishment below — they have developed great firm trunks from what in the beginning were only green stalks; over a hundred feet they rise with a fathom's girth or more at the base, and at the very top are the leaves, the lungs of the tree which must have light and air so that the whole tree may live; here it flowers and bears fruit; so mighty a frame-work does the tree build up to carry its leaves and fruit, the original herb, up into the light. Not every herb has become a tree, for they do not all stand in each other's light, even if they are many together: the grass stays upon the ground, and yet the bamboo has become a tree. Nor is every plant in the forest finished, what they are not, they may become; the plantain is in an intermediate stage, a plant-like growth with a green stalk which still only consists of sheaths, one within another, but has the dimensions of a tree. Even the cabbage has a stalk and is on the way to becoming a tree.

Adversity and luxuriance together make the forest. It is a vast community growing together; the trees stand greedily spreading their roots in the fetid warmth of the soil, watered by tepid down-pours and baked by the sun; they grow up against one another, upon and above one another and into one another, they must come up, every tree stretches itself to bring its top up into the light, to win power and if possible shut out its neighbour; there is not only so much space gained but also the prospect of slaking its roots in the store of strength returned to the soil when the neighbour has gone out from lack of nourishment, so there is a twofold gain in being uppermost. The life of the trees is a pitiless race, but which-ever it is that comes out on top, the forest survives. The *forest* is precisely that which survives.

The strongest? Is it always strength that is uppermost? As the forest; it will answer with a silent explanation, showing what takes place, for instance, between the giant tree and the climbing plant. This is a duel in the forest. Two plants have challenged each other, one of the giants of the forest, with a vast lofty trunk, a fathom thick at the base and anchored to the earth with huge roots, hard as a rock and tough in its wood, tried by many a cyclone — and a poor little thing down in the dark shadow of the swamp, with no body at all, a colourless stalk creeping on the ground without the least hope of ever reaching above the jungle by its own power.

The fight begins, and the colossus grows, adds yearly ring to yearly ring so that it splits the bark, shoots up further yet through the thicket with its mighty column and spreads out its branches at the very top like a dome crowning the roof of the forest. Here it swings up in the daylight, a friend of the sun, the dew and the breezes, and from the green tents of its top the trunk looks like a huge pillar, losing itself far, far below in the dark well of the swamp and the underworld.

But down here the climbing-plant is already at work. It stretches itself, a mile in length though no thicker than a finger; it needs a stem to reach the heights, it knows that, and what readier way is there than to worm one's self up the stems of others? This is what the climber does, it borrows the giant's strong straight mast and crawls up it, not making direct for its goal but in a spiral; as it climbs it strikes its suckers in and nourishes itself with the tree's juices. At last without cost it reaches the light at the great tree's top, and then it spreads in its turn, entangling and overshadowing the giant's foliage with its own hungry leaves, putting out flowers, great gaping funnels with style and filaments projecting like live coals far out of its throat, flame-coloured and overpowering of scent — the underworld that has burst out up in the sunshine and airs its stark nakedness. And the great tree is overshadowed, the long stealthy serpent has actually overcome the giant. When the mighty trunk has fallen the liana remains hanging corkscrew fashion amid the wild growth; of the giant there is nothing left but the idea that may be formed of its girth and length from the empty voluptuous curves of the liana. The forest maintains silence, it exists for the sake of the summits; not even strength, but the result, determines who and what shall live. Such is the cruelty of the forest.

But is it not at the same time generous? The forest nourishes itself only to be able to nourish. Is not the vine a climber? From the corpse of the colossus it has slain it hangs out its grapes, a swelling world of sweetness. Every tree gives, offering its fruit even if there is no one to take it; the coconut palm leans down with its ovary of nuts on the end shoot, from the tiniest up to huge ripe nuts, a whole gamut of fertility; the bushes vaunt their berries, turning them red, food and gaiety at once; even the modest grass conceals a kernel within its prickly ear. The flowers open their calyxes and consummate their lives in perfume, perish in colour; they offer their honey to the bee, which in return helps them to bear fruit — a secret pact which, so long as it endures, will fill the summer with the scent of honey and the humming of bees.

Reciprocity makes the forest rich, this is its law of life; the plant with the reddest fruit gets its seed diffused, unless like the burr it simply hangs on; but a feast to which all who will may come is the more handsome way. For the sake of reciprocity a plant transforms itself, as it does in order to exist; they go to the greatest lengths in order to meet each other, beyond their own nature, if need be, and into another; thereby the forest becomes more manifold. The apple-tree and the briar are both roses, but with no little difference; one form has developed itself from the other, the apple-tree from the briar, by shedding its thorns and turning the little dry stone-fruit into an apple; from prickly bushes growing together in a thicket and armed against their surroundings there has come a fine tree growing in the open which offers its fruit with outstretched arms.

When the apple-tree is in bloom it summons the bees to a banquet, and then each tree is like a white-clad dome full of cool sweetness, sunshine and shade, and the whole tree is one single note of all the humming swarm, a miracle of light, the sphere of blessedness. But when the fruit is ripe it seeks the earth, in dark nights, with an audible fall; the hoof of Time smiting the earth, with its warning that summer is past.

When the first apple-tree bloomed in the primeval forest it told of eternal summer; but when the fruit fell to earth, it knocked to announce the first autumn.

Upon the plains within the great mother-forests stood the apple-tree rounding its fruit to fit the human hand; it offered man of its superfluity and has been taken into his gardens.

For man had his origin in the great northern forests before the Ice Age, the wild joyous forests where existence was bound by no laws but Nature's own, and none knew want.

Man came out of the primeval state together with the beasts, shared their life and became transformed with them. In a forest in

transformation, with herbs on the way to become trees, one species growing beyond itself and into another, the beasts found sustenance and changed after their manner, one leaving another and
on the way to become a third; and as the foremost creature among
the beasts, though by no means the strongest, but the richest in
possibilities, Man arose.

How he tamed fire is to be related here.

III

THE MAN

Down in the valleys around Gunung Api dwelt the Forest Folk,
entirely free from care and without thought for the morrow;
the forest served them out of its abundance. They had no dwellings or fixed places of abode but moved about from one wild or-
chard to another, according as the fruit ripened and offered itself;
when they had cleared one place or amused themselves by shaking
all the fruit down, they went off with noisy mirth to another and
shook the trees there.

But although they were always on the move they had, unknown
to themselves, regularly recurring habits; they wandered in a certain circle, within a definite territory, and in the course of time
left their tracks, formed paths which those who had any memory
recognized from one visit to another; unconsciously their life was
directed by the forest and the year; those who remembered the
paths began also vaguely to notice the aspect of the forest and of
the year each time their steps brought them back to the same place.

A vast landscape was spread out at the foot of Gunung Api, on
one side a gradual slope lost itself in the chain of forests of the
lowland, on the other the ground rose to the first spurs of Gunung
Api; the land was neither plain nor forest but both, open country
and groves alternating, here and there solitary trees, elsewhere
thicket, dense, well-defined woods surrounding a river which
flowed through them; rocks and ravines giving place to level pasture; in this park-like country the Forest Folk moved up and down,
now by the river, now into the jungle, then among the trees and

then out into the open or up the mountain, always something new but within certain bounds, which were so wide that they were not aware of them; all the rest of the world was open to them, but there were reasons for their remaining here. Far or near, Gunung Api's smoking head or the cloud that concealed him was always above their horizon, shutting out the sky on that side; behind the volcano they had never been.

Moreover they had not the country to themselves, for there were all the animals that roamed the forest and the pastures with which they were familiar; with the beasts the Forest Folk lived on the same footing of conditional peace as the beasts among themselves. With some of them their relations were those of irreconcilable hostility, as with the tiger; but it was not man that had started that war: the forest people raised a warning shout as soon as it was seen and were indignant in their very vitals because it did not respect the peace. Before the elephant they lay flat, literally, in the most profound subjection; he was to *see* that they would not stand up against him: down with you, every man, when Father Elephant shows himself; and the great pachyderm had to step carefully to avoid treading on the courteous people in the grass. The tiger shows an evil grin, at a distance; he too has respect for the elephant but cannot refrain from hinting at the unfairness of the match between himself and the pachyderm; it is a low trick of the elephant to wear pegs in his mouth and cover himself with slates. With other animals of medium size, such as wild cattle, deer, horses and other herbivorous beasts, man lived on peaceful and neighbourly terms, but had a tendency to tease and make fun of them, knowing them to be quiet; a frequent sight was a flying beast and a man hanging on to its tail, with unexplained object; on such occasions the human herd raised a special uproar, shrill peals from open throats; it was grand fun to see an honest brute put to shame by one of their like. With the wolf their relations were strained, but they had an understanding with the dogs, which run down a hare when in a pack and fawn so nicely when they are single. All poultry was left out of consideration, though their eggs were not despised. Animals of small size were frightened to death for fun, and everything not too big to be held in the hand was counted as food, from grasshoppers and beetles to worms and mice. It was not every one whose eyes were good enough to distinguish between a berry and a thing with legs, a bug or a spider —

a matter of taste; on the other hand, not many would confuse the durian fruit with a hedgehog. Finally, as for the tiniest winged creatures in nature, flies and gnats, they were only a nuisance. Such was the attitude of the Forest Folk towards their fellow-creatures.

They themselves were regarded by the other animals with wonder more than anything else. Most animals went about in herds, and men did so too; but their herd was always restless, jumping about early and late; if you saw the grass stirring out on the plain and figures leaping out of it with wild gesticulations, you knew that was the men; if the trees on the edge of the forest swayed as though struck by a whirlwind, they were disporting themselves again; they were also to be known afar off by the noise they made; there was a continual chattering in the herd, never ceasing, every kind of jaw-music, sharp, long-drawn-out and deep; long rolling harangues, grunts, and snarls, warning roars and a concert of howls from the youngsters, puling and wailing, and now and then a chorus of laughter, that strange many-voiced neighing peculiar to the human herd, which usually betokened an accident of one kind or another.

Most conspicuous among them was the leader, an old individual, usually of bigger and heavier build than the rest and with a terrific head of hair; from him the chattering proceeded like a prevailing wind, he led the laughter, and if any one gave a piercing shriek it was from one of his pinches. Wherever the herd wandered he was at its head.

The leader, then, was one of the oldest, who had experienced and could put two and two together when the same thing recurred; as was natural, he led the way and gave the direction, cleared the path of obstacles, discovered snakes and gave the alarm, smote his breast in warlike fashion when enemies appeared, and was the first to fly.

The Forest Folk were divided into many herds, each with its leader; they despised and kept clear of each other, but if their paths unavoidably met the result was a single combat; each leader dealt his chest resounding blows and abused the other for half a day on end without budging from the spot, until something or other occurred to separate them, such as a fall of rain or the total hoarseness of one of the parties; such occasions served to show which of the herds possessed the greatest staying power in its leader. The number of tribes was unknown, but among them all was one whose leader had shouted down *all* the leaders without exception in all the other tribes and had always had the last word. He had the most fearsome head of hair in the whole forest and was known to all; they spoke of him as *The Man* and he had no other name; he was always to be found in the best places of the forest together with the herd that followed him; every other herd gave way before his name. The groves were cleared of men, if any were there, as soon as he appeared; he seldom saw his fellow-men except from behind and on the run. He had the most dreaded vocal powers in the forest.

The Man awoke with the sun and shook the dew from his shoulders; far and near among the groves the wild cocks were crowing. With a crash of their wings the pigeons flew out of the highest trees, busy from early morn; the lowing of the wild cow woke echoes in the vales, and between whiles it was so still that the humming of a single bee could be heard. Steamy vapours rose from the grass; out on the plain among scattered trees a herd of giraffes was wading through the morning mist. The peacock spread his tail before the rising sun. The great forest rose like a blue domed wall, but a cloudy outline dominated the whole land, Gunung Api hiding himself in the sky and showing his summit in glimpses through the thick air at a giddy height.

Gaiety everywhere and the song of birds, joy over the new-created day; but the Man was sour, he yawned wide, showing the depths of his throat, shuddered and yawned again, fretful in his soul from evil dreams, empty but with no appetite so early, thoroughly miserable and very, very dangerous.

Those about him knew this from experience and it was very quiet round the tree where the family had rested; the mothers stilled their little ones with silent gestures; a little group of women, every one of them scarred or lame, stole about and put their heads together, occupied with the service of the Man but doubtful whether he could be approached. Fruit had been gathered before daybreak, everything was ready — but would he eat, what would he like, and when would be the right time? An attempt was made, a courageous old individual hobbled up with a freshly gathered pine-apple and made luscious eating motions with her lips to see whether the Man would accept it; she got the prickly fruit flung back at her head and retired bleeding to whisper with the others; evidently pine-apple was not what was wanted.

Another veteran went up: a freshly opened cocoanut, flowing over with juice and kernel; she munched quite irresistibly with her lips, the Man could not help eating, the nut was *so* toothsome and it had cost her a whole morning's toil to open it, an endless filing with a sharp stone to get through the fibre to the nut; but the Man knocked up her hand and sent the nut with milk and all flying into the air. She went back shaking her head to the other women, in distress: he would not eat! Breakfast was tried in vain, grapes, berries; the old women changed their tactics and sent up younger temptresses with the food, not for the sake of their own personal safety, but on the chance of its succeeding; the young girls tried their luck, shedding the light of their own irresistible charms over the food; they lay in the dust, but the Man took no notice of them, and real terror began to spread though the whole tribe — what if he would never eat again? What was to be done? Without doubt the whole world would perish, heaven and earth would fall, if he refused to take nourishment and hold them up. Well-a-way! the women sat down and began to weep quietly.

A last attempt was made, the prettiest thing in the whole tribe, a perfectly fresh, sweet young girl, almost a child, was sent up with a bunch of grapes, which she timidly held up to the Man's lips. He turned his mouth away, and then she made the blunder of persisting, offering the grapes a second time — the next instant she was seized, and the Man gave a loud roar, maddened by such officious impertinence; without getting up he bent her double by the force of his arms alone, held her and, with bristling hair and beard and grinding jaws, bethought him how she should suffer and remember it. Then deliberately he passed his hand to one of her feet and twisted it in the ankle-joint, a whole turn — there, he flung the shrieking girl from him — there, now she could go lame the rest of her days!

The victim was carried off, and the group of women breathed again. The Man had found vent, he was himself once more; they knew him, now he would surely eat, heaven and earth were safe this time. And they were not wrong; as soon as the Man had had his exercise his appetite came back; he deigned to devour a brood of nestlings, alive and warm from the nest, and after this appetiser fell greedily upon anything that was offered, swallowed a mass of dainties, slobbered up the milk of one cocoanut after another, and belched — a good sign; the women nodded to one another with emotion: he's feeling good; and gradually with the sense of fulness he began to look around at the women, one after another, in a different way. They dropped their eyes, sank on their knees, and each one thought to herself: I wonder how I am looking. None had yet had time to finger her hair away from her eyes or to smooth out her limbs nicely.

The Man got up, threw out his chest, took a good look at the sky, and gave the recognized signal for free merriment — instantly taken up by the young men all around, who had kept very quiet all the morning. The brows were working above the Man's gleaming eyes and the women hung upon his countenance, jumping about with shrill bird-cries when his brow was clear, shrinking up ready for a quiet retreat as soon as clouds collected on his forehead.

Soon they broke up, the Man leading, with plans for the day unknown to the rest; next the young men, all intent upon obedience, and last the women, with children in their arms, very happy, sticking green leaves with spittle on their bumps and wounds of the morning. Last of all came the young girl who had had her foot put out of joint, supported by two women with old-standing lameness; they knew what it was.

And so the tribe is on the trail the livelong day, chewing all the time, more or less; wherever they go some food offers, and everything has to be tasted. Everything is turned over, examined, taken in the hand and sniffed, put to the lips and tried by a bite; some swarm up the trees and heave the fruit down, break off branches and get scratched; waterholes are explored, rocks climbed, enemies encountered and a concert of righteous screeching set up; little domestic squabbles arise and die down, and before the end of the day the troop is in quite another country, only remembered by the old leader and perhaps a few besides. The Man's well-nigh supernatural knowledge is shown by his tracking out a bed of salt; the whole tribe gratefully stands on its head licking the salt earth, and after that the fruit tastes sweeter.

The old man walks with a staff, to the inconvenience of the youngsters, who always have sense enough to keep out of arm's length but as yet have not quite learnt to reckon with a stick as well — strange how it extends the power of the Man, ow! ow! And

if they dance out of the way so quickly that the stick can't reach
them, be it never so long, why then the old one *throws* it through
the air, point foremost, and then again it gets you in the back — impossible to find his match, he *is* The Man!

The day is long, no one remembers the morning or other days
that are past; there is only to-day, the summer day without beginning or end, the forest man's day, eternal sunshine and the world
a larder.

But even this day has an end; sunset finds the little troop in another part of the country; a certain tiredness has come over them,
and the Man makes his dispositions for the evening. Careworn and
dangerous he was in the morning when he began the day; anxious
and violent is he now that he sees it vanishing. Few of the others
have a memory that carries from morning to evening; they can't
make out why it is not always daylight, and this gives rise to dis-
sensions; some insist that the twilight is only a passing phenomenon, a wolf coming in front of the sun, or perhaps some indisposi-
tion of the heavens. The Man knows better and proceeds to collect
his flock against what is coming, beating them up to form a square
against the night. If the shortsighted creatures don't know what is
good for them they must be protected against their will, by violence if need be; with tears and shrieks they are driven to bed, even
a brief roar may be heard here and there from some big rebellious
person, who is instantly felled to the ground. The Man knows the
stiffnecked among them: at night, when night has really come,
they don't believe in the daytime; a whacking and into the square
with you, and down with your heads!

Before darkness has fallen the Man has mustered his flock and
keeps them together until night really falls; they grumble a little
but finally have to give in to the old one; soon sleepiness comes
over them, and there is silence. Nobody objects now to sitting in
the bunch; on the contrary, each and every one tries to bore his
way in as far as possible. The whole company, then, is sitting on
the ground, rather high ground for choice, in a place selected by
the Man and judged by him to be safe; in the twilight they look
like a big hairy cluster, a human swarm, all with their backs outward to the dark and all with a head, or at least a nose and mouth,
sticking out of the mass.

Lucky he who feels the pressure most! For the outsiders are the prey of the great cat. The very fact of sitting with one's back in the open air gives an intolerable sensation and many a wrestling bout takes place before they are finally settled and can change no more.

And then they go into the night. It is long and full of terror, not one of the poor wretches realizes from night to night how long and terrifying it is. They quake and hide their heads in one another's bosoms, sleep by fits and starts and wake up again hearing frightful things; and indeed frightful things are happening. When at last day breaks — after an eternity of waiting — the tribe is usually smaller by a few of its members; those on the outside have had to pay toll to the dark, the beasts of prey have been there.

At night the forest is changed; primeval darkness broods over the ground, and the creatures of darkness go about therein, cold gliding things which slay with a stab or crush in limbless coils; the great felines are out, showing their lamps, two and two, in the pitch-dark undergrowth; from above the owl stares down with his two, and from distant ravines comes the lion's paralysing roar, the hyena breaks into his insane laughter, the forest reverberates with terror. It is haunted by a murmur of nocturnal creatures which turn darkness into horror, an element of itself; the darkness is thick with bats and furry things, full of cries, flappings, sighs and rustlings; the whole world is an abyss of horror.

Within the human mass, sitting with arms around each other's necks and eyes shut tight even though they are not asleep, they go through a long death agony, but continue to live and suffer. Nor is their fright without a cause: a wailing cry from the outside of the circle tells when the leopard or the wolf has come to fetch his due. And somebody must be outside, either the smallest or those who were too late to bore their way into the clump; they get peeled off in the course of the night, one or two deep, as it may happen.

But they don't acquiesce in it silently: the victim raises a howl so piercing as to make the ears tingle, and the rest of the bunch are ready to help a brother to the extent of joining in with a monstrous many-voiced shrieking that is heard far and wide and proclaims that man is suffering injustice. And in fact it does happen that even the great cats shrink before it, twitch their ears and give up the meal, letting the thing drop if it doesn't stop howling when shaken; it is almost enough to put a tiger off his food when there is such a penetrating noise with it. The wolf, on the other hand, takes seasoning and all; it is not in the habit of swallowing a howl the wrong way.

But even if the swarm loses a layer or two in the course of the night and bitterly laments the loss, calling the universe to witness — it is a long way in to the core. And then it is the weaklings that go; farther in sit the big strong men who were powerful enough to push their way through; within them are the women, the oldest and their children on the outside, all the young women in towards the middle; and there, farthest in and right in the center, sits the Man! Thus does he form the order of battle in the evening; that is why he is so old.

When the flock raises its cry to signal an attack, he is not behind the others, for he has the biggest voice, of immense compass and timbre; its scaring power is great. But he also defends the flock, often not without success, by human cunning and arts that no one else is able to invent. When a carnivorous beast comes creeping after a little human, it may have a surprise in the shape of something hard flying out of the swarm, a cocoanut or perhaps even a stone; this is the old man in the middle who, protected by a thick layer of family, can keep his presence of mind; indeed it sometimes happens that a long branch becomes as it were alive, in some unexplained connection with the swarm; it comes from that direction and it is sharp, catches one on the tender snout; and then possibly one may prefer to leave the humans in peace and take a rodent instead, or a ruminant, which doesn't make sticks and stones fly in disquieting proximity to one's eyes.

But not every night was so disastrous to the tribe; they climbed into the trees when opportunity offered, and there they had less to fear, only against the snake they were defenceless; steep rocks were a good place for the night, when they happened to be in their neighbourhood before darkness came on. But night itself was not always alike either, it was darker or lighter, and when the moon was up the Forest Folk were not to be scared so easily, they could see what they had to deal with and take precautions in time.

On the clearest moonlight nights the Man gave up forming the tribe into a square, instead of that he led them to open places in the forest, where he had noted a hollow tree, and there the crowd spent the night, not in fear and trembling, but with music, dance and song.

All night long, hour after hour, the old man belaboured the hollow tree with his staff; booming, booming, booming; and at the same time he yelled at the top of his voice, incessantly, up in the most piercing notes of his register, and all the rest of the tribe vied with him, they had nothing like the Man's vocal powers but their numbers made up for it; and in time to this colossal bawling chorus all the men performed a dance, leaping up and down on the same spot, crouching low and stretching to their full height, swaggering round each other and hooting, all night long, while the moon travelled across the sky; and round about the women sat in the grass, in happy deference, hour after hour tirelessly looking on.

And it was as though all the animals kept at a distance, not knowing what to think; far and wide it was still in the moonlight, only the human howling lay like an island of noise in the midst of an ocean of stillness. The wild dogs halted in the neighbourhood and raised a chorus, sat on their haunches and howled with their muzzles turned toward the moon — they could make nothing of it against the Forest Folk; a solitary wandering hippopotamus came out of the woods, and you could see him raise his gaping jaws to heaven; *he* can let out a pretty note when he chooses, but not a sound was to be heard, the Forest Folk drowned him too; all nature was shouted down.

Gradually the concert calls the whole Forest Folk together, troop after troop arrives, following the sound in the moonlight, all the different tribes that are otherwise on a hostile footing with one another; before morning they have come in from every corner of the country and joined their voices to the great choir — a corroboree of all mankind. And the Man is equal to the occasion; his hair and beard bristle up, his madness becomes possession, with redoubled force he whacks the hollow tree, his yelling goes up a note higher, and around him goes the human race in a ring, each one bawling with the full force of his lungs, one beat and one heart, one note and one soul!

IV

THE FOREST FIRE

NEXT day the various tribes parted company, each to its own point of the compass; they had too many disagreements to keep together in one family when sober; it required the fervour of music to unite them. Besides, there were too many of them to find a living in the same tract. But a certain interchange had taken place before they separated; many had deserted one tribe for another, a lively swapping of wives had gone on, and when the Man reviewed the faces around him he didn't seem to recognize them all; some of them did their grovelling like beginners, as it were; they were from another part, had left their tribe that they might still hear the Man's voice and gaze upon his beard.

Without doubt he has a good voice and is able to scare away most animals that are sensitive to noise; even the lion blinks his eyes and feels his appetite going, prefers to walk off; great is the power of the Man.

Yet there is Gunung Api! When *he* roars . . . when *he* flashes. . . . *Fire!*

Terrible is fire. No use shouting then or beating the breast — you run, don't know what you're doing, stand stockstill, and your knees give under you, crawl on all fours — unnerving fire! Man is a small creature when it shows itself.

The beasts fear it and fly before it; far and wide they sneeze and throw up their heads when fire breaks out, wheel round and gallop night and day to get into quite another country. The wild cattle, the horses, rush madly on in herds and trample each other down in flight when the smell of fire has twitched their nostrils; even the elephants lose their heads and prod one another with their tusks, smash into trees and spit themselves when the fire is behind them; every living thing runs and treads its neighbour to death when fire is abroad.

The Forest Folk knew and dreaded fire. The fear was in their blood, they had inherited it from primeval ancestors who still lived their lives in the trees and had no more dangerous enemy than fire. Fire climbed quicker than they and leapt quicker from tree to tree, and no more cruel doom could befall them than to be caught and devoured by fire. Its bite was more painful than that of any other known being; the slightest contact with it left unbearable anguish, with a single lick it took the hair off the whole body, and it ate up everything, bones and all; where fire had fed there was nothing left, though no one could see what became of all its food. For some invisible force was present in fire, with an appetite but apparently without a body like other animals; an invisible being in which Gunung Api revealed himself, a blasting devourer, a *spirit*, the ardent spirit of Gunung Api.

By putting many things together the Forest Folk had attained to the certain knowledge that the fire spirit had its home on the mountain. For every night it glared and threatened like a yawning fiery mouth up in the clouds, and sometimes the naked spirit itself came running down its sides in the form of a glowing tongue as broad as the whole valley and its forest; and then was the time to fly to other forests, right out of the country if possible, a journey of days and nights, if one was lucky enough to get away in time. For when the tongue of fire had reached a forest and begun to lick up the trees, there was not much warning before the whole burst into flame, and then you had the fire spirit roaring over you.

But when the fire had eaten itself into strength it was the greatest and most frightful of all creatures. It might be there in an instant, it came from a tiny little spark to begin with, an insignificant fire-baby, which was born of glowing ash from the volcano or of the lightning, and licked about among the dry leaves, till suddenly it would climb crackling up the trees and grow big. It consumed at a distance through the air, even where its arms could not reach; when once it had taken hold and heated up everything about it the trees for a long way round burst into flame of their own accord, till the forest was one blazing furnace.

And fire was the Bright One, it turned night into day, did not vanish in the darkness like other creatures; it gave out light itself at night, so that everything near it could be seen. At night it was blood-red and visible miles away, but by day in the sunlight it had almost invisible airy limbs, wild and hot. Its face it never showed. But it had a voice and many different expressions, seething, roaring or giving out sharp loud cracks when it sat in a tree and devoured it. At its fullest power, when it rode upon the forest and encom-

passed the world, borne upon the storm, it advanced with a roar
from one forest into another; and then there was no escape, except
for those who had smelt betimes what was coming. For the smell of
fire was not to be mistaken, it was abroad before the blaze had
grown too strong; smoke too could be seen in time by the wary.
Folk who were very wise could even predict the coming of the
spirit long in advance. For the volcano gave out a smell when it
was getting ready and behaved significantly in many ways, with
internal rumblings and much smoke; those who had sense for these
things guessed when it was bent on rapine and removed themselves
as soon as the evil smell began to pour down the sides of Gunung
Api.

It was another thing with the *lightning:* against that there was
no guarding one's self in advance, it might strike at any moment.
It was the Fire Spirit in another form; it manifested itself in company with the thunder, Gunung Api in another aspect as the great
heaven-roarer and flasher who from time to time sported roughly
in the sky and made the woods unsafe to dwell in. Much of this
flashing on high is for his own amusement and does no damage;
every night the fire spirits dance among the clouds, red naked
fellows leaping up in the heavens; but only rarely does the lightning actually strike the earth, so rarely that most men almost forget
about it. And then suddenly one day it happens again.

It begins with heavy swollen clouds that collect about Gunung
Api, beleaguer the whole heaven and turn the daylight sick — the
first lightning flashes in the gloom as when a beast of prey shows
its fang with quivering upper lip; and then comes the roar from
him on high, a long rolling aerial roar which loses itself in the sky
and awakes echoes in faraway forest ravines. The mastodon answers it a league away as he goes through the thicket — a wretch-
edly thin, long drawn-out nasal squeal, like the squeaking of a
mouse in a tuft of grass compared with the noise of him who fills
the world with thunder from his seat in the sky. The great helion
gives his melancholy, threatening cough, with moaning repetitions,
as he stands with his claws in the backbone of a deer: who is this
disturbing him at his meal? The rhinoceros howls, as long as his
wind lasts, and tears his way through the jungle, snapping trees
as he goes, clean out of his wits like a hen; the hippopotamus sticks
his head out of the water and protests with many a loud grunt
against this rumbling up above, as he flicks the water out of his

ears; our Fatty hates noise and doesn't quite know whom he has to deal with.

But all the smaller animals, who have no remarks to make, seek shelter noiselessly. The vultures drop from the sky like stones, with their wings folded, and make themselves small under a bush; the rodents go headlong into their holes; everything that can disappear disappears, in a moment the earth seems clear of all living things.

The forest stands still with outstretched twigs in a pale green glare, as though stricken with sickness, against the blue-black gloom. Farther off it is in wild motion with thrashing branches; the tempest is approaching and lashes all in its path with a sinister howling.

Lightning again, and now the clap comes right on top of it; he is wroth, the Wrathful One, and near — flash upon flash, the whole world full of blue fire — fire and crash right in your eyes! He has struck — a tree droops amid blinding fire, splinters and collapses with crashing trunk, and the fire has seized on it, strikes out with its dazzling limbs from top to root. The forest is on fire!

The fire leaps from tree to tree, blazing wildly up the stems and devouring the foliage with crackling flames, hissing and humming; the smoke rolls up from the forest, and now the fire rages with a mighty blast, the Unseen One is blowing with his torrid hurricanes, long bright flickering tongues shoot up out of the jungle, surround it and tear onward, while lightnings split the sky and the thunder shatters mountains. The forest is dying; fire has it in its grasp and eats into it, swiftly, greedily, visible or invisible, but terrible, terrible.

And the forest dies. When fire and storm have passed on, with a consuming whirr and with an infinity of smoke galloping up into the sky, the burnt-up trees are left, some of them consumed right down to the roots, others, with which the fire has not yet finished, dropping a shower of sparks from their scorched limbs about the charred trunk; till the rain comes to wash the desolation into black miry pools among the gnawed and naked remnants of the stems, a melancholy corpse-strewn field for the sun to shine upon, when at last the thunder is silent and the rainbow gleams in the sky over the mountain. The beasts are dead, those which had not the power or the sense to save themselves; they lie scorched up with swollen bellies amid the destruction of the woods.

But the Forest Folk, how have they fared? Not every tribe has had the same good fortune; some that sought safety with the wind behind them were overtaken by the fire and perished, others that chose the opposite way had a start of it, but not all; some of them in the general confusion came in the path of the utterly frenzied cattle and were trampled out of recognition. It was a question of their leader.

The herd that came out of it best was that which had the Man for its leader. He was old and experienced, had gone through the same thing before and survived it, knew what *not* to do. He was acquainted with fire and its ways — no use taking to the trees and flying from tree to tree as before other dangers, such as floods or when wolves were packing, maddened by hunger, no, down from the trees and out of the forest, out into open country, or failing that a broad glade in the forest where at any rate there was only the grass to burn and one might perhaps escape with singed eye-brows and blistered foot-soles — but best of all water, the river, if it could be reached and put between you and the fire, a lake, if nothing else a swamp, a waterhole, and then into it, take cover in it up to your nostrils, till the fire had passed.

A beastly medicine; ugh, water was the Forest Folk's horror, they dreaded water with every hair of their bodies, with all their ten sensitive finger-tips and noble toes; you drank water, but only with the extremity of funnelled lips, hating to get the slightest splash of it in your face, and as to getting bodily into it, that was a torture and an indignity to man, to say nothing of all the creepy things moving about in it which you got on you — leeches, duck-weed, wet stalks — ugh, the very idea of it made you shudder. Shrill cries of extreme distress were always heard when any one had fallen into the water, and this from grief at getting wet rather than from fear of drowning — so disgusting was water!

But in a forest fire you had no better friend. Water was after all the power that could check fire. Everything else fed it and made it strong, but, like man, it could not endure water. This might be seen when it rained: then fire turned sick and shrivelled up over its prey, grew qualmish and stank unwholesomely, unable to spread its flames; and if the rain kept on properly, it died, was simply smothered, so even fire had its limits and its superior. It was so plainly to be seen that if water came upon fire it hissed, sent out smoke and was angry, but if more came it gave way and left its blackened prey behind; fire and water could not agree. So that the first thing to be done was to drop down from the trees when lightning showed its teeth in the sky, then run, double up and crawl away on all fours or on your feet, whichever was quickest, out into open spaces where it was wet.

The forest fire surprised the Man and his herd down on the edge of the great jungle, far from the river and with no lake near; but the old man instantly broke out of the forest into the long grass, darted a glance around him, at the burning forest in rear, straight ahead and to every side, sniffed the air — which way is the wind? where are the cattle going? — Water? He jumped into the air — a fairly broad glade and looks as if it had a hollow in the middle, and isn't that rushes waving over there, marshy ground, swamp? Then his mind was made up, and he ran into the grass, ducked down, raised his head and sniffed, ran and stopped and ran again, with his staff in one hand and a big sharp flint in the other; and after him came all the rest of the tribe in a long single file, the men with uneasy, shifting eyes and shaking legs, with snorting breath and water pouring from their eyes; terror was in their bowels and they simply followed the Man not knowing what they did. After them again the mothers, silent and swift as shadows, each with a young one in her arms and perhaps a couple of half-grown ones trotting after, all the children uniting their shrieks in one immense earsplitting lamentation. But the mothers were silent, no one knows how frightened they were or what they went through; their eyes were mad with fear, but so they were always; they followed the rest and said nothing. The tail of the procession was made up of all the young people of the tribe, the striplings and the slim young girls — *they* had the becoming halo of terror all over their bodies in the form of bristling silky down; whatever might happen they were not going to run away without showing some grace in their flight; but they had not much to say, they rushed on in the wake of the others and were not going to be the last of all either. The young lads pretended not to care, barked in their rough voices and tried to look as if there was no hurry, but trod each other down all the same if the pace wasn't fast enough.

The whole flock trekked through the long grass towards the middle of the glade, where sure enough, as the Man had guessed, there was a swamp with open water — and so down you go, all hands into the duckweed! Splash, splash, splash, women first, as is right and proper, all the mothers, their eyelids quivering at the first splash in the face, but they take their ducking without a murmur, children and all; then the young girls — they cry over it but have to go: one of the young ladies puts on the brake, on all fours at the edge of the pool, and won't go in — ugh no, it's too nasty — so the Man has to make short work of her, one on the side of the head and a knee behind, and out goes Sister, down among the eels and the leeches. Then all the men, splash, splash, splash; finally the lads, not without giving tongue; and, last of all, when everybody is in safety, the Man, the old leader himself. With a sour grimace he jumps in, carefully, not wetting his head or his hands before it is absolutely necessary.

So there they sat, the whole lot of them, in the waterhole, just at the right depth to have their heads out but ready to dive to the nostrils when the fire came. And now they were in comparative security, they recovered their voices and became communicative, with much modulated grunting and wise wrinklings of the forehead, smackings of the lips and twitchings of the nose. They are small, the end of the world is at hand, but their loquacity is irresponsible to the last.

From the place where they sat they had a view across the level to the edge of the forest, and terrible were the sights they saw. The fire spread with frightful rapidity, black, bellying clouds poured up from the woods, grew one out of another and rolled up towards the sky; sparks flew high at the base of the clouds, a tremendous roaring, crackling and booming was heard and grew more and more intense, drew nearer, spread wider and wider; now the flames could be seen above the trees, an immense extended flaming body running along on the top of the forest, leaping up into the smoke, going out and bursting forth again. Wild red and yellow flames clung to the forest with their bodies waving high up in the air like serpents tearing backwards at their prey, and a frightful hissing was heard, loud thunderous reports; the whole forest was now one raging, crackling blaze, fearful to behold; but it had reached the edge of the woods and was running on, eating its way at a furious pace on both sides; without a doubt it would go right round the glade and on to the woods beyond. The people down in the swamp gave a sigh, knowing they were going to be surrounded; but actually their danger was past; there were no trees near them to burn, they were sitting in the middle of a ring which the fire had to pass round — uncomfortable, no doubt, in water up to their chins and with the heat of the vast furnace stinging their faces, coughing and half-choked by the smoke, but still saved. As for the beasts, their fate was worse, as bad as it could be.

They saw them, saw their wild race for life, and they were still grey in the face with death reflected in their eyes from what they had seen. It came just before the fire had reached the edge of the forest; in front of it chased by it, a mighty herd of animals burst out of the woods on to the plain with a thunder of hoofs, a roaring, neighing and bellowing, for there were beasts of every kind in the herd: buffaloes and horses, elephants, deer, wild boars, bears, lions, giraffes and rhinoceroses, friends and foes all mixed together with never a thought but of flying for their lives; so, far from scattering, they crowded together and rushed onward in a dense billowing mass, in which could be heard the sound of breaking bones. The elephants rolled as in a heavy sea of animal forms, howling in their frenzy with trunks raised aloft; the long necks of the giraffes towered above the rest, trying this way and that way until they fell, their legs broken under them in the crush; a thousand galloping bulls surged in from every side, all trying to get to the middle, plunged their horns into each other's flanks, charged each other with heads down and mad blasts of the nostrils; all smaller animals were smashed up and trampled into the ground — and in spite of all obstacles the herd came on, swift as the wild wind, grinding its own members to death and destruction as it went, over a bridge of the carcasses it left behind in its blind flight — onward it came, in a few seconds it was across the open ground and plunged, bellowing, roaring, howling, and with a crackling of broken bones, into the forest on the other side. There the fire would follow them up and the race would be continued; they had but a short start, you could hear at one and the same time the herd of beasts thundering on through the jungle and the fire thundering on their heels around the open glade.

But now the Forest Folk had something else to think about; their turn had come, they were to be put to the proof — the grass was on fire, the conflagration had spread from the woods to the open ground. They ducked down into the water as far as they could go: this hazard must be faced like the rest. And it was soon over; the fire raced across the plain in an instant, but avoided the

water. Then it was seen that the grass concealed a number of
animals that had taken refuge there — a writhing mass of serpents,
which the fire, incidentally useful, scorched up — a porcupine,
which arched its back and raised its quills against the fire when it
could no longer find cover, but these proved to be highly inflammable, and the poor rodent was roasted; this happened close to the
pool, and the Forest Folk stretched their necks, could not help
sniffing it; a sweet, a very sweet odour proceeded from the porcupine when the fire had dealt with it; even the dead snakes lying
near, with bellies split open and venom issuing from their entrails,
had a particularly good broiled smell; and although the jungle
folk themselves were sitting, so to speak, in the jaws of death, the
present moment appealed to their power of imagination — they
were only human, had been without food for some time; it made
them thoughtful, mumbling with their lips.

But still their trials were not over; a new excitement of another
kind seized them, violently, giving them such a start that a regular
wave washed over the surface of the pool; the youngsters shrieked
piercingly, and even the Man himself gave a cry of astonishment
and alarm — for as though by magic a huge striped tigress sprang
out of the grass just in front of the water-hole.

Tiger-like, she had kept concealed in the grass until the last moment, although only a few feet away, but now she had to move,
the fire had tracked her down — and there she stood in front of the
water with a long look over to the opposite bank; crouched for a
spring with all four feet gathered under her, but did not jump; it
was too far. Then she raised a paw, raised it again, as if to go down
into the water, but each time shook her paw with a cold shiver, a
feeling as though some drops had already reached her — she *could*
not. And then, seeing herself caught, she blinked her great yellow
eyes in an abandonment of grief, opened her mouth as though for
a miaow, but no sound came; the great yellow eyes rested upon
the people in the swamp, but she did not see them, felt too bad to
see anything.

There she stands, hemmed in between fire and water; never
more shall she ride before sundown on the back of a ruminant
with her claws sunk deep in the quivering flesh and her mouth on
the artery, sucking the source of life, thirsty before and thirsty
after the salt drink; never more shall she steal through the terrifying darkness of the jungle's depth, fearless of the dark as darkness

and terror itself; nor stretch her limbs in the midday sun and bake her flaming flanks till the hairs sparkle and thrill with vitality, purring the while like a voluptuous spinning-wheel; nor play any more with her living food, that horrible game after which one of the players is missing and the other sleepy; nor take part in abominable love-duets in the moonlight, nor wash herself with her paw and in her love of cleanliness remove the slightest trace of deer's blood from her whiskers after a murder — now she is to be washed of her sins in an ardent element, the fire is upon her, a flame already has her by the tail.

But then she springs round to confront the fire, which is crackling in the long dry grass; she utters the death roar, tries to fight the hot thing, springs straight up in the air before the fire, fighting with all her claws out, hits at the flames and gets her paws scorched, gets her beard scorched, fans the fire by striking at it; sparks and burning grass close over her head, and amid deafening hisses and sputtering she rolls in the fire, biting herself where the fire bites, tearing long gashes in her face in a cloud of sparks, till the grass is burnt beneath her. Then, madly snorting and sneezing, without a hair on her body, without ears, blinded and naked like a thing all flayed, with the bones of her tail bared, and sweating blood, she gallops across the glade, straight into the forest among the burning, white-hot trees.

The Forest Folk in the water-hole sat with staring eyes, feeling they knew not what and grunting in undertones. Had they not seen Death die? Crueller even than the tiger is fire!

The forest burned itself out. But it was evening and night before the earth had cooled so that the Forest Folk dared to climb out of their place of refuge. And not till the next day could they think of going on. For them existence was to begin again from the beginning; the forest was burnt for miles around; a new forest must be sought, they must wander out into the unknown; and so the Man grasped his flint in his left hand and led off, talking to himself and full of wisdom as he walked in front; the men followed on his heels, after them the mothers, and last of all the young people, in just the same order as they had come.

But meanwhile their number had increased, for one of the women had had a baby, from fright and before its time, while they sat in the pool given over to death — no easy birth. Amid all the thundering noise of the fire and the doomed beasts a dismal note asserted itself, the cry of a woman in birth-pangs, and soon after the feeble whimperings of a new-born babe announcing its entry into the world with wailing.

The little one came into the world half-drowned, the smoke of a disaster was his first breath, howls and heat his first sensations. But no sooner was he born than the little wrinkled imp had strength to find his way, greedy though blind, to his mother's breast in search of nourishment; one creature sucking life from the other, as is the way of things. Happy was the mother to have got this little wretch, that was uglier than death, toothless as a senile but hungry as a leech; she made a nest for it of her arms and breast, hid it from the Man and kept it quiet with her mouth against its mouth, lest he should hate it and in an access of rage fall upon this new whining thing in his company. Weakened and devoted she stumbled on when they had to go, the last of the herd, with a trail of blood behind her.

And so the procession moved off on its wanderings, the Man in front with spear and stone, ready to thrust or strike, the Woman in the rear with the fruit of her body and her sex, a never-healing wound which the Man keeps open.

But on the whole that terrible day showed a balance in favour of mankind; after the fire they entered upon a series of feasts and solemnities; for miles around the earth was laid with a banquet of meat, from roast pigeons fallen from the sky to elephants broiled whole with vegetables in their mouths. The death of the beasts was no loss to men, and they themselves had suffered only an increase.

They increased in days of prosperity, and calamities also caused women to give birth; thus they increased and multiplied. The Man put up with it, though at heart he hated that any but himself should eat his fill, even among his own people; still, numbers were a consideration, especially at night, and for other reasons. It is a known fact that many yell louder than one, the greater the chorus the stronger their rights; therefore company was tolerated.

The new-born child was accepted: it was a boy; the Man pinched him till he cried and beat him till he stopped — the paternal initiation — after that he seldom bestowed any attention on him. He was in his mother's charge and she nursed him into a human being; rounded and straight was her body when she got him, her

firstborn, and her breasts hung like empty bags when he was
weaned; but then he was such a blooming boy to look at, a real
wonder, with his mother's fulness and something of his father's
vocal powers; he soon made his mark in the tribe.

Nature had looked upon him with favour. At his birth he was
baptised and tasted death from drowning, but water vouchsafed
him life; his first breath was stopped by coughing, yet the smoke
did not choke him; troops of frenzied cattle shook the earth close
by him, a stench of burnt horn, blood and sweat was the first he
smelt, and the fright became imbedded in his instincts; but even
the maddened herd let him live, galloped around the place where
he was, on both sides of the swamp — though many were forced
into the mire and perished there, none came where the Forest Folk
were crouching; — the tigress was within his own length of him,
but left him untouched; all creation had received him in a way
apart, all the powers of destruction had revealed themselves in their
frightfulness, life had been wasted as though the whole world was
to be emptied, and just at that moment life was given to him.

Was there any other explanation of this but that almighty, all-
subduing fire had shone upon his birth and held all other powers
in subjection? It seemed that his life was sacred from the very
beginning.

Therefore, in memory of the great forest fire and for the gratification of Him on high who had thundered and strewed fire over
the earth but spared men, they made Gunung Api his gossip, consecrated the boy to him and gave him the name of Fyr.

He became a great man of fire and the forefather of a rich race.

V

FYR'S CHILDHOOD

His first steps in the world Fyr took on all fours, painfully crawling to begin with, then running pretty fast on hands and feet
with his backside in the air; and his mother had many a fright at
the boy's inconceivably rapid disappearance if she turned away for
a moment.

Fyr went exploring in the grass and came upon other quadrupeds who gladly adopted him as a playfellow; a litter of jackal cubs that had strayed from their lair in the neighbourhood and received him with joyful barks. They had wrestling matches where cubs and man-child rolled over on the ground in a downy mass, now the cubs on top with their forepaws victoriously planted on the vanquished, now Fyr uppermost with as many cubs under him as he could get his arms round. The muzzle and eyes of an elderly serious mother jackal were watching a little way off in the long grass, and on the other side Fyr's mother stood on guard, equally anxious and wrapped up in her young one. By such chance meetings acquaintances are made.

Partridges whirred into the air when Fyr walked through the grass, which was so high that he could not see above it; their noise startled him and he pursued the young birds which could not fly and ran chirping among the stalks; but they would not play with him, much as he would have liked it. And the little red-deer calves and baby foals he was lucky enough to see would not stop either when he approached; Fyr stretched out his hands to them, and they nodded, distended their nostrils, were not indisposed, but only sighed and trotted off when Fyr came too near. Other great horned creatures, before whom it was his turn to retire, came and went in the grass; it is a wide and complex world, what may one not meet in it? A long grey form crouches in the high grass, something with a veiled shifting light in its eyes and a long hungry jaw — but scarcely had he seen it when there is a horrid scream behind him and his lame mother appears in the grass with wild antics and keeps up a hoarse yelling until the grey stranger has slunk away; then he is shaken by the arm and dragged home, gets smacked and feels scalding tears falling on him; so now he will know another time that that new acquaintance is not to go any further. There are not a few things to learn before one knows the world of the jungle grass; meanwhile Fyr takes his hands off the ground and gets clever at walking on his feet.

The time arrived when it was hopeless for his mother to follow him; she saw his active head bob up and down above the grass as he moved like a deer in a leaping airy gallop; like the wind running over the grass, like the wild wind he galloped, till he was out of sight in the distance.

Fyr vanished from the tribe together with a band of comrades of his own age who were also able to look after themselves; they were glad to escape the dragging about listening to the grown-up people's endless outpourings about things which as yet had no existence for them: tribal wranglings, women's chastity and the like — things which as far as they were concerned never resulted in anything but a drubbing.

The pace of the tribe was too slow for them; on its day's roaming it never moved so rapidly as not to allow time for the men to wrangle at the top of their voices on the way; they stood still, right up against each other, with clenched fists, stretching their necks; walked away with a scornful laugh and came back with more abuse; picked up stones and held them in their hands; the Man would come up and yell louder than the adversaries, and so they stood bickering, all the men on tiptoe close up to each other, shouting each other down; the troop came to a halt, the women sat down with bowed heads, prepared to wait until the Man had roared the whole herd into silence. It is slow travelling when quarrels have to be patched up on the trail. Why keep together when you wear each other into wrinkles and all the rest of the world is open to everybody?

Well, that was what the growing youngsters didn't yet understand; they swept on ahead, increased their start more and more, until they were out of sight of the tribe and began to make a trail for themselves.

But they too kept together, with one at their head; it could not be otherwise, although as yet it was not violence, bitter compulsion, that held the young herd together — abuse of power at the top and dependence as a primary need below; it came about of itself through one being naturally the most active; he took the lead and the rest ran after him.

Foremost, of course, was Fyr; he walked upon air, it was the wind that animated him in his wonderful childhood; his lips were parted, his eyes wide open from much seeing and wandering, his hair flew out behind him, he was slim, a restless rover, with a careless song on his lips, fond of birds, a friend of flowers, a lover of the least little things: a scrap of down floating on the wind, a feather, a little fir-cone, even if it was not fit to eat — it was still his friend, it was a precious little cone, and he would give it away;

so great was his heart that he must part with his treasures to others. So rich of soul was Fyr.

At the head of a band who worshipped him Fyr first searched the open country, prairies, thickets and rocks, and all that was to be seen and found therein; then they ventured into the great forest, and there they were lost for a long time; they acquired a taste for living in the trees, left the solid earth altogether and did not return to it until they were rich in experiences.

There is a country between heaven and earth, a world entirely by itself, up in the trees: the airy bridge of climbing plants and interwoven foliage that stretches for miles like a connected carpet through the jungle. So dense is the growth that it looks like a green floor up under the tree-tops, a forest within the forest, stretched out and supported by the lofty trunks and with a waving roof of leaves overhead. Whole layers of mould are formed up here from decayed leaves, dust that is blown up, moss and rotting wood, worked together by worms and ants; a green sward in the air, watered by thundershowers and manured by seed-bringing birds; here grow grasses, great fields of weeds, wide hanging gardens filled with the hum of bees and bearing thousands of birds' nests, shaded by green awnings, perfumed by flowers and steaming with heat.

Up in this hanging world Fyr made merry with his companions; on this dangerous quaking floor they galloped around, stuck their legs through and pulled themselves up again after enjoying a dip into destruction; here they swung on a bridge of liana over an abyss, eating fruit and throwing the shells at each other's heads; always on the go, always nosing after a chance of showing off in some daring feat. Fyr works his way up into the topmost branches of a lofty tree, thrusts his head out of the foliage and shows himself, turns recklessly round to every side; *he* doesn't tremble for anything in earth or sky. Nobody dares follow him on such a breakneck climb. Anyhow it is lovely up there above all the tree-tops; it looks as if you could walk along over the whole forest. Here the air is full of swallows with their shuttle-flight in and out above the trees, storks and eagles circle round each other in great dizzy spirals far up towards the clouds and the blue spaces where the sun dwells. In an instant and for ever it all enshrines itself in Fyr's heart: the splendour of the sky and the swallows' airy flight, the superb force of the great birds, the sublimity of the clouds and the marvel of the sun; he has known flight, has been light as the air around him.

From the highest tops of the forest Fyr descended into the underworld by a dare-devil climb down the slender creepers and was lost in the gloom of the jungle's depths till his comrades began to be anxious about him. A little later he was seen scrambling up another tree, with loud shrieks and his hair on end all over his body; a snake was wriggling at his heels and the whole band shrieked, stiff with horror — until they saw it was a dead branch that Fyr was pulling up the tree after him; did any one ever see his like!

After that Fyr coolly led the whole party down into the depths, which no longer had any secrets for him. Looking down from the swinging tents of vegetation up in the trees, the trunks lost themselves in the darkness of the undergrowth, an eternal gloom by day and night, full of a noiseless movement of bats and great sluggish moths; slow, far-away echoes came up from it, the dripping of moisture in the depths of the forest; and viscous fumes ascended, a vapour heavy with dead wood and the resinous sweetness of new shoots.

But down at the bottom, below the heavy haze, a brewing of stagnant waters was going on, the tepid liquor of the swamp; moisture trickled down the tree-trunks, and among the roots were black pools bubbling with the fermentation of their thick humidity, wherein bloated toads warmed their backs; the mud was full of life, the land-crab with his mouth in quivering motion, fat snails crawling among the ferns and making the pale frond nod and show its spotted underside as their sticky bodies glided from one on to another, and centipedes coiling about the colourless stalks of plants that had never seen the light.

Here all was still, with a dense sinister quietness in which the slightest sound was heard — the bursting of a bubble, or when a snail opened its spiracle with a tiny smack — a fly buzzed and stopped still somewhere in the darkness where it caught a thread of light thin as gossamer, and on a pillow of moss, where a ghostly shimmer of light came through, lay a green lizard curled up fast asleep with open enamel eyes.

Fyr and his friends went about down here for a while, tasting the snails, breaking fungi in half, but not saying much, for the echoes had an ugly sound in those dark depths; they drank from the fresh pools and got tadpoles in their mouths, shuddered and looked up, longing for the daylight.

Yes, and there it was, high up above them. Halfway up in the airy space between the stems there was the glimmer of a few slanting rays which penetrated through from the daylight above and painted eyes upon the bark of a tree, a message from the sun. And up at the very top the straight stems lost themselves in a spacious ramification and passed into the dense united roof of foliage which at its dizzy height was illumined by a green twilight with starry patches of blue — the sky and the trembling leaves blending together in a sea of light and colour. At one spot the roof was so dazzling that the eye could scarcely endure it; leaves and sky were dissolved in a ring of many-coloured fire — behind it was the sun. The song of birds came with a distant swell from those green abodes, where the voice of the forest itself murmured continually, a mighty, lonesome breath that turned to music.

They soon had enough of the underworld and climbed up again into the hanging gardens, gambolled joyously in delightful sunny pavilions, in the company of birds and surrounded by flowers and bees, the scent of honey, moted sunbeams in the gaps of the foliage, the song of the cicada, the screeching of many-hued parrots, the cooing of doves — ah, the exceeding happiness of doves which you hear in their thick voices as they sit in their hidden nests — the chatter of the magpies from tree to tree, the cuckoo — that mysterious hide and seek played by a feathered creature which calls its question, Where am I? laughs and calls again and answers itself from the other end of the wood. Magic is at work in the forest, and the forest listens, sonorous, and is still; far and wide the forest lies with noonday, the drowsy present, in its embrace.

Thunder sounds afar off from Gunung Api, a muttering that makes the world seem larger and runs with lowering echoes through the valleys, from one domed wall of forest to the other and from the depth of the jungle comes the crash of an elephant as it breaks down a tree with its shoulder to get at the leaves.

In the deep resounding space between the trunks of the forest the woodpecker taps at a dead branch, beating time with its beak faster than one can follow the sounds, every beat marking the flight of an instant; and yet, as long as the woodpecker admonishes us of the transitory nature of things, so long shall the trees and the feathered creatures therein and the beasts and wondering man have life.

Fyr spent his childhood in the forest, and it wrought a wonder in his soul, lofty and profound, which was preserved in his blood and was destined to remain a wonder in the soul of distant generations when the forest was no more.

He came down from the trees in the same manner as his primeval ancestors had come down; he grew too big for them to bear him. At first he was not too heavy to scale the lightest branches in the very tops of the trees, then he had to stay on the thicker branches lower down, and at last he could no more get across from one tree to another, but had to come down to earth when he wanted to move about in the forest. As small insectivorous creatures, light as squirrels, his race had taken to the trees, and there it had gone so well with them that they had grown into great heavy men of the woods; a gradual descent, through generation after generation, brought them back to earth.

But not all had gone the human way: a remnant of the original stock, side by side with what was derived from it, stayed behind in the transforming forest. The small four-handed creatures who had shared their home with men when the forest was young still swung in the tree-tops, a strange, boisterous folk with restless eyes, without pauses, without memory, always hurrying as if they were too late and must hustle to try and catch up some destiny or other; Fyr stretched out his hands to them, wanted to talk to them; he mimicked their grimaces and threw in a laugh, pursed up his mouth for them, but they did not understand, flew off like a whirlwind and made hostile faces as they turned in their flight; like a band of startled spirits he saw them disappear and heard them scolding long after; Fyr could not win their friendship, and yet he had a place in his heart for every creature in the forest.

Nor would the big, dangerous dog-faced men, who lived outside the forest in the open rocky country under the mountain, receive advances or be reconciled, whatever tricks one might show for their benefit — going on all fours like them, striking the ground with the flat of the hand like them, ducking down or making one's self tall like them, with all kinds of eloquent twitchings of the forehead — they turned aside their striped face, whose grin had stiffened to a mask, wagged their jaws and showed their teeth, unable to sustain a man's gaze but ready for violence if he came nearer; they were ugly and sufficient to themselves, there was no getting a smile out of them. And so one had to let them go; they went about all day long on the mountain side turning over stones and putting everything they found under them in their mouths, worms, snails and ants; it looked as if they expected to find something special under every stone they raised — a forgotten trail, an old, lost destiny — and instead found only vermin, food sufficient for the moment but no sustenance for the soul; they were in retreat and knew not joy.

Far in the interior of the jungle, in the most lonely and inaccessible places, Fyr and his comrades might come upon queer old men of the woods who lived down on the ground, retired and silent, not very different from men and yet not men, strangely wrinkled, as though from great age, and worn by grief; they defended themselves with mute expressions of terror which made horror creep upon the back of him who approached; it was always dark where they sat, in an attitude of collapse, back to the root of a tree; and if one came again they were no longer there, they wanted to be alone and made their way deeper and deeper into the forest to find peace. Change was no longer to their liking; when transformation was at work in the forest they went off to some place that remained the same. They were born old; and, such as they were, the only thing to do was to leave them alone. They too had come down from the trees because they had grown too big for them, but they had remained in the forest and in the shadows.

When he was grown up Fyr sought his tribe again and found it in the open country on the lower slopes of Gunung Api, roaming about with the Man in the midst as usual. The meeting was not marked by any special cordiality: they looked up and observed his presence, with the youthful band that accompanied him, as though they had never been away. An addition to the striplings of the tribe was neither desirable nor the reverse — they knew their place, didn't they? on the outside of the square at night.

But Fyr's return to the main body made no small stir among the women: the raw-boned lad had grown into a handsome joyous youth, tall and faultless as a young tree, with eyes like stars and a big happy mouth; he brought a parrot with him from the forest;

the bird was his friend and sat upon his hand, it could talk like a man. It appeared from one thing and another that Fyr had acquired a secret understanding with the beasts while he had been away; he was seen in the company of wild, roving horses on the prairies, and always had some young animal that he had picked up and took about with him for pleasure.

But Fyr did not stay with the tribe for very long at a time; more often than not he was away on long expeditions, exploring farther and farther into the forest and up the banks of the river towards Gunung Api; it was even said that he roamed right out to the sea, of which the tribe had some vague inkling, but where they had nothing to do. His movements were periodical, at some seasons he was away and at others he came back again, according to the weather; and the weather had habits of its own, fairly regular to those whose memory served to record them.

The life of the tribe had not many attractions for Fyr; it was monotonous. The Man was always the same, and there was no denying that latterly he had begun to be noticeably lazy. The old man preferred sitting still; he sat on the ground day after day, on some little knoll, raised above the rest of the tribe who assembled about him in a ring; there he sat in superhuman silence, only using his eyes, which ranged from one to another or lost themselves in long unfathomable gazing at the sky. He ground his teeth with closed mouth and moved his lips imperceptibly, mutely savouring his own perfection of power and wisdom; he twitched the tip of his nose as cold private meditations came and went. Food was brought to him, and he ate without laying aside his dignity; he just gave a little toss of the head when he wanted to call up some sinner, and he still used his staff to some purpose, but not for beating; there was a shorter way, straight forward, and he stabbed, making deep bleeding holes with the pointed end of the stick. Crying children had to be brought to him to be pinched; but his sight was no longer very good and the mothers could slip a limb of their own in between and rejoiced at the bruises on their flesh if they were able to save their little ones.

Over the women the old man's sway was exercised more and more without the use of words, simply by the play of his features and as little as possible of that; they fell miaowing in the dust if he did but move a hair. Whether because it was beneath his dignity or he had become indolent, he no longer visited upon his wives the sacred act of violence reserved to himself, but he still encompassed them at a distance with a brutal brightening of the eye and indicated his right with a gesture, before which they lay flat as hens shrinking from the hawk. The outrage begun in spirit by the old one was then usually completed behind his back by the younger men; at last their time had come.

Finally the Man lay down all the time and had people brought to him, felt his way with closed eyes until he found a fleshy spot and then dug his fingers in. Ah, at one time he had had such strength in his thumbs that he could pluck a piece of flesh out of a man's body, but now his claws scarcely left a blue mark.

And thus he lay one morning, with scarcely a sign of change, but without movement and without breath, white-haired, long and thin, with stupid eyes open to the sky. He was cold; they brought a child to his hand, but he pinched no more. It was he and yet not he — in silent wonder and fear the tribe stood around him, and for the first time it occurred to many of them that the dreaded leader who in their eyes had towered to heaven, superhuman in size, almighty, unapproachable, was in reality a poor withered old scarecrow and had long been so; it was fear they had feared, not he.

When they realized that he would move no more, one of the men stretched out his hand and took the staff, swung it above his head with a roar, and instinctively all the rest fell on their knees — now *he* was the Man.

For years afterwards, when the tribe passed the spot where the Old Man had lain down, he was still there; they reverently turned aside, but stole a glance and saw him lying in the same position, a long whitened skeleton in the grass and the dreaded head turned to the sky with gaping teeth and great empty eye-sockets.

VI

ON THE MOUNTAIN

WHEN Fyr was quite grown up and had a beard he left his tribe and took up his abode alone upon the mountain. Here he went through a course of learning and acquired arts whose bearing was so great as to bring about a parting in the destinies of the Forest Folk; those who followed Nature remained her dependents and had to migrate in order to retain the conditions they required; those who followed him rose superior to the restraints of existence and became changed men. The elders went in search of warmth, but he showed his followers the way to fire.

Down in the lowlands eternal summer still prevailed, but it fell to Fyr's lot to steal a march on what was coming by making his way up the mountain; here in a rarer atmosphere he became acquainted with cold nights, but at the same time learned to endure them in company with fire. He became familiar with fire and bequeathed to his descendants a power which was to bring them out of the state of Nature and lead them into the path of humanity.

Early in life Fyr felt attracted to Gunung Api, for he had been dedicated to fire as a child and had received its name, it was his kinsman; and when he judged himself fitted thereto he set out to present himself.

No one had ever had the unreasonable, unseemly idea of going up Gunung Api; no one had seen that side of the mountain which looked away from the valleys where the Forest Folk lived, nor the land beyond which was hidden by the volcano — if there *was* land and not simply a vast abyss of fire — what was behind Gunung Api none could guess. All that was known was that the sun came from there; it rose every day behind the foot of Gunung Api; the moon too came from that quarter — likely enough big sources of fire lay behind there. And Fyr felt drawn towards the heavenly bodies, for they must also be of his kindred if they came from Gunung Api. The desire of getting in closer touch with them and fathoming their ways was a reason the more for Fyr's taking to the heights.

On his way up the mountain — which Fyr did not cover in one

journey but in many, day after day, carefully examining every bit of ground as he went and always ready for retreat if the mountain should show signs of disapproval — he first left the forest behind; the palms and warm plants he was used to in the lowlands gave place to a different and cooler vegetation. From the height of Gunung Api's nearest spur he was able to look down into the valleys, which lay steaming with warm haze and growth; a heavy, surcharged vapour came up from them, and beneath this blanket of luxuriance the Forest Folk were now wandering; but above Fyr's head the air was clear, a cool breath descended upon him; all that he met henceforth on his upward way was a new world to him.

He made unexpected discoveries regarding the immense size of the mountain; at a distance it looked like a peak that one simply had to go up, it seemed to rise up close at hand; but it took many days' journey merely to reach the foot of the mountain and wide stretches of country extended over the lowest slopes; what looked from below like scratches in the mountain side turned out to be vast precipitous ravines that lost themselves in an abyss below and yawned to the blue sky towards the mountain top, with a rushing stream at the bottom and choked with lava blocks and bushes. Still higher up lay steep beds of ashes, the end of which was out of sight on the precipitous slope; but here the mountain was already so restless under foot and gave out such ominous smells that Fyr could not make up his mind to go on towards the summit. At a lower altitude, where plants still grew, strange dried-up bushes and dwarf trees, Fyr worked his way round the mountain and to begin with got a view of the other side.

Here a disappointment awaited him. It turned out that the nature of the mountain was much the same on the farther side as on the side he knew; here too it passed through different belts of vegetation and great waves of broken country into a vast lowland filled with haze from countless swampy woods, a country as far as the eye could reach like that Fyr came from. On one side the land ended in a deep bay with an infinite horizon of water in the farthest distance; this was the sea. And now it appeared that it was from this end of the world the sun came, here he rose red and gleaming every morning. So after all the sun was not born of Gunung Api. Fyr saw that he had small hope now of reaching the place of his rising: one of the tasks he had set himself receded into the vague unknown. But during the time of his stay on the mountain he kept a watch on the sun's movements and in the course of years became acquainted with its habits.

Years — yes, he was the first among men to take note of time and keep record of the passage of the heavenly bodies, their return and the regularly repeated changes on the earth that were connected therewith. From his high and airy station, whence he had a free view round most of the horizon, and with Gunung Api as a fixed point for the rest, he gradually became clear about the paths of the sun and moon and the time it took them to complete their course and begin it over again.

Most striking was the behaviour of the moon; it appeared now round, now in a more or less shrunken condition, as though bites had been taken out of it; now it vanished altogether and then began to come again, a little bit of it, which however increased in size every evening, as though it were healing of itself and recovering from its sufferings; and this repeated itself in the course of a number of nights so great that one could not exactly remember how many they were but had a certain definite feeling that the interval was the same each time; that was the moon's time. What else happened to the moon, why it got sick and came right again, Fyr did not attempt to explain to himself; there seemed to be some fairly uniform encounters going on in the sky of the same kind as when the beasts disagreed down on earth: dogs that gnawed at the moon, clouds, monsters that swallowed it, but then it grew again every time; Fyr contented himself as a spectator by counting up how long it took each time: a moon's time, neither more nor less, about as many nights as he had fingers and toes and fingers again; a long, congested calculation and difficult to keep in the head.

But the sun's time was a more difficult matter. It was a good while before Fyr even discovered the fact that it had definite recurring periods in its movement; and, after he had noticed that it rose and set differently from day to day, though imperceptibly each day, it took years before he grasped how this was and how long the interval — years, in point of fact, for that was the conclusion of the matter, when he was able to survey the sun's course and the time it took. It was a long time, and no small mental effort to remember so long; but here Fyr was assisted by his experience of the moon's phases, which divided time into smaller and more manageable lengths. When he had observed the sun's changes they consisted in this: that it rose at a point on the horizon which day by day moved round to another point, so that one might expect it to travel by degrees all round the horizon, but it did not do that; when it had reached a certain point, which Fyr had noted from his fixed look-out on the mountain, it turned and began to rise farther back every day in the direction of the point it had started from, and so on over again. Why? Yes, why cross the sky every day to go down into the depths on the other side, for the sake of the walk, and why shift one's starting point every day within certain bounds, and then turn back again? It must be due to some peculiarity of the mind with which one is equipped as a heavenly body, capriciousness of behaviour combined with the most rigid regularity in the long run. So much is certain, that when Fyr compared his calculations the absolute result was that the moon appeared round just as many times as he had fingers with his two big toes thrown in, during the period it took the sun to travel along the horizon and return to its starting point; that was the sun's time. And by this vague standard, in itself incapable of survey but holding good once for all, Fyr learned also to measure his own existence. From the first time he observed that the sun turned and that it would turn again with the same interval, he reckoned his years; there were just as many of them while he lived on the mountain as he had fingers on one hand, together with the thumb on the other.

Over the nature of the sun he pondered much. It was forbidden to look it in the face, for that one was far too insignificant, and it smote the eye with weakness if one dared. In that respect it was like the fire from Gunung Api; the most natural conclusion was that one had to deal with a fire hovering in the sky. But he did not go deeper into that side of the sun's riddle until he had become familiar with fire.

In connection with the course of the sun and the year it dawned upon Fyr that plants and trees changed their appearance at intervals which occurred, and recurred precisely by periods corresponding with the year. Down in the valleys where the trees were always alike this would not have been noticed, but on the mountain it was otherwise. On ascending from the warm valleys of the lowlands one came upon trees of a different and cooler kind; after the palms came light, fresh leafy forests, and above them again was a belt of pines, and then again more foliage trees, but of a slender, feebler kind; finally wide tracts with nothing but a growth of low bushes and hardy creeping plants. On the mountain Fyr discovered that there is a blossoming time, a fruit time, and a time when plants are barren; after which they come into leaf again and begin anew; all within the same period that the sun takes on its journey back and forth: this was the first observation of the seasons. It was closely connected with the experiences Fyr acquired regarding the weather; sun, plants and weather went hand in hand; for half the year there were good days, the other half less good; it was noticeable too how this changing of the year made itself felt in his own existence.

The first general change he felt after he had come up from the lowlands was that the nights were cold, all the year round; later on he found out that things go worse during half the year; then the days too were cold. It made a very marked difference how high he was on the mountain; it was colder the higher he went, a state of things which for a long time he could not explain, since when he moved upward it was towards the fire; but so it was.

How did Fyr manage to get through the cold nights on the mountain? Well, there was the fire, Gunung Api's warmth; he had to go some way up the mountain, where the cold could be felt, in order to reach this warmth; this contradiction characterized from the first his relations with fire, which from year to year he developed into an art. For he soon learned to retire up the mountain every evening when the cold began to penetrate his coat of hair, right up above the tree limit where the ground was steep and barren, for there he knew it was warm, and he made himself comfortable for the night in caves under the lava or simply under the lee of a warm block.

These advances to Gunung Api required delicate tact; it would not do to offend or annoy the Old One, even if one were distantly related to him; Fyr was very modest about it and came stealing up in the dusk, on all fours like a dog, not wishing to be seen too clearly; during the night he made himself small behind a warm stone with a vigilant ear, even while asleep, for every rumbling in the interior of the mountain. Of course he did not venture *too* far up the hot, naked floor towards the mouth of the volcano, where the clear glow could be seen shining through rifts in its side; it was sufficient if one had enough radiant heat to be able to sleep as comfortably as in the warmest sunshine in the middle of the day. Still, it was not a bad thing to be as near a glowing crack as possible; one slept all the more quietly for venturing there, since it was certain that, where the red smouldering fire showed through the mountain, no other living thing would come, neither snake nor beast of prey: the gleam of fire kept the night clean about the sleeper, though of course at no small danger to himself. With caution and one eye half-open now and then, Fyr found time after time that nothing happened and came to regard himself as on a tacit peace footing with the volcano. Every time he went to rest he courteously asked permission, and as the mountain did not say No, he took it to mean Yes, and lay down in the pleasant warmth.

And when the sun rose and woke Fyr early on the mountain, he crept down refreshed to the forest after mumbling his thanks to Gunung Api for the night — more and more a matter of form, since the mountain did not seem to hear what was said. During the day it was quite possible he might forget his dependence on old Father Fire up above; but in the evening when the shadows fell and he felt the need of a little warmth and protection again, he turned his steps in silent diffidence back to the mountain.

Now and then, too, he contributed to the maintenance of these good relations by a gift, according to his means; if he was well fed and supplies were plentiful it was not amiss to bring some little thing to the fire by way of acknowledgment, such as a bird or a fruit, which was dropped into a rift with fire at the bottom. That the mountain accepted small contributions was beyond a doubt; it answered at once with a voluptuous hissing and consumed in a very short time whatever was given it: fruit with leaves, branches and all, it had an appetite for everything. And it could not be denied that there was a wonderful smell, a most delicate savour, about the things the fire ate.

VII

FIRE AND MAN

𝔜ᴇs, there was no doubt about that, the things the fire had had in its mouth acquired a peculiarly tempting and delicious taste, whether they were fruit, which was made softer and sweeter thereby, or flesh, which gave out a positively sinful incitement in its broiled fragrance. Fyr might sometimes forget to thank Gunung Api for his warmth, but he showed persistence in bringing gifts to the fire and so much sympathy while it ate them that his mouth watered, he slobbered all down himself, and his nostrils dilated till the fire shone right into his head. Would it do to have a taste?

The fire did not always finish its meal, it often left some charred scraps — on purpose, perhaps? Fyr asked politely whether he might, and as he did not get a No he took it to mean Yes and helped himself to the leavings. It was quite a profitable thing to bring presents to the fire.

Fyr had not had much experience of eating meat before he came up the mountain. It was only to be had after forest fires, in circumstances which made its enjoyment a mixed pleasure, as when he had been born — he had heard all about that; then the whole world had offered a banquet of roasted animals which lasted for two days, but on the third the meat had gone off, and the Forest Folk had nearly perished from stench and horror; the whole world had become an abomination to them; so short a step is it from abundance to deadly nausea.

Since then Fyr had tasted fire-sweetened meat after occasional smaller conflagrations which did not spread to the whole forest, and his mouth watered every time he remembered it. Even then there had been some blunting of the deference due to fire when one filched a bit of its meal; the savoury odour of newly roasted cattle on the smoking ground was too irresistible; it penetrated the very palate and positively clouded the judgment; there was really some excuse, and before a man knew what he was doing he would be sitting with the shoulder of a cow in his hands, intoxicated with meat; the fire would have to excuse it.

Besides, was there not a hint in the way the fire made its meal, always leaving something, a nice charred scrap? Was it not actually trying to *teach* men to eat meat in a more proper and decent way than they otherwise knew, well prepared, toasted and blessed by the fire?

Of course in the ordinary way one only got meat in a raw, natural state, as a rule alive; the smaller creatures one ate, nestlings, mice and so on up to the size of a hare, went into the mouth whole, just as they were, and tasted as blood tastes, raw and qualmish; but the delicate roast meat of large animals that had been in the fire was a whole world of new taste; could one possibly be altogether indifferent to it?

Fire was a greedy man with a great range of appetite, it ate everything without exception, the forest as well as the beasts within it. As regards wood, whether fresh or charred, a man could not share its taste; animals, on the other hand, which fire had partly eaten and left in a roasted, half-burnt state as though it could not get any more down — were they to be wasted? was it not something like mistaken modesty, almost a crime, to let them lie?

Experience taught that it was lawful to eat. If one *had* made free with the food of fire and then went in fear of the punishment, and the punishment failed to appear, how was that to be interpreted?

Indulgence in meat in itself made you feel satisfied and impudent, so that you had less fear of the consequences than if your stomach was empty; and it was asking rather too much if you were to expect punishment when you *hadn't* eaten, so why not help yourself till there wasn't room for a hiccup? then you could await the consequences at your ease; whatever might happen, you were full.

Besides which, the fire as a rule had gone, the blaze was over, when the chance of a bite occurred; for you didn't stand in the path of the wind but away from it, so with the exercise of tact and experience of former occasions you could arrange things quite well with fire.

So far did Fyr's knowledge of fire extend before he betook himself to Gunung Api; it was pretty much the point of view of the Forest Folk: complete dependence on fire and the opportunities of eating roast meat confined to the somewhat rare orgies when, after a volcanic eruption or a lightning stroke, fire made one of its big meals; but on the mountain Fyr established daily and lasting relations with fire, to their mutual advantage, as it seemed to him.

Up in the lava cracks, which were hot and evil-smelling by day and shone with an internal glow by night, the fire led a pinched and smothered life, had nothing to feed upon and never flared up unless it was given something; so Fyr saw to that — where the lava yawned like an open mouth and he could venture near enough without burning the balls of his feet, he threw branches and victuals into it, fruit and an occasional unlucky rabbit, and the fire was always glad to get these things; it answered in a brisk blaze, a suffocating smell, with much voluptuous licking up of what it loved best. As a rule it ate up all his gifts, unless he was leery enough to lay them a little to one side on top of the ashes, so that it had to leave something; it didn't seem to notice this, and so Fyr got his share of the meal. Well, one good turn deserves another — you paid the fire a good price and had a reasonable profit out of it yourself; if it wasn't satisfied with the bargain, why it might some day run the risk of going out!

That was it! Not that he was thinking of the big Fire itself, Gunung Api — pray don't think that; but there's fire and fire; the babies it gets, for instance, they are not always so invincible, at any rate while they are small. For it was evident that fire propagated itself and spread; it was not a connected body but a family of many flames and fire spirits; they were born of sparks after being hatched in the glow of Gunung Api, and each of these babies might quite well turn into a whole forest fire, that had been seen before now; the least little wee flame might grow to a terrific size if only it got food enough. But if it got no food, it died; its fate was no different from that of other beings.

So Fyr used to feed the fire up on the mountain, holding branches to it to see what happened; he nursed fire-babies and little by little got an insight into their nature. When a fire had devoured just so much wood as he had given it and got no more, it went out and there was an end of it. If he threw it wood, it was alive and big so long as that wood lasted but shrank up and finally went out when it was eaten up; so it was clear that any fire burning by itself was dependent on just how much it got and in that way also on him who gave it.

If you had dipped a branch in the glowing lava and got a little fire on it, you could therefore quite well take it up and lay it branch and all on the ground, add chips to it, play with it like a fire puppy if you liked and as long as you liked; for if it got too big and dangerous you simply left off adding chips to it, and then what happened? it soon lost its strength if it could not reach anything of its own accord.

To say nothing of water. If there was a puddle among the adjacent rocks one could make the fire very tame; even the glow within the cracks of the mountain side went black and cold when it rained. Filling your hollowed hands with water you could kill even a fairly big and voracious fire baby on the spot. This playing with fire gave you a feeling that after all you were not absolutely the inferior of Gunung Api and his young.

In the evening when Fyr came up Gunung Api to go to rest on the warm lava floor, he took food for the fire with him, fished up a baby out of one of the crevices and amused himself with it as long as he felt inclined; it gave not only warmth but light, it cast a gleam so that he could see the nearest objects; it was a little cave of light, like a spot of daylight in the midst of the darkness, which kept the night at arm's length. Then he had something warm to eat, sharing with the fire — he found the food and got his share of it nicely done — well, that was how Fyr thought it would work out, so that one day he and the fire would understand and help each other.

Fyr had all along lived alone on the mountain, except for some women who followed him; the friends of his childhood in the jungle stayed down in the lowlands and went about with the tribe, exercising themselves in manliness and developing their voices; but Fyr had now formed an acquaintance to which no one before him had dared to aspire, and he began to have an idea of sharing it with the others in the lowlands. But he would not do that until he had reached such a point that he would not have to bring the tribe up the mountain but could take the fire to them.

Nor could he himself keep up this half day's journey up the steep slope to the warm places; it was too far to carry food to the fire, and there was no forest up there: he would have to fetch the fire down! The place where he wanted to use it was down among the vegetation where his food grew, not on the barren mountain side, and he could do without Gunung Api's warmth at night if he made himself a blaze and thus had fire in another form.

So one day, acting on a sudden impulse but after mature consideration and with the knowledge he had already gained of the nature of fire, Fyr took a burning branch and went down the mountain with it. Had he not hardened himself for years against the overpowering dread inspired by fire and acquired a sure insight into its nature, it would have appeared to him impossible to take its young away, to walk off with it, disappear with it — an unheard-of and presumptuous robbery, but he did it!

And it came off. True, the mountain was shaken to its foundations, emitted thunders and reached out arms of fire right down into the valleys to destroy the robber and all men with him, but this was half a year later; the mountain was slow about it and harmless, since Fyr in the meantime had left the volcano.

And there was no need to dwell there any more! The dependence he had lived in — having to keep always in the neighbourhood of the mountain so as to reach his warm sleeping places at night, a pretty hard lot, not to say bondage, since he could scarcely go more than a day's journey away — this obnoxious dependence was now a thing of the past; he carried his own fire, his own volcano in fact, wherever he chose to take up his abode in the forests round about, had no further need of Father Mountain at all!

So rapid was Fyr's progress after he had walked off with the fire. He knew of course what to do to make it propagate. Having taken it prisoner, with greater danger to his life than if it had been a poisonous snake, he carried it in his hands at the end of a burning branch, brought it as far down as he could and laid it on the ground. Then he fed it as carefully as possible, gave it dainty dry twigs and the tenderest of wood to bite at, until it got strong and blustered quite unpleasantly; then he coolly left off giving it any more until it calmed down again with quietly licking limbs; after that he lighted another long branch and went on with that; and thus he came farther and farther down the mountain, for Fyr was an artist and knew how fire was to be controlled.

When he had come down the mountain in this way until he found a place which suited him, he made a fire there and let it increase in power. It was incredible how much it could swallow; Fyr dragged up half a forest and threw it into its throat, till it grew almost sky-high and gave out a scorching heat. Fyr walked round and round, staring into its blazing world as though bewitched, forgot his surroundings, received the element into his soul and became a man of fire for the rest of his days.

But when he had feasted his soul with an immense blaze and seen its consuming might, he let it die down, kept it going for days and nights together with sticks, just a little fire; it could live like that too, if only it got a little all the time; it could be made big again whenever he wished.

He could always take young ones out of the fire and feed them up into a whole family; then he could let the mother fire go out and keep her offspring, could add grandchildren and great-grandchildren as often as he liked and to any extent.

Fire was tamed! The blaze that Fyr had kindled never more went cold. From the fire he first brought down all other fires are descended; it gave him young and young again for all the fires beside which he lived, and afterwards, when he had brought fire to his tribe, for the hearth of its every family; and from Fyr's tribe it spread to all others, to the whole Forest Folk, and with them it was carried out into the world as far as men have travelled.

But this brought about a division of the Forest Folk into the one tribe within which fire had been tamed and which had the tradition of its origin, and all the others who borrowed fire from it for household use without taking account of its sacred nature. This state of things set up a profound cleavage of far-reaching significance.

But even those who were acquainted with fire and its use without having an insight into its nature acquired an enormous advantage over all other creatures. For not only could they eat cooked food at any time without its attending dangers, if they simply carried a burning branch with them and fed it and renewed it on the way, but they could go to rest every evening beside a blazing fire; they had *light;* at last they had become masters of the night and its ancient abyss of terrors — beasts that hunted in the darkness and the awful unseen powers that haunted the night but yielded before light and fire.

Gone was the quaking misery of the square at night, when they sat with darkness pressing on their eyeballs and might expect at any moment to be dragged out by the leopard's claw; now they sat by the fire and watched the wild beasts hovering on the edge of the gleam and blinking palely at man's mighty new ally. The great cats sniffed the air with longing in their eyes, the good smell of men was enticing and called up memories, but the fire came in their way; they stood on three legs with fore-paw ready, but without hope, slobbered up the saliva that came into their mouths at the sight of so much well-lighted food so near them, but they were quite unable to enter the magic circle with which the fire surrounded itself at night.

And there sat the little human, cosy and warm, on good and friendly terms with the fire, and even if you please gnawing the bone of a brother of the self-same beast of prey that was prowling around with impotent sidelong glances at the blaze!

But at the same time they were careful to keep the covenant. If the fire was tame and rendered services, it was of course in return for being fed; it must have its offering. Besides wood, which satisfied its coarser appetite, it had to be given flesh at least once a day; and it must be said that the little men were very eager and ready to procure it, if possible several times a day, provided sufficient sacrificial animals were to be had, seeing that the leavings fell to their share and tasted so gratefully of the fire's lovingkindness.

In the distant tribes, which had received fire at second or third hand or perhaps had half forgotten where it ever came from — most of the Forest Folk had short memories — it might happen that the privilege of the fire as supreme messmate, the whole pious origin of the past, gradually receded into the background; but on the other hand every care was taken that the tribe from which fire came maintained the tradition in full force on behalf of the whole people.

The initiated here, who had their instruction from Fyr, did not neglect to show the fire all the honour due to it for burning, this was their care before all who used the fire; and it was therefore natural for other tribes to honour *them*, the initiates, who kept up the good relations with the Fire Spirit, in place of the spirit itself. Their sacrifices were known to have the right virtue, for which reason it was fair and just to provide them with the sacrificial animals they required; so much could an uninitiated do for the common weal. The tribe of the men of fire therefore never had to

trouble itself, but received as a matter of course all the slaughtered
animals needed by the fire and for their own consumption; an arrangement of this kind continued in force long after its origin was
forgotten; which is what we call a prescriptive right.

But all this lay in the future as part of the vast results connected
with fire, as did also the change in the life of the Forest Folk involved by their great consumption of meat, a factor which was the
cause of their breaking the peace with the beasts and adopting the
life of hunters.

VIII

GUNUNG API'S
HANDMAIDS

BEFORE Fyr returned with the fire to his tribe in the valleys, he
had founded a tribe of his own; this came about almost without his knowing it through his being visited quite often in his solitude by women; at last there was a whole flock of them about him,
and he had not the heart to scare them away.

They came of their own accord, and it said much for their tracking instinct that they were able to find him at all; that one should
have given any hint to another was scarcely likely; each of them
deserved the whole credit herself: astonishing how clever they
were on the trail. Yet Fyr thought he had hidden himself well out
of the way up on the mountain. He did not know that every morning a glorious song rolled down from the height, as though the
clouds were rejoicing, when he greeted the day together with the
birds, or he never gave it a thought; but that was what betrayed
him; the women followed that wonderful voice and came up to
him, torn by the bushes and with wounded feet, and each time he
was astonished anew at their unfailing sense of direction.

They were many and very different women who left their tribes
in the valley when they heard the sound, and that notwithstanding their tribal chief had a very good organ; the charm of distance
was stronger, they could not resist that voice from the mountain
and slipped away under the bushes when their owners were not

looking, braved the rough ground and the steep climb to reach the voice that sang so sweetly.

Fyr saw the first of them one morning when in an ecstasy of loneliness he had crowed at sunrise almost without knowing it; the sun and the wealth of the world beneath him gushed out of his heart in a song of joy, he stalked about on a high place owning the air and the daylight, it was all his — and then it was that he caught sight of a woman; she was sitting in the grass close by, had come quite quietly, and sat down, with her feet under her and her head bent, her long wild black hair falling over her face.

Hish! Fyr shooed at her, disturbed in his hymn to the sun: what did the thing want, what had she come here for? he clapped his hands to make her fly off; but she didn't move either for his shooing or his clapping, sat quite still fumbling with a blade of grass, made herself as small as possible, nothing but a little stick lying on the ground hidden by hair; she was scarcely there and not the least bit in the way, and then — well, Fyr hadn't the heart to shoo her any more.

Nor was she anything of a nuisance, it couldn't hurt a man if she was sitting in the grass off and on when he happened to turn round and his eye fell on her; as a rule she was forgotten; if he saw her again one day — well, there she was, quiet as a mouse, with her head wrapped in her hair; he got accustomed to her coming.

At last one day she flung all the hair from her face and looked up with dark, frantic eyes; she bleated with closed lips, as though a prisoner were calling in her breast, a prayer from a soul in darkness; hopelessly sunk in a necessity she yet knew not, a hot, mute world inextricably blended of outrage and warmth and craving for both. Then Fyr felt homesick for goodness. He cared no more for joy, unless he could share it with her. From that time he was no longer alone.

Some way up the mountain was a plain, it stood high but was of great extent, a country by itself with a fresh air and cool open groves; grass grew among the scattered trees, and wild flowers; none knew the place except the beasts and only few of them; it was the home of bees, and here dwelt the lark.

On this grass land it was that Fyr and the woman met, and here they made themselves nests in the grass, hidden from all the world, except from the blue daylight that poured down on them from

above. Food was here on every side for the frugal who were content to chew most of the day — this was the seed of the wild corn
growing here and there among the grass; you plucked a few ears
and rubbed out the grain in the hollow of the hand, blew the husks
away and put the fresh, still milky corn into your mouth. Honey
you could take from the bees when you had a taste for it, great
dripping yellow cakes which you pulled out of hollow trees; the
wild apple trees grew on the plain, holding out apples to the
passer-by; they were small and hard, but no man had tasted any
better.

In the thicket they found raspberries, a fruit they had not known
before, and they tempted each other to eat, artfully putting a berry
between the lips, the very best, which both must have a taste of;
you plucked a lot and got a little, what sort of a precious, provoca-
tive fruit could this be? In unity of soul they lingered among the
bushes.

The unknown country up there on the mountain had fruits of its
own, not like the pulpy overripe ones of the lowlands, dripping
with thick juices, begotten of humidity and eternal summer, but
small compressed and nourishing things, nothing to look at, like
the good grain in the grass, the nuts in the thicket, no bigger than
one's nail but mysteriously sweet, a condensation of all kinds of
subtle forces which seemed to be in the air here; wild plums that
had gathered the morning dew and tasted fresh and sharp as though
sated with thunder-showers and cool nights.

They witnessed the fall of the leaf, saw the trees turn sick and
cast off their yellowed foliage until they stood naked and the cold
wind blew through their bare branches; they themselves learned
what it was to shiver and huddle together towards evening; but
then they had the warmth higher up the mountain, the first hearth,
and later, when Fyr had tamed the fire, they took it with them
wherever they went.

And they witnessed the spring, the rebirth of the trees, when
the leaves came again and they turned green in a dewy and fragrant coolness, amidst the play of sun and showers; the appletree
blossomed, exhaling freshness, the whole plain was wavy with new
green grasses and a wealth of flowers. The wild sheep brought
their new-born lambs down from the mountain to the meadows
and clear streams; young calves with gristly hoofs took their first
clumsy steps in the grass, with a foolish look about the mouth and

night and the sky in their eyes. Above the plains hung the lark, rising in song upon bridges of light between showers; the wind and the grass talked together in an everlasting nodding and whispering, and a thousand bees hummed, a long, long hushed colloquy between them and the flowers in one vast drowsy note. Summer established its glory, the grasses shed their pollen and went to seed, the newly fledged nestlings attempted their first flight.

Imperishable is summer, as the poppy — as the poppy which cools its red flames a moment in the breeze and loses them when they are reddest — but is it not always summer when the poppy blooms? The wild young couple decked themselves with the poppy and were made drowsy by its fruit. In the heart of the poppy the seduction of summer lies hid, the brief glow and the long black slumber that follows.

So long as the poppy bloomed, their joy lasted. It unfolded his heart, he walked more warily upon the earth, day and night were to him as a marvel; and she became human, with eyes that saw; it even appeared that she had speech, a high shrill girl's note that expressed joy; and she drew herself up, no longer creeping bent double through the grass, but sunning herself erect; she accepted admiration like a bottomless bowl, so long as her hour of summer lasted.

That was their sojourn in a land no man yet knew. Without their knowing it they had dwelt in the forecourt of other ages yet to come and of another humanity.

Afterwards they fell back to the lowlands and the monotonous warm forest, and there their own time closed over them again. The heart shut up within him, and she crouched once more in her speechless solitude. But in the downy youngster that one day crawled between them was enshrined their life's marvel and the germ of a new one.

A troop of women followed Fyr when he showed himself in company with the fire to the Forest Folk in the lowlands; their number had increased — how, he didn't know, but supposed that women never came singly, they appeared in swarms after the manner of grasshoppers. To begin with Fyr had really believed it was always one and the same he had with him, so long as they approached him one at a time; the difference was too trifling for him to notice it — and what of it? They were all pretty.

Ah yes, desirable all of them, particularly well furnished as to the body and with rich limbs, plump beyond expression, a delight to the eyes, extraordinarily alluring, every one! How could he reject any of them; how could he say which was which? Seen from the back there was no knowing one from another, there was the same long hair and the same rotundity of the middle which speaks eloquently in favor of a woman even when she turns away. In front they exhibited another cloven roundness, equally charming in all of them and pretty much the same in all: cloven and double they were all over, as though it had really been intended to make two maidens out of the abundant material that went to each, but there had only been a head for one. Mentally they were not to be distinguished one from another; they were just as short of soul as they were long in the hair, without a yesterday and without a morrow, but greedy for the present; if you heard a sudden whirlpool of utterance beside you, you knew it was one of them, a flood of words all at once, all sluices open and on again, that was their way. Their behaviour towards men and towards each other was entirely different, they had two kinds of manner; but Fyr never got the bearings of more than the one side of their wiles.

He had no idea how many there were in the troop; his notions of number were based on the more thrifty heavenly bodies, two or thereabouts: the sun and moon and some particular big star among the rest; to count the stars themselves, on the other hand, was beyond a man's power, of them there was a whole field; and such things as the sea-sand, swarms of bees, the tides, floods, rain, wind and other obscure natural forces were not to be counted but to be taken precisely for the unaccountable things they were. Nor was he aware of ever having seen them all together at one time and in one place; who was to have precedence was presumably a matter they settled amongst themselves; to judge by what he heard it was not always arranged amicably; occasionally moans and the sound of hollow blows like thumping a cow reached Fyr's ears from behind the bushes, and many a time he found himself embracing a panting, perspiring maiden with a shamefully scratched face.

Gradually, as they settled down, it came about as a matter of course that the women took over the feeding of Fyr; they had been used to this in the valleys and felt the need of having some one to live for; their only trouble was that there were so many of them to do it, each one would have preferred to wear herself out in feeding him alone. They fought in secret for the work, gouged out each other's eyes with their fingers, were always tearing at each other's poor hair and ramming their knees into each other's stomachs to keep each other away from the Man; but whoever might be victorious, the food always reached Fyr's lips whether he was hungry or not; his maintenance was assured, no unpleasant thing for a hermit in the wilderness and a great saving of time, which again was to the advantage of his tranquillity and placid meditation.

For he was occupied all day long with his arts of fire, making paths in the dust with his finger, signs of power which from his frequently looking up at the heavenly bodies were thought to be associated with them; evidently he was giving them their direction and keeping order in heaven, without him the whole thing would soon tumble down, so he had to be kept well nourished.

Often Fyr was entirely wrapped up in his researches into the secrets of Nature, which only revealed themselves reluctantly and after long study on his part; he barely noticed that the food was there, absently took a bite of it, chewed and went on pondering a riddle — a little cry of satisfaction that God was eating might then draw his attention from the food to the hand that offered it, and from the hand to the woman — was she there again, the beauty, whichever one it might be?

That his company of women took him for Gunung Api, the great Fire Spirit himself, the God of the Forest Folk, had long been clear to him. They saw that he ruled over the fire, and it needed no effort of thought to attribute its power to him. Towards the fire itself, which they approached in his company and under his protection, they showed no sign either of contrition or of devotion; whether it was that they had no power of imagination or were unable to form an idea of spirit, they regarded fire with a certain stiffness, avoided it as they avoided water, well knowing that both were injurious to the skin; if they went too near the coals they blew on their fingers, though without its making them any the wiser next time; but more than a smart they were incapable of feeling for the element. No, to them fire existed only as the effulgence it shed over its author and gloriously bearded exorcist; by its light they worshipped Fyr!

Of a surety he was Gunung Api. Had they not heard him sing-

ing on high, roaring with the very bull's voice of the mountain?
Did not everybody speak of Gunung Api as a great male being,
fire and voice and violence in one? Well then, that couldn't be any
other than Fyr!

Therefore while nourishing Fyr as they nourished their own
heart it followed as a matter of course that his fire must lack nothing either. Thus much the women were quick to learn under Fyr's
tuition, to keep up the fire by means of the things it loved; above
all wood, of which it could never have too much, but also with
other offerings, fruit, small animals, eggs and the like, whatever
one could pick up. Voracious he was, that fire, they grudged him
all the good things he ate; yet it did not all go off in smoke, for
Fyr raked the lion's share out of the ashes with a stick, luckily, and
devoured it himself; it made them so glad to see their blessed great
roaring bull buffalo of a God deign to keep up his strength.

Thus it was that the women became tenders of the fire, whether
by day or night, Gunung Api's ever vigilant and responsible hand-
maids.

He was an insatiable master; he had to be supplied unceasingly.
From this time forth the women had a new burden added to their
everlasting young one; they were never seen without a bundle of
firewood on their backs.

The Man, the creator, was meditating upon new things; having
given his family fire, his next intellectual exploit was to be weapons; but the women entered upon their long labour of patience,
their night-watching, their life of repetition upon repetition with
closed soul and an inexhaustible heart, by the fireside.

IX

THE FIRST HUNTERS

THE sensation was immense among the Forest Folk when Fyr
came down from the mountain with the fire and it was ru-
moured that, accompanied by a band of women, he was going
about the valleys with a conflagration which was said to be tame
and followed him wherever he went.

Did a fire burn along beside him or behind him in the grass, did it stop when he stopped and lie down at his feet perhaps? Could it also go against the wind? Did it take a little run into the forest and eat up a few trees and then come back to him when he called it? Such were the questions of the ignorant who had not yet seen the sight; but those who had were able to explain that the fire did not run loose, it did not move of its own accord, Fyr had it lying on the ground and in some way or other held it fast; it was his prisoner, and although it behaved in a very lively fashion, hitting about with long fiery arms and sending masses of smoke up to the sky, it had no idea of escaping, it stayed on the spot as long as Fyr wished and was obedient to him; unparalleled was the power he possessed! But when he wanted to move to another place he made the fire small, took it on the end of a branch and could go long distances with it before he laid it down again and fed it into a blaze.

Herein lay something of the secret, in a purely outward sense; in itself of course the whole matter remained inexplicable, Fyr's own most intimate private property, how he had made friends with the fire; but it was by feeding it he held it fast. It was given wood all the time and now and then an animal to keep it quiet; that was the first principle, simple enough in itself, which had to be grasped.

It was a long time before ordinary mortals ventured at all to approach Fyr and his dangerous companion. It would not do to come erect; they fell flat a long way off and crawled on their stomachs, on no account empty-handed, naturally a gift had to be brought, branches and wood for the fire, some beast or other one had been lucky enough to catch, maybe a pig — and it wasn't so difficult to snatch one out of a litter — many a man owed a good reception to the pig he brought, the fire appreciated that dish, roared high and gave out a beautiful smell when a pig was offered; Fyr himself announced his approval and favoured the choice, so pigs were a popular gift. The final approach to the sanctuary where the fire burned and Fyr went about it as an adept, attended by his female initiates, this final approach was made not only crawling on one's stomach but with one's face down on the ground so as not to look into the fire and annoy it by inquisitive staring, possibly with injury to one's sight; with eyes to the ground you wriggled up, pushing the sacrifice before you with your hands, until it was taken and you could turn round, get up and scamper back into safety. So hard was it to get used to the living incarnate

Gunung Api, even though it was not the Mountain in his own all-consuming person, but only one of his ardent young. Respect for Fyr was commensurate therewith.

But custom dulls all feeling; if you see a fire day after day and have proof, incontrovertible proof that it is tame, you can't keep on quaking before it. Some could, those whose susceptibilities were determined once for all by ancestors and their experience; when they saw the fire they had no peace, couldn't hold themselves, their strength failed them just when they needed it, their knees gave way and they ran for their lives at the best pace they could muster. That kind never got any nearer to the fire and were not to share in a new age; they would eat cold food the rest of their days as their fathers had done before them, that was good enough for *them!*

But then there were others, the young men of the tribes round about; they got used to Fyr and his fire just a little too quickly, came swaggering up with their inquisitive looks and had to be given a physical lesson in propriety; Fyr had to go so far as to throw a burning brand at them to get them weeping on all fours; a stiff-necked generation, but even impudence has its bounds. When they showed a sense of decorum they might be allowed to come with offerings; and in a round about way, through the hand-maids, they might in return come in for a scrap of the fire's meal, a roast pig's trotter or the like, conveyed out of the sanctuary, covertly of course — that kept them hanging about for ever; nothing they had eaten had had such a wonderful taste, all other food paled before it!

Fyr's first congregation came to consist of a mob of these young vagabonds from all the tribes around, with minds open to novelties and just the right degree of recklessness; they always had a "Gunung Api take me" or other unseemly oath on their lips, but could be depended upon if they were put on the right track; from these Fyr trained his first hunters.

For the supply of offerings soon began to fall off, there were limits to the kind of game that let itself be taken casually with the hands; it was true that man lived in profound peace with most of the beasts, but few of them allowed direct contact and not one would let itself be dragged off voluntarily; you had to take their lives first and that was not so easy a matter; you might kill them with a stone, that would answer once or twice in a herd, but then the rest became uneasy and would not let you come to close quarters any more. Formerly men had been able to wander about among the dense herds of wild cattle, deer and horses, shoulder to shoulder with them, and neither took any notice of the other; but when the demand for animals became brisk, they quickly began to adopt another attitude. It was clear that more drastic measures were needed and their capture would have to be put on a systematic basis, if the burnt offerings were to be kept up; the first necessity was implements.

And this is where Fyr's prolific brain began to breed.

Fir and the hearth advanced many things. Down here in eternal summer men had as yet no need of protection from the weather, but they were made safe at night against wild beasts, and they had acquired a taste, not to be eradicated, for cooked meat; another important thing was that with fire came a quieter life, the opportunity for self-communing. They were forced to remain in one spot, at any rate so long as the fire was burning; they could carry a torch about but not a hearth; that demanded permanence. The long evenings when Fyr sat by the fire taught him to devote time and attention to hunting gear, now that there was a use for it; from a co-operation between the insatiableness of the fire and the human appetite — consumption in a new style — proceeded a new art which blossomed in man's first weapon.

Hitherto the only implements — weapons when occasion arose — the Forest Folk had known were the staff and the stone. The staff was a branch picked up by chance with which the Man armed himself, an inventiveness which made him leader of the herd; it was a good friend to have on the trail, it reached farther than one's arm, gave a blow hard as a fist, and if pointed was useful for stabbing, but would also make a hole when blunt if used with sufficient force. As a beginning Fyr improved the staff; he put its point in the fire and hardened it, having the fertile idea that the point must be endowed by the fire with a deadly force through being dipped in it; and he was right, spears of this kind, for which long, straight and slender pieces of wood were to be chosen, did not fray up at the end when they had been in the fire, but kept a hard point. Experience showed that they would even go through oxhide if thrust by a powerful arm, they brought down big game; here Fyr's expectations were realized: the spear that had been hardened in the fire carried with it in a sort of metaphorical sense, but effectively, the murderous qualities of fire. Fyr did not keep this discovery to himself but imparted it to all who would learn; the more men with spears the better prospect of meat.

What did it matter if Fyr put weapons in the hands of his fellow-men, when in the same breath he was after something new, keeping his start? While everybody was coming to him for spears, thinking the whole science of arms was exhausted when you had such a thing in your hand, Fyr was well on the way to thinking out the axe!

This occurred to him as an intimate union of staff and stone, obvious enough but never thought of by any before him. There was the stone, it lay in the hand itself, man was born so to speak with a stone in his hand and an evil look — his aim: how far could he reach with it, either in his hand, when he could keep it, or by throwing, when he would lose it and so ought to have several by him? Throwing stones was an art; women never learned it, they swung with a stiff arm, couldn't get rid of the stone; but there were men who had trained themselves to throw with a jerk of the elbow and a sure eye, and they could bring down a bird on the wing; the stone, you might say, was a tooth far out where one's own tooth could not reach. For cracking nuts the stone was a good thing, and if it had a sharp edge you could file through pretty tough fruit shells with it or cut an animal open, but it was pure chance what you found. However, stones became sharp by being broken; if you struck two together and they fell in pieces you might often get a good sharp one that would serve you a long time. That was their knowledge of the use of stones; it had come about of itself and was common to all, even the women employed sharp stones in preparing food — the ones the men had thrown away as useless; and what did women want with new ones, weren't they born to drudgery?

The hard, brittle flint had long ago been discovered as the best stone for a tool, it split up easily when struck and gave very sharp edges; in shape the raw blocks of flint reminded you of human heads, white-haired old men; there was a feeling of kinship in using flint. It had a ring about it, keen and annealed it was, every flake of it sprang out and bit, drew blood, it thirsted to pierce and stain itself red . . . if staff and stone could but be made to unite, they would surely breed murder.

Cunningly Fyr began to try his hand at what lay in his head — how to get the flint made fast at the end of the stick; thus the connection was to be brought about, the bit of the stone indissolubly wedded to the range and swing of the pole — but how? Other men looking on at his attempts, leaning on the spears he gave them, shake their heads and smile at one another behind their hands: No, now the Fiery One is on the wrong track; what does he think he's doing? They see him lay cudgel and stone together and ponder — is it anything that wants a lot of thought, can anybody expect the stone to grow on to the stick of its own accord? Then it would have to have a mouth to bite itself fast, or the stick would have to gape and close on it — no, the Fiery One is wasting his time!

But Fyr stuck to it, trying over and over again; and one day after countless attempts he actually showed a cudgel which had a heavy, pointed flint made fast at one end; he struck with it and the stone did not come out, struck hard, snapped trees with it, the men round him quivered under the eyes, it dazzled them — it's dangerous, very dangerous, this new thing the Fiery One has made, they see that at once.

How had he managed it? Well, that was a thing they had explained to them and still did not grasp; they saw with their own eyes how it was done and were no wiser. Fyr had fingered his way to the art of binding, of getting two things to hang together by the help of a third; he made use of long, thin, tough things like hair, sinews or gut, and laid them about the objects to be joined in a very complicated and elaborate manner — for they might try to do it after him, twist the thong a few times round, and the whole thing fell apart again as soon as they let go; but Fyr's held, he had his own secret, nothing more nor less than the knot!

That was the first axe. Nor did Fyr keep to himself the advantage this gave its possessor; he passed on the axe to the young and energetic men of the tribes and charged them to become good hunters. They came to take lessons of him and either received an axe of his own making or in some cases got so far as to make one themselves on his pattern. The art of binding was difficult; besides dexterity it required considerable maturity of thought, there was a mass of things to be kept in the head, the practical principle of the knot gave them a headache, and they had to sit and rest with hand to brow before they were finished.

While the axe was now spread abroad among most of the Forest

Folk and kept by them in precisely the form in which they received it — for just as it was, it bit well — the source had not dried up in Fyr's fertile brain; he was quick to see that there was more than *one* weapon and implement in the new combination. If you made the shaft short with a broad, heavy stone at the end, you had the axe, which was good for hewing; but if you made the shaft long and let the stone lashed to it take the form of a sharp point, then you had an improved spear, keener and more penetrating than before. This new invention he also passed on to the Forest Folk.

And now he thought he had done something. Now axe and spear could work for him in the hands of the Forest Folk: had he not secured the fire and his own influence for long years to come? He was by no means blind to the power he had placed in the hands of the tribes; they were many; many axes and spears now against one — but had he not the fire, was he not the fire itself, or the next thing to it? The tribesmen believed he was and would go on believing it, even if he voluntarily undertook to convince them of the true state of affairs; the women believed it, everybody believed it and *wished* to believe it; he was not far from believing it himself. He was not Gunung Api for nothing. In the axe he had made for his own use, which he wielded as a master, not only for striking but for throwing and hitting the mark, in that axe all were agreed that the lightning dwelt, they all feared it more than an ordinary axe, it was the fiery bolt of Gunung Api!

But chiefly his power rested on his possessing the source of fire. His was still the only hearth, but even when he had given the tribes fire, its secret should not go with it; only his sons should know that, they were to inherit his power. And the secret was that he could at any time renew the fire, even if the hearth should go out. The others might receive fire of him, but not the source of fire; that remained in his head; if his hearth went out he knew the way to a whole mountain of fire.

In the midst of the plain burned the hearth, and from every side the Forest Folk came crawling on their bellies with offerings to Gunung Api; so absolute and supernatural was Fyr's power.

But the beasts, what did they say? Little cause had they to be content with the new order of things; it was they who furnished the sacrifices. The peace between men and beasts, formerly as widespread as that among the beasts themselves, was now altogether denounced, and that by what one would have thought the weaker party. The little dancing, chattering forest man had turned uncannily silent; he was beginning to kill off more and more animals of every kind, had power in a way difficult to understand over those which were much bigger and stronger than himself, even to the elephant, unapproachable through his very size.

The ruminants held their peace, they were accustomed already to pay tribute to the flesh-eaters; silently the stag dropped with cleft skull and a spear through him; formerly he died by claw or fang and saw his creeping enemy at the drinking places or in the long grass, now they came towards him walking upright, when he had fallen and could rise no more, they broke into their human laughter and struck him in the eyes; death was more merciful than they. The grass-eaters held aloof from man, first at arm's length, then just as far as they had learnt a spear could fly; but at last they avoided the very scent of men miles away, it was only possible to approach them against the wind and in the deepest silence.

The power of the beasts of prey was gone; they no longer helped themselves to a man at any time of the day or night; hard and deadly things came flying at them now, the issue was decided at a distance before one came to grips; they could bite through the air, these bipeds, they let fly things which did damage; the flesh of the little humans had quite lost its delicate savour, and they comforted themselves in unfriendly fashion. If you tried to steal upon them at night you found them banded together with fire and had to go your ways looking like a fool; better to keep away from them altogether. Soon however the tables were turned; it was the man who came on, a lot of them together and cunningly, from every side, with long, dangerous things in their hands; and then it actually happened far too often that the carnivorous beast went into the stomach of what he would have regarded as his breakfast. The tiger sneezes when he scents men, they have a ranker smell than before, an odour of fire clings to their hair; the tiger too goes to windward and gives men a wide berth.

But the time was coming when safety could not even be secured by avoiding close quarters with men and looking out for their pointed things; they pursued the beasts with other arts, dug pits for them; wherever you went there was a danger that the earth might sink under your paws; the forest was scarcely a place to live any more. In that way even the elephant met his fate, a sad blow to the dignity of all animals, and if the shrewd and mighty beast succeeded in digging himself out of the pitfall with his tusks, there was next time a sharp stake, hardened in the fire, at the bottom, and then he stayed there; certain people have enterprising brains, and how fond they must be of meat!

The wild horses suffered annoyance from the wicked hunters, who in large numbers tried to encircle them, armed with poles and yelling loudly; so the animals made up their minds as one horse to fly from this rabble, quit the country, since it was no longer fit to live in, and they made off in full gallop towards one side which was not closed by the polemen — just what the hunters wanted them to do. Here the ground fell away abruptly in a steep bluff, not to be seen from above, and down plunged the whole mighty galloping herd, one wave of animals on top of the other, down on to the stony ground below. Not one escaped. So many horses were killed that day that afterwards their bones were piled high on the spot — all for the sake of the few carcasses the hunters could manage to devour before the whole mass went rotten.

Oh yes, the beasts had reason to fear the fire's ally and bloody purveyor.

Gone was the peace of the evergreen forests before the Ice Age, where grazing beasts roamed in herds upon the plains and men came out of the groves and mixed with them without fear on either side. An ancient friendship existed between the playful calves of the ruminants and the restless, dancing, variety-loving humans; upon the pastures in the morning of the ages children, puppies and foals rolled about together in downy, sunlit gambols. They had to part. It was written in their fate that they should meet again, but that lay far ahead, and bitter trials, a hard schooling, awaited creation first.

The transformation of the animals had been accomplished in the Forest of Change, so far as eternal summer and easy days could effect it; they had attained their final form according to the conditions in which they lived, according to their place of abode, their food and their mutual relations; deer and cattle in the open forests, with beasts of prey lurking near; on the steppes the whole family of horses, plants with bulbous roots for overcoming barren seasons, and rodents underground which lived thereon; goats and chamois high on the mountains and highest of all the reindeer, seeking peace, but the wolverene finds them there; in the marshes buffaloes and swine, with the wolf round about among the rushes; the otter comes upon the salmon in the rushing rivers, and out in the sea the seal thrusts his man's head out of the waves, and the whale spouts from among shoals of herring into a cloud of gulls; Nature had reached an equilibrium. But now other forces were to intrude upon Nature.

Wherever the beasts might hide, however they might guard against one another, thereby becoming the beasts they were — against man they had no guard, he found them all, and everywhere. A mark of blood was set between man and all other living creatures. Man had entered upon his existence as a hunter; the elements hunted him, and he together with fire hunted the beasts; their life became a hunt for coming milleniums.

It happened thus since it could not happen otherwise; there was that in the air which caused man to draw near to fire, at the expense of all other living things. None could prevail any more against these bipeds who made themselves bigger than they were by all kinds of unbestial arts. Yet the day was not far off when man would turn his weapons against himself and become his own bitterest enemy.

X

THE SACRIFICE

*F*YR reached the summit of his power while he was still a young man; his leadership was founded on something irresistibly new, rather than on an accumulation of experience as in the case of the elders who had formerly been at the head of the Forest Folk. The experience of the old men was no longer at all necessary, all that they knew as a defence against night and famine was superfluous now the fire was there; a single burst of light in man's soul had put all their lifelong bundles of memory to shame. And Fyr did not rule by violence and brutal punishments; his glory diffused power of itself, all submitted willingly to him and his fire.

Fyr ruled bountifully, under his leadership the Forest Folk entered upon an unbroken series of festivals. He reduced the sacrifices to a system, introduced fixed rules for feeding the fire, together with man's occasional participation therein; the whole according to mysterious covenants with the Powers of Fire whom he alone represented; covenants the origin of which was afterwards forgotten but which were kept, all the more stubbornly the less their reason was remembered.

The sacrifice, as instituted by Fyr, rested upon a simple conception of fire as the consuming spirit; at every sacrificial repast it was fire that sat in the high seat, and that men were permitted to partake rested upon an equally simple fundamental revelation, namely, that if one asked the fire whether one might take a bit, it said nothing, which was interpreted as Yes, whereupon one fell to on the fire's leavings. Fyr was always seen to mumble a holy prayer at the opening of every banquet, not a long prayer but undoubtedly an important one, since he never omitted it; thus Fyr asked permission. For a moment he politely turned his ear, in case the fire should say something, and if he did not hear a No — indeed, it had never been heard — and the meat was done, they proceeded to fall to.

What and how much the fire left was a matter of discretion, and here Fyr's insight and sense of fairness were obviously the best guide; in course of time he arrived at an understanding with the fire than which nothing could be more favourable to both parties. The tastes of fire could be ascertained by purely empirical observations; they differed essentially from man's, since it preferred wood to fruit and old, dry wood to green; withered grass and leaves it swallowed in a blazing roar, of that kind of thing it could never have enough. As regards meat experience showed that fire devoured the skin, bones and entrails of the sacrifice with apparently just as good an appetite as it had for the other parts; and, if its digestion was so excellent, why then the tender meat, the shoulders and all the rest was left for the sacrificer and the pious partakers of the meal. If you laid all the meat in one heap and all the bones and skin in another, pointed to them alternately and asked the fire which heap it would have, it said nothing, which was interpreted to mean that you could make the choice yourself. This form also was gone through by Fyr at every sacrifice; they saw him mumble and point and understood that a holy covenant was being concluded between him and the fire. Whereupon they did all honour to the fire, ate as long as they could, till they were full with the last lump of fat plugging their gullet; oh yes, they were ready enough for the sacrifice, both early and late.

Three times a day Fyr ordained the sacrifices, since for some reason unexplained to the others he associated the essence of fire and of Gunung Api with the sun, in itself a reasonable idea but too abstruse to be followed by the general run of the Forest Folk: if respect was to be paid to the sun at its rising and setting as well as in the middle of the day, when it was at its highest, all one could say was that this fell in very naturally with man's desire to take something, when he woke, when the forenoon began to seem long, and before he went to rest; the inner sacred significance of the mealtimes might be left to the Fiery One and his sun.

But not only at the ordinary sacrifices thrice daily did Fyr share meals with his ardent Powers; at other fixed seasons, which might be rather far between, he held great extraordinary sacrificial solemnities, on the occasion of the moon's return, for instance; he also instituted huge meat offerings for what he called the Year and the Solar Solstice; the most popular in every way were however the moon festivals, then there were singing and dancing with a will!

Here a tradition from the past came in; the men of old time had been used to meet at the full moon and delight themselves with song and the sweet sound of hollow trees; now great reeking holocausts were added, a huge bonfire in the midst of the congregation and as many offerings as could be provided, if possible a whole roast elephant, taken in a pit, as the chief dish, or a drove of wild cattle that had been chased over a precipice. Stupendous was then the gorging, well greased were the throttles, down went blood pancakes, baked in the ashes, well charred meat and browned fat one way, and up came a full-throated soulful yell the other; wits took fire under pressure of swelling veins, flowers of speech revealed themselves in their naked splendour, abundance begat eloquence and profusion song — now the dance is not far off.

The old paralysing influence of fire on savage nerves changes into excitement and a breathless craving for motion, now that men no longer lose their wits with fear at sight of the element; no more falling on their faces, they dare go round the fire, go round it many times, half afraid and wholly joyful; they go in a magic circle around the Hot One holding each other's hands, bawling ecstatically, homage and possession in one breath, and this is no brief performance, they delight in dragging it out; the whole live-long night they circle round the fire, shouting their love and gratitude; one will devoutly dip a lump of tallow in it and lick it up when it is nice and smells of burning, and then join hands again with his pious brother and go round the blaze with well-greased gums and a simple hymn of praise on his lips, the joyful howl without words but given with the full force of the lungs and with endless repetition. With a yell in unison to the fire and the moon the dance is kept up all night long, till sunrise appears and it is time to think about *its* morning sacrifice, and a little bit for one's self after so much exhausting worship.

This led to sacred fire-dances in which the whole Forest Folk took part, with imitations of the fire, mimic dances; they flared up and down like fire, threw out their arms and suggested huge armfuls of smoke; they sang the crackling song, roared and whistled with ugly noises, they carried torches, fire-maddened and going on tip-toe the whole night through; in short, they *were* fire, they received it in their souls and gave back its nature in the form of song. The song was a simple one, repeating in an ecstatic roaring chorus a single word, the name of fire, O Fire! the whole night long — lovely! Refrain: A bit of meat and a lick of the fingers! Good, good, O Elephant, tasteth thy foot when thou hast trodden the fire, O Fire, and art passed into eternity; easy be thy rest in my stomach! Yes, there was dancing, singing and feasting with a vengeance.

The festivals however were by no means sheer gluttony and nothing else; the happy eating songs and the transports over the fire contained the germ of a dawning poetry, and Fyr had discovered that both fire and man could live by other things besides those which merely gave work for the teeth — perfume, for instance: the fire evinced a spiritually loftier enjoyment when you gave it certain plants, spiced bark and resin; then the fire sweated voluptuously and smoked so sweetly that a man could not but rejoice over it. On this account Fyr instituted various temperance offerings, where only the smoke that ascended to heaven was regarded as the actual gift; nor was the offering altogether lost upon the sacrificer: in hours of repletion there was a certain gratification in breathing in the spicy smoke and coughing and expanding the soul in flights of fancy while taking one's ease.

Reverently the Forest Folk witnessed Fyr's smoky arts; here it could be seen without any effort of thought how fire and its great adept combined to produce clouds! That he kept up the whole universe in this way there could be no doubt at all.

On the night of the great festivals, when men went in a ring about the fire, the beasts formed a ring outside again, but far, far off; still, they had to see what was going on, why it was they were all to die. And then they heard the Forest Folk's chorus of incantation around the fire and were just as wise as before; the elephant appeared at the edge of the wood and stood there swaying his head, swaying his legs in a checked movement; he was wise but had here come to the limit of his wisdom; the tiger, dazzled, grinned his vexation, a grin he has worn ever since, the grin of a shattered power; the bull stood with slobbering mouth and glared; all the beasts fell into a deeper dumbness, blinked their eyes slowly, seeming to understand that they looked without seeing. Yes, they were left behind, and those of them who were to regain their place another time would not even then know what was happening to them. Only the swine went about his business without forebodings, rooting in the ground with his snout; he was not far wrong in fattening himself, thus he remained centred in his destiny.

From the first hearth, the place of Fyr's fire, a sanctuary developed. It was modest enough to begin with, the bare fire on the bare earth; but it is a question whether greater veneration has surrounded any consecrated place before or since.

To the same extent however as men's terror of fire itself wore off through daily familiarity, the symbols and mysteries with which it was surrounded were multiplied. Fyr saw to this; it grew out of the basis of his relations with fire — that one good turn deserves another. It gave him power, and he saw to its maintenance.

It was to have an honourable dwelling; Fyr built a pile of stones for it, in remembrance of the mountain from which it had come, an altar, a little image of Gunung Api; and round about the altar he placed things which he supposed would delight the fire, skulls and horns of sacrificed animals, so that it might always live in the idea of big game even if it had to be content with smaller for its daily food, when the supply of meat was short and partakers of the sacred meal were many.

Rightly viewed, if the fire got the taste that was its share while making the meat tender, and no more, the odour and the smoke in other words, might not that be sufficient in the ordinary way? Fire seemed to be able to live on an image, as it were, to receive nourishment from the indwelling spirit of a thing without demanding the thing itself.

The fact was that Fyr sometimes happened upon stones which the hand of Nature had fashioned in a certain likeness to animals or animal's heads; it occurred to him that they might please the fire, besides saving the trouble of procuring a corresponding living victim. He made the trial, set up a stone near the fire which appeared to him to resemble a stag's head, distantly but unmistakably, and in order to make the likeness clearer he bellowed and strutted like a challenging stag; then he asked the fire whether the offering was to its taste, and as it made no answer the matter was settled.

To give the image to the fire as direct food would of course have shown a gross lack of imagination, for it was precisely in the contemplation of the image that the fire must be assumed to find edification; it was therefore necessary to preserve it in order that the edification might be of a permanent nature; Fyr set up the stone before the fire and his own soul was actually full of stag every time he saw it, so he was here on the right road to satisfying the fire in a higher and essentially nobler sense.

The image of a stag was not the end of it; Fyr found so many other stones which to a creative eye might look like animals; a weighty round stone with a hint of trunk could easily be recognized as an elephant; almost any clumsy-looking stone passed for a cow, and of that sort of cattle he could get as many as he wanted. Fyr set up a whole animal kingdom about the fire, all the way round, a sacred circle, and these stones, which were to all intents and purposes the animals themselves, were presumed to be taken by the fire as an emblematical assurance that it was always kept supplied.

Yes, and if the likeness was *too* distant there was no harm in helping it out a little, with the free hand of the artist, so that the animal stood out better from the casual stone; an original resemblance was after all unnecessary, you could engrave the picture of any animal you liked on the first stone you happened to pick up, wild horses and buffaloes so true to life that it made the mouth water to look at them — and after all, why must it be a stone, since the spirit was in the image and not in the stone? you could conjure up an animal where you pleased, the soul was in the line, and if you had that you had the whole animal, in so far as it was a question of having it in the spirit.

In dealing with fire, which was willing to feed in such a roundabout fashion, this was a fruitful art; by its help one could rejoice the fire at any time with the outlines of a meal which one was saved the trouble of giving it in the flesh or to which from considerations of health one treated one's self. The fire of course was never grudged wood for its daily needs; that was the women's business.

This then was how the Fiery One had arranged things: the women carried wood to the fire and the whole jungle folk were out hunting early and late to provide offerings for the fire, which was however quite content with the game in effigy; what finally fell to Fyr's share was apparent with increasing clearness in his figure, as time went on he developed into a regular Gunung Api, a sitting mountain of fat.

But after most of the people had got used to fire and all the tribes had been given their own hearths, which they kept themselves and to which they made suitable offerings — Fyr's fire of course receiving the chief sacrifice — Fyr together with his original hearth moved into a cave and there established a great sanctuary.

The cave lay in a rocky cliff and was both intricate and gloomy, you had to go through wet galleries before finally catching sight of the fire in the interior; here Fyr dwelt in awful greatness with the fire, the old holy ancestral fire, father of all other fire; here he had made pictures on walls and roof of all the beasts of the hunt for the edification of the fire, and here he received offerings.

Yes, the Fiery One was an artist; what he created in the spirit, *was*. He had surrounded himself with a reality that was entirely his own, here he was master; for the reality outside he no longer had much thought.

But one day Gunung Api spoke.

Long had the mountain kept quiet, so long that the Forest Folk had almost forgotten his power and attributed it to others in the meantime; he merely smoked as was his custom and carried on warfare with the rain, flashed lightnings through the clouds, muttered too now and then as he always had done. But suddenly one day, without warning, he shook himself in his foundations, and that so violently that huge masses of rock came leaping down his sides, the water splashed out of the lakes and the trees rocked in the forest; whole tracts of it shifted a pace away, as though the forest thought of moving off; deep cracks opened in the ground and swallowed up streams, it was a frightful disturbance. This did not last long, but afterwards a grinding and grating went on inside the mountain, daylight vanished in gloom, the lightning flashed hither and thither, and the thunder rolled, not in single claps but all the time like a vast continuous booming; at any instant a forest fire might break out, the world's last day was at hand.

That day Fyr was sacrificed.

Hastily, by adding one thing to another, but above all hastily, his fate was decided.

To begin with, he was not himself unaffected by the disaster; a part of the sacred cave in which he lived had collapsed. Nobody was hurt, a dozen women were buried in one of the galleries, but it was a bad sign; *was* he really invulnerable, was it he or another that was Gunung Api?

Furthermore, he had bolted out of the cave with the remnant of his womenfolk at his heels in a yelping stampede, when he might have been expected to calm and reassure the rest; worse still, this Fiery One had been seen in a more than human attitude on the ground, lying on his belly, precisely like the others, clutching after something to hold on to when the earth was heaving and jumping up and down — it was too obvious, *he* did not set the earth in motion, he was not even able to stand upright on it!

When the first alarm had subsided and there seemed to be a pause in Gunung Api's wrath, the cooler heads among the Forest Folk tried in all haste to make up their minds what was to be done. The mountain must be appeased, and that instantly. They had taken in enough of Fyr's preaching to know that the aim of fire, as of all other creatures, was food, whence the sacrifice; if there was thunder in the air or the volcano was threatening, anybody might see that it was meat it was after, and it usually got it; but now Gunung Api was angry, a whole forest of animals would hardly be enough to cool his lust, it would take a peculiarly precious dish; and then at the same instant the thought struck their collective mind as the sole means of redemption that it was Fyr himself the fire demanded.

Beasts were not good enough, it wanted men, the whole Forest

Folk; still better, the first among them; that was it, mankind in one person, the intercessor between the Powers of Fire and man, and verily, what Gunung Api wanted he should have!

Ancient cruelty secretly revealed itself side by side with the dry commonsense conclusions laboriously reached by the Forest Folk; Fyr had ruled frivolously, diffusing joy around him; now there was an end of folly, he was to be put to the test. Who was he, when it came to the point, this man who gave himself out to be Gunung Api? it would be seen whether he was not just an ordinary mortal.

What things they had quietly submitted to from that quarter! — slaved for him, hunted for him, and *how* had he discharged his stewardship? He who should have intervened between Gunung Api and mankind, had they been able to rely on him? And when he had given the fire skin and bones instead of meat and kept the tit-bits for himself, put off the heavenly Devourer with images, spiritual victuals — might not *that* be the reason why the whole Forest Folk were now threatened with destruction? Into the fire with him, and let Gunung Api eat *him!*

What had they not passed over in silence, when this vagabond claiming to be a god had told monstrous tales about the order of the world as it had revealed itself to him in so-called solitude up on the mountain! He had asserted, as a result of direct observation of heaven and earth, that the day was not light in itself, it was because the sun shone; as though anybody with the use of his senses couldn't see that it was the other way about; the day of course was light and the sun borrowed its splendour from it. And he asserted further that the sun was a spirit of the same kind as that which manifested itself in fire and in Gunung Api, in the lightning, perhaps it was even the greatest and highest of all fire spirits, since it lived in heaven itself and only seemed smaller because it was so high up — did any one hear the like! when everybody was fully convinced, as you could *see* for yourself, that the sun was a crab-apple. On to the pyre with him!

Oh yes — and it was he who went about with the absurd story that the forms you saw in the water when you leaned over it were not people at all but only an illusion, one's self seen as it were in an image — he and his images! — It was rather too strong that he should deny what was perfectly clear from observation and what was vouched for by older men than he — up and burn him!

No doubt they had learnt the use of fire from him, but now the truth must be told, they learned it reluctantly, in fear, they did not take his guilt upon them. He would have to pay the penalty in person for his audacity in stealing fire from Gunung Api, he was too dangerous a man to have walking about; the old experienced ones, who once more raised their heads among the herd, could bear witness that it was a threat to the whole Forest Folk to have so erect an individual in their midst, he might bring the lightning down on them, all mankind was exposed to the envy and vengeance of the Powers. The proof of it lay in Gunung Api's actual outbreak of wrath, it was best to make the blasphemer cold as quickly as they could do it.

And then those one or two inventions of his which he had presented to men, perfectly obvious things which anybody could invent after him, he had got pretty fat on those, but now he should smart for it!

Nevertheless it was insisted that it was not the Forest Folk themselves who condemned him; to be on the safe side, it was not they. The fire should judge him! If he was really a god, as some believed, then no doubt he would not catch when the fire reached him; fire must be able to withstand fire, and in that case there was plenty of flat ground to fall down on and worship him; as a god he would certainly show himself great enough to bear with the doubts of miserable men; but if he was a creature like the rest of us, then he would assuredly burn.

Ah, no ground is so safe to stand on, even when the earth quakes, as doubt; the Fiery One burned when he was put to the proof. Oh yes, the Elders blinked their eyes in wisdom as his hair and beard went off pretty quickly; he was inflammable as a pig, a man like you or me, what did I tell you? Genuine were his wailings when the fire took hold of hands and feet, he howled just like a man. No need to prolong the ordeal, he had not stood it; they let him taste the axe, his own invention, dipped the flint spear into him, another of his gifts to men, returned with thanks; and then they let the handmaids take him off the fire and open him, for they were skilled at it, and wasn't it intended to try him?

The earth still trembled a little, landslides tore down Gunung Api, and the lightning danced up in the gloom; it was midnight in the middle of the day, a horrid darkness with a sacrificial pyre like a pool of blood lying at the bottom, and in this underworld the trial was consummated; they tasted Fyr and found him fine, of a

rich and delicate flavour, tender, light and volatile to the tongue,
not unlike pig, but of a more soulful sweetness. This was the foretaste of a roast which later on would array men in hordes against
each other and lead to their being mutually swallowed in hosts;
half as many after a battle as before it and only the gnawed bones
and ashes to show where it had been fought; for the Forest Folk
had acquired a taste for meat and seized with bared teeth whatever was not strong enough to seize *them.*

Fyr was good, they hiccuped, turning to each other with bloodshot eyes — to think, messmate, that you and I could take that man
for a god!

XI

THE FAME OF FYR

$\mathfrak{B}$UT they had a multitude of things to think about after Fyr's
death; after all, the doubt about his godhead had been shaky
ground to stand upon; best and safest if a man doubted of doubt
itself!

Sundry prodigies after the sacrifice of Fyr were difficult of impartial interpretation. Gunung Api had immediately settled down,
no more quakings or flourishing of lightning, no forest fire; on
the contrary, the mountain had become markedly quiet, and of
course this might be understood as showing its satisfaction with
the punishment of the malefactor; but at the same time there were
indications that Gunung Api had received a mortal wound; he
stopped smoking, a deathlike stillness reigned upon his surface —
surely it could not be an incarnate god, Gunung Api in human
form after all, that they had put to death?

Many fateful signs pointed to this: shortly after the disastrous
day they found one morning all the palms withered; a rime had
fallen which boded the passing of the evergreen forests. A shudder
ran through all nature, and something strange was seen: the sky
began to fall down in cold white shreds. What now? what had
they done, did the universe stand fast no longer, was it true then
that in their blindness they had gone and slain him who held up
heaven and earth?

The sky did not fall in altogether that time, it only lost a layer; that was bad enough, the whole vault of heaven had evidently suffered no little damage; too late the Forest Folk perceived that they had brought about their own ruin.

Many and grievous were the ideas they formed of their own weakness and of the possibility of the world's being saved in spite of it — if only they had had Fyr's head to see through it all and explain what was error and what truth!

But now their souls were black as the coals after the fire is gone, with spectral lights before their eyes but with no power to penetrate the darkness. Soon every feature of the departed Fiery One was recalled; himself they could not bring back. They had the fire, but not him.

His fame and the images that were used to describe his qualities passed into the language. Fiery was Fyr, a light among men, clear, bright, a brilliant brain; a gleam fell from him, he shone, the eternal fire was in his heart; he was the founder of all enlightenment, he flashed, sparkled with wit, he scintillated, his being was all aglow; and he was fervent, a torch in the night, he dazzled, there was warmth in him, he was ardent, his soul was aflame, he burned, he blazed, he kindled, flared up, shot out beams, in short every image taken from the genial element which he had controlled and made himself one with was applied to him. Never could it be forgotten that he had given fire to men. A pity that he of all men should have perished by fire!

But now it was done. Such things happen. No single person could be blamed for it; the whole Forest Folk had agreed to hand him over to the fire, and it had dealt roughly with him. The majority and the great Destroyer had spoken, who would raise his feeble individual voice against it?

What had happened later was scarcely fitted to be shouted abroad. Two points of view asserted themselves in the judgment of posterity regarding Fyr's end: one, that there was not a word of truth in that story of the sacrifice; it sounded sufficiently preposterous and ought to be received with caution. The night was dark; who had seen it? There was an earthquake and everything had been shaken up; might it not easily happen that the story of Fyr's death and some casual slaughter or other in the neighbourhood had been shaken together?

One ought not to believe the worst of humanity; in reality no doubt Fyr had perished in a natural manner, and the vultures had taken him, as they took all the dead; this explanation actually became the current one and passed into tradition as the more seemly; when all was said and done, it was Gunung Api who had insisted on the punishment.

The other version was never put into words, it was an entirely tacit view which was shared by all but did not call for mention: there were a number of the Forest Folk, a perfectly definite number, who knew the facts, for they had all taken part in the so-called sacrifice, never fully cleared up or proved; and even if they said nothing, they shared the secret knowledge of one thing of no slight subsequent importance — every one of them had a part of the god inside him. Special honour was shown them; the hairs on one's back were apt to stand on end when one saw them, but they were entitled to their honour, one fell down before them. They and their descendants occupied a special position in the tribes; they were regarded with a feeling of holiness as a sort of burial place; somewhere in their direction Fyr was known to have gone.

Apart from this Fyr's power and the mystery of the fire passed to his sons, of whom he had many, all of them active, swaggering fellows who knew very well how to turn their inheritance to account.

In the general opinion Fyr gradually took the place of Gunung Api; it was an easier matter to imagine the god as a man than as a mountain. In sacrificing the thought was more of Fyr than of fire; the latter was worshipped in his person, it was from him that suppliants looked for an answer to their prayers, since he understood men better than the inhuman fire. Thus worship, which hitherto had been somewhat obscure to the Forest Folk, acquired a meaning.

Of Fyr as a man it was said that he had made no resistance at all when condemned to the ordeal by fire; he had gone voluntarily to the pyre. When he had complained it was not of his treatment, so it was averred, but seemingly for other, personal reasons.

As to his treatment, what could be said about it? they were many against one, they had shouted in chorus, and the chorus is right. The caresses of the fire were not kind; yet Fyr suffered torment for other reasons than just because he was to burn and die. Thoughts that came up in him smarted more bitterly, mental images which intruded themselves all too vividly when he was faced by death and had to call all his days to account in a moment.

Then he saw how poor he was become, how short was the reach of man's arm and how far off the sky. Yet he had thought of one day walking on the field of the stars, seeing the moon from the back and touching the sun with his finger. But he had not even reached the top of Gunung Api. Time enough for that, he had thought — ay, that was it. Meanwhile he had prospered only too well on earth. Everything had succeeded with him; he had made himself master of his world, fire had been obedient to him, but one thing he had not been able to bind — pitiless time. He had fashioned a measure for it, set up numbers in the world to hold it fast, but was it not gone?

Where was past time? It was present behind his brow, but itself was no more. Where was his youth? Where was young Fyr, crowing at dawn on the mountain? Where was the Poppy, once his friend? Where was she and the brief flame of their time together? Ah, it had been himself that time, and seemingly it was himself now. Well that they gave him to the fire! A punishment? Oh, quickly, quickly, throw on more wood, you dogs!

In tears Fyr had gone to his death. But when he cried, in human agony, as the years and the fire seized him, a hoarse croaking was heard and a human shadow, an old bent woman, came crawling to the pyre. It was Fyr's aged lame mother, long forgotten by all; far away, from her lair in the ground, she heard her boy crying and crept into the daylight once more, hobbled along with her lame foot and humped herself on to the pyre, lay down and gave a happy sigh; happy was she to share death with the bold lad who once, so long ago and yet how lately, ran from her arms with waving hair and vanished in the waves of the world.

If then she could not pass through fire for him, she could do it now. Her name was Woe.

It was afterwards said among the descendants of the Forest Folk that the sun was none other than Fyr; dazzling and generous he moved each day upon the heavens, sowing his light over all the world.

But the moon is his mother Woe; she goes after him and follows all his doing with pallid face; now whole, now half, she gives away pieces of her heart for him. When the nights are dark she has given all away and succumbed to grief, but when, whole once more, she gleams in the sky, it is well with him.

All women invoke Woe; variable as her heart is their nature, they go to pieces through giving; but every month their being is made whole again.

XII

THE MOUNTAIN
SLUMBERS

GUNUNG API's last eruption was more like a spasm, without very serious results, as when a giant stretches in his sleep; and afterwards he became strangely quiet, seemed to have left off smoking, and never betrayed by a tremor that there was a move-men of life in his interior. Nor was he so continually hidden in cloud, he often stood exposed in all his long black nakedness, and there was such a frosty clearness around his summit. Did he breathe no more, was he really lifeless?

No one who asked the question would live to know the answer, nor would his descendants for many generations. Gunung Api had entered upon a long sleep, had choked up his funnel with ashes, and far below him in the earth's furnaces the fire had coiled about itself, resigned to æons of imprisonment. It seemed, then, that it could not maintain its rule of terror upon earth.

Something different, however, something not of the nature of fire, is in the air upon earth. Let it come, as it is fated.

For now man runs with fire like a tamed leopard by his side; he is grown bold and a great eater, feeding even upon his brother's gall; the little fellow is getting quite hot about the headpiece: might it not be a good thing to cool him down a little?

And one morning down in the valleys the hunters and the hunted see a white hood, with a strange, hard gleam, like a lifeless eye, lying upon the head of Gunung Api; the first forerunner of the Ice Sheet.

BOOK TWO: ICE

I

CARL

F FIRE was burning in the primeval forest, the only one for miles around. It had been kindled in an open space under an overhanging slant of rock which faced away from the wind. Overhead the blast surged heavily through the forest; the night was dark, without moon or stars. It was raining. But the fire burned steadily under the rock, with a clear flame rising from a heap of brushwood; its glare formed a sort of cavern in the deep night.

Around the fire lay a group of men asleep, all near enough for the light to reach them. They were naked. There were only men. Each slept with a club in his hand or lying beside him so that he could reach it in his sleep. Their baskets of reeds, containing a varied provision of fruit and roots, lay in the grass about the fire, whose circle of light in the wild bush enclosed the group. A few paces beyond the shelter of the rock, where the rain fell and the darkness crept near, the remains of a zebralike animal, an offering to the fire, could be dimly seen.

Only one of the party was awake. He sat by the fire and moved but little, but his eyes were never still; he was a tall, large-limbed lad of uncommonly powerful build, though he had not yet reached maturity. By his side he had a huge pile of branches and brushwood, from which he now and then replenished the fire. If it did but sink just so much that the outermost of the party were left beyond the wall of light, they began at once to toss in their sleep; but that did not happen often, the boy had a skill of his own in feeding the fire steadily, he knew how much wood he had stacked up and how long the night was. He tended the fire without having to give it a thought and for the rest sat calmly and alone with all his senses directed outward to the wild darkness of the forest.

In his left hand he held a wedge of flint, as yet only roughly shaped, and when the fire was burning evenly and nothing else caught his attention, he applied a short piece of stag's antler to one part or other of the flint and after long and careful calculation pressed off a flake, which sprang into the fire. Then he examined the effect, weighed in his hand the block of flint, which was to be an axe whose like had never been seen before, and let his eyes dwell intently on its various sides before he applied the antler again and considered the lie of the next splinter which concealed the form he had in his eye. A creative light came over his rude features, a visionary gleam, as he sat coaxing a tool out of the stone; he sparkled with sagacity so long as he was trying and guessing his way, but when he pressed a flake off he put a force into it that would have driven the antler through a man's head, and bent his back as though to raise a mountain, above all when he had to take off a tiny flake and no more. It was to be a weapon like none other. Beside his knee lay the axe he chopped wood with for the fire; it was just an ordinary bit of flint without form or edge, but it was sacred, an heirloom in the clan, and it had decided his fate.

His name was Carl. He was born to tend the fire, belonged to the much respected and dreaded family whose members all had the prerogative of caring for the fire and receiving its offerings.

This privilege was so ancient that no one rightly remembered its origin. Doubtful legends were told of a man of the tribe who once in altruistic madness had stormed the burning mountain, where dwelt the Fire Spirit, the crackling Consumer, and had come down again unharmed with a flame on the end of a branch. Naturally the tribe had flung the possessed one on the midden to the vultures, but they kept the fire and were glad of it. The poor wretch who had stolen fire obtained redress in a goodly posthumous fame, since the vultures were protected and made objects of worship, being presumed to possess the soul of him they had devoured. But after that time the fire and its offerings became hereditary in this man's family, and among his descendants was Carl. He enjoyed the esteem due to his birth, but for several reasons was already not a little feared.

Carl was a warrior. As a rule the Fire clan was not distinguished by manliness; their work was light and they lived too well on the game that was sacrificed to the fire. These trusted men of the tribe were usually feeble stay-at-homes who made up for their lack of strength by magic or other cowardly tricks. In most of the other tribes they knew of, but never came in touch with, the fire was tended by the women, and the work was not looked upon as befitting men. But of course the reason for this was to be sought in the ignorance and general low standing of the foreign tribes in question. Only it was a pity that the sulky Carl seemed to share the views of these distant savages, often spoke of his calling with contempt and replied by a box on the ears when taken to task for it. Carl did not take after his immediate predecessors, he early distinguished himself by a taste for solitude. He tended his fire better than it had been done before, but without any graces, did not fall on his stomach before the burning spirit but methodically gave it something to bite on; he went about the felling of trees with a zest worthy of manslaughter, and men of repute in his tribe didn't like to see it. He had powerful hands and made the most excellent weapons, but then that was hardly the thing for him to do.

As a mere boy Carl had shown a taste for hunting, very improper in one destined for the priesthood, and even then he wouldn't go with the other youngest hunters of the tribe but unsociably and alone; he was still only a youngster himself when he brought down a foal of the three-toed horse with his bit of an ash branch hardened in the fire and dragged the carcass home; then it was a cave-bear cub, and then a plump mallow-coloured rhinocerous calf, still hornless. These things were winked at. But the time arrived when the sacred wood-chopping axe was solemnly entrusted to him and he was consecrated to a long undashing life as tender of the fire. His careless childhood had come to an end. Carl might still try a little run in the forest when some other member of the family had his watch by the fire, but his worldliness was more and more frowned upon and means were found to make things so unpleasant for him after each of these jaunts that he preferred to drop them. But the love of sport was in his blood and sought its outlet in a deeply stirred inner life, he dreamed of great things. His lack of adventure and bondage to the fire made him ungentle of spirit but not poor or malicious, for that he was too healthy. In spite of all his forced idleness he grew strong as a bison and was silent and frugal withal. Young as he was, he had already set up no little tension between himself and the whole tribe. If the elders cut him off from deeds of valour he was certainly going to make it lively for them in return, and Carl made up fires which singed the balls of the sleepers' feet and looked like eating up the whole camp, or else he gave them smoke that nearly burst their throats with coughing. The tribe had to put up with his rude jokes, but he was not loved. They lived in an idyl and did not want to be reminded that there *were* other things. Notwithstanding this, Carl's lot might easily have turned out not very unlike that of his fellows, though he was born defiant: time might have remoulded his forces into spite, so that in him his tribe would have found the scourge it deserved, and the fat of the great offerings would also have settled about his heart, helped by the years.

But the idyl was no longer so secure. The primitive folk had long been aware that the world was changing around them. They no longer had a fixed place of abode, they had entered upon a life of migration. The forest gave them no lodging as of old, could not afford shelter, it was beginning to be in a bad way itself. Something was in the air which year by year grew more dangerous and was now beginning to threaten every living thing. It had grown colder and colder. The rain would never leave off. *Cold* — what was it? *Who* was it? Where did it come from?

Carl was thinking about this as he sat alone by the fire and the others slept, and the boy took it very seriously. He saw that the existence of the tribe was threatened. Within his own memory his people were still living on the northern side of the mountains; he remembered the year when it got too cold and they crossed the pass down to the south side. Since then they had moved each year, and now they were living several days' journey to the south of this place, where Carl sat by the fire troubled in spirit over the constant retreat.

The tribe with its women and children were living in a valley many leagues away, where palms and breadfruit-trees still flourished, and this group round the fire was only an expedition sent up to the deserted haunts to bring back whatever fruit and game might be left in the old groves.

Here in the rock-shelter the tribe had stayed a year, till it was no longer fit to live in; Carl could still see traces of the huts of boughs which rain and slush had scattered over the cold ground. Here in the sunny glade before the rock he had seen the little downy children of the tribe playing with feathers, blowing them up into the sunshine and making them fly like birds among the flowery bushes. Now it was all desolate, the bare rock cropped out of the ground, which was washed barren by the everlasting rain.

But the tribe took their retirement with composure, if they remarked it at all — why yes, they'd have to go farther south if there wasn't a living to be got in the northern forest. If the trees died and food ran out where they had settled, they could just break camp and find a better place, wasn't there room enough to the south? The only one who didn't relish this was Carl. He followed his tribe, gave ground with it from one valley to another, but it was against his humour. There was coercion in it, and that hardened his heart. How long was the retreat to be kept up, was it to go on for ever? Must they not one day turn and face the cold, set their teeth against this silent power that had begun to make everything wither and stiffen, the cold that never showed itself but kept what it had taken? Was it any use keeping up this life of eternal carelessness, when every year they had to transport their security so many weary miles farther south across the mountains? Was it not better to haft the battle-axe at once and fight for their lives in the open?

Carl felt something of this sort every night during the joyless expedition up into the cold among the tribe's former settlements, while he sat watching by the fire. It prompted him to action, murderous action, though this was not clear to him. He was a primitive man, with mighty impulses but no reflective mind. He simply did not turn aside for any one or anything, and this savage strength that blindly revolted against any kind of compulsion was the cause which sundered his fate from that of his tribe.

The Ice was coming on; before it went incessant rain and cold nights which drove men out of their shiftless jungle existence. They would not and could not learn what was coming, and so they had to go. They froze, poor innocents, tried to make themselves cloaks of fig-leaves against the raw weather; they sang sweet songs of lamentation, but the north wind with its cold scourge had come between them and their leafy booths under the plantains. Their home was no more, they were forced to migrate.

It cost them a sign every time they had to give up the ancestral gardens, no longer hospitable; but they recovered themselves in the sunshine farther south, they sang with joy when they had planted the wanderer's staff in a new place and saw it bud; here it was good, here they would stay; next year the cold overtook them there and they had to go on. Yet they were too forgetful to be aware of this gradual retirement, their thoughts were only of the present; but the fall in their existence set its mark upon them without their knowing it and made them first poor and then small.

Carl could not yield. His heart fed upon defiance, he grew in adversity. And when the primitive people were brought to the crossways between the cold and the forest, he was the one who chose the impossible. He became the first man.

II

THE LOST COUNTRY

T HE night was long, and Carl sat pondering by the fire. Watching thus he was the eyes and ears of his comrades and the soul of the dark boundless forest. He focussed in himself every movement for miles around, the slightest sound reached him, every hair of his body was on the watch, not a breath of air escaped him, not a scent passed by without giving him a message. His nose was so keen that he could walk over the turf and track the mole underground to the place where it cast. His eyes flashed and flashed with a never-resting intentness, and when he slept there was a sallow spot on each eyelid which gave his face a dangerous brooding look and scared away every living thing that tried to approach him. He was silent, for his head was continually breeding. No one knew what was stirring in his soul, nor did he know it himself until he flashed into action.

Such was he, and such the fire showed him to be as he sat beside it, a hairy young forest man with rude massive brows, wide-open nostrils and savage protruding jaws. The hollow of his chest was full of hair, his long arms were shaggy, except where the great muscles showed up bare. When his hands were not at work on the axe he often sat with it between his toes, and he used his feet just as much as his hands for pushing sticks into the fire. In all these ways he was no different from the other forest men, his comrades lying asleep round the fire, only they perhaps were generally slighter, with a handsomer coat of hair and of more delicate build. Their savage exterior brought them nearer to the beasts of the jungle, whose grace they still shared. They slept with club in one hand and a half-eaten fruit in the other. Carl alone, who had begun to think for them, had grown hard and implacable of feature.

To Carl's violent appearance answered an inner wrath and energy, grief at the way things were going, bed upon bed of stored experience, which made him more and more highly charged and was bound to lead to a bursting of his very existence. He had forgotten nothing but added one thing to another, and as he sat feeding his heart with dark forebodings of the destruction of the world, his raging blood surged to revolt, to resisting action.

For he saw that the primeval forest was doomed. It was all over with eternal summer. The warm groves were vanishing, and rain and storm had invaded the mountains of Scandinavia. Farther south the forest still held its own with palms and breadfruit-trees, and the vines lay ripening on rocky slopes shelving to blue straits; but for how long? When they came home to the camp where the tribe was living, these young men lying by the fire with cold shudders on one side and hot on the other would take the well-sunned bunches of grapes, heavy as udders, in their hands and laugh as they sucked again the milk of blissfulness. But the year after Carl would have the dead vines to feed his fire on the same spot and the camp would be shifted, and how long was that to go on? The forest was doomed, a Power from the North was marching on irresistibly and inevitably and laying it waste.

Carl looked about him at the trees in the rain outside. Even now in the night-time he could see the desolation, and what he could not see he knew from the daylight. All the palms were dead and leafless and stood with their bare and blackened stems thrusting up into the air like a great gnawed bone. The tree-ferns hung black and blighted, their tops turned to a rotting mass of mud; mimosas and acacias had curled up years before and were washed unrecognizable; all the evergreen trees had perished right down to the roots and were pointing this way and that with pale barked branches. Mighty cedars and gumtrees lay overthrown with giant twisting roots, bared by the rain, sticking up among the ruins of other lifeless trees. All flowers and bushes were killed by the cold rain. The ground was a morass of decaying wood and great naked stones. Only a few of the conifers seemed to be trying to resist, but they stooped and grew sideways, and the resin clotted on their bark and turned white. Ugh! said the voice of the forest.

Ugh! A cold sigh runs through the ribless treetops, and above them comes a tearing sound in the darkness, the rapid gasping wingbeats of flocks of birds who have got too cold feet in the waters north of the pass and are now up and making a streak for the south. They talk to each other through the dark at their giddy height, in broken accents of exile, geese, storks and flamingoes; they are not happy, Carl hears their vanishing farewell and shares their homelessness.

Far in the depths of the forest there is a rumbling from the thousand-year-old path the game has made across the pass; Carl knows it and follows with his omniscient senses the sounds of marching and creeping, heavy footfalls and light trotting all night long over the pass, where the blast urges the pace. It is the beasts migrating nightly in great herds from the forests north of the mountains down to more southerly valleys. Carl recognizes them by their warm smell and knows all about them to-night, though he cannot see them. He hears them and knows exactly where they are.

And as the night wears on long lines of pachyderms defile across the pass, primordial elephants, megatheriums and rhinoceroses, flapping their great clayey ears in the wind, soaked with the rain and fasting. Now and then one of the mighty beasts rumbles like an earthquake in his empty guts, and the elephant curls his trunk and makes the deep forest resound to his sniffling cough. The great cave lion has caught cold and sneezes mournfully, then dries his face with his paw and goes on. The wart-hog is short of wind, snores dismally in his snout and makes question marks with his tail.

Not far behind comes a tripping of many light hoofs, the shy grass-eaters of the jungle, they too are migrating; and among them can be heard the stealthy tread of beasts of prey, who have also lost their continuing abode. Here gazelles fleeting and pale in colour as moonbeams trot beneath the foliage in company with lame, reeking hyenas; wild horses and okapi travel shoulder to shoulder with tiger and leopard, for to-night the beasts are migrating and have forgotten all bashfulness with one another. Behind them the north wind howls across the pass with his long cold lash. Troops disappear into the valley on the south and fresh herds come up over the pass from the north. The giraffe swings his long neck and sweeps withered leaves from the twigs with his crowned forehead while keeping pace with the others, dumb and with moist devotional eyes. Smaller game try to keep up in a busy trot, porcupines, tapirs, anteaters; everything that has legs is on the way south.

But up above the trail there is a procession of emigrants in the trees, the inconstant apes, their time in these regions is over. There seems to be an idea that they have got to do something, take thought for the morrow, what? No more wasteful throwing about of cocoanuts, they are done; no noisy parliament in the treetops as to which of them is to be thrown out; they are all thrown out, the jungle is in ruin. They are on the move, and they are not above emigrating, though of course it is an insult and they let people know it. They don't see why they should take hold of wet branches with their hands; many of them refuse absolutely, but follow all the same when the others have gone on. Not one of the monkeys ever looks back. And there are but few of the migrating animals that do so.

One great beast of the elephant tribe turned and looked back towards his jungle home and then he could go no farther, he faced about and made his way back over the pass; that was the mammoth. A few other animals stayed behind, because somehow they wanted to, and it was no good time that awaited them.

Over the whole forest there was a strange rustling of beasts on the move and in trouble. The hippopotamus landed dripping with mud from its lake which had got too cool; Carl could hear it blow the wind out of its huge belly and nose its way through the withered undergrowth in search of warmer waters. With a queer feeling of pain Carl listened to the behaviour of the few beasts which were going to stay behind in the forest; they could not go, but there was a fear upon them, they complained in a changed voice, their tone seemed to have lost its boldness. The reindeer stands perfectly still under a tree and can't understand the forest, can't understand itself; once in a while it flaps its ears, shakes its head, shifts its feet, wincing in its creaking pasterns. The musk-ox has quietly gone mad like the great sheep he is, and is now on his way due north, clean against the stream of all the rest; that's his business. The bear is sulky about it but hasn't thought of leaving; he lies down somewhere and scrapes up dead leaves for a bed, he has got a cold and wants to turn in. He is not in a good temper, sniffs indignantly at this weather coming on just when he is busy with his bees. Now he'll have a snooze till the sun wakes him, and if anybody treads on him, he'd better look out! Bruin doesn't know that it is a long sleep he is going to. The badger and the hedgehog follow his example and go to earth to wait for better times.

But not all the animals have such practical ideas. The forest is alive above and below with creatures that are neither hunting nor seeking shelter, but only roaming restlessly about, on their legs the whole night because the cold gives them no peace. Carl can hear how they steal up and down, deer, buffaloes and wild goats; they stand still and sniff the wind, trying to understand it all, they shake their ears to see if listening will tell them where the baneful air comes from; and then they turn tail and bow themselves, steal up and down again. None of them comes near the fire; *that* smell they know; they know too that the Bright One it comes from bites and devours worse than anything else in the forest.

Only once, about midnight, Carl noticed two glistening green lights at the break of the jungle not far away and saw the gleam of a pair of long bared fangs; it was the sabre cat creeping up, the terrible beast with swords in its mouth. Why was it unafraid of the fire to-night, why did it venture so near? A shudder passed over the sleepers, who could feel its presence in their sleep, several of them began to utter stifled moans, and all Carl's veins were painfully aflame at the approach of this frightful enemy. But the sabre cat went away again, blinked its hungry eyes in abandonment and went. The rain poured down its gaunt striped sides; it was so cold and its tiger's heart was surely touched by a cruelty more deadly than its own. Carl heard it turn away and roam about in the jungle, without aim, without blood-thirst, without resolve, and he knew that it was doomed, that it was shut out.

But at this Carl was grieved and it terrified him. Had it come to this, that the sabre cat, the great friendless one who hitherto had withstood the hatred and curses of *all* creatures, should seek the fire, not with the object of taking off a man for supper, but to manifest its dejection and go away without wanting to eat?

What was going to happen to the world, what had been secretly decreed, who was the Insatiable One from the North who was laying waste the forest and driving out the beasts, what pitiless Power could it be? Was it a man, or was it a Being whom none could see, a mighty malignant Spirit? Could he not be killed, could he not be forced to show himself and accept battle? Might not an axe in the right spot put an end to his doings?

The night is long. Far away the wolves howl lugubriously in chorus, and in a hollow tree sits the owl chanting a doleful warning. One bird wails and another scoffs, the crocodile blubbers with his mouth full of food, and the hyena doubles himself up with mischievous laughter, his hindquarters shrivel up once for all with dirty amusement; but it does not occur to a single one of the beasts to fill the forest with a howl of challenge to the monstrous marauder who is ruining them all; no cry for vengeance, no conscious plan for murder. Every creature hums and haws composedly, each for himself in his isolation; beasts of prey and wild sheep stray about promiscuously in their abandonment, all defenceless against the cold.

Carl swore to avenge them.

This was in the nights of transition, when the tropical climate of Northern Europe was passing into the Ice Age. But the memory of the warmth lived on in the mind of man, after he had spread over the earth from his northern home — the imperishable legend of the Garden of Paradise. In the North the childhood of mankind was passed, and the memory of this, so profound and rich in pain, is the Lost Country.

Even the beasts, who dream in their own blind, submissive way, still preserve in the cheerful frankness with which they eat each other up the memory of that vanished state of innocence, before cold came into the world.

III

WINTER

𝕬ND the night wore on. After midnight the full moon showed for a brief while in the sky, lending a feeble light to the immense clouds that beleaguered creation, and when the clouds had swallowed it again, total darkness fell, as in a cave under ground, the rain increased and fell in streams, drowning the ruins of the jungle. A foaming waterfall dashed aslant from heaven to earth, solid lakes of rain came down and tore up the earth to its foundations.

Carl heard how the masses of water collected up on the mountain and plunged down among the rocks and trees, with deep bell-like abysmal tones as they rushed in and out of caves, with muffled crashes of landslides and uprooted trees. No sound could now be heard from the distressed and fugitive animals.

It was as though the heavens — which as far back as men and beasts could recall had lashed the earth with barren, never-ceasing torrents, ever denser until they seemed the prelude to eternal darkness, and ever colder — were now gathering themselves for a final annihilating deluge which would drown the whole earth. The stems of the dead palms rang one against another and collapsed in heaps under the swirling pressure of water, whole islands of fallen trees with their roots washed clean of earth came swimming down from the hills; the sky roared with rain.

And how cold the rain was! An icy breath filled the air under the sheltering rock, which the fire, lighting up the steadily streaming wall of rain, could not banish. The sleepers huddled up and shivered, frightened at their dreams; some of them awoke and muttered to themselves as they looked out at the black floods of rain which surrounded them as in a pit; but then they were powerless and unable to form any train of ideas for long; they lay down again with their arms over their heads, heaved a deep sigh and slept on, half dead with cold. It was a long night.

Carl made up the fire and gazed out at the rain with a more and more hostile glare under his bony brows. His heart was hardening, he showed his teeth at the weather. As there was nothing else to be done, he pulled himself together and settled down to finish his new flint axe.

An hour before dawn the rain abated and finally stopped altogether. Every sound was so distinct in the hushed air that the water could be heard miles away rushing down the hills and bubbling as it settled in the swamps of the devastated forests. All the beasts were silent. The man under the rock shelter sank into a torpor, sleeping heavily without the slightest sign of dreams. A faint light appeared among the drenched tree-trunks, leaning or fallen, the sky came forth out of the night in a pale empty hue. There was a dead calm and it was very cold; the air was saturated with a fresh smell from all the earth laid bare by the rain. It was as though the whole world lay naked and freezing and awaited its doom.

And a little before sunrise the dawn was blotted out by a new ghost of blue-black swelling clouds, which grew out of one another as they flew and spread over the whole sky. A sickly darkness fell and for a short time Nature was perfectly dumb, while Carl gazed in stifling expectation at these new clouds, which were blacker and more pregnant than any he had seen before.

Suddenly the lightning flashed from this gulf of gloom, flashed with a cold blue all-embracing flame, in the light of which the clouds showed for an instant white as fire right up to the top of the sky, vast worlds of peaks and white chasms overhead; the thunderclap followed immediately on the lightning in a short tearing crash, and at the same moment the clouds opened and dashed to earth in a headlong fall. But it was no longer water that came down, it was white stinging things, hail, grains of ice beating upon the ground; the shower swept across the soaking earth in a dense, shrieking volley.

The thunder startled every living thing. From the forest came a stifled wailing of many voices. Beasts that had long been fighting with the water in the flooded valleys, deer and tigers mixed together, raised themselves in their last convulsive struggles above the waves and caught the blue flash in their dying eyes before they sank never to rise again. Far, far away in a ravine the unicorn roused distant echoes with an anguished signal of distress, and soon after it trumpeted farther off but more wildly; it had gone mad and was now raging senselessly through distant forests.

All the sleepers under the rock shelter started up and threw themselves on their stomachs as one man before the thunder, imploring, twitching their lips, snivelling and slapping the earth, begging their lives so sorely. But when they had wept and lain in the dust a little while and no more claps followed, they calmed down and crept nearer the fire, stared into the flames with their poor gentle eyes, still wet with tears, and were thrilled through with thanks to the gracious fire which vouchsafed them its warmth; they stretched out their hands over it and involuntarily moved their lips as though eating, so pleasant was it; they nodded again and again in profound gratitude — ah, Fire was their lord and only friend. Then they scratched themselves busily, took another bite at the apple in their hand, wrangled a little — in short, they had once more happily escaped destruction. As for the white stuff that had fallen outside, they could only spare it a casual glance; it looked nasty, of course, but it was cozy here by the fire and they hadn't to go out in it just yet. Soon the warmth overcame them; it was not yet day; they yawned and shook themselves, one after another fell back and shuffled himself into the place his body had kept dry, and soon the whole party was asleep again.

After the hail shower came the sun. The white grains quickly vanished in a vapour which rose from the ground and drifted off under the sun's rays. For a short time there was clear sunshine over the pitiable floods of the forests, as though the sun wanted to survey the work of destruction; but soon an uncanny mist crept over the ground, and in the morning stillness that followed a strange awestruck crackling and starting began in the forest.

Something was happening, something quiet and stealthy that had never been known before. Far and wide all nature lay in a soundless pause, in which the earth yielded itself to a new and painful wonder. Cold could be felt as the only thing that had power in the world.

And now Carl could not keep quiet any longer. The resentment that had been gathering within him during the months of pitiless rain, ran over; he felt that what was now taking place in the forest was a final deadly coward's blow, and the time had come when this Destroyer must be stopped. Now he would go out and find him, whoever he was that was driving men from their dwelling places, drowning the beasts and laying waste the earth, now he should be forced to show himself!

Carl took the old rough piece of flint out of its haft and lashed the new sharp blade he had shaped in its place. After that he made up his fire, covered it well and laid on wood so that it might burn a long time, and then he was ready. He looked round with a kindly eye at his brothers, who lay twitching in their sleep, with their limbs drawn in close to the body and even their toes curled up from the cold; he felt how he was bound up with them, how it was just their irresponsibility, their airy, forgetful nature, that called upon him to go out as their common protector. They should not freeze, they should not perish. Carl made a sign on his breast with the axe as though devoting himself to his destiny, then stole out of the shelter and passed alone into the open.

It was bitingly cold in the forest. A sharp invisible poison seemed to hang in the still morning air. Carl lost his head and started to run, bounded on blindly for a long time through the impassable forest, climbing over or under the uprooted trees. The ground was covered by ice-cold mud which scorched his legs when he sank in it, and on the surface lay cold cutting things, long clear blades and splinters of ice; they made him jump into the air like snake-bites and for a while he was quite beside himself rushing along with the axe before him without any notion of where he was going. Unconsciously he made his way upward, above the lower slopes, so as to reach a safe place where less water was lying and there was a freer view.

Up on the mountain he regained his balance and went forward more calmly, still rather scared and much out of breath, but looking about him again. High up on a terrace of the mountain the forest opened out into bare ground, and with the bushman's distrust of glades he bent double long before reaching it and finally approached it on all fours. It seemed a place where he might expect to meet the enemy, the stealthy spirit of Cold.

Cautiously with both hands he parted a bush at the edge of the open and scanned the plain. No living thing was to be seen. The turf, which the rain had furrowed and broken up, was frozen stiff; the fallen trees over on the other side swam in a white mist. Dead silence. The bush which hid him was feathery and all its stripped twigs were covered with transparent flakes; some of them fell on his hands with a cold bite, till they dissolved into drops on his skin; he tasted them and found they were fresh water with a flavour of the air they came from, hardened rain that yielded to warmth and became water again. The uprooted trees round about were white and feathery at the top with the same cold stuff, like a new kind of strange blossoming; now and then a shudder went through the still forest and the rime dust scattered down with a thousand tiny clinking sounds, the thin and painful song of the forest, as though the whole earth winced in its sleep.

Carl sniffed with wide nostrils and drank in the pungent frosty air which sharpened his sense of smell to the utmost, but brought him no message either of plants or beasts. Instead he had a keener feeling of himself, of his blood and his breath, the singing purity and sweetness of the air made him more alive, he snorted like a horse and shook himself violently, so that the rime shivered down from the bush over his body. He looked about him with a challenge — where was the destructive Being he was after, how should he get at him? Hush!

There was a quacking high up above the forest; Carl bobbed down. A moment later he saw two wild duck dash down in full flight towards a little lake which lay close by him on the plain, a pond formed by the floods of the night, which lay perfectly smooth beneath the mist with rocky borders. The ducks were soaring without flapping their wings, they had almost reached the surface of the pond and had their feet stretched out to catch it — and as they touch Carl saw them slide a long way over the surface, first on their outstretched feet and then, losing their balance, on their tails; they couldn't get down into the wet. At last they got on their feet and rolled along over the pond, slipped and came down clumsily, got up again and stood like a pair of foolish birds, turned and looked about them in a puzzled way with their little eyes set high up in their heads. The pond was frozen, covered with a surface of ice! Carl sniffed knowingly. So that's it. He went up to it and stood looking down through the clear ice at the water, which lay still as death over the gravel and stones at the bottom; he tried the ice with his bare feet and heard it give with a sharp crack; it would not bear him yet. He went on through the rime-covered grass which made his feet smart, straight across the plain so as to come higher up the mountain. Where there was no green-sward the naked earth lay hard as rock and had found a voice; it resounded with an earthy ring under his feet. This was the first winter.

Carl climbed out of the fog higher up the mountain where the sun had power and the ground was not frozen. The forest came to an end and gave place to bushes and heather; finally nothing but moss grew on the wild rocks. At last Carl reached the highest summit and stood in the sun's warmth looking down into the valley, where the frost fog lay like a deep white lake. The sun, which was now high in the heaven, detached whole clouds from the mist and drove them up into the air until they shrank and faded away. Whirlwinds that had frolicked in the sunshine up under the blue sky struck down, tearing deep wells in the fog, and through them Carl could see down to the bottom of the valley, where the uprooted trees lay like sticks in a confused mass and whole herds of drowned animals floated like flies in the frozen surface of the swollen swamps.

IV

THE OUTCAST

CARL did not find his great enemy that day. He was not high enough up. When he had looked around him for a while from the top of the mountain he saw that all he had gained was a free view of yet higher mountains farther off.

Far away to the north they rose, one steep peak behind another, whole hosts of mountains sloping up from every quarter and standing together to support the roof of the world, and above them again came a region of dizzy white peaks reaching right into heaven, so that he could not see whether they were clouds or a new inconceivable world. Was that where the north wind and the frost came from? Ah, then the pursuit might be long, then it would be hard indeed to reach the Mighty One who sent down cold into the valleys. He dwelt high up, and might he not prove over powerful for a man?

Carl's resolution was shaken and he stood a long while lost in salutary meditations, not knowing how time passed. The noonday sun broke up the last shreds of mist in the valley and showed it in its whole extent. What a dizzy depth there was on every side. Carl caught sight of a dot up in the blue, immensely high up, a black speck hovering and descending in great spirals; it was a vulture. It rapidly grew bigger and when it came level with him over the precipice, it folded its wings and dropped like a stone in a straight dive through the air, grew smaller and smaller until at last it vanished again as a speck far below, amid the glare of the sunshine in the wet valley. There was the murmur of a faint breeze where he stood, but not a sound came from below.

From the mountain top the devastation of the rains showed only as holes and channels in the carpet of the forest. It looked as if a finger had amused itself by writing in the soil below. The sun laughed upon the deluge, the clouds shone and went their way. Who was Carl? Did any of the mighty ones who had their being up here above the world even suspect that he existed; *was* there after all any one who was persecuting him and his tribe?

Clouds, wide as whole tracts of country, wandered over the sky from peak to peak, changing as they went, and far below on earth their shadows moved and changed with them. A single white cloud, no bigger than a hand in the sky, darkened the whole valley beneath. The earth sombred or smiled with the passage of the shining clouds through the world.

Did the clouds know of men? They went on dizzy paths above the mountains and sported with the sun, but men were too small for them. They shone in lofty ignorance, they knew not Carl with his avenging axe, Carl the Great, who had set out to exterminate the world.

Carl was put to shame by the smiling face of heaven, he crept under a rock like a worm and for a long time did not show himself.

Later, when he came out again much sobered, the sky had shut out the sun. The distant peaks could be seen no more. The clouds were grey and low, they clung to the tops of the nearest mountains and rolled down their sides. The valley below Carl lay buried in a murky gloom. He began to climb down and had not gone far when this darkness, which proved to be pouring rain, closed over him.

Before Carl reached the bottom of the valley again it was getting on towards evening. He became suddenly alarmed at the thought of his comrades and hurried on till the cold rain steamed off his shoulderblades. On catching sight of the rock where he had left the others in the morning, he was greatly surprised to see no smoke and stopped still. A terrible thought struck him, he caught at his breath and set off in long leaps, came rushing in under the rock — they were gone! The fire was out!

Yes, it was bare and cold under the sheltering rock, his brothers had left the place. Carl saw at a glance that the fire was untouched as he had left it in the morning, but out. They must have slept a long time and the fire had gone out; the wood was damp and all of it had not caught as he had reckoned, and perhaps the wind had changed and blown the rain in under the rock. At any rate the fire was out. And then the poor creatures had waked in the morning and found the fire cold and seen that he was gone! Then they had broken camp and started on the homeward trail in the deepest despair, as he could understand. The fire had gone out. And here stood Carl absolutely alone! They were gone, all of them, and he was left behind alone in the wild flooded forest.

Quickly he bent down and found their tracks in the moist gravel, he knew every one of them and whimpered with his nose to the ground, weeping with grief at what had happened and terror at their forsaking him. The tracks were easy to follow and he started off after his comrades, breaking into a run as he went through the forest. And darkness fell. He turned his head from one side to the other, wept and showed his teeth, as he tore along, terror giving him wings. What if he did not overtake them! What if they were dead! He passed places where he could see they had been baffled and had stood in a body before finding a way round the floods; he came upon some of the miserable bundles of food they had thrown away so as to get on faster, and he stood still a moment and sobbed over their distress and over the calamity that had befallen them. But darkness and the fearful loneliness of the forest drove him on. He saw by the fresh trail that they could not be far away now, and the cold sweat of his body changed to a prickling heat, he laughed and cried by turns as he ran.

And at last he came up with them in a cave, where they had halted and sat together in a bunch, wailing softly in the darkness. He heard them a long way off; their cries of distress had passed into a monotonous plaint, which they had repeated so many times that it sounded like a sort of weary and pitiful chant, the burden being that the fire had gone out and it was a long way home. Carl stood still and called to them, called from the bottom of his heart, sang to them that it was he. They fell silent. He approached them with the last of his wind, ready to drop with exertion, hiccuping with joy.

But when he had come near enough, they stood up and met him with a united shout of rage. They came outside the cave and received him in a body with angry abuse and threats. Through the dusk he saw them turn the whites of their eyes, he saw stones in their hairy hands, and they swung their clubs at him as at a dangerous wild beast. Thus had Carl seen the troop rise up and make a stand against a wolf or a tiger that came too near the camp; but then to be sure he had been in the troop himself and one of the first to shout and threaten; now he was outside.

It was nearly dark and the cold rain beat down upon the troop, who were getting more and more inflamed, and upon the one who stood outside in the deepest dejection.

Yes, but it's me! he called in a broken voice, bringing himself a little nearer and exposing his whole body so that they might know him. Just so, it was he – and the stones whistled about his ears. One big stone hit him full on the chest so that he felt it ring hollow right through to his back. Then he stopped calling and drew back. It didn't hurt so badly, he thought, for they were quite right about his letting the fire out, but *who* could it be that threw such a big stone? He hesitated a minute, unwilling to understand that he had to take himself off. But that was what was meant. They picked up more stones and slung them after him, and as he did not give way, though it was hard to defend one's self in the dusk against so many missiles at once, the band began to move towards him, yelling with rage. One of the tallest of them was at their head and led the chorus in a curse on the traitor who had quenched the fire. *Traitor!* It was Gyuk, Carl's dear friend Gyuk.

What! thought Carl, stiffening all over, what was that Gyuk said? How was it possible that *he* could lead the band and be the first to curse him? Was that Gyuk he saw there with distorted features, his flesh rising with malignity; was that the gentle Gyuk who was pressing on him, closer and closer, foaming at the mouth, with shaking, upraised hands and with the others barking behind him in chorus?

Carl did not give ground, but his chest was beginning to tighten, he gave one or two violent snorts and lost command of himself. But even now he hoped for reconciliation. He wanted to explain, tried to say something, and when the others simply shouted him down he silently enquired of himself whether they might really be right. Was he a traitor? Had he not actually tried to save them in a broader sense than they were able to grasp? Could not even Gyuk imagine this?

A stone hit Carl, and now he got wild, the blood rushed into his eyes, he was shaking, opened his mouth and gave a low howl. He shifted to and fro with a strange buoyancy, lifting his feet high off the ground and shaking them, as though his whole body had lost its weight; he had become inarticulate like the herd that threatened him, like the beast that cursed and would not hear him. They had their limits, but he had none. . . .

And as Gyuk still came on, pouring out his senseless curses, Carl stepped quickly up to him and split his head to the teeth with the flint axe. He puffed with relief and stepped aside from the stream of blood which boiled out of his friend's mouth. None of them could believe it. Carl had done the impossible thing.

Gyuk died instantly. And while the others stood by his body paralysed with terror, Carl turned and went into the flooded forest.

Next day he sat by the burnt-out fire. It lay just as he had left it, the cold ash still kept the form of the wood but was shrunk to nothing. Carl stirred the ashes in a last hope of finding a spark at the bottom; he sniffed wide-mouthed over the heap to catch the faintest smell of a glow, even the tiniest little germ that could be nursed up and fed; but there was no life left in the damp mass of charred sticks and ashes, which had already become one with the earth. The fire was out and remained out.

Carl had passed the night in a tree half senseless with defiance and cold, not far from the cave where his companions had sat clinging to one another and shrieking all night long. Gyuk's name was repeated again and again in their wailing, constantly renewing Carl's pain and at the same time hardening his heart as in a furnace. It rained in drowning torrents as on the night before, and towards morning it began again to hail and freeze. Then Carl heard his comrades leave their cave and start off southward through the trees, until their songs of lamentation were lost far, far away in the flooded woods. They were going home with bitter tidings, without shelter and without fire in the wintry weather.

But still they were bound for home, would only have to endure a night or two more in the open, and then Carl knew that they would be back in camp with their women and children in the mild valley where the tribe's ancient holy fire was burning. There they would be well received and thawed out, and all would soon be forgotten, all but the fire-quencher and manslayer Carl. Of him a tale would be told that would cry to heaven, and the thought that he was doomed to a miserable death in the wilderness would season the food of the whole tribe.

Carl left the extinguished fire in the rock shelter and was now homeless, roamed here and there in the forest for a few days without knowing where he was, staggered around in the cold morasses unaware whether it was night or day. His eyes died away into his head. Now and then he tore a handful of flesh out of the body of one of the drowned animals, he did not suffer hunger; but the cold and the loneliness bent him to the ground like an unreasonably heavy burden.

Then one day he felt better; it was warm where he was, for without quite knowing it he had come into the southward trail and was approaching the valley where his brothers dwelt. He drew near the camp with a hard inward struggle; it was against his will, but he could not resist; he walked without a sound, could not even bear his own footsteps. Then he saw traces of them here and there, the camp could not be far off. And something was stuck up in the glade from which, as he knew, the path led down to the hut; he raised his eyes and saw what it was.

It was Gyuk's cloven skull, which they had set up on a pole. And beside it they had raised another and hung the carcass of a wolf on it. They had set this up for him, if he should venture near. Here was the parting of the ways. Yes, they had made that plain, in case he should come and turn his accursed eyes towards home. Carl straightened himself painfully and went.

He turned back to the north, up into the cold, extinct forests, naked, utterly alone.

V

THE ETERNAL FIRE

IT was snowing. Carl was on his way up the holy mountain, Gunung Api.

The big wet snowflakes thawed on Carl's hairy back, he did not notice them. At first he had thought it was the sky falling down in rags, but he soon knew better; it was only rain in another, still colder form. Carl meant to reach the top of the fiery mountain, from which his distant ancestor had brought down fire for his brothers. He grasped the axe in his hand; he was mad, there was no more fear in him after the nights of solitude and darkness he had spent in the freezing forest. Fire he must have, with or without leave. Carl panted his steaming breath into the falling snow and climbed upward, never once looking back.

The mountain lay far to the north, beyond all the valleys which had been the home of his people before the cold drove them out little by little, but Carl knew the way. Every evening as a child he had been used to peep out through the leaves of the hut and see that fiery red mouth breathing out smoke high up in the sky. He had heard stories of how the fire had once come down the mountain in a long glowing arm, devouring the forest for miles around, and those had been days of terror for the tribe; they had had to fly and hide themselves in swamps and water-holes, till He on high was good again. But in these lamentable latter days, when his folk had been forced to move farther and farther south, the mountain had been lost sight of, and Carl did not quite know what mood it was in now. From a distance he had not been able to see the top for clouds.

But no sooner had he come a little way up the foot of the mountain than he was seized with anxious forebodings. Gunung Api, usually unapproachable for showers of stones and flashes of lightning, was strangely still. Could he be asleep? He never uttered a single thunderclap nor gaped with streams of fire or flaming fissures; he lay perfectly quiet, neither shaking nor rolling down hot rocks; he was cold and still. Perhaps this might be an ambush, and Carl was not too happy about going on, though on the other hand he would have been better served if the mountain had blazed a little.

Carl had long ago passed the line where trees and all growth ceased; he was climbing up a steep slope of oddly gnarled, caked rocks, all of which still bore the trace of fire; but they were cold, and ice water trickled through them, they looked like dead monsters, and Carl's spirits began to sink into despair; he guessed the truth. Late in the afternoon Carl reached the summit. The last steep climb was over rough black ash, which cut his feet, mixed with stinking yellow and blue blocks, all cold and packed with wet snow. Carl reached the top, extinct and cold as the mountain he had climbed.

Yes, the burning mountain was quenched. Carl stood on the brink of the very summit, which formed a wide ring, and looked down into the mountain's yawning mouth. It was cold and full of snow. Around him the heaven and the abyss and the whole world lay desolate.

Never again would Carl find fire. The mighty spirit of Gunung Api was no more. The world was dead.

Icy cold and with bleeding feet Carl stood upon the roof of the extinct world, alone and without hope.

A day or two before on his way north he had crossed the pass by the ancient track of the beasts, now almost washed out by the rain, for all the animals to the north of it had migrated; and then he had halted to take a last look to the south in a vain, misty hope of just catching sight of the smoke of his tribe's dwellings. And there his distress and abandonment had give place to a terrible mood which set him up against all the world, against everything and everybody. He had burst into a roar over the valley in an arrogance of pain, a new song over the fallen earth, a song of defiance, the No song; he had shown his teeth, had sung a challenge as he stood there on the pass utterly alone, with a future before him directly opposite to that which all other living creatures were following. Echo gave back his empty cries in his own broken voice, making him still wilder, surpassing himself in frenzy. And when he had fed his heart full with loneliness and denial, he had turned and faced the north wind, had gone into the winter. Ah, but then he still had hope. Then the thought had not struck him that he might not be able to fetch fire from his father's holy mountain. Was it not Gunung Api, the origin of all fire, the immortal Warmer and Devourer? There was always that resource beyond all others, of going to the great Fire Spirit itself and fighting for a spark to sustain life, and that hope had fed his heart, the spirit of adventure, luck or ruin.

Now he stood on the burnt-out mountain. The very source of fire was dried up. The Great Spirit was dead. Carl had sung for the last time. Here stood the fire-worshipper without fire, the forest man with no forest.

And so his goings upon the earth as a man began again from the beginning, alone in nakedness upon the cold earth.

An ape sat upon the brink of the abyss and grinned with long yellow teeth as Carl turned to go down, an old anthropoid ape which for some reason or other had not escaped from the country with its fellows and which had followed Carl up the mountain. It sat with its cold feet folded together and its hands in one another, shivering with cold. When Carl became aware of it, it returned his glance with cunning, covetous eyes and turned its rainbow-coloured rump towards him, ran down a few paces to the next break in the steep slope and sat down again. Carl aimed at its head with a big lump of ice, but missed; a longing came upon him to eat its heart.

During the descent the ape kept its distance behind Carl, and he threw many stones and blocks of ice at it, but never hit. It continued to follow him.

Carl had hardly come down from the crater before a furious storm burst, blending mountains and sky in one. He killed an elk and slept under the warm body with as much of the animal's blood in him as he could drink. The vital warmth ebbed out of the elk in a course of a few hours, and he awoke under the weight of a stiffened carcass; but he had come through that night.

And when the sun broke through and he was already several leagues to the northward, the holy mountain showed a shining white snow-cap which never afterwards left it. The eternal fire had given place to the eternal snow.

More snow fell on the mountains, snow and again snow, and in the valleys it rained and hailed unceasingly. The Ice Age was coming on in earnest.

VI

UP TO THE ICE-SHEET

DAYS and weeks, Carl had no idea how many, saw him wander and clamber, always making for the north, nearer and nearer to the heart of winter. Much he went through, the cold became so fierce that at last he stumbled along in a dozing state, a stranger to himself from hardship; but he kept going, against the cold, he still wanted to see who it was that lived on the highest summits.

He lost sense of time, walked as in an eternity, only conscious of his existence through his daily struggle to keep alive. This endless journeying through the increasing rigours of winter taught him the nature of snow and ice; they were not great secrets. Ever and ever the North Wind howled: Help thyself!

The frost at night was deadly. All water was frozen solid in the clefts of the rocks, where the rime-covered stone bit the skin and held it. Carl would never have come through with his life if necessity had not forced him to impossible things and taught him to remember its laws.

One frosty night when he felt he would never see another morning, as he lay naked and worn out under an ice-clad rock, he got up half delirious and made for the warm lair of a bear that he had scented near by. He wept a little as he came into the warm hole, which was thick with the smell of wild beast and reminded him of his mother and his lost home in the jungle, where the stench of carrion rose in the sunshine outside the huts. He swallowed his tears, feeling that he had come home, sank down beside the bear and instantly fell asleep. But the bear got up in the dark and sniffed, began to nibble at him; Carl awoke out of his senses and it came to a wrestling match in which Carl would certainly have got the worst of it but for his stone axe. He killed the bear and slobbered up its blood; afterwards he made a hole in its body and crept into the dead beast. He slept until the bear's carcass was cold, but did not leave the place until he had got the skin flayed off. The next night he slept under a rock with the skin on, and afterwards he always dragged it with him on his wanderings. Now he could stand the nights fairly well, and it was not long before he learned to wrap himself in the bearskin in the daytime too. He stuck his feet into the skin of the bear's paws just as they were and could then stand the cold, rocky ground quite well. But in his fight with the bear Carl had lost an eye.

His food he took as he found it, and all he got was the live things he could catch, for there were no more plants or fruits. He stooped as he went along and picked up lemmings or field mice, turned over the stones under which they hid and put them in his mouth as they were, warm and alive. A mouse like that with its paunch full of savoury scraps and with sweet marrow in its little bones was a good morsel to take along on a journey. But otherwise when Carl had need of food he slew and devoured the beasts that were within his reach, from the hare and the wild pig to the great elk. He wielded the stone axe with a strength and dexterity no animal could resist; the mighty aurochs dropped as though struck by lightning when Carl dodged into position in front of it and planted the flint blade in its forehead. But the beasts were far between in the highlands and he often had to track and pursue for days, possessed more and more by hunger, before the saving game lay killed and smoking under his knees. He had no other warmth than the fresh blood and had to eat his meat raw, as he had no fire.

He endured this state of things, because he had to live; he took each day as it came, since there *was* nothing else; but exile set its mark on all his aptitudes, since at the same time he was growing; as a result he was never conscious of his existence except in the bitter regret of a better one which lay elsewhere, and that kept him going.

In his unresting raids he advanced farther and farther to the north. He was now up on the main Scandinavian range, where the snow was already old upon the peaks and had begun to freeze together and glide down towards the valleys through the sheer chasms.

The first time Carl saw the ice-sheet it lay many leagues away glaring blindly with its strange greenish shimmer, which mingled in abysmal depths with the blue of the sky and was afterwards to pass into his soul; he hunched his back as he always did when new mysteries appeared, and made for it.

Mountain ridges and moors lay between; he walked and climbed, crawled like a mite on hands and feet up the precipitous slopes, travelled on and forgot himself and remembered himself another time, somewhere else, still on the way, and time went by.

A day came when Carl was already well acquainted with the glacier and had laid it under his feet like any other road that had been trodden and was worn.

There too, up among the barren icefields, life was to be lived. Carl roamed about among the green ridges and fissures, heard a sighing far below him in the resounding caverns of the glacier's depths; he had no fear of it, for he had wrapped himself in two big bearskins, one with the fur inward, and he had bound up his feet with elk's skin, which he had contrived to hold together with thongs. At night he slept very well in some hole among the great masses of rock which floated on the surface of the ice. And if hard put to it by frost and storm, experience had already shown him that the snow itself was the best shelter, and he dug himself down into it and made himself comfortable with his skins, until rested and fasting he crawled out into the light again and with the skins flying after him raced away to hunt in the snowfields.

Carl outgrew his mission. Originally he had pushed into the north to measure himself with the cold and avenge the mischief it had wrought, but the daily battle for life gradually took the place of his purpose. He found no other master in the highlands than the snowstorm and the glacier, which forced him to use all his strength simply for keeping the life in his wretched body. The peaks held no other secret than snow and ice. But the defiance with which he had started out turned to inflexible will and endurance in his un-equal fight with the weather. The fiercer the resistance, the more resolutely he went ahead.

If the forest man in him had perished as he stood on the burnt-out mountain, the last trace of his animal soul was now paralysed as face to face with winter he lost the habit of imagining a hostile being who was to blame for it. As he trained himself daily and nightly to subsist, not by overcoming a resistance which was in-vincible, but by continual fighting, the foundation was laid in his mind of the first heathenism, the consciousness of the impersonal forces of Nature. His instincts hardened under the necessity of adapting themselves to the conditions he wanted to master. For that matter, he did not think, he vegetated in a sort of blind rage, ate up every living thing he came upon, and developed energy enough for a whole population. Ever and ever the North Wind howled: Help thyself!

Carl stayed in the North. He took up his abode absolutely alone among the cold mountains and began to support himself. The storm and the driving snow became his companions, the distances his home. And the winter increased in rigour. The nights yawned with a deeper and deeper darkness, and almost swallowed up the short day.

The northern lights were kindled like an outburst of mad merri-ment in the clear frosty nights, ghosts in the sky of the world's dead fire; Carl looked up at their spectral play and shook his head, no richer for the apparition. He bent over the tracks of reindeer in the crunching snow — food, food for to-day!

Carl roamed about after game and lived in caves or under rocks, and if there was no suitable shelter where he intended to stay, he piled great stones one upon another with his bear's strength till they formed a hole in which he could pass the night in safety. This contrivance did much to relieve his anxiety about existence and release his forces in other directions. Sometimes he took special pains to build himself a house, or rather a grave, of big stones when he had come to a place where game was plentiful; he might then stay there for a dozen nights at a stretch and even allow himself an hour's rest now and then in the daytime. Then he would sit outside his barrow basking in the pale winter sunshine, while the flint flakes flew jingling about him, as he busied himself in fashioning new implements. His eye wandered from his work, and sometimes he would marvel that the sun should have grown so cold and should be so low in the sky. Nothing moved within his whole horizon without his seeing it.

And with him outside the barrow, a good three paces off, sat the dog pricking up his ears and looking out upon the world with a wise nose.

Carl was no longer entirely alone; for that matter he had never been so, as the beasts were company for him in the wilderness. But most of them avoided him personally. At first the old ape had kept near him, but it did not live long when once the cold became severe. It tried to support itself on the scraps of meat that Carl left, but showed no particular talent for that kind of food and lost flesh. Once Carl saw it pick up a bearskin that he had thrown away and try it on; it dragged about in it for a while, but could not manage going on all fours in it and threw it off again. One morning Carl found the ape frozen stiff on the top of the barrow where he had slept. He stripped the heart out of it, but found it no good to eat; it was broken and wasted altogether with long affliction. After that the dog had joined him.

It began by the wild dogs hanging about his heels, since they were always sure of getting the greater part of the beasts he killed. Carl ate one of the dogs too now and then, if there was nothing else. But there was one of the pack that he spared every time, because he knew him from the others and had got used to seeing him. This one continued to follow him, breaking away from the pack, and Carl put up with his new hanger-on. The dog was very unobtrusive, never approached until Carl had finished eating and ran away most submissively if he did but look at it. It was rather a small dog with a pointed nose and a tail curled up sideways on its back. It gave up howling — Carl cured it by throwing stones —

and learned to bark; for the poor beast couldn't hold its tongue altogether when anything important occurred. Carl and the dog always noticed things at the same moment, their never-resting eyes spotted everything that moved within a range of miles. But the dog was the best tracker. It was marvellously keen on the scent, when it accompanied Carl for days together as he hunted down the reindeer, and more than once it was able to do Carl services which ratified the armed truce between them.

Carl was fond of the dog. In the midst of the hard winter, when days and nights, weeks indeed, might go by like a single long moment of utmost strain, it soothed him to know that the dog remained faithful, never leaving the barrow at night; if his hunting should fail next day, he could always be sure of the dog, there was a good meal on him at any time. The dog seemed to understand Carl, was very polite but never came within arm's length. These somewhat strained relations continued however, and they learned many things of one another as time went by. They could sit together so comfortably during the short winter days, when Carl had secured more than enough food for them both and the barrow was built and the sun shone a little withal on its distant path in the sky.

The flint rang and flew between Carl's hands; he always had a tool to work on when there was time. And as he sat chipping it he would suddenly begin to search the cold air with an eager eye and pass his nose over the flint — it had reminded him of fire! There was something in or about the flint when he splintered it which smelt like embers under the ashes. Carl distended his nostrils wide and drank in the scorched fumes, which also reminded him of grass after rain when lightning had cleansed the air, or of the morning mist in the forest, the heavy night sweat of plants evaporating in the sunshine. He drew a deep breath, sighed, and sighed again. Ah, yes, he missed the fire. He would sit down to work at the flint simply for the sake of breathing in that odour of fire, near and yet so far, which hung about the flakes.

At rare intervals, when Carl did not feel the immediate pressure of life's uncertainty, he would take to examining his person, and then found that his skin was coated with dirt and vermin and clotted blood from all the beasts he had killed; he scraped off some of the crust and ate it; thus cleanliness came into the world.

Gradually his coat of hair grew thinner and thinner, since the skins he always wore on his body took the place of his own fur. But for the rest he was healthy, flourished exceedingly in the keen open air which allowed no lying idle. He increased in strength and expanded his wits, while with a truly universal appetite he walked into all the warm-blooded animals which like himself had chosen to stay in the north and adapt themselves to the new climate.

Meanwhile that winter passed. Carl took some time to understand this. The nights began to get milder and the sun stood high just at a time when he had set his teeth to meet more cold, a harder existence, as the winter had taught him while it was waxing. But now it was on the wane.

And now at last, as the lengthening day brought a little more light, Carl showed signs of what he had gone through in the long and terrible darkness. While it lasted he had raged in a continual state of murderous despair, unconscious of himself, every corner of his soul taken up with self-defence; now the opposing forces were yielding, and he found vent in certain weird noises which spasmodically broke out of his throat; this was laughter. He had had a bad time. But he soon forgot it and recovered himself.

Summer came, and Carl had no other thought but that the cold was gone for ever. But winter came again, still harder, and this time Carl suffered the direst distress he ever had to endure, and came through it only half alive. Summer again put him on his feet, and now he took it in; he had grasped the seasons and got ready for the winter before it came.

Each new winter was longer and colder than the last, and the summer shrank; soon it was nothing but a rainy pause between the everlasting winters. The ice-sheet grew and spread.

The peaks now lay beneath an immense unbroken dome of snow, which grew continually with the ceaseless snowfalls on the heights. The snow pressed upon itself and was kneaded into a mighty flowing mash of ice which slid down from the mountain tops and began to fill the valleys. The short summers could do little to wear away the glacier but melted it into a mass and thawed the snow on its surface, where it froze again to ice; and thus it came about that the glacier stretched naked and gleaming with its greenish blue depths from the peaks far down into the valleys. The blink of this unfathomable green was to be Carl's horizon throughout all the years of his life, as the ice-sheet slowly and imperceptibly spread from the mountains over all the land.

The ice-sheet displaced the earth itself, ground it to pieces, wiped it out under the mountainous weight of its moving ice. In the black nights Carl heard the subterranean thunderings and grindings of the ice, tearing up the rocky ground, as it marched on and on under its own immense cold weight. And he gnashed his teeth at it.

On calm frosty days, when the air bit into every pore, his breath streamed out of his nostrils in thick white jets, and his blood pricked him like a shower of stars under the skin; he felt that merely to be alive was a victory.

VII
THE HUNTER'S LIFE

C ARL was now fully grown and hardened by many winters; he was already leading a sort of regular, assured existence, though still always on the move. His unreasoning fight against the cold had given place to a more carefully planned way of living, after he had made out the changes of the seasons and learnt to make provision for the winter.

He dried meat in the good season and stored it against the cold weather. There was game enough to be had in winter too, but Carl found it best to build himself a deep and solid house of stones and live in it all through the cold season, and this made him turn his attention to collecting stores. Not that he had a really fixed home; every autumn he chose a new place near to fresh hunting grounds, but having found it he stayed there all through the long winter months. He took a great deal of trouble now in setting up his house, as it was to serve him so long, and he did it after a fixed plan. If he chanced upon some natural cave, he took possession of it after killing the bear which as a rule was its former occupant; but if there was none he built himself a barrow by rolling big stones together till they formed a chamber and then filling them in with smaller stones. He deepened this little stone hut by digging away the ground and lined it with moss and deerskins, and there he kept out the cold during the long dark winter nights. He did not give up hunting, but in winter never roamed so far that he could not get back to his house before night.

Though he had neither fire nor light, he found plenty to do in the cave when he could not sleep, and there was enough dried meat for his wants; he prepared his hides, sat eternally chewing the raw, tough skins inch by inch till they became flexible and soft. This way of treating them had been taught by hard necessity, like everything else he knew; in times of hunger he had had to keep himself going by gnawing off the scraps of flesh left on his skins, and in so doing he had discovered that the skins wore better and were pleasanter to have on if he chewed them all over from one end to the other. At the same time he had hit upon preserving meat by drying it.

When he was not chewing hides he sat like a blind man in pitchy darkness, patiently feeling with his fingers; pierced holes in the skins with a bone awl and joined them together with long strips cut from reindeer-skin. He knew how to gather the skins about him in a particular way so as to get most warmth out of them, but this had cost him long hours of labour and much racking of the brains. He twisted lines and yarns of gut, which afterwards served him for various purposes, and all this could well be done in the dark.

Meanwhile the winters grew steadily longer. The ice-sheet lay far down over the country. It could not be seen to move, but month by month and year by year it had come farther. Its extreme edge now lay right down in the lowlands, where the broken green ice came in contact with the remains of the dead forest. Where once bamboo and mimosa had grown, there now arose a shield of ice, high as a mountain; where the pitcher-plant had flourished in the warm swamps, dirty gateways now yawned in the wall of ice, from which cold rivers gushed with white, opaque waters. The icefield ran continually, froze again by its own cold and grew, moving forward and seizing one tract after another.

Carl was well acquainted with its nature, knew that it was coming. He made calculations and comparisons and could then foretell pretty clearly the time when there would be nothing but winter all the year round, when the ice had taken the whole country. Unconsciously he gathered his strength for it, stored up experience, armed himself against the future. Every winter that passed was a hard school in which he learned the broad lines of preparation; there was not much now in his daily doings but had some bearing beyond the moment, even though he was not always conscious of a plan. The ice-sheet was upon him.

But the first few summers he spent alone might still be fairly warm, though very rainy. There were years of sheer deluge, when the mild rain poured down for weeks together and turned the country into a misty morass. Then the icefield lay washed and clear with an abysmal green tint in its heights and depths; it swung round in windings miles across, fissured and strewed with fallen rocks from the snow-clad peaks, bearing them down into the misty lowlands.

Carl became almost amphibious in the short summers of the Deluge, he learned to ferry himself on tree-trunks, which he poled along with a branch; the swollen rivers and lakes could no longer stop him. If the water got too deep, he slashed and dug down into it with the broad end of his pole and got along just the same. The dog went with him, now sitting at the other end of the trunk, now swimming at the side. How wet they always were, with steaming hair both of them, with their skins soaked through and benumbed right up to their eyes. But they did wonderfully well on it.

In the brief summers Carl relapsed into the careless existence of the bushman, threw off his skins and wandered about with nothing on but his flint weapons. He drank in the warmth at every pore, lay all day long baking in the sun, when for once it broke at last through the rolling clouds. But his winter fierceness lay within, only waiting for the cold; he had acquired a memory. He never went so far away as to lose sight of the green ice-blink against the sky.

Carl's summer was a ceaseless roving, when he travelled far and wide in pursuit of all kinds of game. He made little tents of faggots when night overtook him and went on the next morning. In the course of his wanderings he reached the southerly regions of his former home and found that the forest had now almost decayed into a sodden unrecognizable swamp. The trunks of the big trees were hardly to be distinguished; they formed an almost impassable substratum of rotting timber, which was beginning to be overgrown with weeds and bushes.

The jungle never recovered. Every year some of the ruined trees sent out ground shoots, which tried to raise their heads, and the mud engulfing the buried palms was green with fresh sprouts, but they never grew into trees; the next winter wiped them out again.

None of the true jungle plants recovered its vigour, but they kept alive in the form of little crippled offshoots, some of which turned out hardy and were afterwards able to transmit the growth of the forest, though on a very different and dwarfed scale.

There were other forms, however, which formerly had been of no account in the jungle, but which now shot up and began to collect into a new forest: the pines, which could stand the cold. Spruce and fir spread rapidly on the site of the jungle, and even the juniper, which in the warm forest had been a giant cypress-like tree, survived the winter with a few small, slow-growing ground shoots, which showed a resemblance to the domes and pyramids of the mother tree, though only in miniature. Other plants developed in the contrary way in the new conditions, from herbs and bushes into giant trees, showing a capacity for shedding their leaves in winter and sprouting again in the spring. There were the birch and the oak, which before had only been bushes on the floor of the jungle; there were the aspen and the willow and many more; they now came into power and began to form thickets and to stretch out their transient leaves in summer when the nights were light.

Everything was adapting itself to the new order of the changing seasons, since now it could not be otherwise. Many of the animals that had migrated came back to the North in the warm season and continued to do so, though they gave ground from year to year as the icefield advanced.

Nearly all the birds made for the north when the sun began to throw dazzling fans of light over the flooded regions whose outlines they knew so well. They did not mind the abundance of water, if only the sun coaxed up grass and reeds and a sufficient supply of worms in it. There were some of course who at once took to the South and never left it, the flamingo and the pelican and other equally dainty birds of somewhat doubtful exterior but with very delicate feelings in their webbed feet, and thus they go out of the story. All the rest — geese, ducks and swans, plovers, larks, curlews — Carl greeted as they came whirring from the south in flocks as thick as clouds and with a joyful song of homecoming dashed down upon the miles of lakes, where the old forest raised its pallid branches and roots above the surface as far as the eye could reach.

Here the frogs croaked, till the stork came and swallowed them, here worms and swimming small fry bubbled in the sunny water, attracting the ducks; great pike ploughed flashing furrows in the surface, pursued by the otter, and among the heaped-up trees whole crowds of beavers built their towns.

There was an appetite and a hatching and breeding beyond compare, and Carl revelled in eggs and game and passed long lazy weeks among the islands, where the bees were building in the hollow dead trees.

Many of the land animals too made an attempt to find their way back to the north in the warm season. As Carl sat looking out from the high ground he might catch sight of a familiar figure against the sky, far, faw away on the southern edge of the earth, which lay in dazzling fans of sunlight under the clouds — the lion with his heavy forequarters, an almost invisible speck in the distance; or he might catch the fine lines of some chilly antelope that had perhaps travelled hundreds of miles from its new pastures in the south simply for a glance at the northern home it had abandoned. These were only solitary rovers and perhaps outcasts, and they always turned back when they had surveyed the devastated forests from a height. Their destiny pointed farther and farther to the south, and soon their place here would know them no more.

Some land animals came on a visit for the summer and went away again when it got cold, but they were fewer and fewer; they could not make paths for themselves in the air like the birds and fall into the way of annually recurring migrations. The fleet wild horses adopted this habit and a few other light-footed ones, but apart from them the icefield soon set a landmark between those who would stay and those who would go. The first summer or two the hippopotamus tried to return; he came splashing up through the marshes but was piqued at all the tree-stumps and branches at the bottom and did not appear again next year; he showed an ungrateful fatherland his back, and it was a broad one.

The very first summer there was a great rush of the tailless apes who lived on the ground like man; of course, they had forgotten the winter and established themselves, with a great deal of lofty self-assertion and trampling on the rights of all other creatures, in a mountain thicket where there were nuts and berries enough to see them through the warm months in riot and revelry.

When Carl came down into the lowlands next spring, he found the skeletons of the whole band on a little island, which they had

reached in an attempt to escape from the cold. A storm had surprised them, and he could still see by their bare bones how they had
sat huddled together in a bunch with their arms round one another's
necks and had frozen to death. They had always annoyed Carl by
prying on him and mimicking him, so he gave himself the pleasure
of singing a song over the assembly. They were the last he ever
saw. Farther south they must also have died out, in spite of their
always having right on their side and everlastingly canting about
being true to themselves.

Wiser was the mammoth, of whom Carl saw a good deal in the
first long years of his hunting, when time seemed never ending as
he changed and grew into a man; he and the mammoth kept each
other company at first. Carl had not yet taken to hunting this
monster, he was not ripe for that, so they could well go about
together without interference or jealousy; they lived on different
food.

The mammoth no longer resembled his old elephant self; he had
grown a long coat of hair in the cold, so that he looked like a mossy
little movable mountain as he stamped about among the blocks of
granite and shook the rime off the larches before fumbling the
green needles into himself with his trunk. In winter he was a
familiar figure on the mountains, where Carl might come across the
mighty beast in some snow-covered copse of fir, standing under the
lee of a rock with his trunk curled up and the snow driving between
his wide-spreading tusks. There he stood rocking in the snowstorm with his mountainous weight, overgrown with long wool
between his mighty legs, infinitely patient; and under his bushy
brows, full of snow, he looked out upon the weather with his little
lively, experienced eye like loneliness itself.

In calm nights of hard frost, when Carl awoke in his stone-set
grave, he heard the hollow cough of the mammoth echo among the
crevasses and die away in the resonant eternal stillness; so the old
one was on his way up the glacier in the gleam of the northern
lights, careful how he planted his feet among the cracks and hum-
mocks of the ice. He made long journeys over the icefield in
search of the island of rock, often abrupt peaks, where the dwarf
pine grew which was his food.

But in summer the mammoth went about trumpeting lazily with
a dainty appetite among the young birches and played tricks with
his food, twisting it up over his back and twirling it round in his

sensitive trunk before he thought fit to put it into his mouth. Then he shed his coat and left the coarse wool hanging on thornbushes and thickets.

The mammoth belonged to the light nights, when the birch stems glimmered away into the distance like white, flecked limbs; he could be seen far off on the heights, pitching as he stood and flapping his ears for the midges, where the sky still kept a yellow sheen at midnight, and the deep-seated grinding of his sluggish teeth sounded far away like the rumble of the rocks on the ground beneath the glacier.

But as the summers shrank the mammoth came more and more rarely down from the mountains; he preferred to go farther north when spring came, so fond had he grown of cold surroundings, and Carl could not help taking this as a hint for the future; he know the mammoth was wise.

Carl thought seriously. His childhood was vanished now and had left nothing but a feeling that endless years had gone by; the time he had lived alone in the wilderness might well have been a cycle of milleniums. He felt the want of nothing, was complete master of his existence and was always finding new means of making it easier. He feared nothing in heaven or earth, had subjected all the beasts to himself with the axe and the spear that flew from his hand, and with the blind Powers he encountered in the snowstorm and the darkness he kept silence; they were his hard life itself, inevitableness and defiance forced into one and given shape. He had vanquished Nature and himself.

But now he felt very lonely. Why was he growing so strong? Was there no other aim for his forces than simply living? Time did not seem long to him; he either hunted for the day or provided for the future, even in the dark he could work, and if it chanced that there was time for leisure, he sat on his barrow for days and nights together following the movements of the stars, the sun's habits in the sky, and he began to know all about the paths of the heavenly bodies, how often they came back and how long it took.

His eye was always searching high and low, hither and thither, new things were always falling into his hands, and if he had but once seen or touched a thing, it was fixed for ever in his memory and lived on there. He was always open for observation, always occupied, each new discovery drove the blood violently to his head; he ran around like a bird building its nest in a fever of hatching heat when new things came upon him; his head was always creating and everything generated in his hands. But he was not happy.

One summer he took it into his head to follow the trail of his tribe to the southward, which led from one abandoned settlement to another, several weeks' journey down into the country. They had long ago quitted the place where Carl had left them, and the forest had died out; Carl had to cross mountains and go through utterly unknown regions where he did not feel secure, before at last he saw the smoke rising from a camp among the trees and knew it was they. The place was not at all warm, far to the south as it was; how did they manage, he wondered? He looked at the smoke, longingly, but it recalled the picture of the tribe sitting camped about the fire or lying in the huts around and wrangling, pouring out abuse day in and day out, with never a blow. If he had approached the camp that day when he came across the traitor's pole they had set up for him, he would have heard the irrepressible voices barking their spite one against another, and he knew that was what he would find now if he went on. Besides, did he bring fire, had he in his long exile refound what in his own mind he regarded as the one condition of his return? He went no farther. But he spent that summer in the wilderness to the north of the forests where various wild tribes besides his own had settled, far apart and as always at bitter feud with one another.

From his look-out on the heights Carl often saw the smoke of the other tribes' settlements, far to the south, but the thought of trying to get in touch with them or even fetching fire from their camp never once occurred to him. Advances to these strangers could only be imagined in one way.

And that summer it actually did happen that Carl came now and then upon a man who had been inquisitive and rash enough to stray too far north into the desolate marches. On these occasions he was able to satisfy his longings for human beings. It might be a success or it might be a disappointment, according as it was a young person with rich blood or an old sinewy savage that you couldn't get your teeth into. Carl was long haunted by not altogether pleasant memories of such a meeting in the form of indigestion; it was a skinny old forest man that he had surprised catching crabs in a brook and had devoured unobserved, so to speak, on the spot. Ugh, his teeth ached for a long time, it almost turned him against food of his own flesh and blood. His craving for human society fell off not a little after he had tried a dozen or so. Besides which, it ended in nobody venturing north of the woods any more, either in bodies or as single stragglers; rumours had begun to spread among the tribes of a wicked ogre up in the wastes, half bear and half man, who tore and devoured all that came that way. So Carl went up north again towards his own cold regions.

But when for some weeks he had had to fall back upon his usual exclusively animal diet, he began to have visions of a really young full-blooded fellow-man just once, only once again, and the result was that his progress towards the solitudes was somewhat hesitating and full of digressions.

It was on one of these excursions, undertaken in a hope which he half concealed from himself, certain of being disappointed, that he met his life's wonder.

It was a human being, at last another creature with its forelimbs off the ground. Carl sighted his prey one day in a desolate valley making at full speed for a cave, and then, when he had cut off that retreat, running wildly down the valley, over a stream and away behind a hill — and the hunt began. It lasted for three whole days and nights and only ended in a far distant region which was quite unknown to Carl and which helped not a little to make this hunt Carl's great adventure. For the game, which ran fast and with more endurance than any reindeer, brought him to where all land came to an end and there was only water, an immense lake as far as the eye could reach; this was the sea.

As soon as the man took to flight it struck Carl as curious that he tried to make neither for the forest nor the mountains but turned off across the low-lying swamps and steppes which lay for miles to the west towards the sunset. Were there people living in those parts, or had the creature no tribe to go home to?

What surprised him still more was that the man seemed to have something on, not skins like himself but something else that flapped and fluttered in the wind as he ran. If it was a kind of clothes, he might well need it, for the year was far advanced with hail and biting winds; but Carl did not know of any but himself who had thought of clothes against the cold. Another thing he noticed was that the fugitive made no offer to defend himself nor did he try to escape by stratagem, but simply ran straight ahead as the only means of safety, pretty much as the wild cattle would have done. All he could do here was to overtake his game or run it to death.

Carl had to use all his strength to keep the trail and at first for several hours the man in front increased his lead. But then Carl began to overtake him, almost imperceptibly, but enough to make him keep on. That night Carl rested a few hours, ate and slept, and next day he had to follow the trail till past midday before sighting his game.

The next night the hunted man had tried a few feeble tricks, dodging in and out of water and hiding on stony ground, but Carl tracked him down, started him and followed closer on his heels than before. Many, many leagues they had covered and had come into country that was perfectly strange to Carl.

Herds of wild horses rushed up now and then and galloped off in a circle, stood still and looked at Carl, who hurried past in a long striding trot. Carl ground his teeth as he pursued, he was not in any gentle mood now. Otherwise the hunt not very different from his daily experience, only this time his game was a nobler one and more eagerly desired than usual.

On the last day the man in front made but little headway, his limbs seemed to be ailing. They had come out to the great water and were running up along the shore, where the fine sand was mixed with round pebbles and a multitude of curious things. Carl ran on with inquisitive looks at all there was to be seen on the beach, and his nose quivered in the strong sea smell, but he did not give himself time to stop. That would have to wait just a few moments longer; the man in front was not getting on at all, sailing along dead beat, and from behind he seemed to be suffering badly. At last he collapsed in the sand, got up and tried to struggle on, but only on all fours; and the hunt was ended.

Carl approached his prey in long redoubled leaps, but without throwing his spear or preparing to use his axe; teeth would be enough here, and he licked his lips with the tip of his tongue, hungry, but above all thirsty.

Then he saw that it was a woman. She lay on her knees with her face in the sand, awaiting her doom. She made no sound when Carl touched her; he turned her over, and their eyes met. All thought of murder died within him. She should surely live.

But he showed his teeth in a last vindictive feeling of what she had cost him in toil and longing.

Terror at being in his power faded at once from her eyes, when she saw that she was to live, and she too bared all her teeth at his as though to bite — but neither of them bit. And that was the first smile.

They kept together after that. They two were alone upon the ice-sheet, the only human couple in the North.

The sun broke through the clouds and saw that there were no others . . . thus arose monogamy.

VIII

THE SEA

HERE it may be related that many, many years after, when he had lived for a generation up country with his woman, Carl fell a victim to an incurable, but not exactly wasting sickness, a mighty longing for the sea.

It began by his never being able to forget the meal of fresh mussels he and the woman had enjoyed on the beach after he had caught her and they had called forth the smile on each other's ferocious faces. That meal when Carl had tasted salt food for the first time had afterwards seemed like the only real one in his life; when he chanced to remember it he would nod without knowing it, as though he had hit upon some important new thing.

And connected with that taste was a strangely clear and happy recollection of all that he had discovered in those few hours he and Mam — so she was called when the children she bore had given her a name — had rested on the shore, before they started homeward to the icefield. Carl had examined the round stones and other unknown things, a good many of which turned out to be eatable, though of mixed value, and he had sniffed in long breaths from that lake, which was deeper in colour than the waters he knew inland and had no shore on the opposite side, so far as could be seen. Its water had been of a new, wild taste, quite good but not too much of it. White birds with a rank cry of their own flew over the waves, which seemed to be on a great migration.

Had Carl stored up within himself a resolve to come back and afterwards forgotten it, was that what was calling? Why had the day been so lovely, so sweet through and through, that the memory of it was the hidden origin of all that Carl later managed painfully to achieve in the way of goodness? He would shake his head many years after and Mam, looking up from her burdens as they trudged along, could trace a fine fleeting light passing over her man's fierce features, something resembling the smile of that day on the sands. Mam humped her bundles with the everlasting infant on top into a better place on her back; now she knew that her man was longing, longing, but that it was scarcely of her he was thinking. And yet there was nothing in the world before which she bowed more deeply under her load than her man's holy longing, her share in which was to follow him in dumb fidelity till death.

Yes, Carl longed for the sea. The years were taking him farther away from that one moment on the beach, his life had become all winter, but that moment stood by itself, the only one. The unknown had entered into his heart in that brief while, as he sat on the white sand and watched the waves flock together and wander away, out where he could not longer see. There was something in the wonder of that moment that had passed into his blood and was afterwards to be the destiny of him and his race.

But he did not know and never discovered that his longing for the sea was mystically and eternally bound up with the dawn in his heart in that instant when for the first time he looked into Mam's poor hunted eyes.

IX

MAM'S HABITS

And then the everyday round. Winter came and Carl and Mam went to meet it of their own free will, moved northward up to the edge of the icefield, where he was used to lived and felt at home. Here they spent their lives amidst many vicissitudes, at first always on the move but afterwards settled in a fixed home, as the years went by and they became a family.

Cold was nothing new to Mam, she had learnt to pull through every season. Little by little Carl got a glimpse of all the shifts she knew of to keep life going; they were very unpretending and so obvious that no one accustomed to live in the jungle would have thought of them; Mam had simply put them in practice. The clothes she wore when Carl found her were her own invention, and it did Carl good to acknowledge that two people far apart, not having the slightest idea of each other's existence, could happen upon the very same thing; this it was that broke his egoism and made him gratefully admit Mam into his solitude, and they became the first little community on earth. In the forest man and woman approached each other like wolves, and no woman became a mother without the marks of the man's teeth on her neck; Carl and Mam were the first human couple who lived together and looked into each other's eyes.

Mam's clothes however were somewhat different from Carl's as regards material; they were not skins, but a kind of plaited and felted frieze of mammoth's wool, which she had gathered from thornbushes and twisted into a coarse yarn; it was very thick and warm. On her feet she wore plaited bast shoes and she never let go of a cunningly wrought basket of reeds in which she carried all her little things, the queerest treasures consisting of all sorts of trifles such as some birds have a habit of collecting. Here she kept kernels, teeth and pebbles which had attracted her by the colour and roundness, feathers, faded flowers, bog-cotton, all kinds of shining things and everything that was soft, besides of course her food, which was also of a strange nature. When the basket grew too heavy, Mam made caches of her things under stones and in caves, never threw anything away but easily forgot what she had hidden. She was so good.

Carl never really got to know how Mam came to be living in the wilderness or how she had managed to survive the cold; she was very sparing of words. This was not from secretiveness or reluctance, but because no connected past seemed to exist for her. She was all life, but only in the moment; what she remembered flashed across her like the shadow of a past experience but did not live in her. She could shake her wild hair in the most expressive way when Carl asked her how she came to leave her tribe, and she often tried to tell a long story, which judging from the play of her features suddenly seemed very present to her; but nothing came of it beyond an abundance of wealth or affliction in her eyes and a few words, or rather singsong, and with that she thought she had exhausted a whole world. And Carl had to be satisfied with that. What she was he could see well enough, warm and always as near him as possible, and what she could do; what more story was needed?

From what Carl was otherwise able to infer, Mam, for some reason unconnected with her nature, had been an outcast like himself and had taken to the wilderness, and this must have been at a very young age, since she was only just grown up but had evidently spent many winters in solitude. She must no doubt have had something of the same character as Carl's, which had made her different from all the rest of the tribe and given her the power of living alone and without fire. The North Wind had blown the hair from her forehead and she had learnt to help herself.

Strange it was to note how she had acquired in the school of winter the same powers of resistance as Carl but in another way. He came to see this by degrees as they got used to each other and he discovered Mam's habits. She had not taken to hunting; all animals inspired her with fear and nothing else, especially the smallest of all, such as mice, which would send her screaming up the rocks; on the other hand she ate with a tranquil mind ants, snails and anything that crawled, also flies and other vermin, but rigidly excluded spiders; she seemed to distinguish between animals by unfathomable rules of her own.

Beyond this she lived almost exclusively on vegetable food, and here, guided or not by taste, she had invented a whole series of new kinds of victuals. When she could no longer get the fruits of her jungle home, she had fed herself on grass and roots and herbs which she found in the bogs and rocky wastes where she lived, and her very existence, full of life and health, proved that she had sense to discover the nourishing things. This was well enough in summer, and far on into autumn there were plenty of berries in the swamps, which Carl too had found useful, but how had she got through the winter, when there were neither worms nor herbs in the wilds? She had no thought-out idea of laying in stores for the cold season like Carl, and yet she had managed.

It was simply her general hoarding instinct which had been carried so far that she had been able, even for long foodless periods, to make shift with the contents of her basket or of her other hiding-places. She collected every possible thing and as much as possible of it, and this blind impulse had become one with her self-preservation, she *always* had supplies; thus she survived the winter.

Mam knew how to dry various edible roots, or they had dried themselves quite naturally because she hoarded them, and of such commodities she had great heaps laid by. But better than anything she liked the seed of certain kinds of grass, these she picked and stored with special care in great quantities. It must have begun by her loving these grains because they were small and looked to her like babies, tiny little wild lambs, which had to be nursed and were her very own; and here she had known no bounds, had tried to get in a simply endless number just so as to have them, a whole world of dear little babies. Afterwards she had eaten the grains, when forced by want. A handful of them was enough to keep Mam going for the day.

She collected particularly the seeds of a tall grass with a long rough beard, the wild barley. Carl knew it well, he had tasted a grain of it now and then, when it happened to catch in his hair, and it had a pleasant taste. But Mam hoarded masses of it every year, and soon it became a regular addition to the daily food of both.

The years went by, and Mam developed her habits, while they moved about below the icefield and spent a longer or shorter time in each place; and Carl left her to her own concerns, went about his hunting and improved his implements; from time which seemed to come quite of itself. She industriously gathered mammoth wool and the hair of other beasts wherever she went and then sat at home by the barrow and twined it into yarn, which she plaited into clothes. For summer wear she made herself light skirts of rushes and twisted grass fibre, trying one sort after another until at last she kept to a plant that was specially suited for this: a little herb with a blue flower, flax, and this and Mam's tireless finger were afterwards well acquainted. Mam plaited baskets of withies for her corn and smeared them tight with clay, so that nothing should run out; in this way her sex would at last stumble upon pottery; but here as in so many other things there was no real progress before Carl had come at fire again.

There were already several children. Mam had her first baby one day when Carl was away, and next time she left the barrow and retired behind a big stone, where Carl could hear her wailing a little, until an hour or so later she appeared with the new child. They were small blind creatures with a brown nap all over their bodies, and at first they were nearly always asleep in the plaited bag on Mam's back. But they grew apace; the eldest potbellied youngster was already strutting about outside the door investigating everything that lay loose in his path. His father made him a flint axe no bigger than a thumbnail, with which the little man wrought doughty deeds among the puppies that swarmed around the settlement. Then Carl could once more look upon shaggy little children flying bits of down in the air and playing at birds, as they had done in the lost forest; but now it was very different.

Their house had to be built spacious and strong, so that the whole family might have room to sit in it. Carl rolled a big stone before the entrance when he went hunting, and then Mam sat comfortably below with the children and went on with her plaiting. In the daytime she pushed aside a smaller stone so that a little light reached her underground; otherwise it was pretty dark for her in the barrow, especially in winter. They always lived in one spot through the cold season, and in time it became quite an extensive settlement; Carl had to build small separate huts for their stores of roots and corn and wind-dried meat. He always took care to choose a place that was already sheltered, a natural cave for choice, but failing that just a natural rock shelter, to which he built on, or a hollow in the ground if nothing else offered.

The ice-sheet forced them to keep on moving, often literally, when the edge of the ice came marching on over the settlement. In this way they had been pushed so far to the south that their position was now pretty nearly where Carl was born and had spent his childhood; he knew it by many landmarks, it was in the neighbourhood of the extinct volcano. But where the jungle used to grow was now a solid shield of ice extending for leagues and deeper in its green crevasses than the highest trees of the forest. It was a marvellous difference, and Carl, who had witnessed the change, at times found it hard to know himself again.

Meanwhile moving became more and more difficult. Mam had more children and trailed about heartily content with one on her back and one on her arm, leading another by the hand and with several more clinging with their little claws to her skirt; but they had so many other indispensable things now to take with them that it became almost impossible. Mam dragged along more than her own weight, always reserved and always good; they managed the move, because the icefield said they had to, but it could not go on like this.

Carl himself had also introduced so many new things which made it hard to break up when they had once settled down in a place; he had begun to keep animals about his home. For it often happened when hunting that he was able to capture some animal alive, the foal of a wild horse or a reindeer cow, and these he took home with him and kept tethered by thongs near the house. If game chanced to fail, there were then these captive animals to fall back on. In course of time this practice spread, so that he had several wild horses grazing at home, besides wild cattle, reindeer and goats, and they bred in captivity and soon became numerous. The wolves attacked them at night and Carl then put up fences of branches and hurdles. In the autumn he slaughtered most of his stock and dried the meat for winter use, but some that had become quite tame and half belonged to the family were allowed to live over the winter. Mam and the children fed them with grass they had gathered in the summer and dried. The half tamed horses and reindeer were not so difficult to take on a journey, they even submitted to Mam's loading some of her burdens on their backs and thus they did service. The children were soon on good terms with the quiet little ponies, which were scarcely wild any longer, and took it into their heads to bestride them when they were on the trail.

And so the procession is formed, Carl leading with his stone axe, always cool-headed and always dangerous. He has only one eye, but it is everywhere, it flashes upon everything that moves for miles around. He put his hand to the big stones that lie in his path, rolls them over and pushes them aside with his feet, as he goes on with never a halt, his eye clinging to the horizon; and behind him come Mam and her load, the children and the domestic animals in pretty fellowship, the small persons riding on the big. And the rain comes down. Where the sky ends the ice-blink beckons home and drives abroad. Yes, here comes the Stone Age man with his belongings.

But the journeys came to an end at last. One year they established themselves on a mountain height which they could not be persuaded to leave, and here they were surrounded by the ice-sheet.

This height was many leagues in circumference and fairly level on the top, but so high that the ice did not surmount it, though it spread all round. On this island, which soon lay cut off by miles of ice on every side, they made their home, while the ice-sheet grew and pushed on.

The family increased; there were boys and girls beyond their parents' powers of counting and well into the notion of *many*. But each one of them asserted himself sufficiently and ate enough for a human being with or without a number. Mam, who hitherto had only applied her collecting activities to temporary things, had now found her true vocation and seemed to be bent on producing a population. Every year, when the short summer returned and the mountain island was gay with flowers and foliage, there was a new down head peeping out of the bag on Mam's back.

The elder ones were shooting up. Already Carl had sons nearly grown-up, whose eyes were beginning to search the ice-blink on the horizon and whose nostrils quivered keenly with a promise of great hunters to be.

X

CARL STRIKES FIRE

CARL and his family could not have kept alive on their northern mountain isle in the midst of the icefield, with winters increasingly severe and only short rainy intervals of summer, if Carl, after having had to do without fire for so many hard years, had not at last found it again.

But just as he had been taught by growing up in adversity that existence never renews itself until it has destroyed all hope, so did he see fire spring from the heart of winter, in his direst need. It did not come about by a lightning stroke, a shower of red-hot stones or other gracious efflorescence of fire from on high; Carl sat in the midst of the ice, poor and god-forsaken, and fought his way to fire, strove so long with the hard stone that it came. And yet it was a great wonder, that day when fire was born between his hands, a thrilling hour of victory which made him rich for all time and established him as lord of the earth.

Carl had known for many years that in some way unknown to him fire was present in flint or in the air about it; he could catch a breath of it when he split off flakes for knives or hammered out larger implements, a powerful burnt smell which expanded his senses through the memory of all it held within it — the smell of the strong embers beneath the ashes, the jungle, the bubbling swamps, the thunderstorm; and it became a regular habit with him, which Mam knew was inseparable from her man but which she could not grasp, that whenever he was working on flint he would put his face down to the chips and seem to drink a rapid draught with open mouth and wide distended nostrils. Then it was that Carl scented fire and all its nature, then did his spirit take flight where Mam could not follow him. It even happened, and by no means rarely, that the fire showed itself, especially when Carl was chipping flint in the dark; sparks would then fly from it, come and gone in an instant, sprinkling their colours like little messengers from the rainbow and the starry world between Carl's hands and making his thoughts breed fast.

But when the winters became so hard after the ice-sheet had closed about Carl's home, when the cutting frost was all about his cave, with ice everywhere ringing and snapping in the tense air, when it grew so cold that Mam and the children had to stay below, lying packed in layer upon layer of skins — then Carl felt as in the first desperate days when he found himself naked and alone and the cold threatened his life: Now, now something must be done, the impossible. . . .

And then he did what lay nearest his hand, following up what he knew; he chipped flint. Day after day he sat before the entrance of the hut in faint sunshine or wet mist, wrapped to the eyes in bearskins, and struck off flakes. He never gave himself a rest, he hammered and smashed up one flint block and pounding stone after another and watched them flying off in the biting frosty air; he sat among heaps of splinters and did not give up, waded in flakes till the sun which showed far away, lifeless and cold like a lump of ice, had traversed its flat path and was stooping to the horizon behind the endless snowfields. Night came with the northern lights and great trembling stars, and the barrow was snowed under; a brownish hole where the warmth of those below ground ascended was the only sign of life.

A herd of reindeer went past with creaking pasterns in the creaking snow; they bent their frosted muzzles to the snow, hesitated and uttered the strange, flayed guttural sound — *hraw* — which is their language. And the northern lights hung glimmering over the ice-sheet up into the sky like the lone silent laughter of a madman. The Pleiades twinkled mistily, showed all their stars and hung again bedewed in their eternity.

Next day Carl sat before the entrance of his house in the feeble daylight and broke stones, hopeless and untirable, with a tight-shut face; only his nostrils continued to quiver and work. He kept himself warm by his mad labour, that was all he got by it; poor Mam thought her man was bewitched by the cold.

But Carl kept on. If the fire was there, there must be a way of driving it out. It must be sitting in *one* of the stones, and even if it should be his cursed luck that the very last stone in the world held fire within it, why then there were stones enough to last a thousand years, he would grow old in smashing them, but he would do it. When his store was finished, he fetched more, dragged all the loose stones in the neighbourhood home to the settlement and hammered them to pieces. He got no fire. And the bitter winter went by.

In the summer Carl fetched stones home from every part of the mountain isle, all that lay loose on the surface of the ground, a whole mound of stones lay outside the cave; he did not do much else that summer but go out in the cold deluge and carry stones home, stones, stones; and Mam the tongue-tied let him see her tears. She and the children gathered and gathered, though there was hardly anything eatable left on the island. The tame animals were gone, what was to happen? Carl left his hunting gear untouched, and when Mam turned to him with moist eyes, he gave her a look as though he did not know her. He was not like himself, had become so grimy and ingrained about the face and was always covered with chips and dust right up to the hairs about his single eye, which looked uncannily white and heated; the other empty socket was full of dust and slime. Now and then he himself felt something of what was in Mam's thoughts, that the frost had gone into his soul.

But that winter he found fire.

Suddenly one day, after he had broken up stones as usual by the hundred and was sitting half stupefied by the scorched smell which had now begun to affect him vaguely like a dream of sleep, of one day falling asleep and sleeping for ever, he picked up a stone which instantly gave great broad sparks against the flint; he struck again, harder, and the stone rained fire, blue sparks, whole long worms of fire which crawled in the air and lasted a moment in glowing curves before they died. Fire, fire!

Then Carl's strength failed him, he turned hot all over like a miserable sinner and deadly faint, had to sit still a while. His arms sank weakly, he dared no more, looked about him beseechingly, turned his eye to the sun which glittered blindly far away as though dazed by the cold. He looked around upon the snow-covered island and upon the icefield stretching bare and white as far as the eye could reach, and never had he seen his world so clearly as at that moment, he knew for the first time that so it was. And he breathed out a deep sigh.

Then he tried again and saw the sparks fall big and living on the snow, where they went out, leaving a little hollow with a spot of coal at the bottom. He sobbed and sobbed again, a profound weakness fell upon his heart in the pause while hopelessness gave place to a joy in which he dared not yet believe. But it was true. And he arose self-possessed, with a feeling of deep earnestness that came from within him; he scarcely drew breath as he made preparations for a fire. He knew what was wanted from the time when he tended the flames long, long ago in the forests, tinder to catch and spread the fire and wood to keep it going. A few moments later he had a flame.

He let a spark fall on the dry tinder and at once saw a spot of fire form and begin to smoke, turning black with a glowing edge and spreading; he blew on it cautiously till the glow grew dazzling and began to sing, and then he hurriedly strewed shavings on it and left off blowing — and instantly a flame rose straight up into the air, a little blue and yellow soul with a hot breath; it flagged a little, jumped up and down, vanished and came again nibbling at the smoke as Carl blew; he gave a long puff and stopped — and then the flame seized on the shavings with a greedy little flutter and began to burn! Carl lighted a branch. Here was the fire. Now he had it and had nobody to thank for it, it was his own — fire, fire!

Mam heard a yelling outside the cave, huge shouts and songs of joy, and the earth swayed over her head from dancing feet, as though a bear were taking great leaps and coming down heavily on his paws — was that her man's voice? Her soul grew dark within her and she crept out, certain of her doom; now it must be all over with Carl and with the rest of them. She found him up on the top of the dwelling, dancing about and swinging a burning branch in his hand, she saw the *fire* — and then Mam grinned, stood still with her feet turned in and laughed in a dazed way. She grasped what had happened. So that was it; her husband and god had vouchsafed to create fire. It did not surprise her very much. What was he not able to do? Still, it was good. Mam blinked at the fire and laughed. But Carl stormed and howled with joy and exulted at her, Mam, Mam! The youngsters came crawling up, sneezed at the frosty air and saw the fire, stretched their necks and came nearer with wary eyes.

What a day it was! It was the only day, the day without beginning or end. The fire was triumphantly consecrated with dried meat and old tallow, the first sacrifice rose stifling in the frosty air, a delicious savour of broiling rejoiced the family, with mouths full of food they lost themselves in an oblivion of gluttony.

The fire ate itself into strength and held the wood in a ravenous embrace with all its devouring limbs, covered its prey with its whole wild ghostly body, which stretched up and leaped freely into the air, had young, vanished and came again. The wood seethed and gave loud cracks, and the flames breathed fiercely, roared and rolled out smoke which sailed up high and made a cloud. What a marvel! But the greatest marvel was that the fire warmed, it warmed! It was hotter than the summer day and nearer than the great sun. Carl saw his children laugh at the fire with new happy looks on their pauper's faces, he saw them stretch out their hands to receive the warmth, making a caress in return because it was so good. And he saw them draw back in terror when they came too near it, and then he gave a mighty laugh; they would learn soon enough the boundary between what was good and what was dangerous. Mam looked on, her wrinkled face with its young eyes lighted up by the joy-fire; she had brought out her basketwork which the great event had made her drop, and worked on to finish it.

In the evening they had light in the cave! A fire on the floor showed them for the first time the interior of a home in which they had always been accustomed to fumble about with their hands. The family on the icefield had entered upon a new era.

Carl examined the wonderful stone which had given fire on striking flint and could go on giving it. It was a dazzling yellow and glistened when turned in the light, heavy in the hand, and it smelt like raw onion when broken. He ought to have been able to *see* that this was the very fire stone. Never had Carl felt anything lie so weightily and richly in his hand as this stone. It bred a wholly new joy of possession, roused a mighty desire and satisfied it at the same time, since he had it. It gave him unbounded power, it was the first treasure of his race and of mankind. He had not only recovered fire, but if it went out he could *at any time get it again!* The men of the bush could not do that, they only had their hearth, from which all fire had to be taken and laboriously carried about smouldering in a basket of tinder when they moved. If it went out it could not be kindled again. They had not the spark. Here it was. And Carl determined to construct a special little chamber of the biggest boulders he could move as a hiding place for his fire stone.

But when night came and all the others were asleep in the cave, full-fed and resting deeply after all the warmth they had got in their bodies, Carl could not sleep. The day's great find possessed him like a fever in the blood, joy and excitement ran tingling through his limbs, he looked about him as he lay with a supernaturally wakeful eye; it was as though the tension had waited until now, when he had reached the goal through long years of hopeless toil. The fire smouldered without giving any light, smothered in a hole in the floor and well covered over with ashes. Above the little opening he had made for the smoke between the stones of the roof, a star appeared, quite small and intimate.

The low, heavy-walled hole in the ground where Carl lay with all that was his was filled with the smell of the fire and the burnt wood, which had sweated out its summer soul, and Carl thought himself back in the forest, in the pregnant atmosphere of fertility among dewy, resin-dripping palms. A dazzling sunshine kept passing before his eyes and he imagined he was flying, soaring freely in an ocean of mild sweetness above dizzy tree-tops. Did he see peacocks, was he himself a peacock, radiant with the colours of the rainbow, flying over the forest in the mist of sunlight with his train of mystic eyes? Had he returned to his childhood, were the warm forests again swaying upon earth, and was it only an evil dream that the ice-sheet lay over the lost country to the height of its tallest trees?

The familiar nocturnal sound reached his ears, the deep subterranean grinding of the ice on the rock as it crept on, the fall of blocks of ice and the sweep of the north wind in the bare green fissures — or was it the rush of the warm rain in the jungle's foliage he heard, the languid sighing and groaning of the lofty trees? The blood boiled in his ears, he scarcely knew what was the sound and what was himself. Spasms of joy shot through his breast when he came to think of his treasure, he grew so happy that he saw suns before his eyes and lost all sense of time. He did not know himself; what was the truth? Was it he who for endless ages had stood up more and more fiercely against winter, while he saw his children freezing, freezing, without being able to give them warmth, until his heart became like the flint he broke? . . . if the whole earth turned to stone, he would strike fire from it! Was it he who had now found fire? Oh, his heart had come back again, hot, choking hot springs in his breast. . . .

He lay with the fire stone beside him and thought it an eternity since he had tried it; he longed to see the sparks spurt from it again. The blood raged through his veins like a world on fire. He must see fire, calm his heart with the wealth he had made tangible. And he sat up with swimming head, held the stone and a piece of flint before him in the dark, and struck fire.

A great blue spark sprang from the stone, blue as the wildest lightning and of immense power; it lit up a world before Carl's eye. *Now* —

He is not in the cave but in the open, and round about him flickers a green element, in which all that he sees swims away and loses itself; high above his head there seems to be a roof, rocking in lively motion, which refracts the light with dazzling clearness, and he understands that he is in water, deep down where the water closes warm and heavy about his body and runs along his sides with light tickling bubbles. His field of view, which is narrow and blurred, moves with him as he glides on, and he sees other creatures in motion, great armoured predatory fish, which come towards him and instantly turn aside with an oblique stroke of their tail fin; transparent hag-fish vanish in rapid twirls among the sea palms. The bottom, which looks much nearer than it is in the clear water, is like a flowery meadow of open quivering coral polyps, and the glutinous bodies grope about with feelers that are studded all over with eyes and suckers, twisting in and out, up and down in the deep water, which warps the sight so that it is impossible to tell where the polyp is or whether it is only the lobes of one of the long, gently swaying marine plants which rise from the bottom surrounded by crustaceans and with small creeping slimy bodies on their stalks. The deep is covered with whole gloomy groves of plant with leaves or fingers, intersected by green glades, and here glide all kinds of flame-yellow and sky-blue fish which gape over the warm water and expel it again from their gills, as they turn their flat, glazed eyes and look about them. Little fibrous underhung sea-horses sit in the weeds, made fast by their prehensile tails, and let the world go by; their dorsal fin stands set like a little sail, making delicate play in the current.

As Carl glides slowly on it dawns on him that it is himself whose shadow is cast over the wilderness of seaweed wherever he goes, and who sets up a swell that makes the submarine forest rock; he is something or other big and feared, since all the fish, even the most dangerous-looking, make way for him; there is always an empty space of a certain befitting range around him, and there must be a reason for this. He goes over various deep-water passes, where in the brooding darkness of the ocean floor he glimpses the tails of fat mud eels making for safety; he skims over low coral reefs, where he chases whole shoals of glittering fry in headlong flight before him; finally he approaches the dazzling, glimmering roof — and breaks through it. He goes up on to a mud bank among the roots of a tree and is now on the outskirts of a great forest on land, in a damp and resinous atmosphere.

The sky above him is perfectly white with warm steam and appears to rest on the tops of the wide-spreading giant ferns which, interspersed with towering horsetails and lycopodiums, dominate the forest. Gigantic insects fly among the tops of the tree-ferns, prodigious flies, bugs and dragonflies of supernatural size, whose sheeny wings click and rustle audibly up and down. But on the reeking forest floor, which is matted together with mangroves and black fallen trunks, the swamp is almost boiling with the heat of fermentation and here sit great bloated mud toads with witless eyes, making attempts to hop when one of the giant insects comes near. The half rotten tree-trunks are twined round with strange snaky parasites and bushes which seem alive and feel about with fleshy and glandular follicles in the moist air. Tadpoles and snails swim about among the ground shoots of the horsetails, where the sap sweats out in sulphurous pools. The black mud among the roots of the trees is full of holes where crabs lurk, and fish run over it, with movable eyes and fins that serve as feet. All around the hot mud swells and bursts in bubbles.

But there is no sun; in its place a luminous fog over the landscape. From time to time a hotter shudder seems to shoot through the fog, making the sky whiter but not more transparent; this is lightning not far away, followed by muffled thunder. In the south above the misty fern forest a round mother-of-pearl gleam shows in the sky; this is the sun, which never penetrates the steamy atmosphere.

And between the aerial roots of a tree on a mud island near him Carl sees a being which he knows to be his like, a great flesh-coloured scaly salamander with human eyes. It is sitting with its finned tail in the water, opening and shutting long fish jaws of rapacious teeth; it is engaged in devouring a salamander of the same kind as itself, though somewhat smaller. Round about it all other animals respectfully make way. Yes, that is what he looks like, Carl knows very well, and he can feel his salamander soul, a sort of giddy unconsciousness, in which he perceives everything with all his pores and yet knows nothing. At that instant the spark goes out and he is sitting in the dark in his cave on the ice-sheet.

Carl sighed, he knew that he had had a vision but could not remember it. He listened to the children's breathing, they were all sleeping securely in the warm cave. Overhead the frosty wind passed through the night with a lonely sound. A distant cough came from the icefield, where the ice broke asunder in a crevasse. An anguished feeling came over Carl that time was flying past. He would have to strike fire again, only once more. And he struck fire. A long dripping, yellowish blue spark flew from the stone. *Now* —

In that flash it is as though Carl's soul expands so mightily that he knows and is part of all the light reveals, though it is a world incomprehensible to him. It is night and winter, but everywhere is a blaze of light and thousands of human beings pass close beside him. Well yes — he is on a street corner in Chicago, and the magic spark drips from the overhead wires of the trolley-cars. Unbroken lines of street-cars, lighted up and packed full, glide along the street, which is black with a swarm of people, and above them the elevated railroad thunders past illuminating house-fronts. It is snowing, but the city is alive with people on foot and in vehicles, endless trains, steaming locomotives. The city raises its towering houses in miles of cliffs like a glowing forest of iron and stone, and mingles its fiery air and pungent sulphurous smoke with the fine frosty snow of the winter night. Thousands of people, strangers and hostile to each other, crowd among the lofty business houses, which overhang the abyss of the street with their façades as bright as day, lights and lights running up perpendicularly from the ground till the shining columns of windows lose themselves in the smoke and darkness of the wintry sky. In the middle of the sidewalk a long stretch of pavement receives the thick-falling snow with a subdued facetted glare which finds its way up from below through thick glass prisms, and this glare of light throbs with a rapid pulse; it is the shadow of the spokes of a great flywheel down below that makes the light vibrate, the pulse of an engine fed by a coal fire underneath the houses, the beat of the heart of light which sends out the artificial day into the city through copper veins under the ice-cold pavements of the street. The arc-lights over the heads of the busy human crowd burn almost imperceptibly with the same rhythm. This is the *Wheel*, this is the fern forest's marvellous second blooming.

Carl gave a sudden start, from cold and from energy. The spark went out and he was left in the dark with the fire stone in his powerful hands. He had been wondrously staggered and found himself in a painful and ecstatic uncertainty about the world and about himself which he could not bear. He struck fire again.

But now it was half a century later and Carl was an old, old man. His descendants, who dwelt with him on the ice-sheet, had become quite a little nation, all with his and Mam's features blended together, a strong and hardy breed. Mam was no more, but there was no danger of her habits dying out, the race carried them on. Yes, Carl had grown old, his soul had play only within quite narrow limits in his shrunken and ossified body. Time . . . one day he felt longings and went down into the chamber he had built for his fire stone and for it alone and where none dared follow him. He closed the grave after him with a heavy stone, and his sons and sons' sons, who stood around in deepest awe, heard the Ancient turning about and blowing like a bear preparing to hibernate. Afterwards they heard him humming underground, and he sang:

> Early the storms of life
> taught me simplicity;
> the house beneath the ground
> for the weary is fittest.

That day passed and the night too, but Carl did not come out, nor did any one dare to intrude on him. But they heard him sing:

> Once I plucked breadfruit
> where icebergs are crashing.
> Late will men long for
> the land I saw sinking.

Even on the third day they heard feeble tones from the grave. Carl sang:

> I yearn for the shoreless
> sea of my boyhood.
> Memory consoles me.
> Mam, shall we meet there?

They saw a flash of fire from the grave and started back in terror. Not till weeks after did Carl's sons pluck up courage to cover the barrow with earth where the Ancient had gone below.

But the flash they saw was when Carl, after being lost in thought three days and nights, had at last felt in the dark for the fire stone with his numbed old man's hands and struck fire. *Now* —

A flood of unearthly light about him! He is in the midst of the Forest of the Living. The soil is of skin with coarse pores, here and there overgrown with hair and in places hardened to black-and-white striped horn. Hills and the long folds of valleys show where the earth's bones protrude and where miles of ribs run, and the plains are strewed with blocks of old blanched bone. The gravel at the edge of a blood swamp is made of washed up human teeth, and out of the swamp grow tufts of fingers, from tender little baby's fingers not yet opened to strong, fully extended men's hands. But the forest, which grows thick and runs so far into the distance that at last it is only seen as a pink haze, consists of naked

trees with branching limbs and eyes fixed in the trunks; the foliage
is long, hanging human hair. The trees are not all alike, some are
quite red and white in the bark, so that the blue veins show
through; they have greenish eyes and luxuriant red foliage; others
are more brownish in the bark with dark eyes and black tops, but
the forest is so infinitely great that the difference is not very
noticeable.

The forest has the effect of a mass, and yet the trees are not all
of the same sex or age. There are male trees with knotty branches
and protruding paunches, and slender, nervous girl trees with all
their wealth of hair hanging in a tremble over their limbs like
birches in springtime. Little children are shooting up in the undergrowth, with only their round heads yet visible as they break
through the soil.

Some of the trees are old, with perfectly white, scanty hair
bristling from their withered tops, and their stems bent and full
of wrinkles; and there are tender infantile trees and milky skin
and light down on their chubby twigs.

Each tree becomes one with the soil through its horny roots,
but otherwise has most of its organs independently; besides its
eyes there are one or more ears on the stem, a mouth opens among
the branches, and nostrils are spread about over the tree. But they
have their breath in common, the whole forest breathes together
with a sound like one great fever, and from underground up
through all the trees right out to the farthest twig a single common pulse can be felt, the beat of which can be traced in the landscape all the time as a measured, almost imperceptible up and
down; the vast common heart beats far down in the very centre
of the earth. The atmosphere too is common, the whole forest
smells of sweat.

The forest extends, flesh-coloured and boundless, as far as the
eye can see, and the air is so clear that it ranges for hundreds of
leagues. In some places, far and near, it is flecked by shadows, and
these shadows seem to be of a definite oval form and to move
slowly over the landscape. Carl, who is sitting in the forest as an
old gnarled stump with one dim eye, turns his gaze upward, trying
to see where the shadows come from, and notices several perfectly flat, gigantic flounder-like creatures floating up in space
against the red sky. One is quite near and lies above the forest, a
great oval miles long, immensely high up. What it is he cannot see,

but it is in gliding movement, and all the way along its edge, which is thin and translucent, runs a quivering, regular wavy motion from front to rear, like the fins of a flounder, and this is continually repeated. The vast size of these flying ovals makes the forest and everything on earth seem low and small. But the red light in the sky above the flying things draws the eye higher, and soon even they are forgotten like motes in the air, for the vault of heaven ranges away into infinite space.

The universe is of a glorious colour like the flush of dawn, the very source from which all feeble myths of the joy of life are derived. A sun lies quite near but does not dazzle the eye, so that he can see the wonderful gaseous body resting in its prolific spherical being, expanding and contracting, rarer than air and yet tense, like a swarm of bees in the free summer air; round about it hang many planets in their happy orbits, and in the background a host of constellations proclaim that untold suns are circling each for itself, solitary but in freedom after the same blest laws of flight. Blue and yellow spheres hang quite near, so that the lines of their continents can be described. Milky Ways lying billions of miles away swim like fine clouds in the universe.

But above them all and centred in the zenith swings a nebula whose immense shining spiral seems to form a wheel, covering almost a quarter of the heavens. It stands perpetually above the Forest of the Living as a sign of the everlasting centrifugal force in eternity. . . .

The spark went out, and Carl lay alone in darkness — in darkness. The grave closed him in well. It was narrow and poor as the very first stone cists he had made when, naked and alone, he was thrust out into the winter.

Ages passed, and still he could see. There was a hole between the stones, and through it he saw a little piece of the starry sky, and it was his last deep joy that he lay beneath the familiar constellation of his childhood in his own black earth.

It was the Pleiades that shone down upon him, the Pleiades that twinkled mistily, showed all their starry eyes and hung again bedewed in their eternity.

XI

THE SONS OF CARL

THE people of the North increased. As the ice-sheet grew, Carl's and Mam's offspring multiplied into a number of families and clans, which spread themselves over the mountain isle and carried on the life of their ancestors.

At first the Ice Folk drew new blood from their original kinsmen of the forests. Carl's sons made raids among the Forest Folk to the south and brought back women; their sons did likewise, and it long remained the custom for the young men of the icefield on reaching maturity to prove their manhood by going down to the forests to get wives. These raids always took place in springtime and were surrounded by a certain festal humour, of which the younger men dreamed and the old retained grateful memories. For besides the bringing home of fresh woolly girls these expeditions provided an opportunity for making the acquaintance of the young bride's relatives, with a welcome change of diet; merry tales were told of rapes of women followed by banquets where excitement reached such a pitch that the bride was included in the meal, so that to avoid returning empty-handed the whole raid had to be started over again. One was apt to let one's self go in foreign parts.

But these jungle girls, when once the young men had brought them back to the ice-sheet, were thought a good deal of, partly on account of their scarcity, partly because they soon gained respect as prolific mothers; and the half spontaneous grimace with which their husbands approached them, as though they simply intended to eat them up, came to be regarded as the sign of affection and pride of possession.

The distance, however, became greater and greater as the ice-sheet spread, and it might take whole years to visit the natives of the southern jungles and come home again with women. Another reason for the discontinuance of the practice was that in time the Ice Folk became so numerous that the younger members of different families, though distantly related, were sufficiently strangers to one another to be struck with the mutual surprise which brings young people together. Everything has its day, and the woman hunts in spring became in their turn things of the past. Carl's posterity and his original kinsfolk were already two widely different types. Legends more and more romantic were told of the lovely dusky daughters of the jungle, but the few specimens it was still possible to procure in the flesh smelt of civet and were not to the taste of the Icemen. A dream that makes your mouth water is one thing, the unappetising reality another. And when at last distance and time had entirely sundered the two races, any propensity for savage women came to be regarded as indecent; while on the other hand the luxurious dreams to which this privation gave rise took on ever lovelier forms and were bound to end in creating an ideal of Beauty as a world in itself.

Thus the gulf between the two races parted by the Ice became a profound eternal chasm. They were no longer each other's like. The division between them was fateful in its effect. The primitive people who continually gave ground remained the same, whereas Carl, who could not yield, had become another and had passed on his changed nature as a heritage to his descendants. The Jungle Folk continued to give way before the winters, went farther and farther south that they might still live the same life, and this retreat, coupled with their continual increase, was destined to lead them into distant climates and to spread them over all continents. But Carl's race remained settled in the North and adjusted itself to ever more difficult conditions, which necessitated progress at home. They no longer resembled the naked and forgetful savages from whom they were originally descended, they were other men.

The sons of Carl grew big and strong as bears in their toilsome hunters' life on the ice-sheet. The clothes they wore made their own coat of hair superfluous, their skins became red and white from living in the shade. The everlasting wet weather bleached their hair, and their massive-browed eyes, which once had been dark as the confines of the forest, took their colour from the crevasses of the glacier and from the open, blue-green blink of the horizon between ice and sky.

And their nature was different from that of their remote forefathers; they had lost the forest man's way of going slap-dash at a thing and then stopping to scratch himself; their life had taught them to take good thought and strike home when the time came. They did not live exclusively in the moment, the eternal summer of the jungle; they had to remember and think ahead if they were to survive the seasons. In place of the passion, harmless enough, of primitive man, they had assumed a self-command which might have an air of coldness; the wider range of their activities compelled them to think twice and hesitate. This made them introspective and apparently joyless; there was no sound of chirruping about their dwellings as in the leafy booths of the forest. But impulsiveness and joy of life lay deep in their nature and had acquired added strength. In this they all took after Carl, whose lifelong calm was legendary, but of whom it was also related that on two or three occasions he had used his primitive strength with all the violence of rage. It was said that none had seen Carl laugh, and yet there was proof that he enjoyed existence more hugely than any one alive; and then he was immortal. The One-Eyed Ancient was regarded by the Ice Folk with a reverence more and more obscure; every tradition of him was sacred. From him all was derived.

The life that was led on the mountain isle for more generations than any could survey, extending over many thousands of years, was just like that of the first parents, Carl and Mam, and the end of it was that things *had* to be so.

The men fashioned weapons and lived by hunting. Here the only change was that the game grew steadily scarcer and had to be sought farther and farther away; on the other hand every family took to keeping tame reindeer, which were slaughtered when the hunting failed. The chief game was the mammoth, with whom the Ice Folk had broken truce from time immemorial, taking him in pits and bringing him down with the harpoon. Unfortunately there were but few of them and they had to be looked for on distant islands, often after long journeys across the ice.

Therefore it was reckoned a great event, and there was general excitement and blowing of mammoth-tusks all over the island, when the hunters returned after long absence and reported a kill. The signal concerned the whole island, but in particular a certain family circle, that of the lucky hunter who had first tracked down the mammoth. Then the whole settlement was on the move, all that had legs to carry them set off across the ice to the spot where the fallen giant lay. They took fire with them and skins for tents, and a regular camp sprang up around the mammoth, where men wallowed in huge banquets of flesh and ended by eating them-

selves out of their senses. The happy Icemen swarming about the
mammoth looked like slaughtered things themselves, all blood
from top to toe; they threw off their skins and went headlong,
naked as they were born, into the monster's smoking entrails,
each with a freshly struck knife, still smelling of lightning; the
women tucked up their clothes till they hung in a ring round their
necks and a busy hum came from them as they scurried to and fro
between the carcass and the fires. Unspeakable things happened,
everything was allowed at a mammoth feast.

The banquet was opened with the mammoth's warm paunch,
which was full of half digested food, whole stacks of larch needles,
moss, thyme, bark and berries, all stewed and mingled with gastric
juice into a dainty broth which went right into the thirsting veins
of the meat-eaters, who were not used to vegetables. This food
had been the favourite of the One-Eyed in his old age; he used
to say it reminded him of his youth in the sulphurous jungles.
A good part of the belly with its contents was set aside at every
mammoth feast for an offering on Carl's burial mound on the return home. Old hunters told stories that they had heard from their
forefathers, handed down by ancestors still farther back, of the
One-Eyed's taste for mammoth paunch. The legend added, as a
most singular thing, that in the days of Carl and his sons and
grandsons the Ice Folk were no more numerous than that one
mammoth was just sufficient to feed the whole of them with their
households at one time. So long ago was it. Now, if all the Ice
Folk were assembled in one place, there was nothing to prevent
them eating up as many mammoths as there were fingers on a
man's hand, even with all his toes thrown in.

Song and story, bygone days and their destinies lived again at
the great mammoth feasts, when tongues were loosened in the in-
toxication of meat and frightful nightmares fostered the wildest
visions. Long and thrilling tales were told and retold of this or
that mammoth that had gone mad and trampled its pursuers to
death — an unkind mammoth that grudged hungry folk the least
morsel. When the teller was quite full, so full that the last mouthful
stuck in his throat, greasing his speech, he would invariably fall
to romancing about the supernatural mammoth, which had been
seen by every man's grandfather, or indeed by himself one winter
night on the icefield, especially after eating kidney; an immense
old male with tusks towering right up into the northern lights

and a coat white as the snowstorm with age; Father Mammoth himself, the sign of famine. If any one had latent bardic gifts the mammoth feast was sure to bring them out, and many a good lay, with a taste of the fat of the fire, the smell of roast on the icefield and the twinkling stars overhead, passed in later days from mouth to mouth.

The tribe never slaughtered a mammoth without making use literally of every scrap of the beast. The meat left over from the feast was cut into strips, brought home and smoked. The wool was used for clothes and for lining the huts; bones, guts and sinews all had their uses, and nothing was wasted. And when all was collected and carried home, the sharing began. This was perhaps the most elaborate business of all, since everybody on the island had a claim to some part of the beast, greater or less according to certain fixed customs. The Ice Folk had always shared, ever since Carl the Old himself presided at the slaughter and saw to it that all had equal portions. So it had been since his time, only it had become difficult in practice, because the Ice Folk had grown so numerous as to make direct sharing impossible; it had to be done in proportion. Definite traditional laws, which were never set aside, existed for the sharing, but the increase of the tribes compelled new interpretations of the law, which soon became so involved that few could make head or tail of them. First the lucky hunter who had marked down the game had to have his share, and he got one of the tusks, of which he made a grand horn or a set of splendid harpoons. The other tusk fell to the One-Eyed and was offered upon his grave together with mammoth paunch and other good things. The flesh and the rest of the animal was divided according to strict rules, so that the clan to whose lot the slaying had fallen got most, while the rest was portioned out according to degrees of relationship until every single family on the island had a share of the quarry, however small. Specially favoured, of course, was the Garm Clan, which was descended from Carl's firstborn and had the right of receiving offerings to the One-Eyed. A single mammoth, though soon eaten up, might well keep one family employed for several years and the whole island for the best part of a winter, so much hair was there to plait and so much gut and sinew to twine. Strange how much there could be inside a beast which, however huge, looked at a distance no bigger than a midge on the icefield.

Besides the great northern elephant the men hunted the woolly-haired rhinoceros, reindeer and musk-ox, the polar bear and many smaller animals, such as foxes and hares, which lived on the rocky islets or roamed about the ice between them. In their hunting the Ice Folk were accompanied by the dog, who since Carl's time had multiplied through many tame generations and now took up a very hostile attitude towards his former wild kin, which kept company with the wolves and had become merged in them. At home the dog was also useful for guarding the herds of reindeer and keeping them from running away from the island.

But as with their hunting and making of weapons, so with the rest of their life; it was just the same as in the days of their ancestor Carl, and yet innumerable generations had gone by. Their houses were the same pits in the earth, protected by big overlapping boulders; their clothes were the same hides, chewed and tanned with fat and held together in the good old way with thongs of reindeer skin. Any change was unthinkable, for the whole order of things was just what had been instituted by Carl and nothing else was known to the Ice Folk. His ways were good enough for his children and they were binding for all men of his blood.

There was but one circumstance which the Father in his time could scarcely have conceived: that their numbers on the mountain isle should become so great. Wide indeed it was, many days' journey in every direction, but still in course of time there came to be too many of them. And more kept coming, children swarmed up out of the ground, they simply teemed in the settlements like flies on the offal-heap. When the children of several families joined together they formed regular hordes who tore around over the island and almost made it dangerous for grown-up people to go about singly. They wanted food, and when there was a whole pack of them together they let one understand with a grin that they were not particular *what* they got. If it chanced that a youngster of one's own was in the crowd and cheerfully showed his teeth at his progenitor, pretending not to know him, it was enough to make a man feel quite sad.

But there were other difficulties besides that of feeding too many mouths. Supplies were not equally divided, and this precisely because all in the island were equal. Their communal system prevented the individual from developing freely. This and certain aspects of their domestic life — regard for their ancestor's memory — began to be felt as a constraint by the Ice Folk. Carl's laws, which were originally intended for the protection of all, threatened to check the growth of each individual and thereby that of the whole little community on the island. It is true that the worship of Allfather, which little by little had been reduced to a system, united the Ice Folk into a whole, but at the same time it prevented their expanding. Carl's grave formed a centre for all interests, and this could not be otherwise. But a growing injustice lay in the fact that the common worship remained by a natural privilege in the hands of a certain line which traced back to Carl's firstborn, Garm. This clan guarded Carl's grave and received offerings made to him.

It never occurred to any one to believe that the One-Eyed, the Father of all, could be dead. For he had never been killed, nor had he met his death by mischance like other men, but had gone down into his house when it suited him and had stayed there ever since. Many would assert that they had seen him, generations later, and there were still some who at times saw fire issuing from the mound. The Ancient was certainly alive and must of course have food, the best of the hunting spoils was not too good for him. That the seed of Garm, who guarded the Grave, should receive the offerings and more or less openly regale themselves on the victuals, was regarded as only natural; for what went to one family went to one's self. Nor did any man feel wronged at parting with half his kill. But in the latter days the hunter was left with scarcely a tithe for himself. He was practically hunting for others. And the descendants of Garm tried to extend their influence in other matters, not concerned with the division of the spoil, and maintained their position through the awe that surrounded the Grave. They had the power. Theirs was the fire and its source.

Naturally every family had its fire, which was safeguarded and kept alive with the greatest care; in hard times, even if it should cost the last scrap of tallow, the fire could not be let out. But if that did happen there was no help for it but to fetch a brand from the ancient pyre which the Allfather himself had kindled and which was in the possession of the Sons of Garm. That they did not part with fire without ample remuneration or obligations of other kinds, went without saying; the Garm Clan developed a subtle discrimination to their own advantage which lost nothing by being handed down from father to son. Besides the sacred pyre they owned the Fire Stone itself, so they had enough and to spare. Their fire was always assured, even if the pyre should be quenched; they knew the secret of fire. Dark hints were whispered that the One-Eyed had communicated the art to his eldest son Garm with injunctions to initiate the whole people in it, and that Garm had then thought good to keep it to himself; others asserted that Carl had taken the Fire Stone with him into the grave so that no one should have it, whereupon Garm had desecrated the tomb and taken it. However this might be, it was known that the wonderful stone was in the possession of the Garm Clan. It descended from father to son in the direct line, and nobody had ever seen it except the eldest of each generation. There was no supernatural power that was not attributed to it. For that matter it had never been used for renewing the pyre, which had burnt continually since the days of Carl.

The Ice Folk willingly submitted to the Garm Clan out of respect for their common Father. But the effect of this Allfather worship was that all traditions preserved among the clans of the life and customs of the One-Eyed became fixed as the canon for all time, and the Garmings supported this view with all their might. Nothing was permitted unless it had a precedent in tradition, unless it could be said that so had the Ancient acted. All the first simple ways, which in their day had only originated from necessity, though by the hand of Carl, acquired a deeper significance and were followed to the exclusion of any new departure which might have had a liberating effect. The result was a cramping of daily life, in which men hardly dared to move for pious scruples. By degrees the individual hunter lost his taste for sport. But there was no way out of what all regarded as a necessity; for it was not to be imagined that any man should refuse the Allfather's Grave the reverence which was only the natural expression of his own heart. With this view the members of the Garm Clan entirely agreed, and they strengthened themselves in the maintenance of piety by diligently feeding on all the mammoth paunches the people offered before the One-Eyed.

Thus matters stood, and thus they continued as long as the ice-sheet advanced, and that was a long time. Strange luminaries with tails paid visits to the sky and cleared off again, leaving a mystic dread in the minds of men. Generation succeeded generation, the offal-heaps by the settlements grew with one layer of bones and ashes above another. Men who remembered their own early childhood as a yesterday saw their little children grow up and knew that with *their* children it would be the same. And still the Ice Folk shaped their axes and set up their stone huts in the ground exactly as an obscure but inviolable tradition told them the All-father had done and not otherwise. Their minds were shut up in the grey gloom of a monotonous life, while time and the ages passed.

Round about the mountain isle the ice-sheet spoke as it had spoken for thousands of years, with a dull booming and settling in the caverns under the ice, with a muffled scraping against the rock and a subterranean gushing of water; but no one heard it, the sound was old and had become one with their ears.

With the men of the icefield it had come to this, that they were bound and did not even know it. But while they were entirely absorbed in their hunting and in their voluntary bondage, many improvements, strangely enough, were brought in on the part of the women, unnoticeably, of their own accord. It never occurred to any one to give them a share in the men's body politic; they were outside its constraints and in that respect had full liberty. Not that the women were without their own little ways; perhaps they were even more inviolable than the men's, because it was habit and not themselves that had created them. But there was a certain dewy and sisterly forgetfulness inherent in the sex, closely akin to the southerners' jungle nature, which day by day allowed a lot of things to pass unseen by open eyes. Nothing is so unwomanly as to be different from others, and at times this may make a positive crime of any resistance to a novelty.

As far as their daily life was concerned, the women had inherited Mam's habits and faithfully busied themselves with all kinds of plaiting work, with gathering supplies and of course first and last with their little ones. They were carried on the back, you may be sure, even at home in the hut and in spite of the fact that nobody ever travelled nowadays, for that had been Mam's way. In summer there was a gathering of corn and anything else fit to eat that grew on the island, and in winter they twined yarn and plaited clothes; all this was as old as the hills.

But now the women made pots of clay and baked them in the fire. Had Mam done so? Perhaps, and perhaps not. The women had smeared the insides of their baskets with clay for so long that at last one which was hung up to dry over the fire got burnt, leaving nothing but the clay; that was the first pot. It was due to a piece of carelessness. The whole sex had a share in it. It was charming. Later on some enterprising young person must have thought she wouldn't be bothered to shape her pot in the basket first, but made it straight in the clay; a rash thing to do, but it held! — The sex copied her, and now all pottery was made in that way.

But the fired pots led to an important change of diet, since the women got into the way of boiling the food instead of toasting it in the fire as before. But they had not got so far as setting the pot on the fire; they put red-hot stones into it until the meat was done.

The women, hot and greasy, bustled about the hearth with a will during the long days when the men were out hunting. Everything had to be tried, browned, smelt, and poured in and out of pots, then tasted and mixed over again. Sheer inquisitiveness and leisure taught them to bake bread, for they wanted to try scorching and warming all their good things before letting their teeth deal with them; they roasted barleycorns on a sherd, for that made them sweet; they bruised the grain between two stones and dashed water or milk or it before baking and made the most delicious cakes — which the children busily copied in the mud outside — and as the men also took a fancy to these loaves, they became a standing dish, so long as corn was to be had. Baked on the hot hearthstones and seasoned with ashes, which gave a salt taste, they were a favourite addition to the meal, especially in winter, when there were no fresh herbs to be had.

Otherwise everything went into the clay pot, roots and bulbs, meat and tallow; the soup was thinned with water and warmed with hot stones, which besides seething the meat gave it a flavour by adding charcoal and ash. When one of these red-hot stones, which shone in the cave like a little sun, all set in sparks and stars, was dropped into the pot and scalded the water till the vessel rocked and the steam rose thick into the roof, anybody could see plainly enough that an evil spirit was being driven out of the water by the power of fire; it rolled about with ugly growls and you had to hold on to the pot to keep it from capsizing. True, it had never been reported that Mam knew of boiling in her time, though who could tell? What was done now must have been done always. Boiling had come to stay.

When the women were not at their dainty arts by the fire they wove themselves clothes, each finer and more extravagant than the last, but always in the strictest conformity with the general taste. One century it was absolutely necessary to wear nothing but a polar bear's skin which had to be open all down the front; the polar bears were almost exterminated and the women never went out, because the fashion was such a chilly one; but what were they to do? What made it indispensable to dress in this particular way was that nobody on any account might have the smallest glimpse of a woman's back. A later and more sober age found it difficult to understand that people of the olden time could be such unfortunate victims of a one-sided modesty.

Naturally the women of the icefield were always collecting things for their adornment. A necklace of wolves' teeth bored through and strung was very effective in setting off a frail creature who was only a woman. A bone stuck through the cartilage of the nose was one of those ornaments that were within the reach of all and therefore went out of fashion comparatively quickly. A great deal was thought of a fine complexion, which the women tried to achieve by treating their skin with ochre, obtained from the springs on the island. This blooming tint soon spread from the face over the whole body, and here it must be said that the men caught the fashion; they too loved to smear themselves with ochre and fat till they looked like fiery red men and could be seen a long way off in their glory.

But besides these improvements of their personal appearance the women had introduced a custom unknown to Mam the Old, a custom the trace of which was lost in the past, no one ever giving its origin a thought; they milked the half tame reindeer and used the milk in their housekeeping. Perhaps some pretty little sad story lay behind it, inarticulate as a mother's heart, the story of a woman who had had no milk to give her babe and had taken it from the reindeer which grazed about the settlement and were kept for winter slaughtering. Since then people had themselves acquired a taste for reindeer's milk. Now there were always pots of fresh or curdled milk standing in their storerooms and many reindeer were allowed to live on this account. This custom was afterwards to be carried further.

Taking it all in all the people of the icefield were fairly contented and led an honest, simple existence. But the continual increase of the population was pressing upon them, and they made no advance. Perhaps the Northerners might have remained for ever in this stage as a poor and upright race of hunters, cramped and shut in by sterile retrospect, if the solid ring within which their existence had stiffened had not itself served at last to exclude another individual, as it had once excluded Carl; a new outcast and liberator, who against their will led his people on beyond themselves.

And at the same time a fundamental change came over the conditions of their life on the icefield — the icefield which for all time decided the fate of men.

XII

THE UNICORN

THERE was a man called White Bear who was not born of the race of the Sons of Garm.

Early in life he heard of injustice and oppression from that quarter. White Bear's father used to sit at home in his cave with his back against the farthest corner and move his lips with every sign of curses seething within him; this was when the Garmings had offered him an insult which lay like glowing stones about his heart; but no sound came from him, he swallowed his wrath. White Bear's father was a great hunter who every year brought a heap of mammoth tusks and other spoils of the chase in tribute to Firegrim, now chief of the Garm Clan.

White Bear's father was very strong, and Firegrim was a weakling, who never dragged his bloated limbs farther than from the storehouse to his sleeping-place. White Bear marvelled as a child to see the two together and hear Firegrim give orders to his father, whose chest was on a level with his head. When White Bear ranged about the island in a pack with the other children and their boyish appetite made them bold, the talk was always of when they would be big and eat Firegrim, and their mouths watered as they said it, but they shuddered all the time; for Firegrim had the sacred stone which killed people and returned to his hand itself, my word!

Afterwards, when White Bear grew up and became a hunter, he learned to reverence the Allfather and was initiated at the Grave, taking the oath to offer the greater part of his spoil to the Garmings. On that occasion Firegrim gave White Bear to understand, as others before him, that his zeal in sacrificing would stand him in good stead when presently Allfather came and took all his people with him home to the rich country he knew of. Oh yes, White Bear knew all about the beautiful summer land which had been lost and which Firegrim said was to come again, but he never gave it much thought; the icefield was good enough for him. As for the sacrifice, White Bear made up for it by taking ten times the quantity of game. He became a mighty hunter and was the cheeriest man on the island, full of song, never on bad terms with any man, not even with Firegrim.

But White Bear cast his eyes upon a girl, and then there was an end of peace. The custom was that, when young people wished to be united and have their own home, they were to be blessed at Allfather's Grave and to receive fire for their hearth from the sacred pyre. All other fire was forbidden as unclean. No decent person objected to following the custom, and there were only decent people on the mountain isle. But the consecration cost a good deal and was binding for life; moreover it rested with Firegrim the priest whether he would allow the union at all. In White Bear's case he forbade it. Firegrim had never looked upon White Bear's family with favour, and he secretly desired the girl for himself. Her name was May and she was lovely.

Now it was not to be expected of Firegrim that he would refuse pointblank and no more to be said, that was not the way of Firegrim the priest. White Bear got his refusal in the cautious form that May should be his on the day when he laid the Unicorn's horn on Allfather's grave mound; but that was of course impossible.

White Bear smiled. He went out upon the icefield and was away a year, and when he came back he had laid the monster low. It was the greatest exploit that had ever been achieved by a man of the Ice, no one had believed it could be done. Only Carl the Old was thought to have possessed strength and courage enough for what White Bear had accomplished. He was called the Unicorn-slayer and was celebrated in song and story.

He himself made a picture of the whole hunt on the blade of his spear in everlasting remembrance. First you saw a long stroke with four strokes under it and a slanting stroke above, that was the Unicorn. Then you saw one stroke with another across it, that was White Bear himself with his harpoon; all the rest, the fight and the end of the Unicorn, was obvious.

Now the animal was of the rhinoceros tribe. Not the ordinary woolly-haired and cross-tempered rhinoceros which followed the tracks of the mammoth and was often brought down by the Ice Folk. That one was wrathful and dangerous enough and a big lump of a beast to have to deal with, but nothing to the Unicorn.

This beast, which was of a kind by itself, had only one horn and was nearly three times as big as an ordinary rhinoceros. It was longer in the body than the mammoth, but not so high. But the fearful thing about it was that it ran and jumped like a stag in spite of its immense weight, and it attacked without provocation; it was certain death to come within the same horizon with it.

If it got wind of the hunters, they had it upon them instantly in full gallop, letting out a deafening roar, and with its six feet of horn, which grew in the middle of its forehead between the eyes, lowered to split the wretch who ventured within miles of it. It was enough to paralyse anybody simply to see a beast of such supernatural size leap and turn as airily as any dog; it was the swiftest and heaviest beast in the world. When it came on, galloping like the lightning, it left holes in the ground big enough for a man to hide in, and it flung itself round before you had time to think; there was no escaping it.

The uncanniest thing about it was that it was scarcely to be distinguished from the icefield or the willow-covered rocks which it haunted; it would lie down and look like an oblong block of stone on the ice or a clump of dwarf bushes, until it suddenly rose up and was *there* in a second. The hunters knew their fate when anything on the ice which they thought was dead suddenly came to life; it meant that they had seen the Unicorn and would be spitted or trampled beyond recognition within a minute. Only very few had escaped it, and from them came all that was known about the dreadful animal.

The Ice Folk believed that there was no more than the one specimen, which was a female and had been in existence ever since the beasts were driven out of the Lost Country. Then, it was said, the Unicorn had found no mate, but had been forced to live alone and become an old maid on the ice; and that was what made her so long and wiry of body and so cantankerous against all the world. The few who had survived the sight of her reported that she had quite small red eyes, as though she had wept for an eternity; and when at the new moon a baleful sound of groaning was heard from the icefield miles away, it used to be said that this was the Unicorn standing with her tail to the north wind and lamenting as though her heart would break the mate she had never had.

It was because she had never had young that she retained that terrifying youthfulness of movement; she still galloped like a calf and yet was so old that flint had formed on her shoulders. Eye-witnesses who still shuddered at the thought of it related that she was so wrinkled about the face and wherever you could see her skin for the white hair, that you could cut yourself on it; her hide positively lay in stony folds from age. And her horn had grown so long, much longer indeed than on a male, because though a virgin she had reached this great age.

To get the better of such a creature who still possessed all the speed and fire of her youth, had added to her childlessness the experience of immortality and hardened the two together in ice and loneliness, was regarded by the Ice Folk, not without reason, as more than impossible.

In what manner the hunt took place was never properly cleared up in detail; White Bear had had no one with him and had after-wards told the story in a rapture of song but with extreme conciseness. He had played with the old girl so long that she had fallen into a fissure in the ice and stuck there; and so he had finished her. The horn was as long as White Bear when it stood on the ground beside him, and White Bear was a tall man. It had so many rings that no one could count them; it was like the very thorn of affliction which had grown layer upon layer in all eternity.

Besides the horn White Bear brought back the Unicorn's heart; it was quite young and tender to look at, but so hard that no flint axe could bite on it.

Firegrim took charge of the Unicorn's horn on behalf of Carl the Old. To all the songs and jubilation with which the island greeted White Bear's great exploit, Firegrim turned his fat back.

He appeared to have entirely forgotten the agreement.

But when at last White Bear bashfully suggested that now he supposed he would get May according to promise, Firegrim made an obscure speech which might be interpreted to mean that in asking White Bear to go out and slay the Unicorn he had really intended it as a harmless joke and imagined it would be taken as such. Any impartial person would certainly support his view that the proposal could only be interpreted as a delicately put refusal. But since White Bear with ingenuous precipitancy had taken him literally, he was disposed to construe his proposal as a pious wish to see White Bear duly mangled for his pains. Therefore, in returning with a whole skin, it was in point of fact White Bear who had deceived Firegrim and was in debt to the Allfather according to the turn things had taken. Such were Firegrim's words.

The palaver took place at the settlement of the Garmings, Carl's old home, which was holy ground, and events developed rapidly. When White Bear saw that May was denied him after all and that he was not to have fire for a hearth of his own, he was angry for a moment and involuntarily made a butting movement with his head, over which he wore the skin of a musk-ox with the horns on; and Firegrim misunderstood this, drew in his stomach and began to quiver about the eyebrows as though he felt a cold draught. White Bear smiled; his blood calmed down at once.

And now he took to scanning Firegrim long and leisurely, looked him well up and down and finally laughed aloud. Thereupon he smote the weakling with a little rod, the very smallest he could find, and turned to go. But Firegrim flared up and gave a screech like all the pangs of childbirth, and the Garmings rushed in on every side with thongs and cudgels to bind White Bear and give him a thrashing.

Then the spirit of Carl came upon White Bear, and before any one saw what was happening he had done the impossible thing, slain one of the sons of Firegrim, of the inviolable race. And while the others shrank back, dumb with horror, White Bear in his rage seized the corpse by one arm, put his foot on it and tore the arm out of the body, the arm that had threatened to beat him. With a loud roar White Bear slung down the torn-off limb at the feet of Firegrim, and now he was appeased and went his way.

That day White Bear carried off May, and they fled to the ice-field.

XIII

WHITE BEAR AND MAY

Nobody on the mountain isle approved of White Bear's misdeed, even in his own family. The murder one could understand, but he had flogged the priest, and the transgression had taken place on holy ground; it was a mad thing to do. Not a single voice was raised in White Bear's favour, when before a general concourse of the people he was proclaimed an outlaw from Allfather's Grave. He was now torn out of the hearts of the Ice Folk, and any who gave him but a friendly thought, let alone food or shelter, was outlawed with him. White Bear and May were abandoned to the icefield, fireless and accursed for ever, and if seen they were to be regarded as all other game, ripe for every man's harpoon.

The curse passed unheeded by White Bear and May; they had settled on a distant rocky island, miles away across the ice, where they had ample solitude for tasting young people's delight in each other's society, but at the same time the unsodden food of exile.

They were without fire, and raw meat sounds strong but in the long run makes such a tender appeal to be cooked. Still, it was summer, they lived in grand style in a tent of skins, and their skerry grew a trifle of herbs and corn, which May gathered as a seasoning to the raw joint. She patted together little loaves of corn, but unfortunately had to offer them unbaked and fresh to White Bear when he came home from hunting. White Bear ate them with much facial expression and sang a lay about warm food being after all an unmanly refinement. Later on towards autumn they had a few berries from the mountain tops that rose above the icefield to flavour their raw diet; they were as well as could be in their frugality. But soon the air was chilled with night frosts and the first snow, and winter was upon them.

White Bear had built a good strong house of big stones and was well supplied with furs for it, and May had dried meat and herbs in store. Besides, White Bear had brought home a couple of wild reindeer, which were to be tethered upon the skerry until they were tame and could give milk. Thus they entered upon the win-

ter. It was stormy and desperately cold. The couple were to experience going through a winter without fire. White Bear knew
that it had been done before, but now he almost doubted the truth
of it.

The nights were long and dark as in the bowels of the earth, at
last they scarcely knew where they were or *whether* they were; it
was well they were two, so that one could find the other. In the
long black nights White Bear fell to meditating. He saw in his
mind the home tract with all its rich fires, his eyes almost caught
their brightness and his skin remembered their warmth when he
thought of it. Now the Garmings and the rest of the dutiful crowd
would be sitting round the fire, hugging themselves and saying
that that murderer White Bear must soon be sunk so deep in
poverty that he would beat his woman and say it was her fault.
Before midwinter they might expect the pair begging around the
settlement. White Bear smiled in the dark.

When the year sank in deadly cold and ceaseless snowstorms,
so that sun and moon were threatened with extinction, White
Bear was still laughing with May in his arms. But she shivered.
They kept alive, owing to their youth and strength, but they
suffered badly. The two settlers were too rich to grieve, they
uttered no word of lament, but they were frightfully cold. White
Bear decided to find fire.

First he set aside, one by one, every thought of getting it in any
way from others. The simplest thing was to creep home and beg
or steal fire from one of the hearths, but that was the very first
thing he would not do. Less impossible it seemed to fetch a brand
from the Garmings' sacred pyre itself, in a sort of formal visit
with harpoon and axe and so on, but — no, White Bear could not.
If Firegrim and his clan had inherited the pyre, it was theirs and
no other's. His thoughts dwelt long on the mysterious Fire Stone,
which he knew Firegrim preserved in Allfather's Grave. Supposing
he broke in one night and took it? Of course Carl the Old was not
walking about alive down there any more, that was a superstition;
at most his bones lay mouldering in the grave and they wouldn't
do one any harm. But still the Ancient had once lived and given
his race fire; the proper way of course was to let all that concerned him remain as it was. It would be a shabby thing to offend
the Forefather, so long as any other way out of the difficulty could
be thought of. And there *was* the way of getting fire of one's own

accord. This was what White Bear proposed to do. Yes, of course.

He collected fuel from the fir copse on the island and built it up in the form of a pyre; that was as far as he got that winter.

The year after they emigrated. They stayed over the summer on their skerry, and a remarkably hot and violent summer it was, with scorching sun and almost daily thunderstorms which drenched the ice-sheet and wasted it visibly. The skerry was cleared of ice to double its usual extent, and the surrounding islands also appeared much larger. The ice-sheet blinked in the twilight of its green abysses against the lightning in the light nights. When the rain was not actually pouring down, the clouds were piled up high into the sky, white as fire and strangely alive, growing out of one another with a swelling brightness beneath the sun, till they closed again all round and let loose a warm shower over the icefield. The lightning struck the ice and split it to the bottom, the thunderclaps echoed in the dripping crevasses. It was wild weather. Neither White Bear nor May missed fire that summer. But White Bear had not forgotten the winter, it still stuck at the root of his heart that he had seen May suffer. He knew that they would have to get fire.

The wild summer passed without anything particular happening in the cave except that they got a prodigy of a baby, which White Bear carried up into the rain, shouting with joy. He was born with two little bits of teeth and was dedicated to great deeds by the delighted father. And a great eater he became.

But when the air began to grow cold for the second time on the skerry, White Bear got uneasy. For he had not found fire. The nights turned first blue and then black. White Bear groaned in his sleep, when he was not lying awake and pondering. One night he took May in his arms and she heard that he had been weeping as he confided to her that he could not find fire anywhere. But didn't she think they ought to leave the place? Yes, May was willing to go with him to the world's end. That decided it. White Bear's plan was to go south. If he could not get fire, they must go and live somewhere else. Far to the south he had heard that the icefield came to an end, and there was said to be a warm country with great forests inhabited by naked savages; they would have to try a journey in that direction.

Autumn was far advanced when the little family made a start. Late as it was in the year, the thunder gave them a farewell salute of crashes and deluging streams over the icefield, which gleamed with its abysmal green beneath the lightning. White Bear looked about him — flash upon flash all round the sky, a world full of fire, and not a spark for him! He smiled, but it was an old worn-out smile which ran in deep, fixed furrows in his face. Then they left and never once turned to look back.

A little herd of half-tame reindeer and a quantity of skins for tent and clothing was all the family possessed besides White Bear's weapons and May's baskets of all kinds of odds and ends, and thus equipped they set out on their way to the south. Winter overtook them, and it was severe, but it helped them to get on when the new-fallen snow on the ice-sheet froze together into vast snow-fields which gave better going than the fissured ice.

All that winter they were on the trail, though without coming very far, and White Bear felt that he was growing into an old man. It tried him to the marrow to keep famine away from the little wandering tent in the midst of the snow; he often had to follow a trail for days and nights before he could come back with game, and all that time he knew that his two in the tent were fairly unprotected; before him the fleet-footed beast that would not let itself be taken, and behind him the fear that dragged at his heels, but on he had to go so that he might turn back. When he came home he found the tent snowed under, while his few tame reindeer stumbled about in the snow, a scattered flock with hobbled forelegs, breathing rime.

Upon them White Bear never laid hands, however hard it might be to find meat; their milk was May's resource when he was away from the tent, and they formed in themselves a reserve which was only to be attacked as a last shift. May got them moss and lichen from the loose blocks and shingle that travelled on the top of the glaciers and defended them against the wolves when White Bear had the dogs out hunting. But when he had brought down a good head of game, they struck the tent and pushed on.

When snowstorms came on there was nothing for it but to go to earth in a cave and let the storm spend its rage outside. In this way they passed weeks in unbroken darkness, during which they almost lost the power of speech. They endured hardships which were not to be recalled in after days, since they paralyzed the soul and blotted out their own traces. That winter seemed so long and bitter that the minds of the two were clouded by it, and at last they no longer remembered that they had left their home, or where they were going, or even who they were. Thousands of years might well have passed over them. The northern lights stretched over the sky in silent frenzy and began to hang like a spectre of eternity, near and yet far, over the heads of the fireless family, lost in the snow and in their wanderings.

And yet that winter was shorter than usual, the thaw came early and in a rush. But that did not help White Bear so long as they were travelling on the snow. Of late they had been getting on faster, for White Bear had found out how to drive what afterwards became a sledge. Instead of making the reindeer carry the tent and the rest of the gear, it occurred to him to let them drag the load, underneath which he placed the birch spars he used for tent poles, to make it slide more easily over the snow. The reindeer were able to pull more than they could carry, and it was not long before White Bear and May sat up on top of the load and let themselves be drawn too. This was a great improvement, which united the reindeer and the family even more closely than before. White Bear was pleased with the sledge and soon found a form which he kept to as the best. He had no need to place more than two birch spars under the load, but they had to be curved at the fore-end to keep them from sticking in the snow and to keep the lashings from being worn through. To prevent the load dragging in the snow he laid bent pieces of wood across the runners and lashed them fast, and then the sledge was finished. White Bear provided the hands and necessity did the rest.

In fine weather, when the sun shone upon the crisp snowfields, White Bear made the reindeer break into a trot, shouting lustily to them; and then it was as though he and May awoke to life and knew each other's dear grimy faces. Their hardships might lull them into a sort of mental blindness in which they lost sense of time, but real sadness was unknown to them. They came to themselves again in sunshine, tearing along on the sledge over the frozen snow with the fresh coughing reindeer in front pulling at the traces and the dogs giving tongue at the side, hey ho! The youngster stuck his head out of the bag on May's back and rolled big dreamy eyes at the world that swung past the sledge. Thus they covered the ground.

And then they reached the sea. White Bear had set his course for the south but had veered away to the eastward towards the sunrise, and this took him off the icefield and down to the coast of Upland. When spring thawed the snow, which also covered the land south of the ice barrier, White Bear saw that they had come down on to an ice-free lowland intersected by lakes, bogs and rivers and studded with rocky heights which continued out to sea as holms and skerries.

The ice-sheet lay far to the northward, but it was not long since it had been here, stretching right out into the sea. The coast and all the skerries were still naked and worn to roundness by the ice; White Bear saw traces of the ice-sheet everywhere in the lowlands. Farther up the coast to the northward an arm of the ice-sheet still came right out to the shore through a fjord, and White Bear could hear it crashing and sighing when the ice broke off in the sea and floated away as icebergs. But not many years were to pass before the ice receded altogether from the coast, and what icebergs were still to be seen swimming far out at sea came from the extreme north.

No doubt but White Bear opened his nostrils, sniffed and sniffed again when he made the sea's acquaintance. There was something hidden away in his soul which the salt smell awoke, something he did not understand; it was Carl's longing for the sea which lay innate in his blood. His dream of the sea was a love-child of Carl's soul, and it implanted a dormant instinct in all his descendants which a salt breath from the beach was enough to awaken. White Bear drank in the sea air with great open nostrils, and the sea took him in its arms.

The first sign of this was that he immediately wanted to go farther. He was already on a journey, the goal of which was the south and its forests, but the sea's billowy wandering and wandering out beyond its own limits added its call and changed his whole being to outward longing. Here, where he could come no farther, he seemed only to have reached his true starting-point. The sea barred the way, but it was to be his path.

Here it was that they settled in the lowlands, among copse-ringed bogs and lakes, so far south of the icefield that it could only be glimpsed in the distance as a greenish shimmer under the northern sky; on the other side their horizon was bounded by the belt of skerries and the open sea. There was game enough in the country, and soon there was more, hosts of game, as the animals made their way into the ice-free land. The freshwater lakes and streams up country were alive with fish, salmon, pike, and eels, which White Bear soon acquired a taste for and learned to entice with curly worm and a hook inside it. The very sea was like a flashing field of fish; the whale chased shoals of herring up on to the beach, where they lay so thick that you waded in them. Ah, it was a fat land, and White Bear's heart fed on it so that his outward longing grew stronger. His soul dwelt on the moonbeam bridge from skerry to skerry, when the sea was rising and embraced the world in its stormy, roaring infinity.

But they stayed there. Years passed, and they were still living in the low country between the ice-sheet and the sea. May added one child after another to the family. Although they could come no farther, White Bear for his part was always teeming with plans of travel, his thoughts were never busied with anything but the means of getting on. In winter of course he had the sledge, with which he made long journeys round about on the frozen lakes, or out among the skerries and sometimes a long way to sea, when the ice was frozen fast, but wherever he went the open water stopped him at last. In summer the sledge was useless, and the spring thaws often changed the lowlands almost into a single swollen lake, which shut in White Bear just as emphatically as the sea. Something had to be done.

On the icefield there had been nothing to make men take to navigation, though it was likely enough that the mammoth hunters knew how to get across a chance stream in the spring thaws with an ice block for a ferry. There was a dim legend that once in the beginning of the ages the Allfather had been good at sailing on the water; that must have been how he came from the south, some said on a tree-trunk, others on the back of an enchanted tortoise; in any case through powers which ordinary mortals did not possess — what had not been possible to the One-Eyed! White Bear had never dreamed of equalling Allfather in supernatural powers; he was only a man trying this way and that, since that was what his hands were for. Nevertheless White Bear acquired the art by the path of experience.

Big timber was not to be found in the country; but that it had once grown there White Bear could see for himself on clear days, when the sun shone down into the brown bog water, at the bottom of which lay a muddy, confused floor of fallen tree-trunks of all thicknesses. It was evidently a drowned forest and it suggested all kinds of ideas to White Bear when he looked down into that still and sunken world which belonged as he could understand to a bygone age. The sky with its dizzily distant clouds lay upon the surface of the deep bog lakes, and only when he looked right through his own image lying lifelike beneath him did the water become transparent so that the bottom and the sunken forest stood out. Strange, when he could see the sunken forest, he himself was gone, and when he saw himself, the trees below vanished!

Whatever might be the truth about the forest that had been, it was a *forest* and nothing else that White Bear was looking for, but it ought to be a living one for choice, and it lay far away, in the South, the very embodiment of the future he yearned for. One day he slipped a thong with a noose in it under one of the big round logs, which looked so fresh with traces of where the leaves had grown and still some resin on its bark; it had struck him that perhaps he might turn the forest of the past to account by getting a craft out of it to take him to the South. And the idea was not a bad one, but the trunk broke in pieces when he began to haul in, and a piece which he got up turned out to be nothing but black, liquid mud inside. Thus White Bear's forest sank in a double sense.

Meanwhile he was on another track, less pregnant with sentiment but more in the direction of his goal. What White Bear wanted was to cross the water; the sea lay between him and the South, and he had to get on. Without knowing it he had long been making progress in a small way. The wide fens and morasses of the low country were overgrown with scattered thickets of birch, aspen, and various kinds of dwarf trees and bushes, of which only the birch attained any size, though without growing into timber; White Bear had to put all thoughts of tree-trunk navigation out of his head. The tortoises he came across were no bigger than a hand, so if it was one of them Allfather had sailed on, there must undoubtedly have been some magic in it. All the same it was worth noticing that the empty shell of a tortoise floated very well on water, it was just shaped for that; but of course it could not bear a man.

White Bear was above all heavy and he was aware of it every day. But when he wandered about in the wet marshes, intersected by innumerable watercourses, he was in the habit of crossing smaller streams by throwing bushes and branches into the water until they choked it up and formed a bridge; and if the water was too deep he had also found out how to heap together enough branches and whole trees to float under him and had poled himself across. To prevent the mass floating apart he tied a thong round it. And this, with time and repetition, became a raft. White Bear was now a skipper.

He was everlastingly splashing about in the water with new and improved craft, it became second nature to him. Everything had to be tried on water, whether it would float, whether it was watertight, whether it made good headway and kept its balance. White Bear was always busy on the beach, barelegged and lost to the world in his wet experiments, blue with cold and dripping at the nose; the sun came and went over him. He developed into a great carpenter and a regular waterman. And yet, strangely enough, there was nothing White Bear dreaded more than the wet, with an inborn horror which made this giant who knew not fear start twitching all over and roaring like a wild boar when he got into deep water. White Bear could not swim. He saw that all the animals gladly trotted out into the water, but it didn't suit his paces. Just when the sea bore him up, when he felt its yielding and heavy power carry his legs off the bottom, he was seized with a frenzy, an impossible desire to climb, which he never got over in his life. His boys, though, were born swimmers who slipped in and out of the water like otters, and the numb flesh always lay in folds all over their bodies from taking refreshing baths and then reviving themselves in the rain ashore.

All White Bear's sons were fair, with a perfectly bare white skin which was coarse and fulled from always being wet. In summer they got freckled in memory of the dark blood brought into the race by mothers fetched from the jungles, the sunburnt skin coming back in spots. They were blond with a reddish yellow tinge, like a lingering suspicion of the dark hair the North had bleached. Their eyes had the summer blink of the icefield. They were to be great sailors.

White Bear, who was so helpless in the water, had every reason to meditate upon things which could float and bear him up. But behind it all lay the great thought that he would travel on, on over the sea, and this yearning he bequeathed to his sons as a heritage. It is not saying too much that while they were living on the coast White Bear never for a single day had an abiding place, and yet the family stayed there till the children were grown up. The boys had become men with prolific hands and memories, rivalling their father in carpentry and thinking. The tool created the work, and the work created the tool; White Bear and his sons now ground their stone axes and chisels, unlike their forefathers who had left them roughhewn. It took much time and pains to smoothe off a hard flint axe on the grindstone, but then it went into the wood where you wanted it to go and did not spoil its own bite. White Bear and his sons invented, and novelty brought the wisdom. They had Carl's vision, the keen, close-set eyes that flashed and flashed over the things they worked on; they drank in life from what they produced. And at last, they got so far that the first ship stood built upon the beach before the settlement.

It was a long raft of light birch spars joined and lashed together, with a rounded bottom and made watertight in the joints with tallow and animal hair, so that it would not only float but kept a dry space inboard. It was not small, could carry several men and made good way. The poles for driving it forward were flattened at the ends so as to work better on the water when it got too deep to reach the bottom. White Bear and his sons rowed on long trips on the lakes inland and were well satisfied with their ship. If they were going with the wind they cut leafy branches and held them up, so that they blew along without having to use the oars; a skin on a spar drew still better.

White Bear shaded his eyes with his hand and looked out towards the south, where sea and sky merged in one on the horizon; now they would soon be off! But the ship would have to be made bigger, or they would have to build more, to take the whole family.

May looked at her husband in embarrassed silence when he declared, with happy blue eyes and the air of an eagle flapping its wings, that now they would be off. Her man had said that for so many blessed summers that May's children had grown as big and — no harm meant — as unaccountable as their father. May looked with profound admiration at her White Bear, who could keep on beaming with hope as in their first boundless youth, though neither of them was young any more; but she was afraid of his plans and when he was holding forth about the voyage she embraced her home with the look of one who has been struck down and cannot rise again. May had something to lose.

She had not been idle through the long years while White Bear every day, so to speak, *had to be off;* while they had been settled she had imperturbably entrenched herself in her daily life and added to her household. No future existed for May and no far-reaching dreams, but she was faithful in small things. While White Bear in fervid forgetfulness of everything around him was busy with his boats, May was dutifully building up a practice which was of a very real nature and which grew with the years under her hands. She never got excited, never changed her habits, that she knew of, and yet, in her beneficent, woman's way, she had produced many new and indispensable things in the course of years.

White Bear perhaps did not see much of her little daily efforts, being always on the go and always blinded by his sailor's dreams; but she saw herself as she was, reserved and set in motion once for all as a kindly fate, to be White Bear's support and the other half of himself. May was always there, had always been there, full of vigour and gentleness in the pouring rain with her long fair hair flowing over her shoulders, always a child with her, always about, backwards and forwards on the short paths of the homestead, feeding and protecting. To see her beyond a call from the settlement was a rare thing, and it meant extra herbs for dinner.

There was much thunder in those years, and in a chance flash White Bear would see May standing in the drowning rain, surrounded by her children and domestic animals, reposing in herself with calm eyes in the midst of the storm, while all sought refuge in her arms. The thunder was beyond her comprehension, like all that was the affair of the Great One on high or came within the sphere of *Men,* but the children and the timid animals came to her to share the calm that proceeded from her heart. And thus White Bear remembered her afterwards, when youth had vanished; the taste of rain like clouds on the tongue, the fiery fumes of lightning close at hand, and then May with her hair rained down her back, smelling like the wild Dane-wort, which stretches up flowery hands to sun and rain.

But now May was a weatherbeaten, case-hardened mother who defended her own, armed with taciturnity and with experience in biding her time and letting well alone. She gave a candid smile every year when White Bear exultingly announced a new ship and off to-morrow, feeling sure in herself that it would have to be improved upon and rebuilt yet again. Only when he talked long and seriously about leaving, making her think she could see it happening, did she grow perplexed and let her eye range uncomprehendingly over the homestead where they had taken root. What about the cows? Were they to go sailing on the water? May had a growing field of barley and another of flax, besides a whole kitchen garden with beds of peas, thyme, onions and roots; could she take her fields with her? What was that he said?

Yes indeed, May had something to lose. She kept domestic animals and carried on agriculture. It had come about entirely of itself, first when they had no fire and necessity forced them to every shift, and afterwards when they had found fire again and there was no end to what she could do. The cows were near to her heart; she had got them while the hearth was still cold and they had been the half of life to her and the children; she would never have lived through the cold days without them.

The wild cattle migrated into the low country when the ice-sheet receded; light, slender, deer-like animals with big wet eyes and as inquisitive as on the first day of creation. The little new-born calves, which still sailed in their walk as they followed their mother, appealed to May's insatiable girlish heart; she squatted down and spread out her hands to entice them up to her knees.

At first they were scarcely shy at all, they only became so when White Bear had hunted them for some time, and even then the cows in their innocence would stand a little way off, spread out in a semicircle, all calmly chewing the meadow flowers as they turned their horned heads towards this unknown creature. If he came too near, they trotted off, but soon had to turn again and stand and look, cautiously leaning backwards on all four legs, with moist nostrils and eyes that darkened as a night. One or other of them was forced by unconquerable curiosity to advance a step or two out of the circle and even tried to adopt quite a threatening attitude, raising a forefoot and setting it down again hard in a very dangerous-looking way, and the cow drew a deep breath; but the mild eyes did not altogether carry out this warlike bearing, and indeed the cow soon fell back of its own accord, cast its head to one side with quivering eyelids and turned about.

White Bear's spear flew when the time came, and one of the animals lay rolling with the shaft in its body, while the herd galloped off. He preferred to kill the big bulls, which gave better sport and sometimes stirred his blood by themselves taking the offensive.

There were now dense herds of cattle in the lowlands; on sunny days you could look from a height over miles of bogs and water-meadows, where the shadows of clouds above which flecked the land mingled with herds of beasts as far as the eye could reach. Not all that roamed there were wild cattle, deer and aurochs were equally thick, herds of wild swine broke in and out of the brush-wood, the bear haunted little islands among the bilberries, and by the brook the fox whipped out a trout with his paw. The elk wandered in great herds through the young birch copse, the dwarf fir took wings as you looked at it and gave birth to the mighty capercailzie, the heather became alive with black game wherever you went. The foreground was full of beasts, and in the distance the herds floated together into misty streaks which were merged in the horizon and continued beyond it. Here it was easy to get meat, there was more than enough, and White Bear had ample time to work at his shipbuilding so as to get away.

But the very first year May asked White Bear to catch some cows alive which she would try to tame; the reindeer did not thrive, they were homesick for the icefield and left off giving milk. So she got her first cows, and the very same day they were caught they lay down compliantly in their tethers and began with deep and satisfied eyes to chew the cud. They had far more milk than the reindeer and they were so gentle. They became the children's best friends. May loved them, they were her treasures and her gossips. She was always about them in confidential chat, the warmth of their hotblooded horns passed through her hands into her heart. They had a sweet smell from the grass they ate and from the nourishment they had to spare for others.

May became an artist with the cows' milk all over her big motherly hands. She made cheese. This came of itself through her keeping milk in a chaudron, and May always had a supply of it pressed into round cakes. When the men came in from their wet exertions in fishing and floating on the sea, you may be sure they were thankful to Mother for a slice of cheese.

In return the boys made her knives and awls of bone. White Bear's interest was attracted by the yarn May and the girls sat patiently twining in their fingers, especially after he began to make nets for fishing and had use for a lot of yarn; as usual he tried a short cut and after experimenting for a day with sparkling eyes he came and presented May with a *spindle*, which could twine ten times as much flax in the same time. It was a little stick with a round disc, which was whirled round till it ran of itself and span the yarn so nicely; what was sufficiently twined you wound up on the stick, so that you could go on spinning without the yarn getting fouled; the spindle was a great success with the women and henceforward it hummed continually in the home.

After fire came back and May was able to bake herself a large outfit of pots and pans, she also made butter. If the truth must be told, this discovery was due to May's personal requirements, her fondness for anointing herself with fragrant things. She and her daughters began by smearing themselves with the thick cream which lay on the top of the milk and could be skimmed off; but the salve became stronger and more penetrating by being allowed to stand, and especially by being thoroughly shaken in the pot. This was a long job, at which they had to take turns, but they did it with a will, till at last the butter came and they could rub it into their skins. White Bear took pleasure in the salve, but his grosser nature preferred it for internal use, and May then prepared it for his palate in larger portions. Thus by degrees butter was introduced as a luxury and a relief to the monotony of their daily diet.

In the baking of bread also May had accomplished much. But everything connected with corn and the husbandry she had introduced was based upon a special mystic pact with the earth, May's own little womanly worship, which traced back to that spring and that day of joy when fire came again.

XIV
THE THAW

To White Bear all things came as gifts. When he was sent into exile, accursed and banned by his people, his fate willed that he should find his way to milder climes, to an Eden of game (where this man never felt at home); but he was to have more than enough of good things, since even the weather itself changed and turned warmer. He had directed his steps to the south, and the South came to meet him.

The great thaw sparkled in the eye of the sun over the North. The ice-sheet was in rapid retreat. From the place where White Bear lived, down in the lowlands, he could see at first the green ice-blink on the edge of the horizon in the north-west, but it shrank more and more and finally disappeared altogether; the ice-sheet had withdrawn beyond the range of vision to the northward. This was not to be wondered at, for the weather that had come on was enough to melt mountains. Thunder-showers and warm rain gushed down incessantly. All through the spring drowning showers passed over the earth, and between them the sun broke through, so smilingly powerful, so full of hope, that even the beasts raised their heads from the wet earth and looked upon the world as though it had become new.

Lurid hail-showers crackling with lightning chased over the sky in the midst of the sunshine and thrashed the earth white, and when the shower was past and the thunder rolled into the distance, the rainbow stretched its airy vault over the greensward, where the drops hung sparkling like tears on a child's eyelashes. One, two and three glorious rainbows swung themselves up across the sky, one outside the other, bridges in the colours of Paradise, standing and yet not standing upon the earth between the clouds and the victorious sun. Every shower was a lost battle which gave new birth to hope.

Days and nights together the rain streamed from the sky, straight down, and the earth received it flayed and furrowed, the lakes swelled, the rivers rushed foaming and deep to the brim through the low country and whirled into the sea. But the rain was warm and bore a new age in its inexhaustible womb.

The eyes of White Bear's children were full of life from gazing at the rain, which tore up the puddles so that they looked like a lot of little people jumping up from the ground, stretching themselves an instant and then going back again, while the rain constantly bred fresh ones. The rainbow stood above their childhood and promised them a whole world.

Winter still came every year, but the cold did not last so long and the spring thaw set in with ever-increasing force. The low country was flooded every year, and more than once White Bear would have been hard put to it to save his household but for his boats. There were times when the country was under water for miles with only the heights showing up as islands and holms, and there the wild beasts took refuge in black frenzied herds which it was pitiable to approach, while just as many floated about drowned in the deep. White Bear, who had built his ships half for the pleasure of it, began to suspect a destiny behind; stern necessity might find a use for what he had produced in sport. White Bear smiled so that his whole blond face crinkled.

Was not the sun his friend? Could he not put his trust in the earth? For it had given him fire of itself, when he had no fire and was alone. Sun and earth had joined together to thaw the ice-field and give him fire. Never did White Bear forget the day when the rock outside his homestead opened in a smoking gulf and sent forth fire from the bowels of the earth, an hour that had begun in unspeakable terror and ended in mad joy.

The whole earth rocked as though its doom was at hand, there was a deep booming under ground, frightful shocks, so that even White Bear fell flat; and from the fens came unrecognizable roars of fear, the beasts lost their wits and were thrown into confusion without regard to friend or foe.

And in the midst of this paralyzing deadly terror White Bear saw fire shooting up from the crack in the ground, the bushes were on fire; and then he got up and laughed like a madman, seeing the whole joke, he staggered towards the fire, for the earth was running in waves beneath him, he fell down and laughed, got up again and at last had hold of the fire. His heart was ready to jump out of his mouth with happiness and thanks. Fire! He had fire and yelled in his immense joy; he came storming home to May, who was lying on her face and holding on; he swung the burning branch over her head. Fire, fire! Yes, the earth had given White Bear fire, for it was good.

The day the fire was lighted in his house he went out and wept in the warm rain; rain and tears ran down into his beard, while, dazed and drunken with gratitude, he looked up into the sunlit sky.

That was many years ago now, and White Bear had grown-up sons to whom he could talk of his friendly relations with the earth and the sun. But every spring White Bear kindled a great bonfire in commemoration of the earth's wealth and bounty. He brought a young bull for an offering, and while Heaven was gracious enough to receive the smoke, White Bear and his sons regaled themselves with the delicious roast meat. It was at the time the cuckoo's note is heard and the northern sky begins to gleam at night from the not too distant sun, that White Bear had received fire, and at that season he lighted his joy fire in memory of the first blaze the earth had given him.

White Bear's sons ever after kindled bonfires at the same season, even when they were dispersed and lived so far apart that they could not even see each other's fires. And this custom never went out of use in the North.

But May, who was naturally excluded from the doings of White Bear and the sons, the immoderate men, approached the earth secretly in her own womanly fashion, thankful for the dear fire which now burned upon her hearth.

She went out when no one knew it, and while she saw that the night was light and the sun at rest behind the distant icefield, which would never more threaten her and hers, she offered a bowl of her corn upon the earth, the fat grains of barley that she had gathered ear by ear the autumn before and patiently rubbed out of the husks in her hands. She knew of no better gift, and as the earth had now vouchsafed them fire so that she could bake bread again, it should have an offering. It was such a small one that nobody might see it, but she did not think the earth should be left without a gift in the light night. May strewed her barley on the naked earth, bashful as a girl, and went in when it was done.

In the course of the summer the barley came up and made a fine field of corn. This May interpreted to mean that the earth had privily accepted her gift, and she flushed with humble gratitude when she grasped that it had now replied by privily giving back her corn many times over. Should she pluck it, was it for her? It must be, for how could a woman be offered a favour without yielding to it in warm submission? May explained the cornfield as a great unselfish wooing, which she accepted by making obeisance to the ground she stood on; her knees lost their strength at the graciousness of the earth. As a mother and as a child she took what the Strong One offered. Thus the first yellow cornfield waved in the summer wind, a secret pact, a beautiful and innocent tryst, between the rich Earth and May's dumb girlish heart.

Next spring May went out again and offered her corn to the earth, while the men folk were up diverting themselves with their bonfire and greeting the sun in the north. And that summer she had still bigger fields of corn. But she did not harvest them entirely in the autumn; she left a part, which she thought the mighty Earth might deign to keep.

After that she arranged her gifts with some shrewdness, like the practical woman she was, according to what she wanted in return; she offered the seed of flax, which was no good to eat, and got back plants for her spindle. Quite unfeelingly she sowed turnip seed and afterwards took the turnips, though by their nature they ought to be the earth's share; to make up for this she let the roots of her cabbages stay in the ground and took the tops herself. But whatever she did, the earth tacitly abode by the pact, and sun and rain gave growth to the private arrangement between the two.

And that was the beginning of May's husbandry. Her pact with the earth and then the tame cattle had been May's joy in all the years she was bearing her children and watching them grow up, while White Bear had been talking every single day about breaking up and going on. But so long as they only stayed where they were, May had found her whole existence in the days and had made a home for her children.

Her goodness was never forgotten. May was so great-hearted that her eyes moistened when she saw the birds flying with straws in their beaks to build a nest. She was so gentle that for her sake the rough men folk, her sons, never hurt an animal except for food. For all ages to come the memory of May was bound up with the calves and the little lambs which early in the year lay upon the ground newly born and cold beside their mothers; the very month of spring was called after her and blessed in her name.

But the day came nevertheless when at last May had to lose her home and go through a world of fear and pain before a new one was given her. One year the thaw came so suddenly and violently that it tore the family out of their homestead and threw them upon the sea.

It began with unusually early thaws and freshlets from the mountains; the rivers overflowed their banks even before the ice was thoroughly broken up. Great fragments of glacier ice were carried down so rapidly that they had not time to melt on the way. That things were serious in the highlands White Bear could see by the number of dead beasts floating down the rivers; up there every living thing must be up to the neck and beyond. Human corpses too came down in the early spring flood, and as a rule White Bear knew them; he began to be anxious about how the Ice Folk were faring.

One day he saw a corpse floating on the waters with its swollen paunch sticking up; a raven sat on it tugging at a long strip of skin in its effort to make a hole; White Bear sailed up to the dead man and saw that it was Firegrim the priest. From that day White Bear held the raven dear.

But he had other things to think of than his former persecutors; earthquake and spring flood came, the one overwhelming mountains and with thunder and fire in its mouth, the other swift, silent with strangling arms. Far to the northward where lay the icefield and the mountains White Bear saw a pillar of fire miles high shoot up into the air mixed with immense blocks of ice, whole icebergs which were thrown up to the sky amid flames and lightnings and rained down again. After that a chalk-white cloud of steam rolled up and in an instant filled the whole sky. Then followed darkness, then a hurricane, and mud rained down from heaven. Fire traversed the darkening world.

And there arose a thunderous foaming from the mountains which in a short time reached the coast and was met by a howl of storm from the sea; it was the flood rushing down from the violent melting of the ice-sheet. It came in vast wild streams with a roaring breast of solid water in front which advanced towards the sea, where the storm wave reared itself to receive it. Shores and skerries vanished in the foaming conflict.

And when the storm subsided and a dead calm followed, the lowlands appeared as a single swollen lake which made one with the sea. Slowly the surface rose and sank with all the stars of night in its black, drowning embrace. Swimming islands of perished animals floated quietly in great herds on the same spot, gently heaving up and down upon the deep like a forest of bodies, legs and antlers, under the rays of the moon.

But White Bear and all his house had long lain out on the open sea. When White Bear saw that the icefield and the earth were in conflict and that there was no longer any abiding place on dry land, he made ready his rafts and ships, took in provisions and fire and went on board with his whole household. It was like the hour of death to May. But the burning mountains and the rain of fire prompted departure. So they confided themselves to the sea. They were already far out when the flood burst down from the mountains, its wave had lost its strength ere reaching them and did not capsize their craft. It fell dead calm, and the fleet lay in the same place rising and falling slowly with the breath of the sleeping sea. White Bear and his children sat in their ships without hope, dumb as the constellations above them and in the deep sea. Huge sea monsters broke the smooth swell between the icebergs, blew out hot breath and dived again, their wet dorsal fins gleaming in the moonlight.

But morning came, the sun rose in the east, red and all-powerful. A fresh breeze hurried over the sea to meet the sun. White Bear and his sons set up skins to catch the wind, and the ships began to advance.

And when they came well out to sea, the interior of the land they had left rose before their eyes and they saw that the mountains in the north lay naked in every hue as in the dawn of time. But at the highest point a mountain rose with a round top from which a pillar of smoke ascended calmly and gracefully into the blue sky. It was Gunung Api whose youth had returned. Then White Bear knew that peace had come again. The sun had conquered and accepted the earth's sacrifice.

But the wind drove the craft from land, out towards the east, till there was nothing but the wild open sea on every side, and they thought they must die. On the tenth day, when they all lay exhausted, land appeared in the east. White Bear saw then that they would be saved and called the land Lifeland.

Here they settled. White Bear kindled a bonfire and took possession of the new country beneath a whirring flight of birds coming from the south and making for the northern lakes.

Here was the same conflict of sun, water and clouds, and the earth lay bared and steaming from the bath, now brightened, now shaded by the hastening clouds with which the sun sported. But spring triumphed. The rainbow stretched its airy bridge over the greensward as a sign that here too man was at home.

White Bear looked about him and found birch trees, good and plentiful timber for shipbuilding; here he could build prodigious vessels to take him all over the world, and here he would stay.

XV

THE SETTLER

I
N Lifeland White Bear met with the primitive folk. It never occurred to him that the little scurvy savages who infested the thickets like vermin were the beautiful naked people he had dreamt of finding in the southern forests; and yet it was they. They were directly descended from the same people who long ago had thrust out Carl and left him at the mercy of winter.

It took White Bear a long time to reassure the shy natives sufficiently to get a proper sight of them; at first they hid in the bushes like foxes and took to flight when any one came too near. They usually ran off on all fours to avoid as much as possible being seen, and as they crawled through the grass with a stiff hide over the back for protection, they had a trick of turning their faces over their shoulders, showing all their teeth and then running on. When they had come a certain distance, they stood up and ran straight before them till they thought they were in safety. White Bear called them the Badgers from their tracks and from the smell there was about them.

It dawned upon him that they regarded him and his tall, blond sons with the deepest awe and terror and probably took them for supernatural beings. And what indeed were they to make of giants with fair hair and blue eyes who came over the water in *ships*, something of which they had no conception? White Bear had to make many signs of friendship and go with green boughs in his hands instead of weapons before they would approach, and even then they came creeping on their stomachs and squirming like puppies with fright and submission.

May the gentle squatted down before them and enticed their little ones with barley cakes on her knees.

At last friendly relations were established, but even after the Badgers had learnt that the tall white men did not intend to eat them up, they continued to lie in the dust before them as before supernatural creatures. Thus White Bear met with no difficulties from their side when he established himself in the country.

It was rich in pine and birch forests, full of game. Inland lay endless steppes, where herds of wild horses and sheep grazed as far as the eye could reach. Here White Bear saw the wild horse for the first time; it had left Scandinavia long before his day. True, there were legends that his forefathers in a distant age had known an animal that had only one toe on each foot and ran like the wind, but White Bear treated them as fables like so many more that were told of old times; here however was clear proof.

White Bear expected great things from a closer acquaintance with the wild horses. They were handsome animals with traces of black stripes on their dun flanks and big lively ears. They were very inquisitive and spirited, full of play, always ready to kick up and dash across the steppe in a joyous gallop. White Bear's boys were greatly taken with the dashing animals and tried to approach them with a piece of bread in one hand and a coiled thong in the other, and the wild horses answered with an eager snort, dancing round in a most engaging way; they were very willing, but still, if the boys came too near, they set off at such a gallop that there was nothing to be seen of them but the hollows of hoofs in the air. They gave fiery ringing neighs, especially the high-mettled colts with flying mane and a white half moon showing in their eyes; the boys called to them with every show of affection, and the horses curtsied with their heads and answered in a glad whinny, but would not let them come near at present.

The fact was that the natives only knew of killing the horses, they had no notion of taming them and making brothers of them. They were altogether unfeeling towards animals, in a way that struck White Bear as both foreign and revolting; not content with killing them in the chase, they tortured them in cold blood for their amusement; the idea of approaching them fraternally was the more remote, so far as White Bear could understand, in that these cowardly plantigrades considered themselves elevated in a positively transcendental degree above all that bore the name of beast. But the Badgers had many peculiarities of which they were proud, and which White Bear was glad to let them keep for their own.

The fortunes of the primitive folk had been very various since Carl the Old parted from them in the Lost Country. The majority, we know, had gone due south and scattered into distant tropical lands, where nothing was heard of them until the best part of a geological period later, when a descendant of Carl, Columbus, found a branch of the family in the West Indian islands. Still later another of Carl's descendants, Darwin, met with their remotest offshoots, in the state in which they had begun and ended, in the Land of Fire.

But at the time in which White Bear lived they had reached no farther than Southern Europe, with the beginnings of an immigration to Africa and Asia. There were always northern outposts who stood the cold better than the rest, and when the climate of the North became milder, many of them found their way back into the old tracts, following the migrating birds and moving regularly with the seasons. When the primitive folk emigrated from Scandinavia it was continuous with the rest of Europe; afterwards open sounds came between, which they were not yet able to cross; meanwhile they turned off along the shores of the Baltic countries, while at the same time sending offshoots far into Russia; and here it was that White Bear found them.

In the beginning they could not understand one another, and each was apt to think the other had no speech at all, only meaningless sounds; but they soon learned to infer what was meant from what was said, and this difference of language was the first thing that led to the formation of ideas, which afterwards took firm shape. Moreover it was not long before White Bear discovered words in the Badgers' apparently outlandish tongue which seemed familiar to him and must once have sounded the same in both languages. The Badgers could repeat lays and ancient legends; amongst others they had a misty tradition about a man who murdered his brother and was banished to a desert land. White Bear heard of the evil deed with much sympathy and gave the narrator a piece of bread.

The northern primitive men were not altogether the same as when Carl left them. Homelessness and want had changed them for the worse, had made them sickly from birth and more jealous of one another than they were before. There was nothing left of the freedom from care and softness of fur in which their jungle ancestors had once rejoiced, they no longer swung in the treetops with an apple in one hand and all the rest of the fruit shaken down on to the ground for amusement; they had lost their coat of hair, which was worn off by bad times and replaced by sweat and the dust of exile. The only thing they had learnt was to cover their backs against the winter they always fled from; and this was the literal truth, since they did not know how to clothe themselves properly but dragged about an old sheepskin, with which they protected their backbones from the weather. But they had no idea of preparing it, the skin was stiff and hard. When hunting and on every occasion they used it as a protection, they slept under it and crept behind it when in danger. They did not build themselves houses but slept miserably in holes on the bare ground or in a bush, and on the approach of winter they started for the south in a body like other birds of passage and did not appear again before next spring. And yet they had always had fire. They carried it about with them in baskets with tinder, exactly as in primitive days, but had made no progress in the use of it. They knew nothing of pottery. Of baking bread they had no idea and never guessed that there was such a thing as corn, though they were wading to the necks in it; the country was full of wild barley. That they should make the corn grow themselves was not to be expected. They did not know how to build boats; on the other hand they could swim and in this way crossed minor water obstacles. They did not throw the spear and only struck the simplest flint flakes.

But to make up for all this the Badgers possessed an implement which was altogether new to White Bear; they knew how to give a flint-tipped reed a long and sure flight through the air by the help of a pair of antelope horns, the points of which were drawn towards each other by a cord of sinew. This was the bow, and how they had come by it they were unable to explain, but they showed with a grin how they caught a poisonous snake and stuck the arrow points into its head to make them powerful, and White Bear shuddered the first time he saw a wild horse fall to one of these arrows and die in convulsions, though it had scarcely received a scratch. This was dirty sorcery. White Bear for his own part never learned the use of the bow.

The boys on the other hand could not take their eyes off it and soon made similar ones, but of ash. The poison they would have nothing to do with, they didn't hunt in ambush, they were strong and in time became so practised that, if the range was not too great, they could shoot an arrow clean through the body of a bison.

Besides the chase the Badgers had another use for the bow; they often sat down and made music by plucking at the taut string with their fingers. It gave a seductive clang, like the wind playing over distant worlds.

The Badgers were devoted to music, and when one of them struck the bow, the notes of which gained resonance from the empty skull to which the horns were attached, and another thumped a hollow tree with a cudgel, while a third piped with all his might into a shinbone, and at the same time a whole lot more formed a ring round the artists and raised a full passionate chorus of moaning, it was really enough to make the deepest impression, even on others besides the abdominal contortionists who made the music. There was a magic in the way the sweet blending tones made men and even beasts recall and lament the past, a voice from the forest which awoke sleeping memories of the lost Eden.

Originally no doubt the Badgers had only used the lure of their playing in the service of the chase to catch the attention of the game, and then, when the wild horse approached with his head sagaciously on one side and his big down-filled ears cocked to catch the lovely notes that sounded like the wind on distant blissful pastures, then it was that the poison arrow flew from the harpstring and planted the fire of death in the beast's veins. It was an art that paid, the whole soul of primitive man was contained in this instrument, viper and harp in one.

But by long practice the Badgers had acquired such skill that they now cultivated playing as an art independently of hunting. They added more strings to the bow, as it were winds of different force, and gave it deeper resonance by freeing the horns from the empty skull, the teeth of which jarred, and setting them in a tortoise shell instead. The bone flute they provided with holes, that it might have more wounds to bewail; the hollow tree they cut off from its root to make it portable, and they learned to lament with a certain rhythm, whereby misery and regret became a gift. Oh yes, they were masters of music.

White Bear and his family had no talents of this sort, but they were very strongly susceptible and listened in profound ecstasy when the Badgers obliged them with a piece; they fetched deep sighs from their innermost recesses and went red and pale by turns under the influence of their feelings. The music made them meek, they stood as though nailed to the spot, fascinated by the bewitching lure that called them out of themselves.

When they listened in this way, they must have been very like the handsome wild horses which the music inspired with confidence; they bent forward in the same attitude of enchantment, with fetters about their limbs . . . and it was the Badgers' music that won over White Bear and led him to commit himself to their friendship.

Otherwise White Bear did not learn much the Easterlings. The influence was the other way. The Badgers showed a surprising capacity for imitation, learned in a twinkling how to clothe themselves and boil and drive a sledge and sail on the water and everything that White Bear could do. In fact they assimilated all this so well that it was not long before they began to hint among themselves that they had really been well acquainted with all these simple things beforehand. They were not far from jeering at this Firebeard who gave himself out to be the originator of the most obvious things; luckily it was not *they* who had invented any of them. All the same they never got any further with the new things they had learned until they had gone and pried on White Bear's fingers while he was at work.

Tools and wood bred fast in White Bear's big freckled hands. Nothing remained as it was, but leapt into a more perfect form when he had gone over it with his flashing blue eyes; not a new boat or sledge left his hands that was not different from the last. The Badgers' best efforts at doing a thing well were directed on the other hand to getting it just as it *should* be, the old familiar form, and in this they went far, they achieved the highest that could be done in the way of jogging along in rear of the obvious.

They transmitted the new things to distant tribes of the primitive folk, who accepted them readily but often stood still for ever at one stage or another, as they came too far away from the source.

White Bear and the Badgers got on well together. They each kept their own customs, and these were pretty different. Thus the Badgers burned their dead, now a symbolical act derived from a past when they roasted and ate them. As though in memory of the ancient custom, the family still ate a little bit of the deceased on the pyre, simply for the sake of honouring the person in question; this however would not be proper if any one should pass away in a totally uneatable condition; but after they had learnt the use of corn from White Bear, they took to making little cakes in the likeness of the dead man, which they ate at the funeral ceremony, and this custom became permanent.

White Bear took no offence at the burning of bodies, though he disliked the smell; he was used to a different custom on the ice-field, but did not expect all peoples to be alike. The Ice Folk did not believe in death. Ever since Allfather had gone down into his house and had not been seen again, they used to let those who perished from sickness or old age stay in their graves, which they had inhabited while alive, and give them something to live on, after which the grave was generally closed with earth. Whether they continued to live after that was not for others to determine; at any rate they were given every possible chance.

In daily life also the habits of the Badgers differed radically from White Bear's. The lot of the women was simply miserable. Licentiousness flourished as the most natural thing in the world. Thievery was the only form of lawful property known to the Badgers. They were timorous to a disgusting degree, but very courageous at a distance. Reverence for superior power was unknown to them, they ran away from the smallest animal but did not hold their peace when Nature spoke; in the dark they were as noisy as a pack of wolves. They squabbled perpetually, black-guarded each other like the dirty wretches they were, but without ever coming to blows.

A proper division between White Bear and the Badgers came about of itself. While White Bear stayed on the coast busy with new big ships, the Badgers came and went on their barren migrations up and down the same tracts, southward when it got too cold and back again with the spring. White Bear received them well when they came, but no closer connection arose. Every spring at the time when White Bear kindled his bonfire and held a sacrificial feast, on which occasion he now slaughtered the wild horse for choice on account of its sweet meat, the Badgers would put in an appearance, old acquaintances who were welcome to a share of the feast and nearly always had news from the outside world. This might lead to a great banquet, followed by musical performances and bartering. The Badgers often brought things with them that White Bear might want, and he on his side had treasures which the Badgers eagerly desired.

One year a wanderer had with him an axe of a strange nature, which White Bear immediately acquired and set to work to investigate. It was of a fine red colour and so bright that you could see your face in it as in water. But the striking thing was that it could not be treated like any other kind of stone, it did not crumble or split up when struck. On the other hand it could be beaten flat, whereby it became warm, and hammered out into another shape again. The stuff was tough but not particularly hard. It had neither taste nor smell and lay very heavily in the hand. It was copper. However, White Bear did not do much with the new stuff in the meanwhile, though he got as much as he could by barter, as May liked to have it to hang round her neck. For tools it was unsuitable, not nearly hard enough, so flint was better. White Bear owned certain ground chisels and axes which no other stuff could replace; they bit into wood with a greedy tooth and stood all the force he put into the blow.

But afterwards White Bear went more closely into the properties of copper and learned that they were great. It was in working the stuff into ornaments for May that he discovered it would melt in fire. For it got warm when hammered and at the same time a good deal softer; White Bear then tried warming it in the fire, and saw it suddenly run away like a red worm among the embers; he hardly knew what to believe. Afterwards he found it in the ashes, run together and cold, and began with it over again. By degrees it served him for many things. The Badgers said they got it from the tribes far to the south and east, but for the rest they knew nothing of its peculiar qualities as compared with stone; they always brought it beaten into the form of little axes or pins to wear in the cartilage of the nose. Later on White Bear bought little pieces of another somewhat similar stuff from the Badgers, who got it on their travels; it was yellower in colour and still softer, so that it could be used for nothing but beads and earrings for the women. A white metal White Bear also became acquainted with, besides many other things the Badgers carried with them, mussel-shells, pretty stones and the like.

Their intercourse lost the stamp of novelty. The Badgers knew very well that the white men were no more supernatural than themselves. One year one of the tribes stayed through the winter and got on very well, for now they had learnt how to build houses and prepare skins. After that they settled permanently and set about imitating the White Bear family. They showed a certain constancy as far as watching White Bear's work and copying him went. They developed a peculiar sidelong look through always stealing with their eyes without a word of thanks to the owner. White Bear let them stay. They supported themselves by fishing, after they had learnt to go to sea. Yet they did not *build* ships, preferring to imitate the dug-out, of which White Bear had also furnished the pattern, since there was big timber here. A trough of this kind could be hollowed out by fire without much trouble and served the needs of the Badgers. And truly it was no longer with abject wonder that they looked at the great masterpiece of a ship that White Bear had under construction on the beach; it rather weighed on them like a burning internal sickness from which they were suffering and which there was only *one* cure for. . . .

White Bear's ship grew. And his plans grew with it. It was to be so big that by itself it would be able to carry him and all his clan to the world's end, right into the Lost Country! His head swam in one fit of frenzy after another as he worked. When he was producing he ran hither and thither in his excitement, his brow brooding hot, his hands congested with blood, his eyes flashing and flashing again; he made himself so wary and deft-fingered, with such intense vision, as he directed the tool, and he cut trees through with *one* blow, went at it like an ox when he had made up his mind what he wanted. He shouted, drunk with victory, over his work when the sun shone, himself a little sun upon the landscape with his fiery red hair and beard, and there were times when in a fury of impatience he smashed up all his work with his biggest hammer, went mad like a bull till there was not a splinter left whole; that was when something had offended him and would not come right at once. Next day he came down to the empty place sober and fresh and ran his fingers through his red hair and began all over again. His sons helped him in everything.

The ship he was building had a keel for the first time. He had forged bolts and nails of copper to hold the timbers together, and as the whole ship would be so big that neither he nor the boys nor any human power could move it, he had begun by laying the keel on round tree-trunks, taught by previous experience, so as to roll it out when it was finished.

Now the fore-end of the keel, which was to rise up beyond the stem, had already been shaped by White Bear, with the most glowing effort of his craft, into the gaping head of a monster.

What sort of a creature it might be was not altogether easy to see, and White Bear himself was not quite clear about it. But he, whose blood was still haunted by blind memories inherited from forefathers who had seen the foul sea-serpent, now sleeping its eternal sleep at the bottom of the sea, had only imagined some kind of indication of the Impossible created and held fast by his hand, and this gave him the idea. The head might scare off whales, and that was part of its use. Besides, it was to stand looking out to sea while the ship was being built and absorb longing for the lands of wonder that White Bear intended to visit under its sign.

Meanwhile, like the lightning seer he was, White Bear had already started on a new track, even before the ship was finished. It was the steppes and the view to the eastward which never came to an end however far he went inland, it was the infinity of the earth, like that of the sea, which gave him no peace. Would he never come any farther? Was this round horizon over by the rising sun to be his limit? Would the world on that side never be his? What about the wild horses, how was it they could range to the eastward as far as they liked?

Ha! White Bear catches horses and tames them, and the sledge of old days on the ice comes into use again; in winter he tears away on journeys across the endless snow-covered plains. The homestead is in a whirl of horse-breaking, neighing, laughter and shouts. May comes out with bits of bread for the beasts which she gives them on the flat of her palm lest they should nab her fingers in their greediness, and the horses pick up the crumbs with their soft flexible muzzles. And when it is all gone she dries the foam on the animals' manes and smiles at them when they follow her, sniffing at her hands. White Bear makes a cunning whip with a lash that whirs in the air and stings just like a gadfly; that makes the horses jump and throw their heads about. He and the boys go on the Wild Hunt over the steppes.

The dear wild horses are more than ready to run, they set off on full gallop before the sledge in the impetuous belief that all the time they are running away from the sledge and their captivity, which is just what they have to do; behind them sits White Bear roaring with laughter and is carried on with them, the horses' flight is what he has use for.

But in summer White Bear can't get anywhere with his sledge. He ponders.

He ponders again. Look here — those rollers he uses for running his boats into the sea . . . what if he made fast a round block of wood under the sledge so that it came along and went on rolling under the runners all the time? White Bear couldn't get the roller out of his head. He tried, fastened thongs to both ends of a thick block of wood and hung it under the sledge; but the thongs caught and wouldn't let the roller go round. There was no need for it to touch the ground in its whole length either; White Bear hacked it thin except at the ends and then actually got it to hang on, but it was like nothing at all until he gave up the thongs and made holes in the runners themselves through which to put the thin part of the roller. Now the sledge was really fit to run on the bare ground. But the round wooden discs at the ends had to be made bigger, taken from thicker trunks, and it was a long job to hack them thin in the middle; why not make a pole fast to the sledge and bore holes through the discs themselves?

White Bear's hair tingled at the thought, he got the carpentry done, and then, after many summers' laborious attempts and endless hacking with his stone axe, he saw himself in possession of the first car.

Now in with the horses! White Bear fetches a pair, and you can guess they turn the whites of their eyes at the sight of this contraption with two possibly very fateful wheels underneath it. They hum and haw and quiver a trifle, get ready for a gallop to the world's end, if need be, for freedom; and let them do it, thinks White Bear, but they are to stand still till they have got the leather traces on; a little taste of them along their flanks makes them both willing to have them on and more eager for liberty, thus serving White Bear's purpose. A stag's antler bit in the mouth to foam over — away from their heads, boys, and the happy White Bear is off. . . .

Not two minutes after he had fire!

Yes, as true as the sun circles in the sky! White Bear was run away with on the spot, the wheels, wood against wood on the axles, began to smoke almost as soon as the car started, and the horses, who thought it was a steppe fire they smelt, set off at a tearing gallop. The smoke streamed from both hubs, began to shoot out sparks, and suddenly the wheels burst into flame, the whole car was ablaze about White Bear's ears. Then all the Badgers, who had stolen up to look on, fell on their faces and twiddled their hands above their heads in the deepest misery — surely the Mighty One would not let them die!

But they recovered themselves and nearly smacked their thighs to pieces with fun when they saw the end of the show. White Bear was upset, and the horses, now clean mad, broke everything and ran off; and there lay White Bear battling with the fire amid the remains of his smashed car. He got hair and beard singed off and was well burnt all over, but he noticed nothing, not even the Badgers who came and roared with laughter in his face; he laughed heartily himself, with wide eyes staring from terror and delight, he swung a bit of the burning car over his head and howled with crazy joy. *Fire!* He rushed off home to his workshop to start making it all over again – and suddenly he fell silent as he ran; now his head was going again, he was working!

Behind him cackled the savage laughter of the flat-footed, blighted folk who could see nothing in it but that the man had had a spill and got singed.

And after this they permitted themselves to grin more and more openly when White Bear was out driving his car like a headstrong fool; they stood in line and laughed in good faith, held their breath with polite interest; but they let themselves go like frisky swine with delight at the Thunderhead's doings. For when White Bear drove fast the car rumbled pretty loudly, especially as the wheels were not properly round, and as fire had broken out on the first trial run the Badgers had really believed it was the *Thunderer* himself they had amongst them and had cast themselves on the ground before him. That was a blunder he would have to pay for! Behind their laugher lay a corroding malice, a hatred that only the heart of a thief can hold. They had generosity to avenge.

But White Bear did not see what was gathering against him. He was entirely taken up by his car. He straightway built himself a new one and prevented its catching fire by pouring water on the wheels; one of his sons sat in the car by him with a pot and kept the axles wet, and this answered the purpose until he had tried other ways and learned to smear his car with grease and tallow. He improved the wheels; discs cut crosswise from a tree-trunk would not last and it was an inhuman labour to hack them out; he laid two strong pieces of wood together in the form of a cross and made the hub in the middle; outside this he bent a strong ash shoot of the thickness of a wrist all the way round and lashed it together with pigskin thongs. He protected the lashing by laying another band of ash outside to take the wear and tear, and now the wheel could hardly be better. He prolonged the hub so that the wheel should not work loose. The car itself he also improved, giving it a pole to harness the horses to and splinterbars for the traces.

But now White Bear knew that he need only drive with ungreased wheels to get fire. And thus fire had come to White Bear, as to his ancestor Carl, through the work of his hands.

The art of making fire he afterwards pursued in a special way. He made himself a wheel and axle for the purpose, only reversing the movement so that he turned the axle while the wheel lay still. Experience showed him that the axle was best made of ash and the hub of elm. Thus he had the means of renewing his fire whenever he wanted it.

And as this wheel was not to be used for driving, he left out the band and only left the spokes with a hook at each end to make it fast by. This instrument afterwards became a secret sign for all members of Carl's race, when they had spread over the earth; a solar symbol to which all kinds of incomprehensible meanings were attached; but the only secret of the sign was perseverance and fire, labour first and last.

Now White Bear had thoughts of leaving. The ship would soon be ready, and it was a big one. It was to hold the car and several pairs of horses — aha! for there would be driving in the land beyond the sea.

And the ship was to be victualled with corn for weeks, the country was far away. White Bear himself helped May to grow corn. He watched her scratching the ground with a stick to open the mould for the grain, and he came at once and beamed over the field, gave the stick form and harnessed an ox to it, so that May's strength was spared. One more crop and they would be off.

XVI

THE VOICE OF THE BLOOD

T HE GREAT year of departure arrived and the ship lay ready with her dragon's jaws gaping hungrily out to sea.

White Bear had burnt his joy fire for the year and hoped to light the next one in new realms. But May sighed this time as she laid her corn in the earth; she knew she would not reap it. But she sowed it, for the earth which had been the first to give should be the last to receive.

The Badgers had come with the birds of passage and had been liberally entertained with horseflesh at the spring bonfire. White Bear sacrificed to Sun, Moon, Sea and Earth in view of his approaching voyage. There was great feasting, at which the Badgers contributed the most affecting concerts. The harp twanged confusedly like storms coming from every quarter, the drums throbbed like a heart overwhelmed by sadness, and the bone flute puled so sorely; The Lost Country was nigh. Between the numbers the Badgers who lived on the spot had much to tell their friends returned from travel, they put their heads together and whispered all sorts of things into each other's ears; White Bear was glowing with the music and saw nothing.

Having the impression of a certain melancholy on the part of his guests he went driving in his wonderful new car; perhaps it would cheer them up to see him manage the horses and thunder about on the steppe. White Bear's flashing eyes, which usually saw everything, did not discover that the Badgers were shortening their necks with suppressed rage, he did not hear them grind their teeth behind closed lips, speechless at his rashness.

It offended the Badgers in their very souls to have to witness this madman's speed. It was dangerous if not fatal simply to see the wheels whirl round so furiously that they were quite invisible, rumbling in a way that was more than insulting to the Thunderer himself and a scandal for folk to listen to. Were people no longer allowed to walk on their feet?

What would be the next thing? And what idea of himself had

this foreigner with hair that had gone light from sickness, since in his indomitable insolence he persisted in dazzling the world with fatuous devices? Were old ways not good enough for him? Would he perforce make himself different from other people? And yet he had himself shown that he was nothing more than an ordinary man by mixing with them as an equal.

But they had let him exploit them; all the copper he used for his ship and had now mounted on the wheels of his cursed car, had originally hung on their necks or in their noses, it was green with their sweat and properly belonged to them. And then that thing he had said. . . .

White Bear had said something which more than all the rest had riven the Badgers' bile into their blood and given them yellow eyes. It was only just a chance remark White Bear had carelessly let fall and forgotten again, but it had affected the natives as a deadly insult, a piece of spiritual coarseness never to be forgiven.

On an occasion when several Badgers were listening he had said, expressly intending to give them a cut of the lash, that it was after all a lucky thing it had occurred to him at the start to propel a ship end on, otherwise they might have seen people sailing broadside foremost to the end of time.

That was what he had said, and it was a heartless thing. The Badgers discussed nothing else at White Bear's feasts, while pouring out their whole souls in music and song, which threw White Bear off his guard.

A day or two after the bonfire White Bear made a trip inland after game. Some supplies still wanting for the ship, and the Badgers had brought word of a great herd of buffaloes wandering in such and such a direction inland. They had advised him to go in a body, and White Bear had taken his four elder sons with him; they were on horseback, and he himself drove the car.

Later in the day, when White Bear had been gone some hours, the Badgers came creeping up to the settlement from different sides, surrounding it and hid themselves, while three or four of them went openly towards White Bear's house.

May was at home with her three daughters, the youngest of whom was still a little child, and a half-grown boy called Worm. To him the Badgers addressed themselves, and they talked for a while of this and that. Worm knew them well, they were in the habit of coming to the settlement and asking favours of White

Bear. This time they only wanted to borrow a clay pot, and as
Worm turned his back to fetch one, they threw straps about his
arms and legs and pulled him down. Worm defended himself desperately and nearly struggled free, but more Badgers came to help
and Worm was overpowered.

The confusion brought May out with the little girl. The two
grown-up daughters stayed below in the stone house. Not a word
was spoken between May and the Badgers, but when she had
looked round at them and seen Worm lying bound, she took up
a heavy piece of wood, lifted the little girl up on her arm and
began the fight for her life and the children's. She fought as long
as she could see, raging like a she-bear, till she could feel no
more.

The settlement was thick with Badgers, whole armies of them
had swarmed up from the grass and undergrowth, they were so
many that they pressed each other backwards and forwards like
a tideway, they swayed in and out, almost too numerous to get
anything done. But that came after a while. Some of them made
for the ship, others split White Bear's sledges to pieces and killed
the domestic animals. The daughters were brought up shrieking
from the house, but soon their cries were stifled by skins thrown
over their heads and died away as they were carried off.

One group took Worm and led him to a tree to be tortured.
They looked at him with eyes ready to burst with rapacity, they
foamed and bristled like beasts at night, they blew and snorted
and twitched spasmodically. They were past speaking, their jaws
were stiff with cramp and set in a cold grin, and Worm's voice
sounded so lonely and abandoned among all these men. He had
much to say, words enough for a lifetime which he had to pour out
all at once. He kept his grave voice, the rough voice of a growing
boy, even when they were maltreating him.

When he could not help trembling, standing naked before his
tormentors, he remarked to them that his limbs seemed displeased
at having to lose their power. It worried him to be hustled by the
crowd, and he turned up his nose at the sweat and stench they
smothered him with. They wanted to make him complain and
fetched brands to put to his feet, they broke his fingers with a
cudgel; he stretched himself but said nothing. He was of a sort
that did not yield in adversity. After a while he made a remark
about the weather. Then they set to work to torture the boy in

earnest, thoroughly, bit by bit. And so they made him cry.

Far out upon the steppe White Bear saw smoke and knew that it could come from nowhere but his own homestead; he wondered at it, stopped the hunt and turned back. The smoke increased, he saw flames at the root of it, and now he hastened on, making for home as hard as the horses could go. He reached a hill from which there was a view of the coast, and saw it was his *ship* that was on fire.

Between him and home lay a dense birch copse, and from this a numberless swarm of Badgers suddenly burst and rushed towards White Bear and his sons yelling with all their might. But even before they were within bowshot the sight of the giant with his stone hammer coming at a thundering gallop in his car unmanned them, and the whole swarm turned their backs all at once like a flock of sandpipers and fled back to the thicket. Their little plan of campaign was stifled at birth. White Bear did not see a single one the rest of the way during the final wild race to the settlement.

Nor were there any Badgers to be seen here. But their tracks showed that they had only taken to flight a very short time before. White Bear only gave a brief glance at his ship; it was enveloped in flames and destroyed, the charred dragon's head gaping to seaward; outside his house White Bear saw things that were worse. Here they had spent at least an hour amusing themselves at their ease, the whole settlement was bespattered with blood.

May, May was dead. In her arms she held the unrecognizable body of the little girl. Both the big girls were gone.

But dying and bound to a tree White Bear found his son Worm. He was resting with his head upon his shoulder, but raised his pale face when his father came and smiled at him. There was a faint trace of tears on the freckled boyish cheeks under the eyes, which were half closed and dim; he could not see but still moved his blue lips, trying to say something.

They had cut his back open and torn the lungs from his living body.

Once more he moved his lips, and White Bear bent down his ear and heard his boy whisper that he was all right. And then he laid his head upon his breast and was dead.

In the light northern nights the birch stands with all its rich foliage hanging down over the rounded stems, which glimmer in a twilight of white flecked limbs; the whole delicate tree trembles like a woman whose long hair has fallen forward over her face; and the northern sky, which smiles and blushes with the sleeping sun in its embrace, knows not whether the birch has hidden its face because it is quivering with happiness or because it is weeping. Ah, the birch hangs its light young leaves in deep sorrow, since it has dreamt that its foliage will be turned to a crown of bloody hair, each leaf a bleeding wound, until it is swathed naked in the snow-storm's winding-sheet. The tree that quivers under the sympathy of the lovely northern night is May, the gentle May.

But the great white Star that wanders ceaselessly about the sky while all other stars have come to rest and twinkle in one place, the star that does not sparkle but hangs calmly and hard like a boy's tears, that is Worm who died too early. How he shines in his pallor as he pursues his course, which was broken off before he had lived; how he wanders eternally about the earth with his fine, defiant heart!

And the little girl who was killed on her mother's breast shines now as evening, now as morning star, white and pensive like a child's soul full of its own affairs and playing so happily by itself on paths of infinity.

XVII

THE SIGN OF THE HAMMER

B̶UT as the dark sea of blood where the sun sinks at midnight, as the long black nights of the North was White Bear's suffering.

Ages passed before his spirit dawned again, and all the while the darkness lay upon his soul he raged as a terrible avenger. The steppe was swept by a storm of slaughter and burning, White Bear thundered far and wide in his car, which had become death's vehicle, accompanied by his darting sons on horseback, and wherever he passed the Badgers writhed stricken in his tracks. He swung the great stone hammer which before had done him peaceful service in shipbuilding; it did not sink in the wound like an axe, but crashed down and was free again in his hand as he hunted on; up and down it went and the Badgers sank back dead behind the whirling wheels. White Bear laid waste the country for leagues, burned the Badgers out of the undergrowth with fire and exterminated them in masses. Every sort of wood or cover was laid in ashes, the steppes lay scorched and blackened as far as the eye could see. It was like a visitation of winter over the whole earth, not a blade of grass was spared. The Badgers were swept away like the leaves of the trees in a ravaging frost wind.

But slaughter and reprisal could not in the long run expiate the deed. White Bear's eyes were not sated by watching the death shudder flicker across the faces of the wretches he had doomed, but who did not even know what they had done. He saw that the Badgers had acted in profound ignorance, they had only followed their nature, and it was he who had been most to blame for not guarding himself against it. He had been as one who releases a wolf caught in the forest and instantly has the brute at his throat. They were jungle creatures who were incapable of thought and had not learned to remember. The outrage had been committed without a scrap of reason, as an urgent momentary impulse, and now they had actually forgotten their guilt and looked upon the whole affair as though it was he who had begun it and had been butchering them in his fury for all eternity. An inarticulate hate was the only feeling that filled them; they did not even know what it was to die, though they were cowardly enough; he looked into eyes that returned nothing but blank hate when he marked them for death, nothing but the momentary guiltlessness of the animal, until his hammer scattered their brains upon the ground. At last he could strike no more. They were the many. They must be right.

And another thing helped, which seemed stronger than White Bear. Far to the eastward he at last came up with the band that had run away with his two grown-up daughters. Instantly the sky turned red before him, revenge and slaughter were in the air — when White Bear witnessed the sight of his and May's white-armed girls, his own flesh and blood, falling at his feet and interceding for the ravishers who had violated them and carried them off. Then White Bear wept and gave them peace.

He gave up his reprisals and turned home, sat for months inert, dumbly lamenting like the forest in autumn. His hair turned white.

But the man's designs and constructive passion came back. At last he had thought it all out and decided his fate and that of the Badgers.

May and the two children lay in the house White Bear had lived in! he threw on earth and raised a great mound over it. He himself left the place and camped on the coast in a forest of big timber farther to the south. Here he built a new ship. It was of such vast beam and length that the Badgers, who had begun again shyly to draw near to his settlement, puzzled their heads a good deal as to how White Bear would get such a big ship to move on the water. White Bear set up a dragon's head on the stem with gulping jaw to seaward, and it seemed to laugh with a silent uncanny laughter.

But when the ship was finished and afloat with thwarts for twenty men besides White Bear and his sons, he went ashore one day and caught that number of Badgers, strong young men, and brought them bound to the vessel. For every seat he had made a copper shackle and this he attached to the foot of each of his captives. They expected to be put to death. But White Bear gave them food and looked after them so well that they cast down their eyes. Then he told them to take hold of the oars and row. And now they saw how White Bear had thought of moving his ship.

Afterwards, when they grew homesick and drew distant comparisons between their dog's life on the steppe and their present altogether carefree and regular employment, with sighs for the past and detriment to their working powers, White Bear cheered them by remarking on their muscular strength and suggesting that it would soon be supper time; they were immensely vain of the strong arms they developed at the oars and showed all their teeth in a pleased grin when White Bear praised them; supper was also a fine object for a little extra exertion, another hour or so every day. The Badgers made good rowers. They lacked nothing; White Bear took a number of their women on board in the bottom of the ship, to make them feel at home and to add to the crew during the voyage, if it should be necessary.

Besides them White Bear brought everything pertaining to his life on board this roomy ship, his cars, horses and cattle with their hay and corn, and all he possessed in the way of skins and tools, copper and weapons. On a hearth in the after part of the ship burned the fire, which White Bear had the power to extinguish and rekindle whenever he chose. The order of the ship was that White Bear stood at the great after-oar and steered while the captives rowed; his sons lived in the forepart and looked out for land, always playing with weapons in their hands. Thus they stood out to sea.

And this ship with all that was assembled in it, with all that it *was*, now moved with the wind and the currents and its own indwelling force like a little living island, a type of that growth of power in adversity and its consequences, which transplanted itself from the ice-sheet over Europe, and later expanded over every sea into what became in time the white man's social order.

But White Bear's eldest son, Wolf, stayed behind in Lifeland. He had taken one of the daughters of the Badgers to wife, a twinkling brown girl of the steppes, and wished to remain in the country and share his lot with her. From them and from White Bear's two white daughters who had native husbands was descended a great people who ranged over the East and South in chariot and on horseback.

White Bear sailed so long under the North Star that he grew homesick for Upland, where he had lived the best days of his life in longing to get away. He felt he must see the place where May's first yellow cornfield had waved in the summer breeze like her own rich hair. And he found his way by steering by the burning mountain, whose smoke marked his course by day, while the glow of its summit against the sky guided him by night.

In Upland White Bear settled. The waters from the melting of the ice-sheet had long since fallen, and the land was fair with greensward and young trees which clothed the moist banks of gravel and the furrowed hills. The deep cauldrons which the ice in many places had left in the rocky soil were full to the brim with clear water, so that you could see the pebbles that had been churned round lying still at the bottom and collecting moss; little water-newts with mottled bellies lived here as though there had never been another world. But even on warm summer days a breath cold as the grave might strike the face, coming from century-old ice that still lay in some cleft facing north under a protecting bed of gravel.

The forest was full of beasts which looked out from their secret paths among the trees with eternity in their eyes, as though they had always been here. The spruce sweated resin in the midday heat with a scent of the days when it was a tropical tree. Aspen, birch and mountain ash whispered together, beckoning significantly with their leaves, of the Lost Country. *Just below here,* they said and shook their heads, all-knowing. But in the thickets was the scent of raspberries with a new, finer sweetness than any forest had known before, the rich concealed intensity of the northern summer.

The bees hummed busily and gathered honey from flowers that only lived the summer through but drank up a condensed soul from a mould ground by the glacier out of the primeval forces of the mountain's heart, bared and enriched by all the moist whims of heaven, frost, rain and sunshine. Lichen and moss clothed the naked, scored rock, brought by the winds of heaven; birds of passage flew over the country with seed, or it was brought as motes sailing upon September gales from over the sea, and the land put on its new green garment.

In every crevice of the hard rock was a grass or a tiny flower with spicy scent. And in every calyx the gasping bee tumbled like a furry little elf, and the flower nodded and nodded again when he had flown away, smoothed out her skirt and blinked on at the sun.

White Bear brewed himself a drink of honey, which went dizzily to his head, as though he were spying upon a love-tryst between the sun and the nakedly fragrant herbs of a southern slope. When, drunk with mead and warmed through from lying on a slab of sun-baked rock, he looked up at the swarm of bees hanging before the sun like a great hovering globe swelling and shrinking in its heat and spinning like a fiery song in the sky — then the Lost Country returned, with a world to boot. At last White Bear found where he came from.

He let the years go by. He looked round the Upland forests after timber for shipbuilding. The trees were but young, of no use yet; but here would be forests for his successors, enough for fleets, for hosts of ships. The young smooth-barked trees were already swaying as though they knew they were to grow into keels that would sail the farthest seas.

For himself White Bear felt glad to settle and had his ship hauled up on land. He canted it keel upwards and built underneath it for a hall; and this was the first Gothic building. Afterwards, when White Bear's descendants found a new land and settled it, they turned their ships into halls and travelled on under the vaulting in another, spiritual sense.

White Bear went up to the island that had lain enclosed by the icefield and found his people again. Many of the Sons of Carl had perished in the thaw, but the rest were living in exactly the same state as when White Bear was outlawed. Now he came driving back, with his hammer and his fire and his ships behind him on the coast, and his kinsmen, who still remembered him, repented of the old story.

White Bear deposed the Garmings. He ordered the Ice Folk to disperse. There they were living on an island, which had long ceased to be an island, with the whole world open on every side but without a man to show them that the limit only existed in themselves; White Bear showed them that.

And lest they should continue to crowd round Allfather's Grave, White Bear took authority to gather them about a new sign, the fire-bearing Wheel. But he placed the sanctuary in Upland, with the open sea for a boundary on one side. He instituted great sacrifices to the returning Sun in spring, in whose fire he charged the Ice Folk to worship the One-Eyed Ancient. The young men he bade travel, as he had done, but he himself now stayed at home and founded a realm whose spirit should inspire the young, that they might remember where they came from and carry white man's customs with them into foreign lands.

The Ice Folk then gathered round White Bear under the sign of the Fire Wheel and the Hammer. Many of them crossed the mountains, now that they were freed, and founded Norway; others settled on the coast with White Bear and learned agriculture. Later on the young men made their way to Britain, Denmark and Germany, the Mediterranean; they made the waters round Europe their country, spread abroad but held together.

In the last years of his old age White Bear was much occupied in following the course of the heavenly bodies. He became more skilled in the days of the year and more intimate with the stars than any before him, and he bequeathed his knowledge to his sons. It was to be their secret and no other man's to be able to foretell the sun's position throughout the seasons and advise the people accordingly.

Otherwise White Bear did nothing to strengthen his power by dark and hidden lore, so long as he kept his bodily strength. The art of making fire, as he had introduced it, was known and in the possession of all; he would not have it used to any man's subjection. But he caused the Fire Wheel to be holy in the hand of every man as a sign of everlasting gratitude to the earth and the sun and a symbol of fertility. His influence White Bear maintained in his own way, by the Hammer and his almighty hand.

In a leisure hour White Bear composed the story of his life and engraved it for ever in the earth itself, a slab of bed-rock which the ice had worn smooth, the first tablet; the narrative consisted of two signs, whereof one was to represent a ship and the other a wheel. That was the beginning of art and literature.

As long as he could use his eyes White Bear continued to work in wood and metal. He kept affectionately to his stone implements that fitted his hand so capitally, but in leisure moments his curiosity was busy with the copper and other new things his sons brought home from the East; he tried everything in the fire and observed the nature of the stuff. On one of his visits Wolf brought home a big lump of an extraordinary new metal from the East, which he laid in the old man's hand; and this was long before even copper had come into general use. White Bear held the lump at arm's length and examined it carefully, weighed it and felt it all over with his big, scarred fingers. It was of a cold bluish lustre, something like ice, very heavy; a stone made no mark on it. White Bear put it to his tongue, it tasted bitter and raw like the sea; he sniffed at it, it smelt like blood. Then White Bear fell into deep thought. It was iron.

From that piece of iron White Bear forged himself a hammer, deserting his old tried stone implement for the first time. He was still so strong that with one blow of the iron hammer he could stretch a horse dead on the spot before the stone of sacrifice, and that without leaving a whole splinter in its skull.

Now when the wisdom of old age came to him he saw that the people would insist on submitting to his power, even when it was no more; and this insight into the nature of the heart of man once more gave work for his cunning hands.

White Bear lived almost entirely inside the hall, which was somewhat gloomy, and here men were accustomed to see a glimpse of his great frame and to show him the respect due to him and his Hammer. White Bear now privily shaped a block of wood into something of his own likeness, gave it his Hammer in its hand and set it up in the murky background of the hall, where he was used to show himself. And he actually had the satisfaction of seeing that the people bowed just as reverently to the image as to the reality. Then the old man laughed in his white beard, tickled with pride at the work of his hands — and at the same time by another master-thought of cruel merriment. Then he yielded himself to repose.

But afterwards, when he no longer showed himself outside the sanctuary, they could still catch a glimpse of him in the inner twilight with his Hammer raised; and his son, the only initiate, sprinkled the blood of the sacrifices upon him and gave the folk greetings from the old skipper-charioteer.

White Bear, who had been more human than any before or after him, was worshipped as a god by the Northerners and received affectionate surnames — the Thunderer, the Hammerswinger, the Truthteller — and he was given a place in the heavens by the side of the One-eyed Ancient. But their living blood flowed in the veins of the race. From Carl, who could not yield in adversity, and his posterity through White Bear, father of open fight, are descended all kings and husbandmen.

The Northern folk advanced in agriculture and seafaring. They fetched thralls from the eastward and lived together with them for hundreds of years. In the course of ages they became crossed and blended into one people, but a border-line always persisted, although they came from the same root, the line drawn by the ice, a fundamental difference in their stages of development. There were those who once for all had the lead, and whose fate it was always to drag their past about with them; and there were those who were burdened for ever by the impossibility of overtaking others, to imitate whom was their one desire. Of freemen and bondsmen and their mixed offspring, labourers under the yoke with the souls of freemen, as well as severe masters with the spirit of thralls, the population of the North and of the countries to which it spread was made up for ever after.

But when White Bear had got his substitute well set up, he yearned for solitude. One night he left the hall and secretly went on board a ship which he let drift away from land. He was oppressed with age and longed to lay his bones in the sea. Out in the open sea he sat quite still and looked at his hands, while the ship rocked broadside on to the waves. Time no longer existed for him.

Dawn came, his friend the sun arose. Broad and red it sank again into the sea.

The moon passed over the heavens with May's gentle, lifeless features.

The little dead girl came out in the morning sky and looked down, shining quietly till she too paled away.

Then he closed his eyes and saw no more.

XVIII

WOLF THE HORSEBREAKER

WHITE BEAR was the first to sail on the water in a ship, he tamed horses and invented the chariot, but, as has already been related, White Bear's adventurous boys were the first on earth to *ride*.

It was not for the old man to trust his heavy frame to the bucking wild horse to the extent of climbing on its back; there was a certain fatherly dignity to be thought of too. White Bear was content to develop his powers as a charioteer. Nor, though a mighty skipper, had he learned to swim, whereas the boys had taken to the water from sheer curiosity and daring and had risked drowning so often that at last they swam like seals. The fact was they were restless creatures and had to be on the go, up and down, in and out, wherever there was a chance. Many things that they started as purely thoughtless pranks afterwards stuck and became permanent acquirements, part of the everyday life both of themselves and their successors. They learned horsemanship in the same way, through play and passion for novelty, and above all through the necessity of constantly risking their necks which seems to be essential to every boy. It came about in this way:

Behind White Bear's settlement on the coast of Lifeland the steppes began and stretched eastward to infinity, so far that nobody had ever seen their boundary, right away to the place of the sun's rising. The country was fairly level and clothed league after league with high grass, but in the coastal district and many other places inland there were young forests of birch and stretches of thick scrub, besides bogs with bushes and reeds. Game roamed everywhere, bears and deer, aurochs, wolves and wild cattle living as neighbours; the sea was full of fish, and farther north, where the steppe passed into endless frozen marshes and hills, the reindeer dwelt in countless herds; in winter they came south and at that season supplied all the needs of White Bear and his household. But in the summer the wild horses came in from the warm pastures in the south and roamed over the open steppes and in the glades of the bush; then *they* were the quarry and daily fattened the smoke of May's kitchen fire with their sweet flesh. The wild horse tasted so good that White Bear preferred it to all other animals as an offering to the distant powers he honoured; every year he had his days of mark when more than one of the handsome refractory animals was led to the pyre and sacrificed.

But he also domesticated the wild horse, partly as a good food reserve which might be left alive against a shortage of game, partly of course for use in his car and sledge. This latter the horses did not seem to object to, and thus a mutual confidence soon grew up between them and White Bear.

But the boys especially had more and more to do with the spirited animals. Wolf, the eldest, was quite irresistibly attracted by them, and it looked as if they on their side were willing to make a special friend of him.

A secret sympathy arose between horse and man, a feeling of kinship that seemed to belong to a very distant past, forgotten on both sides. Perhaps it was due to the horse having once been a primitive animal in the same period when man's ancestors still lived in the trees, so that the obscure memory that linked them together dated from the Lost Country.

While the jungle man, in the days before Time came into the world, hooked himself from branch to branch in the tropical forests of Northern Europe, the primitive horse padded about down below on the hot swampy ground as a beast of just about the size of a rabbit, with four well-developed toes adapted for spreading themselves over the mud and with a mouthpiece that craved for water-plants and fruit; a plump little animal that might be something between a rodent and a ruminant, half-way to becoming a lazy tapir but possessed by an ambition to follow the distinguished career of the okapi and peaceful enough to join the herds of antelopes. Here in Paradise, the eternal springtime of the forests, the jungle man must often have dropped a juicy fruit to the beast in the swamp below, which devoured it in good faith as a gift from on high. Cocoanuts on the head it received from those above, but also the goodly breadfruit — the primeval horse was fond of that. Later on, when the tree-dwellers found themselves entitled to descend to earth and in that connection took to eating flesh, the little, widespread, easily caught swamp horse became their favourite food; that was the origin of *their* warm feelings.

Afterwards, when the ice came and overwhelmed the forests, they parted; the jungle man entered upon the inclement existence, under the law of the icefield, which made him human, and the horse went his way, which in course of time and in a literal sense was not without influence on his toes. Instead of the soft forest floor and the secure hiding places of the jungle, he came out upon dry steppes, where there was no need to spread his toes to prevent sinking in, but where on the contrary they were a hindrance, when for thousands of years he had to run for his life with packs of wolves and other hungry beasts of prey at his heels. Instead of plantain and young bamboo shoots he had nothing to live on but grass. But better to change little by little than give way to bad times. The horse had to travel long distances every day, and that quickly, so he raised himself on his middle toe and it gave him a feeling of greater freedom, of being more in alliance with the wind; and as the other side toes were not used, they shrank and became superfluous, while the nail hardened into a hoof; thus time and the road turned a fugitive beast into a horse. And it thrived so well that the puny creature of the forest floor gradually rose into an animal of size, one of those that are seen at a distance.

Its youthful dreams of subsiding into a tapir or a ruminant vanished of course together with the Lost Country. This beast of many possibilities, then, had now become a horse with no chance of retreat nor any desire of it; no more rabbit existence for him, he was a horse right through. And now it had met man again and felt strangely affected by an ancient memory, inexplicably attracted — but at the same time instinctively warned. There was something in man's gestures which promised fairly, and then the horse through all its trials had preserved the sweetness of Paradise in its blood, the great curiosity, it was so ready to come on. But a rather uncanny light in man's eye, something like the taste of an old and much-loved friend and a newly awakened appetite, could but induce the horse to keep at a suitable distance.

Such was the position when the boys made the acquaintance of the wild horse. Their closer relations began in the neighbourhood of the settlement, where White Bear kept the half-tamed horses he had caught for driving. They ran loose in a big paddock, a sort of island that White Bear had contrived by digging a ditch on the fourth side of a pasture which was naturally surrounded on three sides by water. Here the horses lived just as in a free state, there was open ground and trees where they could roam about or stand in shelter as they pleased. Every time they had to be brought to the settlement to be harnessed it was a case of catching them over again, and as the enclosure was so big this gave rise to many skir-mishes and much strategy on both sides.

It was the boys' task to fetch the horses, and if they could not succeed in any other way in getting near enough to throw the leather noose about their neck, they would entice them with a bunch of tempting grass or a particularly succulent root, or per-haps even a bit of bread Mother had given them for the dear horses, and when they couldn't resist any longer and let the boys come near — then hey! catch hold of his forelock, out with the halter and slip it over his head, and the dainty one was caught.

Now it was no little way from the paddock home to the settle-ment, and the boys, who naturally wanted to get out of the tramp when there were others to do it for them, often coolly tried to jump upon the horses so as to be carried home instead of trudging by their side. This the horses invariably took in very bad part. The halter one could put up with, if there was no way out of it, and a good-natured pat on the muzzle might also pass; nor need one object to sniffling up to one of these humans now and then and tripping a dance round him, for company's sake and three paces off — but to be clawed by the mane and mounted like a tree, to have this biped on one's back! Every time the boys attempted it you could see the offended horse spring straight up into the air with all four feet to send him to the stars, and if he actually kept his seat, then, a vertical rear with the hindquarters and the next instant up with the forelegs the same way, and if this pitching didn't make him seasick, then a wild jump to one side and up with the back in an arch that nobody *could* hang on to; but if he stuck

on all the same, as Wolf did more and more often, why then there
was nothing for it but to fling yourself down like a dog and roll
on the ground, or a heap of stones for choice, with all four legs
in the air, to get rid of the vermin; or it might be necessary to
rush at full gallop for a tree with a low bough that would scrape
him off — in short, it was not to be thought of that the horse would
tolerate a man on his inviolable back. The inherited experience of
generations, the bloody consequences of getting anything on one's
back — the *lynx*, the *wolverine* — made the horse blindly resist
the slightest advances of that kind.

And then, in spite of this, May witnessed one day from the
door of her house a half terrifying, half ridiculous performance in
which Wolf played the chief part, sitting redhaired and glorious
on the back of one of the horses on the way home from the paddock — dreadful boy! The other brothers were decorously leading
theirs by the halter, but Wolf sat astride his horse with his legs
proudly dangling in the air and guided it with a strap on its neck.
And the horse seemed to submit with a good grace, it walked with
its head down, pondering deeply, as though it had an inkling of
the bearing of this first complaisance, but without any attempt at
revolt. Cheers and great reception of the boys! Even White Bear,
who was ardently engaged on his new ship, looked up from his
flint wedge and cast a fatherly eye upon his offspring, shook his
head in thoughtful approval; he knew what might result from
heresies. He himself had made his way by doing the impossible.
The boys might well behave a little differently from just what one
had expected of them.

Wolf had at last achieved it. The stallion he rode had been his
friend from a foal. It was born in captivity and reared in the paddock, looked after and petted by Wolf with all the good things he
could get hold of and spare for it; it knew him from any of the
others and liked being taken round the neck and patted by him,
even after it was grown up. True, its innate shyness lay so deep
in its blood that it was ready to start off all the time as though possessed by a thousand promptings of flight, quivering in every joint
and with wide, fleeting eyes; its ears twitched nervously, lay back
flat while its teeth showed in an ugly grin; its nostrils stretched so
that daylight gleamed through the rosy cartilage between them; it
wanted to be patted and yet did not want it, swung its flank forward and drew back ticklishly, as though it was fire it felt and not

a human hand, its mood shifted like a breeze on the water; only after a long, long time of tireless overtures would it accept the relationship, but really *tame* it never was.

Only Wolf could approach it. He came so calmly, controlling every single step, and put out his hand so cautiously, lest its limbs should be seized with instinctive flight; and when he had once come up to it he took care never to make the slightest unexpected movement or do anything suddenly, which would have sent it off with stones and turf flying from its hoofs. The wild horse itself always stood perfectly still when it was not grazing or actually on the move; when at rest it stood straight up with its head out without moving so much as an ear; even at a short distance it was not easily sighted in the field before it moved; that was its protection against pursuit; moreover it is only ignoble animals that always have to be fidgetting and cannot be restful in themselves when there is no real need for exertion.

When the horse stood like this, probably under a birch if the sun was shining, Wolf would approach it with every sign of profound calm in his gait, and then it stood still and awaited his coming. Wolf might then take it round the neck and stay talking to it a long while, with his hand laid against its fine skin; and the horse did not move a hoof, nor tremble, only now and again it threw up its head as though it didn't want to hear a word more; but it stayed with Wolf, and he patted it here and there, stroked it and made it feel safe all over, until every fibre, every hair of its body, which had been timid at first, was calmed down by gradually being accustomed to the strange touch.

And Wolf was clever. With his experience of the others which had never allowed themselves to be tamed, because he had taken them by surprise, and had only become more unmanageable, he was wary of attempting to jump on the back of his friend; it was not to know *when* he sat there. He began by leaning against the horse's flank and laying an arm across the handsome, faintly striped back, just casually as it were, and yet the first few times the horse received his arm with a tremble. Later, when after long and patient repetition it learned to bear his arm and allowed him to lay his whole weight on it, he proceeded as though in play to hoist a leg now and then on to its side, and he kept on at that until it found nothing odd in his pulling up his body after it little by little and hanging over its back for longer and longer at a time.

Then the day actually arrived when the horse without noticing any difference allowed him to sit right up and stay there; but then it is true he had talked to it as long and as sweetly as the south wind and summer days. But when he *sat* there and the horse still stood quietly under him, Wolf laughed, laughed only too well, his heart leapt in his breast for happiness.

Now the horse was to begin to walk with him, and he had to be very careful not to do anything to scare it. Afterwards, when besides walking it came to trotting and galloping, some of the difficulties were indeed transferred to himself; it was not directly in accordance with human nature to sit a horse in *all* dispensations; it had to be learnt. But as Wolf was very willing, and the horse had no objection, and there was time enough, it came quicker than he knew, and soon his younger brothers, yelling with admiration, could see the pair dashing at full gallop first round the paddock and then out on the steppe.

The first horseman, with a scrap of wolf's skin tied about his middle and his fiery hair flying about his ears, Wolf's red elf-locks that he used to dry his fingers in, always full of last year's burrs and affording shelter to all kinds of crawling things up to the size of a grasshopper; Wolf moulded in one with the wild horse, still half striped like a zebra, its shoulders marked with the lightning, with a dumpy head like a foal all its days, and with the thunder-bolt under each of its heart-shaped hoofs!

When Wolf had won the first victory, his brothers gradually followed his lead; each of them chose a pet among the foals and caressed it and hung upon its neck so long that they became confidential friends and united as one figure in the landscape, to the stupefaction, terror and disturbance of all other creatures. And this somewhat strained but never changing friendship, half based on deceit, half with the character of a providence, has since per-sisted between horse and man.

When once White Bear's boys were mounted it was not always easy to know where to find them, they almost showed a capacity for being in several places at once. White Bear covered the ground pretty well in his jolting two-wheeled car, but as for keeping up with the boys, it was not to be thought of. The daily hunt took on a new, undreamt-of pace: the sons rounded up the game and made dashing inroads where before they had had to get within spear range by a long and troublesome creeping, taking cover and making detours. A new age was latent in what the boys had origi-nally hit upon quite aimlessly.

Meanwhile they were growing up. Wolf had begun to detach himself from his brothers, not that there was any disagreement be-tween them, but because he had changed. His voice was now deep and hoarse; at one time he would be very serious and would then join his father, skilfully chipping and hammering at the ship, at another he would go back to games and larks with his younger brothers and sisters, but he easily got wild so that they could not make him out, and was apt to break off the game by some exu-berant vagary.

It was Wolf and yet it wasn't he. Sometimes he would be subject to fits of laughter, when he would seize an unfortunate calf and roll about with it in his arms till it was scared out of its wits, or he embraced the first inanimate thing he could get hold of, a tree or a rock, howling with laughter; he threw himself on the ground with outstretched arms, trying to embrace the whole country; he jumped into the sea with a big stone clasped affectionately to his heart, took it to the bottom with him and then came up again sorrowing and alone. He had fits of mighty generosity, when he presented his delighted brothers and sisters with all his possessions, still treasures to them, to him wretched toys. At other times he would begin the hunt in high spirits and work himself into brutal cruelty; then he slew without mercy, exposed his life in cold blood; on days like this he went out alone against the wild boar or the great elk armed with nothing but an axe and came back from the fight shaking with a rage which the death of the beast by his hand had not sufficed to quench.

If any one had sought the explanation of Wolf's state of mind in the time of year, he would have found that it was the spring, what-ever that may have had to do with it; but Wolf had of course been through other springs without being half beside himself. Had he been bewitched?

Spring came with some force in Lifeland, it set in with surging wet east winds and warm nights, the steppes threw off their snow and lay bare as far as the eye could reach, with open blue-black pools here and there in the grass. The water sank rapidly as soon as the ground was thawed, and in a few days the new grass made the country green far and wide. Birds of passage filled the night with a vague whistling, and suddenly everything was ready for the great spring festival: trees in leaf with resinous scent, the song of birds and the dreamy music of frogs in the light evenings, the capercailzie's crowing tryst in the birch copse, and the horrid nocturnal miaowing of the predatory beasts of the steppes in distress of love.

And the wild horses were there, the real ones from the steppes. The first herd was sighted one clear day, immensely far off, like a dot on the horizon just under the sunrise; afterwards more came every night, and soon the steppe swarmed with their herds as usual in springtime.

There was unrest in the enclosure among the half-tame horses. The old mares were foaling at this time, and the stallions parted company, each with his own group of young mares, and fought furious battles, in which they reared and bit and scattered foam like a landward gale and their neighing could be heard far off in the magic stillness of the night. The horses felt their confinement and often went up to the edge of the ditch and stood there nodding, reflected in the water, with long looks eastward over the steppe; but there was no help for it, the ditch was their boundary and there they had to stay. When it chanced that a group of the free steppe horses passed near, the captives showed their distress, you could see them leap in the air where they stood and turn about with their necks stretched to the utmost, as if they were trying to fly straight up and away to their wild kin. Alas, there was a ditch between that kept them back. . . .

But not the horses from the steppes! One night several wild stallions leaped the ditch into the enclosure. What had never occurred to the captives the free animals did without a thought, they jumped the ditch. There was a terrific battle that night in the enclosure, the horses roaring and the ground thundering, and next day when the boys came to fetch their horses they found that the wild strangers had driven all the stallions into a corner and had divided the mare's among themselves in friendly fashion. The defeated stood in stooping, broken attitudes, badly bitten, but the victors, who were nevertheless far fewer in numbers, trotted with proud gestures of the neck and great swishes of the tail round their many new obedient mares, now and then glancing with bloodshot eyes at those they had ousted, but otherwise fully taken up with provisionally reviewing one by one the additions to their herd.

Wolf flew into a passion when he saw all this horse presumption;

with a death-defying howl he plunged forward in great leaps and before his brothers grasped his intention they saw him fling himself at one of the wild stallions, dodge it behind a tree, dash for its mane and swing himself on to its back in one great flying leap . . . and instantly the horse bolted with him! Running away was its everyday business, but now that it felt somebody on its back clinging fast with two muscular legs and with heels planted in its stifles, its soul was all thunder and lightning, and with snorts and explosions it made like a streak for the steppe in tearing flight ——

The ditch! The brothers hold their breath in almost unbearable excitement when they see the wild horse dash straight for it in blind career; now — *over* — they see Wolf hang a long moment in the air and dangle with his head in his stomach as the horse lands on the other side, but he sticks on, and now the horse picks itself up and gallops on towards the open country, mad with terror, still with Wolf on its back. Horse and rider were already so far away that the brothers were beginning to feel a grip at the heart on Wolf's account, when they saw him deliberately throw himself on to the steppe and roll over and over in the grass in a fairly breakneck fashion, while the horse continued its senseless flight. The brothers breathed again, they knew how much Wolf could stand in the way of falling off. And presently he came back quite calmly, feigning complete indifference for the benefit of his prostrate brothers; he was bleeding at the nose and blowing like a bellows, as though his ribs were trying to creep out through his skin, but otherwise he was of course the man; and now he knew that even the untamed wild horse could not throw him.

It was clear that Wolf was the one great horsebreaker, and his brothers, who for that matter had become good enough horsemen, never tried to rival him, but regarded his mastership with cheerful disinterestedness; he was the eldest and the first to have the idea, and what a man starts from the beginning ought to be left to him. And in fact the horse was to be Wolf's destiny, and that of the people which sprang from him. The germ of a nation lay in his blood; that was what had made him so restless, full of a tempestuous craving to perish, with or for something, and yet with the feeling that he could not die.

Meanwhile the ice broke up along the coast, and White Bear and all his sons were busy with navigation and new, improved ships. Thus the summer went by in a fever of work and tossing on the sea.

In the autumn Wolf disappeared.

His brothers tried to keep it quiet, but when their father pressed them and insisted on knowing what had happened, they could only explain that Wolf had gone with the wild horses. That was all they knew.

The truth about Wolf was that he had grown melancholy in the autumn, when the steppes withered and all the birds of passage were preparing to leave. Even the sun had no abiding place, it rose farther and farther to the south and crept low in the sky to go early to rest; it was already far away and would seek yet more distant paths. But the days were so clear, the steppe lay in a cool farewell light which made each withered blade of grass rise up in the tranquil air, no longer green but strangely luminous and sorrowful. The buzzing of a single belated bee was heard brokenly from place to place, where it still found a lingering flower. The flocks of birds. darting in and out, up and down, as they practised their flight, could be heard miles away on those still days. High up in the transparent sky gossamer threads sailed giddily and drew off, the wild geese drew off in the moonlight, the summer drew off, *memory* drew off, all things drew and drew away.

But when even the wild horses were gone, when herd after herd broke up and made for the east and the south, until they were only visible as a misty speck, now swelling out and getting bigger, now contracting again, as the horses, indistinguishable singly, joined or left the herd; when at last the speck disappeared immensely far out and finally vanished beyond the edge of the world, then Wolf thought his heart would burst his throat to follow them. He wept over their tracks abandoned in the earth, the last ones; the loss of them, the steppes now so deserted, and the thought of their distant world, over where the sun came from, caught him chokingly in the throat, he could not draw breath for pain. It hurt him so to think that that tiny faint cloud of dust far, far away was the herd, how they were now trotting close to one another, the old leader in front, the mares in foal in the middle and the young stallions outside as a protection. How he knew them. There were always some in the herd who ran in pairs, two friends who once for all had looked each other out and were not happy unless they ran together. Horse friendship! And they had no hands to give each other, only a horny hoof, they could not say anything, but who could tell the deep-felt joy of laying one's head across another's neck; was it not enough to feel the warmth of each other's skin while travelling side by side? Ah, no warmth and no smell is so sweet as the horse's! Wolf did not know what was happening to him. Something must be done; he wanted to dig himself into the earth with his hands, he ran round and round himself, shaking his head violently, for if he stood still in one spot and felt all his longing, he could not live.

In general Wolf hated emotions and being touched, he preferred to give himself vent in some mischievous prank or other, which at any rate made him less ashamed; but now he felt that nothing but a mad act, a leap into the fire, could bring him relief. Then one day chance and impulse came pat. One of the last herds of wild horses had just started on the way to the south-east, trotting in a compact body, and Wolf lay out on the steppe behind a bush, following their movements. The leader, the strongest steed of all, was at their head, and suddenly Wolf saw him make straight for the bush, he would have to pass quite close to him; he turned giddy, and then did what he knew by an inner flash had been in his mind all the time; he gathered all his strength and dexterity as the horse came past, jumped up just as it discovered him and reared to throw itself around; Wolf, without knowing how, got alongside it, felt its mane in his hand and kept up in two or three long leaps, until he stamped on the ground for the last time and swung himself up. And there he sat as he had dreamt!

A couple of his brothers saw him disappear, from another part of the steppe; they saw him settled in his seat as though grown fast to the horse, which was tearing at a mad gallop towards the horizon, with the herd behind it in a cloud of dust. In a few minutes Wolf and the wild horse were away behind the curve of the earth. The brothers knew that Wolf had done what he had to do, even though they did not yet understand him. They did not expect to see him come back on foot.

White Bear had his own ideas and was not alarmed for his first-born. But when some weeks had passed without Wolf returning and May was mourning for him, White Bear made up his mind to drive a couple of days' journey to the south and seek news among the nomadic Badgers who pitched their tents here and there in the interior. Oh yes, they knew all about his son. He was living somewhere a long way off to the eastward with a beautiful girl — the

Badgers had good reason to know it, since she came of their people and Wolf had stolen her in broad daylight; a thing, they respectfully suggested, for which compensation was due, and no doubt the Chief would be ready to settle the matter on his son's behalf. For the rest the two young people were carrying on like simple fools; they had cut themselves off and lived on distant pastures with the wild horses, it was said, and chiefly on mare's milk! Ay, you hear strange things. Nobody could feel safe for him, for he had the crazy habit of getting on to the beasts and tearing about all over the place with them, and if he wanted anything he came flying along on the back of some wild creature and fetched it, no matter *whose* it was. Some people would have it he was a downright supernatural being, made like a horse with four legs below and like a man above, but they'd have to take that story further across the steppes, for here they had seen him get off; and he must have human tastes too, to run off with a woman. *She*, by the way, seemed to be just as cracked as her man, she climbed up on to the dumb beasts and followed him in all his jaunts. But, they added, with eyes aslant, if such a Chief could own to a regrettable offspring, what was to prevent a Badger claiming a mad flighty creature as his bantling? . . .

White Bear thanked them for the information and went home again. Well, well, so Wolf had done the impossible again! Ay, every new generation had its own ways, it must be hoped. In his own mind White Bear did not deny that the boy's exploit displeased him; he regarded the natives with pity rather than with anything like respect and had never dreamt of being mixed up with the riffraff in this way. But what could he say, when the immigrant White Bear family were the only whites in Lifeland and there were thus no other women to be had? There was nothing to be done but to let Wolf act for himself and take the consequences. May was inconsolable; that she herself had once run away with White Bear did not make the misfortune any less. Wolf was lost to the home.

In the course of the winter he came home unexpectedly, in a sledge drawn by two splendid, fiery, well-broken horses. The sledge was laden with frozen reindeer carcasses, which he carried into his mother's store room, just as in the old days when he came home from hunting; but she thanked him as for a present. There was great joy at the meeting, but no one showed any surprise either at Wolf's absence or at his reappearance, and no questions were asked. His brothers found him unaltered, except that he had grown a beard, which unfortunately could not be seen properly because it was so fair, and which Wolf therefore blackened in secret with soot from the fire. His eyes had got hollow and he was pretty gruff but heartily pleased with himself. In spite of his thinness he astonished his brothers with proofs of immense newly acquired strength and accomplishments. Of the rest of his adventures and the mysterious world away in the wilds which he had made his own, not a word was said. He only stayed a couple of days and then went off again to the eastward where he had come from, on the empty sledge behind the two beautiful horses in a stretching gallop.

But at his leave-taking the old man had let fall a remark to the effect that travelling was better fun when you were two and hadn't to feel anxiety about the one you left behind, and Wolf had nodded as one who is his own master but is not above taking advice.

And now it was over a year before they saw any more of him. Then he came on a visit and this time he brought his whole world with him. It proved to consist of an immense herd of horses, Wolf had no idea himself how many, though he knew each one of them. They were not exactly tame, but were kept together and looked after with or without their consent by Wolf always riding round them, giving the herd the direction he wanted and preventing any of them from straying. In this he was helped by his wife, whom his family at last had a sight of.

Her name had a sudden, explosive sound — *Tchu* — and not without reason; she was like the whirlwind over the steppe, swishing along with joyful shout; she was as daring as Wolf in clinging to a horse's back, full of fire and with seven lives in her, lithe and gentle as a kitten. If the White Bear family were blond and fair of skin like rain on the icefield, she was as brown as the sunburnt, cloudless steppe, with the blackest hair in the world. Her eyes, which lay quite flat in her face, were dark as old honey; she was not pretty, but tingling with life, her small limbs agile as a squirrel, but with a strength in her teeth that was marvellous to see; if anything had to be held and her hands were busy, she snapped her mouth on it, and when she had got a firm bite she would hold on with all her weight, even to being dragged after a horse; she was all grip and energy with a careless smile to boot, wiry and full of laughter from top to toe. In a skin bag on her back she carried a baby, which was nicely jolted when she was on horseback for days at a time and which got the galloping rhythm into its blood only too early. May took the bag by its corners and shook the youngster out to have a look at it, and it proved to be doing splendidly and took more after its mother, swarthy and flat in the face; but it had Wolf's blue eyes and his hands. And when it stretched them out to Grandmother, she instantly raised an altar in her heart to the new idol.

The family, however, were only passing by with their herd, with which they were always changing pastures. It was all the property they had, besides a little tent of hides in which they slept at night. As to their food, they kept to mare's milk, for which they had acquired a taste once for all in the first sweet crazy days of their exile. All things that are new and that endure have their origin in love. This is what White Bear guessed, and thus Wolf's curious taste was approved.

They roamed about for a few years with the horses, but when both these and their masters had quieted down through mutual familiarity, Wolf founded a settlement on the coast in the neighbourhood of his father's and continued his horse-breeding there with a fixed establishment.

From Wolf's and Tchu's progeny are descended the restless horsemen of Asia with an equal share of North and South in their veins; the kumiss-drinking tent-dwellers, all the free nomads of the steppes, who go galloping through the centuries.

But from the wild horse, which followed White Bear back to Upland and afterwards made the circuit of Europe in his son's ships, came the warhorse, which made its owner, the knight, the cavalier, master of the world. From it came also the peasant's faithful draft-horse, drawing the plough for the corn, that itself and many more might live.

In memory of the nettlesome steed that bore Wolf and Tchu to lawless wastes where they learned to dwell in each other's vital warmth, like two horses that will always go in a pair flank to flank, in its undying memory there shines a constellation in the sky.

The soul of the wild horse lives in the legend of Pegasus. Eternal youth, fore-time and all-time, is in the rush of his wings; but it is not he that has borne me; I have my myth from home, from the *Hell Horse*.

Yes, from the Hell Horse, the old Danes' friend in war and peace and favourite food; the sacrificial victim before all others, which they dedicated to their ancestors and ate with faces devoutly smeared with its blood. Later, when our fathers were persuaded to honour another origin than their own and were prescribed the lamb as the only sacrificial food with power to save, the horse was forbidden as unclean — the horse! — and buried alive under the threshold of the new house of God. Here it arose as the spectral Hell Horse, oh, ho, ho, and they say that whoso looks upon its ghost must die. Can it be so dangerous as that?

From a ride on the Hell Horse, a glorious devilish gallop in company with the dead through the Lost Country — from that I have my myth.

XIX

THE LARK

SWAIN was a seafaring man, he came in his ship to a land which almost made one with the sea and consisted of many low islands with fjords and sounds between. In one of these fjords he lost his way and ran on for so long among headlands, broads and islands that he came to like the country.

It rose gently above the sea with miles of low, fleeting slopes, strewed with gravel and boulders, new-born with a fresh scent of rain as though just left bare by the ice. Swain went ashore and found the beach friendly, covered with the finest sand and edged at the break of the waves with a mass of round pebbles of every hue, which rattled cheerfully against each other; the grass came right down to the blue sea. Inland were rich meadows and marshes, bright young woods and wide heaths between. Splendid game moved everywhere and the fjord, fed by streams which flowed between flowery banks with dimples in their sluggish course, was flashing with fish. The sky stood mightily above this land which scarcely showed in the sea, with swelling worlds of cloud and shafts of light slanting down from the hidden sun.

Swain sailed to other parts, but he did not forget this low-lying country and he came back. Then it was early spring with chilly winds. The showers came and went with a homely industry all their own; there was nobody to keep them up to it, but they got it done just the same.

Away in the grey fields stood horsetails that had shot up beside the molehills like thin skeleton fingers. In the mould, which sucked and oozed beneath the sun, lay little stones like wet eyes, and in the pale grass were yellow flowers with musty stalks. The southern slopes were green with new growth, where rare and fragile pansies peeped up like tiny faces blue with cold.

Shadows of the clouds travelled and travelled over the moist meadows, now it darkened about one, and now the sun broke through imperiously, wooing the earth, expanded like a wheel, shed fire over the world and was gone again. The shadows breathed over the land like the ghost of a wandering sea, they ran up over the hills, pursuing one another, chased by the wet wind that smelt so pregnantly of earth.

But up in the restless sky, where the clouds cast gloom and the sunshine sported, warm to the eyelids, the lark hovered, singing.

Slowly, drunkenly, it went up, now in light and now in shadow, singing unceasingly, be, be — bebebe — be, be, until, caught up in the rapture that was simply its own heart swelling with the air it drank in, it rose so high, straight up, that light and clouds swallowed it, and it was as though the moist air itself sang over the fields, where springs gushed clear and bubbling from the naked mould.

And the nights grew warm. The toads sat to their necks in water and croaked like little trolls in the rushes, where the afterglow lay in the still barren water. Down at the bottom the black, twisted roots of the sweet flag shot out their green claws; the willows clothed their buds with white fur against any whim of the weather. Birds of passage were on the way, everywhere was growth.

But Swain had hearkened to the lark and determined to stay. Here was the place to rear his children, that they might one day possess the land. It was afterwards called Denmark. Swain settled at the inmost end of a sheltered fjord by the outlet of a river. Up through the valley lay bogs and woods, and above it on the long hills began the heath.

As soon as Swain's children could crawl they lay out in the heather with their fair mops of hair and made themselves acquainted with the things of this world. They crept up to the big grey stones that lay scattered singly, each with its own particular look, or in sociable crowds about the heath, and would post themselves in front of some silent mightiness and wait for further signs of life, themselves quite reticent the while. They put out the end of a very little finger to the juniper bush, which stood domed and bellied but headless among the heather, and when they found that it pricked they did not come there any more.

But with other things they soon made friends; with the heather itself that stood like a tree of iron with scaly roses at every branch; with the evergreen leaves of the whortleberry, shaped like little boats, and the bog myrtle that bore whole flocks and herds of fine and wild-smelling cones. The broom blossomed like fire and then put out black pods that looked like swords which had been scorched and might just as well have been a yard long and hung from the top of a big tree. The mottled orchis stood apart in the heather with its plantain stem, the lycopodium crept in the rough carpet of lichen under the heather and sent up long shoots here and there to keep a look out, the most childish of trees, pale green all over.

The children had never been told that all these weather-beaten plants had once been tropical trees in a forest that formerly stood in the same spot, but they knew it quite well in their hearts. By the taste of a sprig of heather they knew that it came of a great family and from a warm place, it left a balmy and bitter taste in the mouth. They could tell that the juniper bush had seen better days. And they loved to pretend that the sedge reached up to the sky like a palm with smooth, ribbed fruit as big as loaves.

On warm summer days, when the grasshopper's pse, pse was heard everywhere and nowhere in the heather like a gasping breath, an airy mirage of groves and lakes would rise over the heath; the children could plainly distinguish giant trees up there and found a great forest in the air perfectly natural.

In the light nights they would wake and fall to thinking of their round pebbles which lay in their pens like cattle up on the heath and must be feeling lonely. They would raise their heads and look out into the light night, and the second sight of the half-waking child's mind would see a vision, a glimpse of a wonder of the past, when the tropical forest of the North once spread beneath light nights. Childhood, that is the Lost Country.

Here ends the myth of Carl.

The Cimbrians

BOOK ONE: NORNA GEST

I

GEST COMES INTO THE WORLD

E was born in Sealand. The first thing he remembered was a rowan tree covered with berries, which waved above his head, a lovely red revelation, and carried his eye up into a world of leaves and airy tree-tops, right into the blue sky, where great white things passed in a blissful depth; this was the first time his eyes saw the day.

Somewhere up in the blue there was something that shone and gave warmth; he turned his face that way and met a mighty white fire which glowed like a molten ring; dazzled, he closed his eyes, and then the darkness under the lids was full of strange living colours. When he opened his eyes again there were livid spots, ghosts of the sun, on trees and sky and wherever he looked.

His mother had laid him on his back under a tree at the edge of the wood, and she could see that the little one was beginning to take notice, he was so full of thought; wonder was depicted in his tiny features. He drew in his arms and legs and gave a frightened glance when a bird broke out of a bush and stayed for an instant fluttering in the air before darting in again; and no less fascinated was he with a little green worm that lowered itself by an invisible thread and curled in the breeze above his head. His mother laughed over him from joy and sadness, in the way mothers laugh — the little stranger couldn't make out at all where he had come to!

That was how he got his name. For he had arrived as a little helpless, dumb, strange person, on a journey from one unknown world into another. His mother had been in a swoon when he came into the world, and the women who were with her were afraid she would never come to herself again; but when in her torpor she heard the little stranger cry, she opened her eyes and saw what a tiny creature he was; then she signed to them to give her the child and they placed it on her breast. It was as though the mother had been absent and would fain have stayed away, for when she woke she had not the look of a living creature; but when the new-born babe fastened itself upon her, the desire of life returned. Thus each of them came from an unknown world and they met in life. The little stranger had come on a long visit; Gest should be his name, and a welcome guest he was.

When once he had come he behaved in every way like a proper child. It was not long before he began to use his hands and thrust them out after anything that his eyes coveted; often he made a bad shot, but if he got hold of the thing, whatever it was, it always went the same way in a stiff curve right into his lips, and many a time his mother had to force open the little mouth and clean it out with her finger, until he had learnt to distinguish between what was eatable and what was earth.

Otherwise he spent most of his time sleeping securely in the bag on his mother's back, and he was well shaken up and ducked now and then, when she stooped down on the beach to gather mussels; this gave a savour to his dreams without disturbing his sleep.

He had scarcely learnt to walk before he tottered away from his mother's knee, one day after a thundershower, to grab the rainbow, which stood with one foot in the grass apparently close by; but the rainbow moved as he approached it, and when he had come right down to the beach it was hovering with both ends over the water; without hesitation he lifted his little leather apron and started to walk out into the sea; his mother had to hurry down and carry him ashore, shaking her head and full of laughter at the little man-child's precocity. It was evident that he had great aims. And in fact while still a boy he left his tribe of his own accord.

Gest's mother was a Stone Age woman, by name Gro. She was the mother of the whole tribe. The settlement swarmed with children, Gro herself had a number, but she didn't distinguish particularly between her own and the others', all of them were in her care. Wherever Gro saw a child with its little arms outstretched, she took it up and gave it a drink and then a sleep at her breast. She was the first up in the morning at the settlement and the last to go to rest; no one had ever chanced to see her asleep. The tribe held together of itself without coercion, thanks to her; among the men it was undecided who was at the head of affairs, and if a dispute arose it was seldom long before Gro was consulted. She was loved by all men.

Under Mother Gro's protection Gest spent his childhood, on a sunny strip of sand between forest and shore.

II

THE SETTLEMENT

EST's birthplace in Sealand lay well concealed, not on the coast itself but a little way inland, in a sheltered fjord on the Great Belt side.

Looking at this coast from the sea no one would have thought it inhabited; it had the appearance of a long, compact forest floating on the waves, so low did the land lie. Behind it, where the coast came to an end, another wooded headland thrust itself out into the sea, which might be a fold of the same island or another of the low Danish isles which floated between the Baltic and the Cattegat.

The sky above was in a movement of great clouds, like islands slowly wandering; isles in the sea and isles in the sky; the sea roared, the day showed white and blue with a primeval stillness, only gulls and seabirds wrapped the shores in a light sea-music; silently the seal came up with his wet eyes and looked towards land; a column of smoke rose above the forest, and the seal caught a smell he did not like, pinched up his nose and dived head first among the big weed-covered rocks at the bottom.

But inland where the column of smoke rose above the forest dwelt men. A shingly beach and a narrow belt of sandhills separated the forest from the sea. The outer edge of the forest was made up of low, tangled bushes and dwarf trees, which lay pressed close to the ground, held down by the wind, and were more impenetrable than a brier thicket; only little by little did the trees grow higher, as the outer ones screened the next; from the sea side the forest looked like an even, sloping roof rising landward from the shore, apparently less impassable along the top than among the trees. It was as though the land had turned its back on the sea.

But in one place by a headland a gap ran up into the land, not very noticeable if one did not know it; inside it widened out into a fjord, and here the forest opened up.

It was more sunny and still inside the fjord than on the wind-swept outer coast; the sun was on it most of the day, and in a bay the water lay quite shallow and smooth, bright from the sandy bottom shining through and dazzling with the reflection of the midday sun. This sandy bottom was one great oyster-bed.

The bay was enclosed by a beach of shingle and seaweed, above which were low bluffs with bare gravel and big fallen boulders. Above that was forest. But unlike the forest on the sea side, which stooped and made itself thorny and impenetrable, the forest here rose into an airy, open vault with lofty trunks that stood like gates towards the bay. The great full tree-tops formed domes in calm sunshine; here the day was always calm.

Here were great crowds of gulls, the banks were white with them, where the tepid water was only a few inches deep; they screamed and quarrelled noisily all day long, flapping their wings and always on the move; they sat on the big rocks out in the bay and poured out their eloquence to each other till it roused echoes from the shallow water and from the forest and even from the other side of the fjord, where again there was a bluff crowned with domed and sunny woods. Above it all lay the blue summer sky with domed white clouds, which were mirrored in the bay and mingled their whiteness with the gulls'.

The still air held a thick warm vapour of fermenting seaweed, of salt water with the sun on it, of gaping mussels left by the tide and beginning to smell, of the gulls' white dung, and blended with it all was the green spicy smell of the woods, breaths of raspberry perfume and the scent of honey from the sunny glades within the forest, where wild flowers and grasses rose in a confusion of long stalks.

At evening the slightest sound could be heard. The seal came cautiously in from the sea and slid up on to a big rock out in the bay, flung itself on its side for a doze — and then it might be that one or more low trunk-like objects, each with something queerly alive about it, would creep out through the dusk. These were the hunters of the bay, who had caught sight of the merman and were trying to surround him. From their point of view the merman was favourite game, giving no little food, and the skin of him was specially coveted; it was worth trying to outwit him and get a harpoon in him before it grew quite dark. But if he smelt danger too soon and made for the sea, they stole back as quietly as they had come and drew their dugouts ashore. The women, who in joyful expectation had already made up the fire, were given to understand that it could scarcely have been a proper merman, but more likely a supernatural creature, since it had proved so entirely superior human cunning.

A little way above the beach and up towards the bluff lay the settlement. There was not much to be seen; the dozen or so of dug-out canoes that were hauled up on the beach might at a distance just as well be fallen trees, of which a good many lay over the bluff, and the huts up on the edge of the forest could not be dis-tinguished from it at all; they were lined holes in the ground roofed with turf and made one with the greensward. In summer most men preferred to sleep outside, by the fire, with a skin over them, spread on a couple of sticks; only the women and the younger children lived underground the whole year.

The days were spent on the beach itself, where the fire was always burning, when the men were not in the forest or out on the banks fishing. Here they went about their work and here they ate, seated on the remains of what they had eaten in years gone by; on the long and comfortable heap of empty oyster-shells and other refuse they were filled with the memory of their meals; here they were at home.

A penetrating, pungent and raw smell hung in the still warmth of the sun under the woods and the bluff, where there was almost always shelter, a greasy mixed smell of ancient fish and the fer-menting remains of dead molluscs and seaweed, and of washed-down lime and soured seawater, together with the smoke of the fire, the spicy juices of fresh wood, the hot exhalations of the em-bers and the stink of wet ashes, not forgetting the dogs or the human smell from bodies clammy with salt water and unkempt heads. You could not come near this settlement without a sneeze refreshing the heart; a good place this, here you felt at home.

The dish of food was the seat, close by was the open beach, which was a huge larder, the walls of the room were the mild summer breezes, nothing less, and the roof the great open sky.

It lay so calmly above the shallow tepid shore, where the domes and abysses of the clouds were repeated in the water; the tern dived silently in the noonday heat into its own reflection, sea and sky reposed in each other like twin worlds.

Far away below the horizon came a sound of thunder, short subterranean shocks like something moving in the earth's interior. It was as though there had never been anything else but midday and midsummer.

III

THE MEN OF THE STONE AGE

WHO were they? Were they the first men who set foot in the Danish isles?

In the myth of the Ice it has been told how the Ice Folk originated, the descendants of Carl; the first of them were mammoth-hunters, afterwards their lives were bound up with the wild horse and the reindeer, and at the time the latter was on its passage through Denmark it may well be that here and there a family of the primitive folk came into the country with their reindeer herds, but then they must have followed them out again and lost themselves to the north and east in the tracts which the reindeer still inhabits. In the age of the steppes Denmark was continuous with Asia; afterwards the sounds formed again around the islands.

The men of the Stone Age were seafarers. They came to the islands from the south, from the shores of the Baltic, where the Ice Folk had settled and become mixed with the natives, descendants of the Forest Folk; the oldest Danes originated from two sources.

If they themselves had been asked, the answer would not have been very satisfactory. Few gave a thought to the past or formed any conception of where they came from or how long ago it was, least of all the youger ones who had been brought up in the settlement and who only knew it and the immediately surrounding country as their world.

Some of the elders had legends, transmitted by their fathers and grandfathers, of which they sometimes talked among themselves, of a past when men dwelt in a land far away, a voyage longer than from new moon to new moon in dug-out canoes. through many sounds and along the coast of one island after another; in that country the winters were said to be very mild, there were years when no snow fell at all. The people lived on the banks of great rivers and could always get fish. It was supposed to be one particular man who had first found the islands in the sea and settled in them; afterwards many followed him and brought their families. In the beginning they used only to travel out to the islands in summer and stay there hunting and fishing as long as the weather was fine; it was mostly young men who had pluck enough for the voyage and knew the way; but when the nights grew cold they rowed all the way back and wintered on the mainland.

In time they learned to get through the winters on the islands too, either by choice or from having waited too long and been cut off by the autumn storms; they found that it could be done, and many families stayed in the islands all the year round and never saw their old country again.

The islands were uninhabited when the first of them arrived, the game was untouched and in abundance, perfectly tame; you could catch the birds in your hand and the deer came of their own accord and sniffed at the ax; the hunters had not the trouble of going half a day's journey from the camp to look for them, they lay down by the fire, and when the deer came out of curiosity on a brotherly visit they slaughtered them without going two steps. But soon the animals knew better. By and by as the hunting became more difficult there were fewer immigrants to the islands, nor did they all have such a kind reception from the first settlers who had taken land; occasionally whole boats' crews disappeared without leaving a trace. Finally the way thither was forgotten, and there was no longer any one in the islands who knew the way back; those who had sailed it and knew the sea-marks were dead long ago. But nobody wanted to go back either, they were perfectly contented where they were, so long as they were left in peace.

The families became small tribes, scattered far from each other over different islands and with long intervals of coast between them, with no mutual acquaintance nor any particular desire for it; each tribe was sufficient to itself and not disinclined to regard itself as the only human community in a true sense, in contradistinction to all other quasi-human, totally inferior foreigners.

A position of this kind as the centre of creation was assumed, then, in their own comfortable conviction, by the inhabitants of the little hunting and fishing station within the bay where Gest was born.

They were not so numerous but that each knew all the rest individually, though they never attempted to find out how many they were. If a stag was brought down and each had his share of it, with as much shellfish added, the tribe might be fairly supplied, so that it was not such a very small family either, and the daily provisioning gave them all enough to think about.

The tribe's world was not a wide one. There was the bay and the stretch of fjord nearest it, and then the forest inland which was known in its smallest details, but no farther afield but that a man could range through it in a day and be back by evening. What lay beyond was pretty well unknown and for the present did not tempt further exploration. What they especially avoided was penetrating into the forest beyond the known tract; there was no knowing what might be in the interior of the country. It happened not unfrequently that a man came back to the settlement almost broken-winded with running and so terrified that his friends had to sit on him a long while to keep him down and bring him to his senses; this meant that he had taken liberties with the forest and had been scared by it.

The outer coast was seldom visited. Here the sea beat upon the shore and was rough, and this was the way up or down the coast to other settlements, whose inhabitants they did not care to meet. With the nearest of these, who were not so far off but that the smoke of their fire could be seen from the entrance of the fjord, there was some intercourse, though of a reserved nature. Curiosity with regard to the foreigners was soon curbed; even distant tribes did not look or behave differently from what one was accustomed to in one's own settlement, apart from certain absurdities which were to be expected of people who had learnt no better. Within the forest the different hunting-grounds met, with tacitly accepted boundaries; if foreign hunters were encountered here both parties preferred to retire, with a very formal stiffness of demeanour, whereas of course the dogs on both sides instantly flew at each other's throats. Often on their return home the hunters from the bay had stories to tell of these strangers who had behaved arrogantly, though without making any impression, while the narrator was convinced of having conducted himself with tact and of having inspired respect.

If then the ancient territory of the tribe was the boundary of the forest side, the known world ended at the sea on the coast. It was not open sea; on clear days from the top of a tree a coast-line could very clearly be seen on the other side, a long, low country like that they themselves dwelt in; but they believed it certain that that was not the old home of their ancestors, no reasonable man would go so far to sea in a canoe; more likely they had come up along the coast from smaller islands lying to the south of the one they lived on. For that it was a big island they inhabited was maintained as probable by the elders, though they had not themselves made the voyage round it.

When the hunters sat around the fire entertaining themselves with questions like this which lay outside everyday experience, they might notice one of Gro's boys standing near, leaning forward and straining his ears, listening with nose and mouth into the bargain; then perhaps they condescended to throw a brand at him in fun, or he might be allowed to stay, as the insignificant quantity he was. This was Gest drinking in knowledge with every hole in his head and hoarding up every legend he heard as a precious treasure.

Here he heard the first mention of a wonderful country from which all men had come in the beginning; not the land of the great rivers, which lay comparatively near, but a land so far away that no mortal man could reach it, even if he travelled all his life; it was so long since men had left it that the tale had passed from generation to generation more times than any could count, and most of it had been forgotten in this immense course of time; only an obscure memory of the legend itself and a few surviving features of it had been handed down. In that country, it was said — but few could believe in the likelihood of its still existing, or ever having existed — there was never any cold at all, clothes were not needed, the trees had breasts which you sucked, and you slept in their arms at night! Of course everyone knew that the trees, even now, were sacred and protecting beings, but the rest sounded incredible, albeit no one had ever been able to forget the story. The first men had been cut off from this country by a vast Flood, wherein all of them had perished, with the exception of a few who had canoes and could sail; from these the Stone Age men were descended, and their canoes were a sufficient visible proof of the truth of that part of the story!

Gest listened, and what he heard sank into his soul.

He would have liked to ask questions and get to know more, if only the direction in which the country was supposed to lie; but nobody would answer a boy, and no more information came of its own accord. Then Gest gave a quiet sigh and buried the fragments of his precious knowledge in his heart. Everything he knew he had to pick up by snatches.

IV

THE WORK OF GEST'S HANDS

A SWARM of children infested the settlement, where the men chased them from one end of it to the other like the troublesome breed they were. The mothers on the other hand spoiled them and took their part, made great to-do with beating stocks and stones when the little ones fell down and hurt themselves, and found a scapegoat for their troubles by pretending to take big handfuls from the place that hurt and throw them into the forest; from that quarter they could always count upon sympathy. The third Great Power in the settlement was the dogs; relations with them were apt to be fickle, sometimes they fought over a bone or a piece of gut, dog at one end and youngster at the other; at other times they played together in sweet concord and slept in one another's arms at night; the smallest, who had scarcely begun to walk, tottered about with puppies in his arms; a large share of the children's time was spent in playing with the dogs. Otherwise they splashed about all day long in the shallow water of the beach, where they could come to no harm, or were busy digging in the sand and making all sorts of small scale copies of what the men did. The forest was forbidden, there the wolves might take them, and the men would not have them out hunting until they were big enough to be taken into their company; but then that meant the end of their childhood's world.

Gest was early to feel the narrowness of this world, but without exactly longing to be adopted by the grown-ups either; his relations with them were strained. Gradually, then, the plan matured in him of taking part in the men's life without asking their permission or becoming dependent on them, and in this he found an ally at critical moments in his mother Gro.

From the time he was quite small he busied himself with making all kinds of things himself, first toys, but afterwards regular implements such as the grown-ups used; he had his own little workshop beside a stone he had chosen just outside the settlement.

Here he sat through the long summer days making his first ax. He felt the want of an ax in everything he tried his hand at, and as nobody would give or lend him one he had to get one for himself. Everything in the settlement belonged to somebody or other and was not to be touched, and if it was not the property of one of the grown-ups then it belonged to the forest, or to the sea, or to the spirits; you could not get anything without giving something in return, and if you had nothing, why then you were thrown back on what you could make yourself. That was Gest's early experience.

Now a shed stag's antler had come into his possession; he had found it himself on one of his surreptitious rambles in the forest and picked it up, in the conviction that it had been placed in his path expressly that he might have it. He gave the stag a grateful thought and interpreted the fact that he had come upon it in the forest as a sign that the silvan Powers were also favourable.

Gest hummed to himself as he studied the antler and considered what the ax was to be like. His would-be playmates found his back turned, and one of the dogs who came fawning up to him was rudely pushed away by his elbow without so much as a look. The antler was long and slender, with not many tines, and when these were removed the whole antler could be used as a haft, with the handle at the thin upper end; the other, heavy end had a thick branch, which would have to be cut off at a suitable distance from the stem and hollowed out to receive the flint blade — altogether a complicated and difficult piece of work, but the day was long and Gest began to sing louder as soon as he saw clearly what he had to do.

As he sat singing at his work he heard with half an ear that somebody else was singing near him; it was a little girl called Dart, who had been Gest's playmate since they were quite small. Her mother lived next door to Gest's mother, so they had always been together. She had been given the name because she was so straight and slender, just like a dart, and when she was born she was covered all over with white down like the buds of a willow. She had bright, smooth hair like sunshine and was always smiling; she was the gentlest of girls. Like Gest she was fond of playing alone, but was always to be found with her little lonesome games somewhere in his neighbourhood.

He saw that she was busy picking bast fibre from the fallen branch of a lime-tree, just sufficiently decayed for the bark to come off easily without the bast being spoilt; she was separating the long pieces of bast into fine strips and laying them side by side on the ground, in silent rapture at the way the pattern was already coming out; she sang in her thoughts like a summer breeze, it was evident that she had some plaiting or weaving on hand.

Gest set to work at once, and it occupied him so deeply that for hour after hour he had no sense of anything else. First he hammered off the superfluous tines between two stones, as near to the stem as he could without spoiling it, the stumps were to be removed afterwards and the whole thing scraped smooth; then he began to hack off the thick branch in which the eye for the blade was to be set. This took time, he had to strike off one flint flake after another, and that too took time; Gest might well smash away at the blocks in the way he had seen the grown-ups do and as it ought to be done, but it was not every time that he got a useful flake, generally he had to put up with a fair splinter, more or less oblong; and then he cut and hacked round the hard horn and filed until the flake was so worn and blunt that it could do no more, and yet he could hardly see that the groove was any deeper. It was hard having to wait till it was worked through and Gest's blood reached boiling-point; no more song came from his lips, they were tightly compressed as he exerted all his strength, quarrelling with the antler for being so stupidly hard, and with his flint tool, which always broke if it was sharp and of course would not bite if it held. He worked madly at the groove till his arms ached and the palms of his hands were cut by the sharp blades; they would have to be hafted and he could scarcely spare the time for that; he borrowed some bast from Dart, who made friendly remonstrances. Gest seized half her work, wrapped up his flakes, and sawed and cut and hacked for half a day, until at last the groove was so deep that the branch could be knocked off.

Passionately he examined the broken surface, where he now had to make a hole in the horn. Luckily the tissue was softer in the middle, not so difficult to penetrate, but he had to make special flakes for the purpose, and Gest hammered and banged at the flint and a lot of it went into splinters. The noise he made was enough to show he was a busy and a wrathful man; and then he bored again, blew into the hole and bored, with burning cheeks, his hands trembling with impatience, but without giving up, for the ax was already so far advanced that it spoke to him, it was going to be a good one, it said, and he wanted to have it finished instantly.

Shouts of triumph sounded from his workship among the boulders when the hole was done. The day was far gone, Gro called to her youngsters from the fire, there was a dainty meal of baked oysters, fresh from the ashes, steaming in their own salt water; Gest flung his food down, with eyes on the unfinished haft in his hand, he ran to the brook and drank, ran back and threw himself upon his work.

The most difficult and most critical part of it was still to come: how to shape a flint wedge that was sufficiently sharp at one end and of such a form at the other that it would fit into the hole and sit perfectly tight. But the flint did not split off at all as he wanted it, the blade would be irregular, even if the edge proved serviceable; he made one attempt after another, smashed up whole heaps of flint, but if it was as it should be at one end, it did not fit at the other, wobbled in the hole, was too large or too small. He was in despair at his failures and wept a little in his pain, with a burning oppression on his brows that tortured him; he smashed the unsuccessful wedge into little bits, ground them into the finest powder, it was to be destroyed utterly. He could not see for tears and anger, the hairs on his body bristled with defiance, and he began again, blew his nose and began all over again, more thoroughly this time, haste did not pay; he fought his way with deliberate force against the abominably refractory, the perfectly idiotic material; this miserable stone which laughed when it went to pieces was unnaturally stupid; but now he changed his tactics, made the hole a good deal deeper, since however he contrived it the flint would always wobble, and set to work to strike off correspondingly long and narrow blades. Of course the first one broke right across when it was nearly finished, that was what it would do! A roar escaped him, he dealt a furious blow at the fragments, hit one of his fingers and crushed it nearly flat; it turned first white and then blue, he quaked but then became viciously quiet, pretending it was not his finger at all, though it hurt atrociously. Quiet! he whispered, foaming at the mouth; over again, you wretched boy! And with a terrible calm, deeply hurt, he took a fresh block of flint and started again, with nine fingers and the tenth useless, swollen and numbed — and he got what he wanted, at last, just what he wanted!

Partly by design, partly by luck he succeeded in getting a wedge of the right length and symmetry, so that with a little careful trimming of the edges and a corresponding adaptation of the hole it would fit in and hold fast. The ax-edge at the outer end was broad and substantial, suitable for every kind of work, but it would also be a powerful weapon if need were. Gest fitted the ax-edge at right angles to the haft; it was to be an adze, which would be better suited to the work he had in mind.

Now it was a question of the lashing, and this gave him trouble, he began to fear that the ax would not be finished that day, since for a really durable lashing you want fresh sinew or gut. He roamed all over the settlement, crept down into his mother's hut, but could not find what he wanted anywhere; no animal happened to have been slaughtered lately and there was nothing lying about that he could use, though there was plenty of carrion which the dogs were licking and tearing. Gest was disheartened; gloomy and sorrowful he wandered about, and went over to see how Dart was getting on.

She had laid aside her bast work and allowed some girl friends to tempt her to play with clay. They were up under the bluff where a trickle of water oozed out, ochre-laden, and stained the gravel red; here the women often came to decorate themselves and make their bodies attractive; Dart and the other girls also put on some colour, laying it on thickly wherever they could reach; the only undyed spot was between their shoulderblades. Then they dug clay from the moist bluff, fine clay which was to be found hereabouts, brought great lumps of it down to the beach, sat down on flat stones to knead it, flinging the hair from their eyes, and began to make pots. Water for shaping them they fetched from the beach in big blue mussel-shells. First they rolled out long strips of clay, which they laid one above the other in a ring; when they had reached the proper height they kneaded them together and smoothed them with a flat stone, until the pot was finished and could be put in the sun to dry. Unlike the impatient Gest the girls took plenty of time, lingering over their clay while they chatted together and letting it grow beneath their hands as they themselves grew.

With many a sigh Gest hung about, watching the girls' pastime. But suddenly he went back to his own place with long strides — eel-skin!

Eel-skin, of course, if sinew or gut was not to be had! Eel-skin was the toughest in the world — if he could just take one of the canoes and pole out with it and get what he wanted! But that was just what he could not do, and that was what lay at the root of all Gest's plans, the want of a boat. The canoes belonged to the grown-ups, and if you touched their things you got beaten like a dog; Gest would not ask for the loan and be denied like the other boys, he preferred to do things for himself, and he put to sea astride of an old tree-trunk which he had dragged down and which would just bear him. The pole he used, a long hazel shoot, he had ingeniously provided with a slit at the upper end, and if he saw anything at the bottom of the shallow water, he turned the pole round and used it as a clutch. There were eels enough and to spare in the tangled mass of weed and more than once Gest got one in his cleft stick, but they regularly got away again. Of course, the fork spread out on the sandy bottom, and the more he pressed, the more room there was for the fish to escape. The men's fishing-spears stood leaning against the trees at the edge of the forest, but it meant a thrashing that would make your head ring for a long while after if you just happened to upset them, to say nothing of using them. They had several prongs with barbs of bone or stag's horn, lashed in a bunch to the end of a pole in such a way that the barbs were turned towards each other; splendid, but not to be borrowed or

imitated on the spot. Gest went ashore and improved his cleft
stick by giving it a lashing, so that the slit could not open any
more, and in the middle between the two prongs he inserted a big,
sharp fish-bone. Then he poled out again; and this time the eel did
not escape when once he had got one on his pole, it was caught
between the prongs and held fast by the point. It was a big, long
eel and he had a severe tussle with it, even after its head was off.
The trunk went round with him and he got a ducking out of his
depth, swallowed a lot of salt water and was sick as soon as he had
scrambled up again, but he never let go of the eel and he brought
it ashore.

The skin he flayed off with the best of tools, his teeth, but then
it had to be divided into several narrow strips, a difficult and tire-
some work as long as it was wet. He went at it as hard as he could,
but still had not finished when it was growing dark and all the
children had gone in, leaving a whole assemblage of the girls' little
jars drying on the beach. Not until it was quite dark had Gest
finished his strips and put on the lashing, with one end in his teeth
and his mouth full of eels' slime; when once the binding was dry
it would be immovably fast. He woke in the night and got up,
half-asleep, to feel whether the lashing would soon be dry.

Next day he was up early to test the ax; the blade was fixed so
firmly that no human strength could move it, and to split the handle was impossible with that binding. He went into the forest and
tried it; it lopped off hazel shoots as thick as his wrist quicker than
you could say it. It almost went to his head; although he himself
had made the ax he was not far from attributing supernatural
properties to it. It was not for nothing that a stag had a share in
it; that gave it swiftness and the power of fury; it was destined to
be dangerous in the chase. And that a fish had contributed something to it would certainly make it powerful and lucky on the
water.

But what it could do in the work Gest had in mind, felling heavy
timber and boatbuilding, was soon to be seen. A little way from
the settlement, at the edge of the wood overlooking the bay, an
oak stood quite near the beach, a tall, straight tree with a perfectly faultless stem which one could see was just made for a boat.
Years ago Gest had picked out this tree and had lost himself
deeper and deeper in dreams of what a splendid canoe it would
make. The trunk was about double the thickness of a man and

longer than was needed; the canoe would not have much beam, on the other hand he could make it unusually long; it would be a fine and a quick sailer and would easily carry two people. The tree stood on the extreme edge of the forest just by the sea, as though it had come as far as it could of its own accord and was only longing to come farther. When his ax was finished Gest wanted to set about felling the tree, so that at last he might have a proper big dug-out like the grown-up men.

Almost since he had been able to stand upright it had been his ambition to sail; he used to wade about all day long in the warm shallow water, making sticks float from one island to another, for he pretended that the big rocks off the beach were islands; afterwards he hollowed out his sticks in imitation of real boats and undertook long voyages to distant shores, rocks far out in the bay, where the water came up to the armpits of the skipper wading alongside. In these games he always had the help of Dart, and they were so absorbed in them that they might really just as well have been transported to strange worlds; they forgot everything around them and had neither eyes nor ears when they were on a voyage. But now their play was to become earnest.

Gest had thoughts of emigrating. This was not quite clear to him, but all that he had picked up in childhood and all that he had lately turned his hand to led him in the same direction, like a fate.

It was no mean undertaking for a boy entirely singlehanded to try to fell the big oak and set about shaping it, but not even this was the greatest of his difficulties; other and weightier obstacles stood in his way. In the first place of course he had no right to cut down the tree; it was taking a liberty with the forest which could not be allowed unless great services were rendered in return. In the second place it was altogether forbidden to take fire from the settlement, the fires belonged to the grown-ups; they were sacred and he might not touch them. But without fire of course the work was hopeless.

The same morning Gest finished his ax and tested it he took a brand from his mother's and began to build up a fire close to the tree; as soon as the smoke was noticed he had one of the men down on him, who took him seriously to task and stamped out the fire, in doing which the clumsy lout fortunately got his toes burnt. As soon as his back was turned Gest nursed up the fire again from a brand still smoking among the ashes and started afresh; this time there was a regular commotion in the settlement, several angry men came up, and Gest was dragged home ungently by the ears. Gro appeared at the entrance of her house, the men made their accusation with many words and gestures, the dogs chimed in as usual when there was a quarrel, barked and went for each other with bristling hair — general excitement on the kitchen midden!

But the men soon let go of Gest, in consequence of something or other in the expression of Gro's face. The abuse went on without anything further happening, and Gest callously went back to his fire and got it to burn up for the third time. And this time he was left undisturbed, though he could hear distant growls and threats hurled at him from the settlement.

The day came when the oak fell, after Gest with a great deal of trouble had got it burnt through at the root; the great tree heeled over with an ominous crack which could be heard a long way off, a scream of its branches as they were broken to bits and a booming sigh which shook the earth as the trunk with all its weight thundered down on to the beach. It woke the men out of their midday nap and they began at once to make a row about it; they were not going to put up with such doings from a boy who broke the peace with all the Powers of the forest and the sky, and Gro had to come out again to give them a piece of her mind.

The children of the settlement followed the battle at a safe distance, crowded together in a body, and watched with wonder how Mother Gro quite by herself tamed all that excited swarm of men, simply by what she said, and with a smile on her lips too, while all the hairy men were roaring with all their weapons about them and a look of murder in their eyes. Just as they were on the point of leaping on the blasphemer with harpoons, axes and bows to make an end of him, the murderous weapons dropped from their hands and they stood there looking like fools, just because of some words Gro had uttered with a hearty laugh; she must be full of witchcraft! What she had said they could not hear, or it was above their heads, but the battle was over, that was clear, and Mother Gro had won without the slightest effort.

Now what Gro had to say to the men was this, that if they wanted to put her youngsters to death they really couldn't expect to find the passage of her hut open at dusk any more; she was not going to have them running after her and fighting like mad bulls

for her favours and then see them exterminate the offspring afterwards! Gro snorted a trifle, this was just a little too strong!

The prospect of falling out of Gro's good graces was more than
any of the men could bear. One after another laid his weapons on
the ground, eager not to be the last; there was a regular rain of
lethal weapons. And as they stood empty-handed and abashed, Gro
gave them the parting shot, after enjoying a laugh at their expense;
there was one thing she would like to ask: was there a single
one of them who was certain it wasn't his own son he had come
so near killing?

At this the men hummed and hawed in a feeble way and shook
their heads like oxen. The baring of Gro's revelation taxed their
minds, paternal feelings worked in them with difficulty; there they
stood, and the children in the background saw them shove their
beards into their mouths and chew them with downcast eyes,
while Mother Gro laughed at the whole lot of them, but now with
a more genial laughter which they knew and which told them that
peace and reconciliation reigned once more among the grown-ups.

But that day's sun was not to set without the band of children
being reduced in another way; the affront the men had swallowed
and the predatory spirit that Gro had checked in one direction
found vent in another.

The noisy and threatening commotion over Gest had died away,
the midday sleep was resumed and the warm day was already sinking to its close when suddenly a roar burst out again from the
settlement; this time it was the men who were laughing — not a
pleasant laughter — and a single thin little scream was heard in the
midst of it.

It had been discovered from various signs that one of the girls
in the children's band was a child no longer, and instantly the
signal was give for a bride-hunt. The man who first made the discovery clapped his hands and began roaring with laughter, and
then all the men of the settlement clapped their hands at once, like
a flock of birds taking wing, and burst into uproarious laughter,
a tempest of merriment; the band of children broke asunder and
the poor little woman who had been found out knew what it
meant, made a dash for the woods and ran for her life — and the
whole crowd of men laughed and clapped louder and louder, for
she had done just the right thing, trying to run away from it, run

she should, ha, ha — and with loud yells of the hunters and fierce baying of the dogs the pursuit began.

It might be short or it might be long, according as the girl was light-footed and knew how to hide herself; sometimes even the dogs let her off and would not follow the scent because she had been good to them. Who would be the first to reach the victim was hard to say beforehand; it would show who was the swiftest and fittest of the men of the place; but the hunt always ended in the same way, with the girl being caught.

Then the poor thing, who that very day had been one of the playmates in the children's flock, might be found crouching in the darkest corner of one of the winter huts, bleeding and trembling many hours after, with her head buried in her hair, inconsolable.

And with that she went over to the women's side of the settlement, was given a digging-stick and set to provide shell-fish for the hunters when they came home from the chase and yawned round the fire; she was never allowed to play any more.

From Gest's workshop at the edge of the wood came the sounds of the ax all day long, one summer day after another, enough to send any one to sleep who was lying in the settlement, so regularly came the blows of the ax; now Gest was at work.

Near him sat Dart with her sunny hair, not disturbing him at all; she was busy weaving her finest patterns, talking to herself, whispering and plaiting, happy as usual in playing alone. Only when a chip flew from Gest's ax and got her on the head would she look up with a chilly quiver under her eyes; Gest must be angry, quarrelling with his work and red in the face; yes, it was terrible how that boy carried on and made his own life a burden.

He was at work shaping the outside of the canoe, after the tree had been felled; he walked round the mighty trunk like a little giant, attacking it with his flint tooth of an ax, a hopelessly unequal fight by the look of it; the trunk lay bare and heavy, resounding dully through its immense wooden mass, of which the greater part had to be removed; but Gest was stubbornly gnawing his way into it, as though sick to be finished.

First he had made holes in the bark and pulled it off in big flakes; then, when the trunk was bare and he could get a better idea of the form, he made up a fire under the root end and burned that away; he did the same thing up towards the top at the length he had decided on for the canoe: a piece of work which the fire could do almost by itself, he only had to stand by and put it out with water when it ate its way too far in. And then came the shaping of the outside, and here he had to hack at the trunk as it lay, doing the best he could; it was to be more or less pointed, of course, at any rate at one end.

This took many, many days, and Gest was perfectly silent all the time; he hacked and hacked, chip by chip, sharpened his ax again when it would not bite any more, which delayed him for half a day at a time; young as he was his toil brought furrows to his face and a hollow between his brows; all the time he was ahead of his work with his desire to see the ship finished as he had it in his head; he pressed on with a passion which made him forget himself entirely and become one with the tree-trunk, with the chips; every one of them spoke to him with its individual nature and offered its own tough resistance; he was absorbed as though for all time in the astringent smell of the fresh oak wood, which makes the hands black. And at last, at last the outward shape was as he wanted it.

Without a minute's delay he began on the hollowing out, to which he had long been looking forward impatiently. First the upper rounding of the stem had to be taken off down to about the middle; this he did with the ax, a work of many days, with blisters on his hands which turned to sores and healed again; then he laid on hot stones and began the actual hollowing, with the consolation that the end was in sight; but now he had to watch very carefully how far the stones burned in and be always ready with water to put out the fire in time. The burnt and charred part he went over with the ax, then burned more and chopped the surface clean; and so he went on till the oak was hollow right down to the bottom like a long narrow trough. Now it was all ready for the sea. Great shouts of triumph were heard from Gest's workshop one day, as though somebody was killing himself with joy, and though the men had tacitly conspired to take no more notice of the boy's doing, since they had come to grief in trying to put a stop to them, they could not help walking past the place, just to see how he was getting on.

And there they found Gest silent, with the shouts of joy sticking in his throat, standing dejectedly beside his completed craft.

One thing Gest had forgotten to take into consideration: how he was to get the trunk from the place where it had fallen out to the water. It was only a few paces, but the first time he had put his hand on the gunwale to move it, he could feel that it lay as though grown fast to the earth, immovable as a rock, as far as his strength went. He had forgotten to put rollers underneath before the tree fell! How could he forget that?

A couple of men came out of the wood where they had been watching and asked him with an assumption of sympathy how it was the canoe wouldn't move? They were nearly bursting with suppressed laughter; more came up, a whole crowd of men with their beards all in a grin, and all together they burst into immense roars of laughter over the wretched boy, leaning against one another so as not to fall; their amusement simply took away all their strength, it was a long time since anything had done them so much good.

Suddenly Gro appeared amongst them, attracted by the howls, and she too laughed, Gest could see her laugh — but while she was still cooing, for Mother Gro always laughed like a big wood-pigeon, being rather short-winded with all her fat, she went up to the prow of the canoe, lifted it without more ado and with two or three tugs pulled the whole craft out into the water! When she saw it was afloat she gave it a little shove and waded back again, with a smile at her son, and watched the inconsolable sorrow in his face change in a second to joy, he was laughing through his tears.

"There, now you can take a hand," she said to her son in a sing-song voice; she gave the men an offended glance, turned her back on them and went calmly away to the huts.

There the men stood. They saw the ground smoking where the stern of the canoe had ploughed a furrow, they glanced askance from there to Gro's back — never had they known that she was so strong! It was the strength of four men, nothing less!

They looked at her back as she walked; what a woman she was, massive and slow, her immense flanks and loins shook with every step, her knees turned in a little as was natural in a woman, her arms could not fall against her body but rowed freely in the air on each side, so big was she; she swayed as she walked — how beautiful she was!

But to think that she was at the same time so strong . . . the men looked at each other quite foolishly. One of them scanned the sky, trying to make out what kind of weather might be expected; another absently rolled a straw between his fingers; a third sneezed violently and blew his nose. Some of them had already stolen away, the rest went off in different directions. The affair was never talked of again.

But Gest had snatched the paddle which he had long ago split from a branch and hacked into shape; with a leap he was in the canoe, which received him with a grand wooden resonance and splashed the water under him; it lay perfectly on the water, proclaiming its nautical nature from the start, and a little later Gest could be seen sailing out in the bay in his bright new canoe with the paddle walking away first on one side, then on the other.

That was how Gest got his craft launched. A few days afterwards it occurred to one or two of them in the settlement that they no longer heard or saw anything of Gest. It takes a certain time to notice the absence of any one, if he has not been constantly under one's nose; at last it becomes clear that he is gone. Gest had vanished together with his new boat. Also the little girl they called Dart; her fair hair no longer showed up among the band of children either. The women knew of it first, then the men discovered it and felt injured at not having been asked; they put down the theft of the girl to that presumptuous boy's account together with his other sins. But Gro was able to inform them that Gest had indeed left the place and taken his playmate with him; Gro had not opposed it. That ended the discussion.

It was not long before the two children were almost forgotten, and perhaps Gest's name would never have been mentioned again but for an event which recalled his crime in a painful manner.

One of the men lost his life while hunting, in particularly striking circumstances. He had not returned at evening with the others, and on searching for him next day they found him impaled on the stake of his own pit, into which he had fallen in the dusk. He was still alive when they got him up, and was able to walk back to the settlement, holding his guts in his hands. Outside Gro's entrance passage he lay down, and she held his head on her knees till he was dead. He was one of the best hunters of the tribe and a merry, handsome man; Gro had loved him dearly and wept for him a night and a day; all over the settlement they heard painful subterranean wailings from Gro's house-grave, where she lay mourning in the innermost darkness.

Gro's sorrow shocked the other hunters which, to say the least, was unbecoming in her. The dead man had been a good friend and comrade, but still, when they buried him, they took good care that he should not walk; they heaped a goodly cairn on top of him. An excellent man he had been, but in future when Gro's eyes had a kindly look for one or other of them, it would not be on *him* they would light.

But as to the warning pointed by the accident, its cause, the men had no doubt. They said nothing about it before Gro; she was too dull to draw even the most obvious inferences and besides she was personally interested; but among themselves the event gave them a lot to talk about. For the case was perfectly plain: it was Gest's iniquity that had called down punishment upon the tribe, as they had very truly foretold; the forest had been outraged, and now it had taken its revenge.

But Gest had disappeared, and nobody but Gro knew whither he had gone.

V

THE THREE NORNS

THERE was a secret connected with Gest's birth, which Gro revealed to him privately before he left home.

When Gro had recovered after his birth she wished to have the boy's fortune told and sent for the Norns that they might take a look at him and read the omens of his destiny. Some of Gro's men had to sail after them, for they had to be fetched from another tribe up the coast, where they had been in the exercise of their calling. They had no fixed place of abode, but wandered about among the settlements on their momentous and at times somewhat dreaded mission.

They came, and they were three very ancient sibyls, rocking to and fro on their staves and nodding their noses with age; they had beards, but not a tooth among them; they were clad in old garments of fur that had not been off their backs for twenty winters; but they were wise.

Gro received them well in her cabin below ground, entertained them nobly and took special pains to put them in a pleasant frame of mind. The meal was oysters and mussels, taken out of their shells and put into a pot, all ready to gulp down; after that hard roe and wild pig's liver cut into strips and intended to be swallowed whole; and the drink was spring water well sweetened with honey. The old dames were pleased with the fare and did it justice, they grew loquacious and told many a good story, brought to mind by the food, of hunting that had taken place before Gro was born. Gest's birth reminded them of their own childbeds and marriages, the merry outrages they had suffered on the part of hunters long since turned to dust; their children too were dead, they were homeless sibyls now, but they still mumbled with their toothless gums and hee-hee'd with pleasure at the thought that they had once been human and had known all that a human being has to bear. One's trials were not so bad. Ah, now they might walk alone in the forest; even the wild beasts puckered their lips at an ancient sibyl. Yes, indeed.

When they had eaten their fill and their eyes began to sparkle — the Norns' wisdom taking fire within them — Gro emptied out her bag on the floor and bade them consider the boy.

They found him big, placed a finger on him and declared him to be well bred, they opened his mouth and felt his gums, sharp already, forward with his teething. They all felt and nothing happened with the first two, but when the third had her finger in his mouth the boy gave a bite and the sibyl had to waggle her finger to get it out. Mother Gro didn't like that and made a note to punish the youngster, but in her heart she thought him a brave boy. After that they went over his limbs, poured out a wealth of experience; they nodded their appreciation, whispered together and nodded; yes, he was a proper man.

Then one of the sibyls got up and started to prophesy, talking wildly and singing a horrid incomprehensible song which made the whole place seem uncanny, but it was all with the best intention, a magic incantation against evil Powers of every kind, and she ended by predicting that the man-child would have much good fortune and would see more than most people. The second sibyl nodded several times, concurred entirely in this prediction, it was exactly the augury she herself would give, and Gro smiled with pleasure, took the boy by his heel and dumped him into the bag again.

But the third had not said anything, and when Gro gave her a questioning glance she could see that the old woman shut her mouth tight so that her chin and the tip of her nose came together; there was something smouldering in her eyes that boded no good. It was she who had been bitten so unfortunately.

As a matter of fact she had been displeased long before, ever since she arrived, though she had concealed it. The first thing she had taken offence at was that Gro had set nothing but soft food before them, as though to let them feel their toothless state. Besides which, Gro's person in itself was something arrogant and insulting to small, thin people; for she was as big and fat as a whale, with limbs of indecent size, on which account she was desired of all men, it was said, no doubt truly, considering their coarse taste; furthermore she was audaciously dressed for the occasion in nothing but a thin summer mat, woven with the utmost vanity in open meshes, a porpoise in a net couldn't be less concealed, an altogether too obvious contrast with other people's slightness and sharp angles. Round her neck she vaunted a loud ornament, a necklace of more bears' teeth than anybody could count, one for each of her men — as no doubt one would be right in guessing — and she didn't make any secret about it either, for when they were examining the child and the other two agreed that judging by certain signs he would be kind to women, Gro had laughingly remarked that she wished him as much luck of that kind as she had had herself, a piece of impudence that was enough to damp the spirits of a lonely person. Moreover Gro was proud, as you couldn't help seeing the moment you entered her cave; it was clean, Gro had swept it, as good as an insult to such as maybe had a couple of feet of filth and offal and overlaid children at home!

But the worst thing, the thing that offended the eye most of all, was that Gro had lighted a candle. Not like other simple folk a fire on the floor or a bowl of grease with a handful of moss in it, but a big dip, in her high and mighty way, made as it seemed of tallow with a rush for a wick, mad newfangled ways that one heard tell of and a slight upon the customs of simple old people; to say nothing of the light, nearly as bright as day, not being equally advantageous to everybody's appearance and of a certain smokiness and gloominess being more the thing when there was magic to be done.

All this hurt the feelings of the third sibyl, and therefore, when Gro frankly asked her what fortune she would tell, the old dame rose and made ready to go, rocking on her staff and dipping her nose time after time, neighed to clear her voice and finally croaked out with a nasty bird-like glance at the candle that for her part she couldn't promise the boy any longer life than that of the candle his mother had lighted over him.

Gro launched out for the mouth of the bird of ill omen, but too late, the augury had been pronounced and the old woman made for the door-passage, chattering. But before she reached it she bent forward and spewed, bringing up all the dainties on the floor, then tumbled on all fours and crawled like a toad towards the entrance. Gro snatched up the crock with the rest of the food and threw the whole broth over her back; if the hag wouldn't keep the bribe inside her she should anyhow take away the marks of it behind.

Then Gro, like a raging she-bear, turned to the candle and blew it out.

That solemnity ended in pitch darkness. But Gest's life was saved.

And when he went away Gro gave him the candle-end, well sewed up in a bladder bag with a cord of sinew to hang round his neck; she bade him never to part with it and to remember what it meant. Gest thanked his mother much for the gift. And with that they parted.

VI

THE SQUIRREL'S NEST

At the extreme end of the fjord where Gest was born a river entered; the people of the settlement knew it for half a day's journey or so from the mouth, but higher up, where it lost itself in dense forest and totally unknown tracts, they never went and never thought of going. This was where Gest and Dart had gone in the new boat.

At first he had intended to put to sea at once through the bay and follow the coast to the islands and the great far-off country he had heard the elders talk about, but his mother dissuaded him. When they talked it over secretly she had proposed to him to travel up the river and into the heart of the country and try to live there first; afterwards he would be able to come back and set out on longer journeys, if he still had a mind to it. Gro gave him a look and screwed up her eyes, trying to recall Dart and guess at the ages of the two; after which she advised Gest to stay away two summers. And so they started out.

The canoe was long and crank and as Dart at her end rowed just as well as Gest they made no little headway; they had set out very early in the morning, before anybody was awake in the settlement except Mother Gro; by the middle of the day they had left the fjord behind and were up in the river, past familiar ground; from now on the country was all new to them, perfectly safe from any possible pursuit in their rear, whereas in front they might expect anything as they travelled on.

When they felt well secured behind many projections of the land and turns of the stream they rested for a meal, which meant that they had to fish first. Gest landed to get worms for his hooks; fish they had seen all the way in the river, nor was it many minutes before they had a catch; the worm had scarcely sunk below the surface when a shoal of black fishes' backs darted up to it from the bottom, the hook was seized and dragged hither and thither till the line stood taut and tore the surface of the water; the first they got up were broad fish with big scales and red fins; Gest killed the floundering fish in his teeth, got his mouth full of fresh water and the sweet juices of the fish; he ate on when he had once started, the whole fish went rapidly in at one corner of his mouth and the cleaned backbone ou ut the other; the long row had give him an appetite.

Gest was delighted with his hooks; he had made them himself out of fishbones with a cunning calculation, for with fish are fish to be taken, and it was in itself a merry thought that the fish should swallow its own bones the wrong way.

At her end of the canoe sat Dart modestly turning her back while she ate a little fish she had caught, for she had manners enough not to let any one see her eating. None of the grown-up women did so either, they took a bite now and then in the course of the day, unseen, but never sat down to a meal; no one had ever seen Mother Gro eat.

Fish were here in plenty, they were simply fighting to get at the hook. Soon they had eaten their fill, wound up the lines and paddled on after lapping up a couple of palmfuls of the fresh river water, smelling of vegetation.

They rowed that day and the next through entirely strange country, in and out with the twisting of the stream. It flowed towards them with a broad, calm surface between high banks of rushes which usually hid the view, lightly ruffled and rocking in the narrow places where there was a current, resting over deep pools in the bends, where little eddies broke the surface over the depths, and clucking against the hollowed banks; the river had its secrets, they could understand. On turning a corner sharply they would startle some living thing below; a deep furrow ran in front of them with rings on each side, a big fish or the otter, or perhaps the river sprite; often the heron flew up from some place they had passed quite close and took to his wings with curved neck and spindle-legs dangling behind. The swallows dived in their flight after midges on the surface of the water; frogs or water-rats flopped in by the banks, and the snake swam in great curves from one bank to the other with its head and the two poison spots on its neck above water. A long way off the wild duck rose in flocks from the stream, the coot hid among the reeds or dived; once where the view was open they saw a herd of roedeer make off in great leaps through the grass, hanging an instant in the air at every leap. The forest spread its domed vaults far away on each side of the stream.

At its outlet into the fjord and far up the country the river wound between broad stretches of marsh and thicket, impassable quagmires, but gradually the valley grew narrower, the woods on each side drew nearer, and the land became a winding valley with meadows and scrub at the bottom and great compact forests beyond.

On the second day, when they had rowed so long and so far that they felt quite lost, swallowed up by the stillness and solitude of these new wild regions, the windings of the stream brought them right in under the forest on one side of the valley; the land sloped upward here and was fairly open with lofty trees. Something about the place attracted them, the sun was beginning to sink over the valley behind them, and as there was an opening in the rushes and a broad place which seemed of itself to invite a landing — the bank was low with a sandy and stony bottom and many tracks of beasts, no doubt a drinking place — they decided to go ashore here, drew up the canoe far enough to keep it from floating off, and began to look about them.

The forest opened to receive them, they were quite one with it and felt they must draw near, whatever it might conceal; with it they were now to live. They took each other by the hand and went in among the trees, slowly; the shades of the forest fell upon them, they heard it resound with their footsteps; vast and cavernous and lonely it was within.

There was a rustling in the bushes in front of them, they stood still with all their limbs a-quiver, seeing nothing, but somewhere farther in the leaves of the hazel trembled, an animal had broken through; they nodded and looked at each other, opened their mouths but found nothing to say.

Cautiously and with wary steps on the forest floor they then examined their nearest surroundings. Here the forest stood on a long slope which thrust itself out into the river valley; on both sides of it the meadow ran up into smaller lateral valleys, the forest as it were extended an arm here; it gave them a sense of security to know that this piece of it had its limits at any rate on three sides, and for the present they tried to make themselves at home.

At the bottom of one of the side valleys they found a brook, which joined the river lower down, and by following it a little way they suddenly came upon the source. It lay at the end of a cleft, a deep gash cut by the stream, like a portal opening upon the forest and the country beyond.

The source itself issued among rocks and twisted roots beneath a great forest tree and with other huge trees standing round about. It was a cool, deep hole with a floor of the finest sand, and in the sand was a strange pit looking as if it were alive, a mouth which blew the sand from its lips, stirred it with its tongue, made itself round and shot up water from the bottom, closed and opened again, all without the slightest sound; and you could hardly see the water coming, so transparent was it all in the deep, clear hole, but you knew by the sand in the pit being continually in motion that water was coming up all the time; it domed up and spread away down in the clear, clear depth with the fresh water that was always coming up; it was the underground spring that brought forth water and sent it up from the bottom of the hole, keeping it always brimful and running over to form the brook.

A strange and mighty gloom there was here under the tall trees, which inclined towards each other over the spring and talked together with their murmuring foliage under the sky, where they shut out the daylight. Farther on the forest rose darkly, trees and trees with their roots down in the earth, losing themselves in an airy wall of distant trees and shadows blended together, whence came a solemn breath; but through a gap in the trees on the other side you could look down upon the meadows, which lay sunlit and open with the blue surface of the river winding through. Under the trees lay a deep shadow, and in the heart of the shadow was the source.

Gest and Dart plucked up courage and leaned over the spring; its mirror gave back their faces and they took it for a welcome and drank, mouth to mouth with the silent water-giver below, the first long, sweet drink that this new world offered them in welcome, laden with the country's innermost taste of earth and pure coolness. They drank and their faces were wet and refreshed, it did them good within and without.

And when they had drunk they laughed and felt that a miracle had happened; the feeling of oppression vanished from their minds, they were as though new-born, a sweetness penetrated all their veins, so good was the water of the spring. All at once they felt at home here, scarcely remembering the settlement in the bay and all that lay behind them, though it was only two days since they had left it; all that had lost its reality, a new life and a new reality had taken its place. Here they were and here they felt they would remain. Such power had the water of the spring.

Therefore, when they had drunk and been refreshed, they thought they ought to make a gift to the source. The only thing Dart possessed was the necklace of wolves' teeth which she had had from her mother to guard her against wild beasts; it was hard to part with it — her only possession and for the moment all she had on — but she decided to give it away and dropped it into the spring. It was well received, it sank right to the sandy bottom and lay there. Gest had come into the new country just as naked as Dart, with the exception of his amulet, which there could be no question of sacrificing. But he felt in his hair and took out a long awl made of bone, felt elsewhere and found, not without bringing away a good deal of hair, several bone fish-hooks, a good roll of sinew, some flint flakes and other small necessaries; he offered them all to the source, and his gift was also well received.

They had now entered into relations with the Spring Man and felt that they might stay here and dwell in his neighbourhood, until perhaps they would one day find themselves on a good footing with the forest as well.

The forest, they could see, was bigger and loftier here than they had known it in their former existence, and no doubt it offered at least the same difficulties. At present, however, it seemed to take no notice of them; it talked endlessly to itself, as forests and old people do, and they for their part had not the slightest intention of taking any rash or precipitate action against any kind of visible or invisible Power in the new country.

The first night they spent in their boat by the river, quite comfortably; they drew the canoe ashore when it began to get dark and fell asleep in it without a thought of danger, forgot everything and slept on undisturbed until it grew light again; but that sort of thing would only do once. The trees were safer.

They chose for their sleeping place none other than the lofty tree which had the spring beneath its roots. It was not easy to get up, the trunk was far too thick to clasp and the lowest branches were high up, but from a slenderer tree close by you could climb over into its top. Between the branches and the trunk, high, high up, there was a nook which would suit; when it had been enlarged with other lopped-off branches and a wattle-work of twigs it would make a comfortable and perfectly safe lair.

While Gest went up into the tree to cut branches and build the nest, Dart plucked grass, which she laid in the sun to dry; this was for lining it.

There was one who lived in the tree before them, a squirrel. It received Gest with mixed feelings the first time he came up; ran out on a branch and showed every sign of curiosity, sat up and raised its broad furry tail again and again, pricked up its ears and twitched its nose, quite unable to keep in hiding though it guessed the danger of showing itself. It approached in bounds and dashed off instantly when Gest made a move, chattered loudly from the top of the tree among the foliage; soon after it was there again, sitting up on its hind-quarters and scrubbing its cheeks, its beady eyes sparkled, it held itself stiff, came nearer and then again dashed madly off in two or three long bounds. The little man, whom Gest knew very well but had never before seen at such close quarters, was evidently much interested in his arrival and in doubt as to its meaning. When Gest began to chop away among the branches of the tree, the squirrel was right up in the topmost twigs, making a most abusive noise; Gest did not care to disturb it, not knowing what power it might possess here, but as he had no intention of do-ing it an injury he might surely be allowed to come into its tree. He might always do it a service later on in return. Gest lopped off the biggest branches he could manage and put them in place in the fork where the nest was to be, making them fast with a binding of honeysuckle stalks, and above them laid sticks and twigs, in the way the stork builds; soon he had a good and secure lair ready.

The moment Gest began to deprive the trees of their branches and help himself to withies and whatever other growing things he wanted, he knew well enough that he was taking liberties with the forest. The squirrel's behaviour was worth noticing, perhaps it knew more about the matter than one would expect from its size; it would be better to do something to appease the forest at once. As soon, therefore, as the nest was finished and he had come down from the tree, he betook himself farther into the forest, not liking it, but driven by a feeling of the necessity of approaching it and trying to establish a tacit mutual understanding.

He walked up over the wooded slope that formed a sort of forest promontory, came down into a valley on the other side and over another hill; the forest closed in his rear, he was now within the deep main forest and felt himself in its power, but went on in a hesitating way in the vague hope that something might happen which would bring him face to face with the very spirit of the forest. But nothing happened, and yet it was very near all the time.

A good way in he discovered a glade, and in the midst of it stood a very big tree almost by itself, an oak; he at once had the idea that this must be a mighty tree, it was old and very thick with an immense trunk and long, gnarled branches, its foliage made a whole wood by itself. Some smaller, strangely black and crooked trees grew near it, creeping along the ground, uncannily alive, with eyes on their stems and queer limbs; of these he was afraid. But the big old tree did not inspire fear. The whole of its huge spread of branches was covered with the thickest foliage, and among the leaves grew acorns like a lot of green babies; the tree was with child, teeming with fruit; without doubt it was a rich tree and it must be the strongest in the forest. When Gest came right up to the oak he saw that the trunk was hollow, the tree had a gash in its belly, and at once he followed an impulse and placed his best flint knife, a half-finished ax of red flint and five good fish-hooks in the hollow.

It struck him as quite appropriate that the forest should have just those cutting tools he had used against it, and he went away feeling confident that now he might use all the wood he needed. But he ran the last part of the way; it was not good to have the forest at one's back when one was alone, and he did not stop to take breath until he was well out of it again.

Having got over this formidable visit to the forest Gest set to work in good heart to carry grass and leaves up to the nest. He made a regular little island of it up in the spacious tree, floating between heaven and earth.

The view was wide, on one side the whole winding valley with the river in its midst lay spread out before their eyes, and far away they saw the fjord they had come from reflecting the pale blue of the sky; behind it, a darker blue, the sea beyond the coast, which lost itself in a bank of mist. But on the other side the forest extended into the country, a green domed roof of tree-tops, woods and woods as far as the eye could reach. On the edge of the horizon the forest rose like a wave towards the sky, and at the highest point the forest wall was pierced, an opening between the stems through which the sky was visible, a distant blue gateway, with slanting shafts of light falling from the cloud above against the sun; they had the idea that this was the gateway to the wide world and that they would one day pass through it.

And when they had set their island in order up in the tree they set out, sailed a long way up the river and made themselves acquainted with the valley farther in. It ran deep into the country, they could not see the end of it that day. They came across many new things, surprised beasts and birds that they had never seen before, and the river revealed to them more and more of its nature. It was full of fish, flashing down below when one of a shoal turned and showed its side; the big fish swam in the deep water, on the surface stickle-backs swarmed in dense little crowds. In shallows the pike stood still as a stick with its striped body and ugly lower jaw, disappearing in a cloud of mud if you came too near; the brown eel wriggled deep down at the bottom in the brown sun-warmed mud among the stalks of the waterlilies. Underneath the banks they discovered little caves deep down, where crabs hid; they were not difficult to get and were a very pleasant bite as a change from all the fish they ate. They left nothing untasted, every single thing had a soul which entered into their soul; the fresh muddy smell of the water, the strong breath of the banks made up of wet water plants, of sweet flag and curled mint; the meadow grass invaded the river, strewing its light seed in the stream among the swaying rushes, and over the meadows was a dense wilderness of fragrant plants and flowers surrounded by bees, a mist of honey wherever one turned the eyes; in the little groves of willows and bushes that grew in the quagmires the birds chirped lustily, here they were in safety with their nests.

The day was warm, the sun poured down upon the narrow boat, baking its timbers and bringing out a scent of tan; strong and fresh was the smell of the fish that lay at the bottom of the canoe in the sun, its occupants themselves had a smell of fire about their hair and the nearness of the water tempted them; they plunged in, ducked below the surface in the deep, cool water which pressed against their limbs, holding them up, got water in their mouths and water in their souls; good was the river. Afterwards they sunned themselves till they were scorched between the shoulder-blades, with cooling waterlily leaves on their heads. Close by on the bank the otter rolled in the grass, getting his coat full of thistledown and pollen; he darted a swift wet glance at the two unknown, sneezed and took to the water again like a snake.

In a bend of the river up on the firm ground they came across the wild sow luxuriously stretched on her side in a mud-hole with a litter of little pigs on top of her; she turned her small red eye as they passed but stayed where she was. The osprey swept down on a broad reach of the river, made a mighty splashing on the surface and took to its wings again with a salmon held fast in its talons.

Their voyage of discovery lasted the whole day, but before evening they were back at the spring and went to rest up in the tree before darkness fell, tired and fed and content with everything, on a springy, swaying couch of grass with sticks below. They heaped grass over themselves, especially over their heads, so as to be well hidden.

And here in their airy nest they fell asleep, insensibly swinging and held in the arms of the lofty tree, rocked to sleep without knowing it, delightfully warmed and cooled at once by the fresh grass. And in their sleep they glided into another airy, hanging world and were cradled, rocked and swung through infinite existences, warm and cool, in a profound and peaceful trance.

Above their heads, higher up in the tree-top, a forest creature watched over their rest.

That little man the squirrel had his house under the sky, up among the lighest of all the twigs, just strong enough to bear him and his house, but inaccessible to any animal heavier than the squirrel. Here he had patched together his nest, a summer house built upon an old crow's nest and covered over with a roof of twigs, leaves and withered grass, with a little door to it and lined inside with moss, all very dainty; and here he dozed at night, but only lightly, nothing could happen without his hearing it with his furry ears and being wide-awake in time.

That the two ridiculously big, tailless and naked, pink and altogether misshapen and unhandy man-things had now come and built their nest in his tree did not make him uneasy at first though he could not control his curiosity. Now they were there, and now he would see what would happen. To tell the truth, it was not the first time the squirrel had shared a tree with Man; though he did not exactly remember it, it was in his veins that he knew them. So now a couple of unprotected man-children had taken to the trees again, and the squirrel received them as one receives very distant relations, with reserve but with a deep-felt attraction; they came to be on quite good terms with one another.

The squirrel meant something to them simply because he lived in the tree, and they too meant something to him; since they had moved in the marten and the wild cat came there no more, nor the birds of prey which threatened the squirrel from above; they had a respect for the new inhabitants. The lynx came up to them one night, but then the squirrel made such a noise, behaving as if he had gone mad, that Gest awoke just in time to see a pair of greenish sparkling eyes quite close to him in the dark tree and to plant his flint ax between them. The lynx sneezed and dropped from the tree, and it never came there again.

In time they became very intimate, the squirrel grew so confident that he would come quite near, when the children had anything to give him, and take it out of their hands. To watch him eat was a great delight; he sat up and took the food between his forepaws, with brisk and gusty movements, examined it in a flash, turned it upside down, took a quick bite and munched busily; his teeth went so rapidly that you couldn't follow them, he stretched his tail, munched, took another bite, it was a sight to see his long sharp front teeth working; they smashed up a nut or an acorn so that the splinters flew; Gest watched the little carpenter with admiration and would have been glad of some tools like the four splendid little chisels the squirrel carried in his mouth.

But when the squirrel was fed and wanted nothing for the moment, it was fun to watch him hide what had been given him in the first place he found, a crack in the bark, or in his house; another time he would fetch out what he had hidden, dart down the tree and start digging vigorously somewhere at the root of another tree near by, where there was not the slightest mark to be seen, and up he would pull an old earthy nut which he had buried perhaps three months before and just happened to remember. This hoarding was something to follow, and Dart took the hint.

Dart loved the nimble little elf and often gave him things for the sake of enticing him so near that she was just allowed to touch his fine coat and feel his little warmth; but as for taking hold of him, it was not to be thought of, he was too quick and too sensitive for that, the least touch of his hair sent him off instantly; tame he might be, but he kept to his own air, visible but in reality a spirit of the forest.

He showed what strength he possessed in spite of his smallness when he had one of his flying fits, and these would come over him like something very important that had to be done -- unless it was his play -- without apparent object he chased wildly from tree to tree, flew in long daring curves like a bird from one tree-top to the next, streaking like a flame along the thinnest twigs, and if it was too far to the next tree he landed on the ground, galloped on like a red snake in the grass with his billowy tail on high and in

a second was up the vertical tree-trunk again, throwing himself
from branch to branch; in a moment he was away in the depths
of the forest.

It was such a temptation to follow him. Gest and Dart were infected by the joy of his flight and made attempts at climbing
after him, laboriously from one tree to another, when the branches
came near enough together; it was a very poor copy of the squirrel; they were too heavy, slow and careful, and never made anything of it in the trees. But the giddiness and the difficulty of getting from tree to tree without having to touch the ground had an
attraction of its own which they could not resist; it was like a
happy dream to see the world from the trees, the airy elusive view
from above was at the same time something new to them and an
obscure repeated experience; it gave them a kind of drunken feeling, they forgot all else, were simply in an eternal forest and
eternal sunshine, an eternal summer, so long as they practised
crawling about from tree to tree.

In this way they penetrated by degrees into the forest. On their
expeditions, which became longer and longer, they could at any
moment run up the trees if anything at all unusual appeared. They
covered the distances on the ground but most of their observations were made from the trees, where they could look down and
themselves remain in hiding. Thus the squirrel became a guide who
gradually enticed them into the forest and made them familiar with
it for miles around.

The nest up in the trees had been roofed over, after the squirrel's model, with a few rafters placed against each other and covered with leaves; there was just room for them inside, and the hut
was hardly to be noticed from below if one did not know it was
there. Here they were sheltered at night from rain and wind and
all the evil things of darkness, here they were rocked into dreams
and hushed to sleep by the murmuring trees and the airy soliloquies
of the forest.

They went about in mats of bast which Dart's skilful hands
had woven, rough things to wear at first and superfluous most of
the day, but in the morning and evening they were glad of them.
Dart adorned herself and was different every day, now with wild
flowers, always some new sort which she found in the forest or the
bog, now with feathers shed by the birds which she stuck in her
hair; she beautified herself with ochre, which was also to be found

here by the springs in the ground; but she was not alone in this, for Gest was not above improving his appearance with a couple of broad red streaks on his face. They were always occupied, always had something on hand, no time of the day was without its business or pleasure, if it was only plucking the little pointed calyxes of certain flowers and sucking the almost inperceptible drop of honey they contained.

They found honeycombs in the meadows and sucked out the round cells with a straw, put them back again in the nest and might afterwards return when the bee had filled them anew.

But one day they had a visit from the wolf. It came prowling down in broad daylight from up country, long, gaunt and footsore, and on catching sight of them halted underneath the tree they sat in, raised its forepaw and seemed to have come just on their account. It raised itself on its toes and spread its whiskers, with a bright look, an expression quite sunny with kindness, and the children almost began to think they had wronged it. For in fact they had never seen the wolf at close quarters and had perhaps formed an entirely false idea of its nature. If they made friends with it, it might be just as good to play with as a dog, and they wanted a dog. It looked so like a dog.

Though tempted to come down and open an acquaintance they stayed where they were for the time being; for if the wolf meant well it could easily come up to them. Their grey friend kept walking up and down below, as though in thought, licking its thin chaps and hanging about much longer than one would have thought the acquaintance was worth. The children amused themselves by throwing sticks and bits of branch at the wolf, who blinked his veiled yellow eyes and pretended to enter into the sport, feigning to bite at the things they threw and showing himself as ready to play as a puppy, though he was a bony and experienced old villain; he jumped skittishly and played with his paw, put on a pathetic air and tried a tender bark, curled his thin lips into what was meant to be an outburst of merriment, ingratiating himself so sweetly; and the children really felt the strongest desire to come down and pat this playful puppy; they looked at each other, shifted a little farther along the branch, in doubt what to do.

The tempter down below sported more seductively than ever,

jumped off into the wood and turned his head to entice them to follow; but one thing struck the children as odd, they didn't think the wolf's smell was nearly as sweet as his laugh, whiffs of ancient carrion were wafted right up the tree to them, and the wolf looked as if you might hurt yourself against him, with his bones sticking out of his mangy grey skin; it was probably not worth while going down to him, and they stayed where they were.

When at last the wolf had recognized the hopelessness of waiting to captivate the couple, he dropped his mask and yawned like a pit with boredom, exposing four long rows of fasting teeth; hunger and murder were plainly written in his eyes. Then, after sitting on his haunches and howling, a bitter uncanny lonesome wail, he lifted a hind-leg against the tree, scratched up the dust with his feet and prowled off, long, gaunt and with drooping tail, never once looking back.

The couple in the tree looked at each other and turned white in the face; they felt that in broad daylight they had been visited by the *Night*. The wailing of the wolf was what resounded every night in the forest, nothing else; and what they had taken for the voice of the forest and half a world full of supernatural Powers turned out, when they saw it close at hand, to be nothing but a famished and disappointed old eater of carrion. So much had they learnt.

Gest followed the wolf with longing eyes till he disappeared in the forest — if only he had had a bow and arrow! Perhaps he could have shot the deceitful old prowler and given Dart a new necklace of wolf's teeth in place of the one the spring had. Without a doubt it was her having parted with it that had made the wolf so bold.

Next day Gest sat at a big stone near the spring that he had chosen for his workshop and made the place ring with the finest flint work. It was a delicate job he was on, arrow-heads, which you make by splitting suitable flakes across; a lot of them go to splinters before you get a few as they should be. Gest had a fancy to make himself a bow and arrows. He had been to the young ash trees for the wood, was wondering how he should get the string and thought of every place he knew of in the neighbourhood where there might be reeds.

Gest saw the bow as he wanted it and attacked the wood with

his sharp flint; the slender ash shoot had to be carefully scraped so that the bow should be equally pliable at both ends; notches were to be made for the string; he could not wait till the thing was finished but worked as though possessed, longing for the string while still at work on the wood, with the arrow in his mind while he was on *that;* he had neither eyes nor ears.

Dart was at work plaiting and had to lend Gest some bast for a string; he called to her when he had got it stretched tight and plucked its first singing note with his finger while she listened, smiling the smile of the creator — didn't the bow sing well? By his side lay a bundle of reeds that he had fetched from the brink of the stream and peeled, long straight wands, they were the sort for arrows.

The day wore on and Dart got a lot of plaiting done, busily whispering to herself and with frequent casts of the head to throw the hair from her eyes; she went back to look at what Gest was doing but this time found him close and gloomy, uncommunicative, quite a different Gest; he had had trouble, the first time he pulled the bow-string hard and released it again it broke with a snap, it could not stand the sudden strain. No, of course, bast was no good, unless you made the string so thick that it would have a dull note and no spring in it. A bow must have a note or it has no soul. That his bowstring ought to be of gut Gest knew very well, for what is to reach the guts must come from gut, but here his plans led him in a circle; how was he to shoot anything before he had the means of shooting?

For the present then he would make the string of hair, and so Dart had to suffer, since her hair was both longer and finer than his own; laying her head on a stone she meekly allowed him to saw off as much hair as he wanted with another stone, and even helped him to twine the string.

It proved to be durable and gave quite a good clang. The fact that it was of human hair gave it a significance of its own, which other human beings would have to beware of, should they meet with any; but of course it held a fate for all other hairy creatures.

When the bow was finished Gest sat down and played Dart a piece on it. It sounded quite lovely, monotonous but lovely, and he lingered over the string while Dart lent her ear and delighted in the music. That was Gest's first harp. He afterwards became a minstrel.

But now it was a hunter he thought of being. The first arrow that was ready he shot straight up, and it rose like a worm against the sky with its little flint point, went higher than the highest trees, and when it had looked about in the blue for an instant it turned again and sought the earth head downward; it stood with shaft straight up, buried to the depth of a finger in the mould, when Gest after some search found it again in the grass.

He broke truce with the birds the same day. In time he became a practised archer. At first the bow was but short and the arrows of reed, but it grew with him and his arrows were of wood, long and tough. Gest had now taken up a thing to which there was no end, each new bow he made was an improvement, he grew and it grew, became long and powerful in its stroke, soon it was no longer a plaything with a little innocent clang; Gest's bow began to make itself heard in the forest with ferocious voice.

One night there was a gaunt old dog-wolf who left the pack and went on the prowl by himself; silently he came limping down through one of the side valleys towards the stream, impelled by a memory that was always running in his wolf's head, of a pair of pink half-grown man-children that he knew were to be found hereabout, and whose savoury tracks he came upon more and more thickly as he neared the river.

He was hungry, desperately hungry, though it was not so very long since he had had something; he was always hungry, always had been, hungry through and through and all his life long itching to eat himself up, a fallen creature who couldn't understand that the more he ate the more he was feeding his unquenchable hunger. Now there was a voice in his ever-burning entrails which deluded him with the notion that tonight he should regale himself with human flesh.

But just as he was prowling along with his nose to the ground and had got it full to drivelling of a lot of fresh scent, an inconceivable thing happened: the earth suddenly vanished under his feet, he sprawled in the air and hurt himself badly; when he reached firm ground again and on recovering himself after the somersault he found that he was in a hole with vertical walls of earth on all four sides. He tried to jump up again, but the hole was as deep as a shaft, there was no chance of getting out.

So he sat there all night and had a view of a square of the starry sky, until morning came and the square turned blue. Then the wolf got uneasy and went round and round the hole many times; he was so hungry that he felt an extra wolf in his entrails, as though there were two of them, and both dreaming a day-dream over again: of a couple of pink man-children, not big enough to be judged dangerous, but still a fair mouthful, just what a wolf could manage. Twice he had filled his nostrils with the rich near scent of their flesh, one night when they had unsuspectingly lain down to sleep in the grass, but then they had unfortunately raised such hideous shrieks that any one would have thought there were hosts of humans about the place, the wolf couldn't stand it, he had cut and run from a safe meal. The second time was when they were sitting up in a tree, from which however they had been too cowardly to come down. The wolf was so hungry and his dream was so vivid that he could almost see what he wanted so much to see.

And at that moment he actually did see them for the third time, up at the edge of the pit, where they lay on their stomachs with their hair hanging over their faces, looking down, unpleasantly amused and holding their noses in an impolite manner.

They knew him at once, saw that it was the same old rascal who had tried to get them to play with him in the forest; he was running round himself like a shadow, glancing up and blinking at the light, and they saw him staining the pit yellow with fear of what awaited him now. For it had never occurred to the old murderer that one day *he* would be faced by a violent death. They laughed at him, and for answer he sat on his haunches and gave his carrion howl, hoping to make their flesh creep so that their hearts might be softened; but it only made them the merrier to hear the miscreant performing his own dismal elegy.

So then Dart got a necklace again. The teeth were very long but half decayed, the old rascal had had a diseased jaw. The skin stank and had chafed bald patches in the hair, but it would serve until they got younger and better skins. The nights were getting cold and they felt the want of more covering than hay and bast mats.

But from the wolf's guts Gest got his first real bowstring, hard and tough as though tempered in the fire, springy and yet so strong that no human strength could tear it apart. Neither the wolf nor any other beast was safe from one of the shots. Thus it came about that the old wolf's appetite was stayed, while Gest secured food for his own.

VII

LIGHT NIGHTS

INLAND on the edge of the horizon the forest rose like a wave, pierced at its highest point by a gap in the stems through which the blue sky was visible, like a gateway to the wide world; through this Gest and Dart passed one summer day when they were out roaming; they had broken into a run, the distance had passed into their souls and they went on running.

The day was both warm and cold, the sun gave heat but there was coolness in the breeze; for the first time that year they had thrown off their clothes, crept out of the nasty old sooty skins, which lay like a cast-off larva, and had rushed naked out into the sun and the air, but the air was cold, though the sun baked them; they ran and running made them hot and red all over, they cooled themselves in the breeze and felt thin and airy as the wind and burning like the sun, air and sun united about them, the cool young woods united about them, the blue sky and the swelling white clouds foamed and swelled over them; they ran, were caught up in the air, they flew — now, now they would go to the end of the world!

Running they came up to the highest point in the forest, an opening with a few big trees at the top of a hill; from here they could see far into the country, more green forests, valleys unknown to them, a new horizon with distant forest portals, and towards it they ran, ran on and on, up hill and down dale, without once looking back, they were the air and the sun, they were the wind, they were the wide world!

Gest ran in front, bow in hand, and as he ran he shot his arrow, which flew before him, leading him into the strange country; he saw it climb towards the blue vault of heaven and raise its point against the clouds, and Gest was with it on high and sought the ground with it, ran till he found it and shot it again upward and forward. His shot carried far, with a mighty whirr of the bow each time; the bow was long and heavy, the twin to his arm in strength, and long and slender was the arrow with a double-barbed flint point, akin to the lightning-stroke and winged with stork's feathers to make it go high; it was his longing, it went before him in a leap between heaven and earth, as he himself leaped.

And thus they ran on into Sealand, into widespread waving young forests, with here and there a glade and a hill, where glimmering aspens blended with the shafts of sunlight on the horizon. They saw what no man had yet seen, lakes in their primeval stillness surrounded on all sides by the walls of the forest, heights clothed with heather and juniper which gave a view of new forests and new blue sounds, stretching far into the country from the sea. And they came upon wide grassy plains strewed with big stones and framed afar in waves of warmth, with a scent in the stillness of wild wormwood, a web of larks' song as of everlasting fountains in the air, alder woods and streams where that wet man the beaver splashed about swimming in the shadow of the woods with his gnawed logs — and again the open country with rolling wild pastures and rocks, flowers as far as the eye could see, and above it the airy swallows weaving their flight in and out, up and down, and above them again a hawk high up against the blue, hanging and diving in its flight. . . .

At the hawk Gest shot his arrow and ran, flew after it through the long grass, with a swish of his own hair . . . and as he turned he saw his playmate come running after like the wind, almost without touching the ground, with her long hair flowing out in the air like a flame and her necklace of wolf's teeth flung the same way, a bunch of wild flowers in one hand and a pretty feather she had picked up in the other, her mouth wide open, she ran, she flew . . . and then Gest saw that it was no longer " Little Dart " but a long-legged young maiden with fair arms who came flying like a summer breeze over flowery grass.

But she for her part saw that it was no longer a boy running before her, but a young hunter holding his head high on a strong pair of shoulders; she heard his cry, a hunter's halloo to the sky, and on he ran, shot and ran again, leaping above the grass like a stag to catch a scent — she shook her hair, filled her lungs and followed him, and so they lost themselves running in the wilderness, in a shimmer of sunlight they vanished on distant plains.

The fox came up on the top of his house between blocks of stone and sniffed with his nose in the air after the couple, when they were well away, scenting a drama. What strange creatures were men! He had seen before now a lot of men running after a woman, but here it appeared to be a great hulking youth seeking safety in flight, pursued by a maiden. Uf, the fox cleared his nose, men were strange things! He turned about and disappeared with his brush after him between the stones.

Empty, in primeval stillness the wide plains lay, wrapped in the song of larks above and the high summer note of bees among the flowers below; the clouds pursued their airy life, the sun marched on in solitary might, the long sweet summer day reposed in itself, until its being had an end.

Sated with shining the sun sank behind hills. Then with the dew the larks came down from the sky, falling obliquely out of space and hovering an instant over the long darkening grass, before they slipped down and vanished in their nests, sated with song.

Green and cool was the world; for a brief while sheer silence, while darkness grew among the stones and blended with the evening mist; the stars came out, chilly and small. Soon other evening voices made themselves heard, the twilight hooting of the owl, a wandering beetle's ticking in the gloaming. From dark groves came a long-drawn enchanted note, the night raven's, and from swamps and pools the cool dream-chorus of the frogs was heard on every side.

And the day was gone. But it did not grow dark; in the north where the sun had gone down the day still slumbered, the sky shone light, fields and forest lay in a gloaming, and the white clouds could still be seen with their sleeping summits reaching up into the night, a blue night; the bushes filled with mist, and out of them came white nocturnal forms. Soaring free the moon rose grandly over the edge of the earth, with a dazzled stare at the other side of the sky where the sun had vanished; a great calm white star attended on the moon. Far away echoes sounded confusedly among the woods — the wolf barking at the moon, angrily, with a snap in his voice from annoyance at the marvel. But the moon lived her round life up in the sky, rising and soaring in her solitude, advancing over still lakes with her mirrored image and staring blindly upon sleeping woods and sleeping heights in the distance.

Somewhere far up the country by a tarn among birches a fire was burning; far around the animals sniffed and stood still before open moonlit glades between the groves, not daring to cross over; never before had fire been seen in these vast uninhabited tracts; a smell of roasting — what now, were they to be burnt and eaten? Clear flames rose from the fire and the smoke was visible in the light night; now and again a black upright shadow passed in front of the fire, there was no doubt about it, man had come with his hot arts.

Now it was Gest and Dart who had lighted their evening fire here and delighted themselves with its warmth after running all day in sun and wind. They had not lost heart; naked and taking nothing with them they had run from home that morning; they did not know where in the world they were, but the thought of turning back never occurred to them. The night had no fears for them, it was so light, and they had the fire. Gest kindled fire with the first two sticks he came across and made free to miss out a good many of the mysteries connected with the act, not even forbidding Dart to look on at it; anyhow he got fire, it smoked and glowed in a moment beneath his strong hands; a full-throated song did duty for the incantation, and when the blaze flared up he threw a brace of birds into it, sacrifice and supper in one. The great fire ceremony and the sacred meal were now celebrated every day. Gest had left all his tools behind in the winter house; the nearest sharp stone had to serve for the present as a knife. When they had finished eating, the feathers, beak and claws together with the picked carcase were given to the fire, which seethed with satisfaction; then they broke off branches and built a booth for the night.

Thus they returned to the simplest way of life, older even than what they had known where they came from; they began again at the very beginning, in freedom and alone. And the light nights held them, they stayed out the rest of the summer, quite forgot their home by the spring and the settlement on the coast; they moved on and slept in a new place every night, saw new worlds, became like the birds, like the flies, like the light — nothing but flight and light, outside time, animated only by one another. The love-star shone above them, as it shone above the innocent who cleave together and evoke vital warmth and multiply upon the green earth; they lost themselves among them, among birds that sat on their eggs and deer with new-born young, and swallows that rustled together on the wing, and dragon-flies on their bridal flight, two and two like *one* winged creature, and cuckoos that played at hide-and-seek and gave their cry wherever they might be, and hedgehogs chasing each other in the twilight, and snorting buck hares — everywhere an enticing, calling and crowing, a mad miaowing of the wild cat in the moonlight, a tortured scream from the rutting lynx — but drowning all the rest came the bison's roaring challenge from one end of the country to the other like the voice of a deity from heaven, multiplied by echoes and swelling through every valley.

The fox spying upon the human couple seemed off and on to have a fly in his ear; never before had he come across such joyous people nor heard such wild, meaningless songs as they sang while they were tearing about.

In the autumn they came back to their home by the spring, sunburnt and matured, and resumed their life there.

The spring welcomed them with its familiar, intimate voice, they looked at their reflections in it and remembered the childish faces they had seen there; they were now gone, and in their place had come a pair of well-developed young people who could scarcely find room side by side in the mirror. On Gest's face a beard had sprung out, he was now a man. More beautiful than any other earthly marvel was the cleft of Dart's young breast as she gazed at her reflection.

Deep down in the source, at a giddy depth, they saw an eagle soaring on his wings in the abyss; they looked up, the same eagle was soaring sky-high beneath the clouds; the reality was linked with its image in the source.

Their house stood untouched as they had left it but had nearly collapsed; they rebuilt it and lined it with great stones to keep up the walls. With wonder Gest found his tools again, weighed his old ax in his hand — to think that he had once hewed out a canoe with that fingernail of a thing! Now he struck big, heavy ax-heads, slender but nearly a foot long and hafted in proportion. The bow he had with him was twice as long as the old one; he had taken to carrying spears now when he went hunting, long flint-tipped poles that were dangerous even to the biggest game when he got within throwing range.

There was no difficulty about providing all they wanted for the coming winter; Gest was more intent on making his things agreeable to the eye than on their mere usefulness, which had been well proved; he would spend months grinding an ax to get it perfectly smooth all over, and he set about it with extreme persistence, sitting the whole day long before a big flat stone and working the piece of flint backwards and forwards as far as his arms could reach, pouring on sand and water and grinding, pressing and grinding, till the stone was hollowed out and the flint too began to feel it, but slowly. Gest was strong and the work made him stronger; many, many hours, day after day he ground away, dumb with passion, nothing but a tight-shut, immovable beard to look at as long as the fit was upon him, and he did not give up till the last trace of flaking was effaced from the flint, even though for the sake of symmetry a layer had to be taken off the whole ax; in his mind's eye the tool was perfectly smooth, and it had to be made so. His spear-points he made quite round in section and absolutely straight, he had no love for them until they were perfectly rounded and straight.

Dart was just the same with her things; it had come upon them as a sort of flowering of their nature, this desire that everything they produced should be well done, just as they saw it in their mind's eye and not otherwise. Dart decked herself over the source, mirroring her loveliness and thinking out new and graceful trappings for it, trying and turning the skins on her person, this way and that way, before she cut them out and joined them into a new skirt. She talked to herself about it half aloud, spread out the stuff on the ground and pondered over it; she plaited and invented new patterns, plaited everything she saw, her hair too; and Gest had to fashion a comb of bone, with many teeth, to comb it out with. When it began to get really cold she sewed fine otter skins together and made mittens of pole-cat's skin turned inside out, which she decorated on the outside with scraps of many-coloured fur.

But the smallest and finest skins Gest could bring in were tanned by Dart with special care and laid aside; and when she was making pots, which she decorated and covered with the richest designs, she made for her own amusement a whole lot of little jars besides, like a row of children the big pots had got.

In the course of the winter Dart gave birth to her first child, her little bud, and now there were three of them in the nest, the first feeble whimpering of a new life was heard in the cave underground, a little human supplication never to be forgotten.

It was a hard winter, the snow lay late, and the house by the spring was snowed under in a great drift and lay buried for weeks, while the world above it lay buried in darkness. So long had winter lasted that summer was forgotten. The memory of it remained, but summer itself could not be recalled — it had always been winter. Even the river was frozen over, and Gest went out on the ice, wrapped to the eyes in furs like a bear, and speared eels. The muddy fish tasted distantly of summer slime and fresh open water; summer was a long way off.

But now a springtime had come to them in the dark days, a little harbinger, tender and defenceless like the very earliest spring flowers that come up with their bulbs under the snow and hang their white bells in the moist wind; like the furry buds on the willow that raise a smile of spring to the thawing clouds and the first powerless sun; Dart had repeated herself and produced a bud just like herself when she was little, with a white nap all over, downy and sunny-bright about the head, a little girl too, the smallest, sweetest and liveliest little woman in the world. Gest had a catch in his throat, a change was wrought for ever in his heart when he lifted the warm little creature in his arms for the first time and saw how tiny she was. She was a bud, and Bud should be her name. Gentle as her mother she was, only uttered a few little whimperings when she came into the world and then sank back into the long sleep from which she had come, like the long sleep of spring, lingering in repose before it comes out as spring.

It was a wondrous child, strangely fair, silent and full of life. Gest fitted another string to his bow-harp, the two he had did not suffice to express her nature, in the new one he put her soul, a high, delicate, joyful note. During the long winter days he sat playing to his Dart and his Bud and singing songs, till it seemed as if the narrow underground cave were filled with sunshine and the notes of birds, the summer wind and the quiet talk of leaves in fresh-clad woods.

And even as he sang this all came about, the loveliest spring broke in upon them that year, when at last winter's time was past and the storms had raged out and the showers were spent and the sun grown warm.

The first green day, with warmth on the sheltered side and yellow flowers in the grass, Dart took her Bud up to the spring and let the surface of the water kiss her, that she might have its strength and be pure and inexhaustible as it was; she held her up to the sky and gave her to the daylight, held her towards the forest and prayed that it might shelter her; and then she laid her down under the big tree by the spring that she might touch its roots and acquire fecundity. And as she lay there they could see the wonder of the earth reflected in her clear eyes. The little hands shrank shyly from their first touch of the world — but then what things they were she saw! a great frog took a huge leap and hopped right over the Bud — no doubt a happy omen, but what *was* she to think of it!

But it was not long before Bud showed a predilection for devouring not only frogs but anything else that moved within her reach, and from that time forward she behaved like most other marvels in human form of the same age.

Spring passed in blissfulness and song, and summer once more established its summer eternity, high summer, midsummer, a dazzling realm full of sport and good days; winter came again, and winter too was good.

But when another spring arrived the little girl could totter by herself out into the air and stretch out her small hands to the sun and forest. And that spring the family broke up their home by the source and prepared for a long journey. Gest wanted to see the world. He had made up his mind to go down the river, out of the fjord and on along the coast in search of new countries. In the course of the winter Gest had built a new canoe, bigger and broader than the old one, out of a real giant among trees, but boat-building was only an amusement to him now with the big sharp-ground axes he had.

When all was ready and the season come, they set out proudly with all they possessed and desired to possess in the roomy new boat. There were Gest's new weapons, bow and arrows, lance, and his good tools, all they required of skins and clothes; and there was Gest's harp which had grown out of his bow and become his friend; there was his firestick, for which the bow had again had to adapt itself; Gest passed a slack bowstring around the fire-drill and turned it by drawing the bow backwards and forwards with one hand while holding the drill in place with the other; it never failed, whether he mumbled or sang to it. They would be able to cook food in the boat, Gest had made a fireplace of earth and stones amidships, he was thinking of voyages where perhaps they would not have a chance of landing every day; the hearth was to go afloat with them. Fish-spears, hooks and nets they took, of course; where one can float one can fish.

At her end of the boat sat Dart, and the paddle in her hands was a work of art, decorated with carvings and ornaments by Gest in the long winter evenings; and at the stem of the canoe he had carved an image which was supposed to represent a squirrel; it was to go in front and bring them luck.

Round her neck Dart wore a necklace of many rows of animals' teeth, all of them picked eyeteeth, a costly piece of work which held within it the souls of all the beasts Gest had brought down since he became a hunter. At her feet in a nest of skins sat the Bud, blue-eyed and holy, in an ermine hood and holding in her hand a bird's bone inside which her father had put little pebbles, so that it rattled enchantingly when she waved it in the air like a sceptre; it was a thing to scare away evil spirits. And in the prow of the canoe sat Gest broad-shouldered, dipping his double paddle in deep, slow strokes that made the boat jump forward each time.

Thus they set out. Against the stream they had come into the country in distant days now almost forgotten, when all was beginning; downstream they went now, back to the fjord and bound for new shores. Gest's nostrils expanded at the thought of meeting the sea again.

The voyage lasted a couple of summer months and took them round Sealand, as it turned out at last, for they lost their bearings on the way and were not quite clear about how the world was pointing.

They sailed out of the fjord by night, silently and in mid-channel, saw nothing of the people of the settlement and had nothing to say to them either. Gest had always had an idea in his head that he ought to have the coast on his left hand when he came out of the fjord and wanted to follow the land in the direction of the unknown foreign country the Elders talked about; he sailed that way and they soon came into pretty rough water and hugged the coast as closely as possible. They knew that there was land on the other side, but it was no part of Gest's plans to try that way, and besides the water seemed too wide. So they kept along the coast in the hope sooner or later of slipping out of the country and finding their way to the great rivers the old men prosed about.

But the coast proved to be indented with many bays, several times it ran up into extensive, branching fjords, and as they always sailed in the immediate neighbourhood of land they had to take all the ramifications before they got out into the open water again; it was a long voyage, they turned completely round time after time and lost all direction, but in the end they left off worrying about where they were going. There was no hurry, they supported themselves on the way, lay still and fished, and Gest went ashore to hunt where the land invited thereto. They saw a great deal and had many strange adventures, though none of a fateful nature.

The coast was everywhere pretty much alike, low and with woods or bluffs down to the sea, in some places sandhills; dense, close forests inland wherever they came. As a rule they could see other coasts or islands on the far side of the water, sometimes fairly near, but they still followed the land from which they had started, with the coast on their left hand, as Gest knew he ought to do. Now and then they saw smoke rising from the forest or in the neighbourhood of the coast, and then they proceeded cautiously, hiding in the daytime and only passing the suspicious places at night; they had no mind to encounter men.

Thus they lost themselves in the world and became experienced travellers, having their eyes opened by constantly seeing new shores. At last they came again to a fjord that ran up into the country; there were many of them, it couldn't be denied, and this one was not particularly broad; Gest considered whether it would not be best to cross its mouth and sail on beyond, but decided after all to follow the land; there was no knowing whether it was closed at the end or perhaps might be the very opening he was looking for.

But what was their surprise on going a little way up the fjord to see it open out into a bay with shallow water and masses of seagulls, shores and headlands opposite that seemed familiar; strange how it resembled their native fjord which they had left in the morning of time! Could it be possible that two fjords, with at least half a world lying between them, could be so exactly alike? Absolutely the same woods with their bent trees creeping up from the beach! And with the same settlement inside the bay — they swung round a headland and at once saw smoke, boats hauled up on the beach — and now at last it dawned on them that it *was* their native settlement to which they had returned by unspeakably roundabout ways. They had simply sailed round the whole country, and as it was an island, that could only end in bringing them back to their starting-point.

They were well received. The meeting was really cordial, without a trace of bitterness on either side. That the old quarrel was forgotten and not to be dug up again was a matter of course, now that the tribe's prodigal son had come home and had made himself famous as a seafarer. So at last it had been proved, by actual circumnavigation, that Sealand was an island. Well, wasn't that what the Elders had always said? And it resulted of course from direct observation that the face of the earth was circular, that could be *seen*, the earth was an island in the ocean, as everybody had naturally supposed, and now it had been proved. Which was the more meritorious, to supply the tangible evidence by a voyage, or to sit at home and think the whole thing out by inner sagacity, was left undetermined; both parties had every reason to feel respect for each other.

Gest found his mother Gro unchanged. She did not walk much now, preferring to have things brought to her; people she wanted to talk to had to be at the trouble of calling on her. Dart and her Bud were presented to her on arrival, and she pronounced herself appreciatively about the child's condition and obviously good nursing, paying at the same time a handsome tribute to the young mother.

After the inspection was over Dart mixed gaily with her friends, young mothers who had been children with her but had had babies while Dart was away; and she had to lift her Bud in the air and measure it against all the other buds to see which was biggest. There was a great difference, some of the young mothers' children were short and fat, others more in the form of a ball, but Dart's Bud, though plump, was slighter and more slender than any of the others. Great was the joy at that end of the settlement on meeting again; it now appeared that Dart, though she had never breathed a word of it, had always had great longing to see other women she knew and to exchange motherly wisdom with them.

Gest was duly received into the company of the men of the settlement, submitted without turning a hair to all the bloody and cruel ordeals prescribed before one could be initiated into the men's traditional mysteries; it turned out that he knew most of them pretty well beforehand. Gest soon became one of the foremost hunters of the tribe.

VIII

THE VOYAGERS

ʙᴜᴛ he could not keep away from the sea. On the voyage round Sealand the clouds had got into his soul, they had passed over him like great creatures of the air with outspread wings travelling through the sky — where were they going? It was plain that they were carried along by the wind, for they always went the way the wind was blowing — where did the wind come from, and where did it go to?

If the wind could take the clouds with it, why should one not commit one's self to it in a boat? Gest began experimenting with a sail in his canoe, a mat stuck up on a pole to begin with; it bore but little likeness to the spacious clouds, but still he drifted along the same way as they, not so slowly either, it was clear that he was on the right track.

The Elders shook their heads at Gest's sailing freaks, they had heard the like before but never wasted any trouble on it; but he got several of the young men of the place to join him and together they made prolonged trials with sails in their dug-out boats, first inside the bay, then more and more boldly out in the open sea. They soon reached the limit of sail the narrow canoes could carry, they capsized easily, and of course they could not be made broader in the beam than the thickest tree in the forest; so they tried putting two together and connecting them with cross-spars, or they gave the canoe an outrigger, a trunk floating a little way from its side and fastened to it by several wooden stays; this gave a boat the power of carrying as much sail as if it had had three or four times the beam, and without taking anything off its way.

With new and complicated craft like these the young men made longer and longer voyages to sea, as by degrees they assured themselves that it was perfectly safe. The Elders had no desire to sail in winged ships of this kind; their motto had always been that you ought not to go farther from land than you could reach bottom, better to pole than to row; ships with sails were immodestly conspicuous at sea, you drew attention to yourself; it was more manly to row than to let the wind do the work; and finally it might look safe enough with that outrigger in the water to prevent the boat capsizing, but then the very safety of it was a challenge to the Powers both above and below, the stormy as well as the wet ones, which might involve fatal consequences.

As always happens in a conflict between the impetuous new generation and the circumspection of its elders, they separated. One fine day the young men went off on a longer voyage than usual, they had hinted at the coast over on the other side, and they never came back. The Elders had carried the day, they stayed in the settlement where they had always lived, and presumably the youngsters had come to grief; at all events the rash skippers were never again seen in Sealand so long as anybody was alive who could remember them; they were dead, or the world had swallowed them up.

They had as a matter of fact gone over to the other side; Gest and his companions discovered Fyn and found settlements there pretty much as at home, a similar population of shell-fish-eaters, friendly rather than ferocious, few of them cannibals and none at all supernatural as might have been expected. They had a merry time there, but as they had set out in search of new and strange things it was not long before they put to sea again. With very much the same result the young sea-rovers visited one after another all the rest of the Danish isles.

Thus they cruised about the Baltic waters until at last they found the great continental rivers, ascended them and penetrated far into Central Europe; they fished their way on, and when they could no longer float they went ashore and turned hunters, shot their way on through wastes and dense forests, came into wild mountain tracts, until they found rivers again on the other side;

then they turned fishermen again and sailed thousands of miles into Asia, lost themselves on boundless steppes and became reindeer hunters, were carried northward through sparse forests and over frozen swamps to the Polar Sea where the sun was almost lost. Here they hunted seals and made themselves boats of skins for lack of timber, found their way along the cold coasts to the outlet of other mighty rivers, which carried them back as fishermen thousands of miles into Asia again, and once more they turned hunters in new wild forests and made their way across other mountains of terrifying steepness which raised snow-capped walls to the clouds between heaven and earth; but where the mountain goat could go they too found foothold and food — namely the goats; these mountains they conquered in their turn and came down into the warm valleys with rivers that drew them on to the south; the great tiger showed his stripes as he turned among the reeds on the bank; naked they now sat in their boats and the sun opened gates of fire above their heads. Thus they reached the warm countries, through the tropical jungles and out of them again, to the borders of Asia on the south and east, the whole immense circuit of the coasts, and northward again to the farthest arctic islands in ice-bound seas, wheer they took to seal hunting again; from there they passed over to the American continent and found the moose, lived in forest and mountain, made themselves bark canoes and bored their way through rivers and lakes into the interior, came out upon immense prairies and hunted the buffalo; tropical America swallowed them and kept some, just as some had stayed behind wherever they went, but others emerged again and spread over the bleak plains of South America; on to the south they pushed and could not understand how it was this time that the farther south they went the colder it grew. Here they hunted beasts like camels which they caught with a noose, and their wanderings only came to an end at the extreme point of South America, on cold, gloomy winter island not unlike those they had come from in the beginning; here some of them settled, in a sort of consciousness that they had arrived at the world's end and yet to all intents and purposes were back at their starting-point, no way forward and no way back, discontent taking the place of longing — and they are there to this day!

But others found their way from Asia to great islands in the ocean and pushed on south of the sun, became snake-eaters and pursued beasts that hopped; their souls too were closed, they had come into a pocket of existence and had forgotten who they were. And others again set out at random upon the South Seas, committed themselves to mighty billows in their miserable out-rigger canoes, riding half in the water with naked feet which the sharks snapped at; on *them* they lived, fishing their way on, and came to little palm-wreathed islands, smoking volcano summits, in the immeasurable ocean, remote and forgotten by Time, like the seed that floats on the wind, whose fate is never known.

It was the great Stone Age migration which Gest and his com-panions had been caught up in, and which absorbed their instincts long after they were dead; new hunters and fishermen, generation after generation beyond all count; they were a part of this human wave which spread in ever-increasing rings, until it was cast up on the farthest shores of the uttermost sea.

Nor were they the first, for other waves had gone before, a procession of generations, the early Forest Folk that had lived before the Ice Age, whom the cold had driven out and who now hid themselves, shunning the daylight, in the hot vaults of tropical jungles in the heart of Asia and Africa; all the distant, widely-scattered border folk, who generation after generation had thrust each other on towards the extreme coasts of the continents; their waves broke over these wherever they went, peaceably or in con-flict; and the march went on, the ages passed.

But at last there came a time when Gest bethought himself, went over in his mind the long way he had come and was home-sick for the place he had set out from. Many generations he had followed, and they were all dead; there alone he could not follow them, for he could not die, he was the very spirit of travel. He did not even grow old, so long as he was on his wanderings. But now he had a longing for an abiding place.

He was on an island in the outer ocean, the farthest of them all, hundreds of leagues from the other islands, when this despondency fell upon him. The deep sea ringed about the island on every side with a succession of long, slow-rolling waves; he was in the cen-tre of the ocean swell, and over his head leaned a palm-tree with its top full of fruit, like a breast with many breasts; then it came upon him that he could not stay, the old unrest which hitherto had always set him off on his travels, but he did not move. He was homesick for the big old tree by the spring in Sealand and the northern stars, and so violent was his longing that he could not bear to think of the same endless journey back again as he had come. Then he determined to die and took out his candle, which he had kept so long, and lighted it.

It was a strange candle, it burned quickly, but the present and eternity were in its flame. It was as though time had not gone by, there was no time, Gest had his whole life about him at once, far-off things were near, Mother Gro, whose hands had fashioned the candle, was with him, his beloved Dart was beside him, breathing into the flame; the only unreal thing was that he had ever been parted from them. For a brief moment he had turned away, and now he was at home again. Then he felt so glad that he no longer had any wish to die, and hastily he blew out the candle.

After the dazzling light black darkness fell. But even as he sat in the dark he could feel that he was in a different atmosphere, he no longer heard the long roaring thunder of the surf on the reef of the island; all was still, and close at hand he could hear the tinkling sound of running water.

Little by little the dawn spread around him, and he saw that he lay beneath the cool foliage of lofty trees. A distant ring of hushed music surrounded him on every side, the cool nocturnal witch-craft of the frogs; it was a clear night, and above his head were misty stars, the old familiar constellations. For he was in Sealand, where he had always been!

The grass where he sat was cool and the night refreshing; he sighed out all his sighs in a single sigh, sank back with closed eyes and slept on Sealand's breast.

IX

THE RICH VALLEY

H E woke at the sound of his name, a laughing voice that asked what kind of a guest this might be. . . .

On opening his eyes he was dazzled by the sun, and close by in the pale green wood he saw a woman.

For a long, long time he looked at her. Well what kind of a guest was he, where was he, who was she?

Gest could not take his eyes off this wonderful woman; he knelt in the grass and looked at her. Was she supernatural, some friendly forest deity? Strange were her garments, a dark brown woven skirt of cunning workmanship, and a tunic, neither of skin nor of bast, made to fit closely to the body and arms. In her hand, with the frugality of women, she held a long stick that chanced to have a crook in it, and at that moment Gest discovered a new marvel — behind her in the wood moved several cows of a kind that he did not recognize at first, neither bisons nor deer but a sort of cattle; and they did not seem to be wild, grazing quite quietly among the neighbouring trees; from one of them came the sound of a bell every time it moved, from some hollow thing or other on its neck; what was it, were they her animals, were they supernatural too, how could they go about so peacefully together? She must be a great sorceress, since she could put a spell upon the beasts; but she was no sibyl to look at, neither old nor ugly, quite the reverse.

His staring at last put the young goddess out of countenance, she laughed and would have turned away, but he hastily reached out for her skirt; it was real, his hand could feel the thick, soft stuff. She stayed still, silent and with a smile on her lips, a smile he knew — it must be Dart! Was it Dart?

She shook her head at his question, understanding his language; and he too understood what she said, though their speech was very different. What was she called, who was she?

Well her name was Skur, she was a cow-maid and a thrall at the homestead yonder — she tossed her head in the direction of the wood.

Thrall? Homestead? Cow-maid?

Gest asked no more; riddles multiplied with each fresh thing he was told. Cautious observation was better than exposing himself by too many questions.

Thus the conversation dropped, but they still looked long at each other and a liking grew up before they were aware of it; to him she was not of this world, a wonder in human form, with Dart's warm smile and yet not Dart, and she could hardly resist his obvious admiration. Slowly they began to walk in company, she with head bowed as though to warm waves breaking over her, he rich of soul and uneasy already with the fear of losing her.

From the first they were a pair. They influenced each other powerfully, he as a stranger, she as a mystery; but even when they had come to know each other better they remained a pair; it made no difference that she was a mortal, nor was she disappointed that, though a stranger, he was a man like other men.

They spent the lovely spring day together in the forest, and Skur taught her friend how she tended cows, he helping her, though as a hunter it took him a long while to get used to such a tame sort of game. She ruled her cows with gentleness, kept them together by her voice and made them go in the direction she wanted simply by leading the bell-cow, which all the rest followed. Gest examined the bell and found that it was a hollow piece of wood with a clapper in it, very clever and pretty work.

In the evening Skur drove her herd into an outhouse in the wood, a fairly large building of logs, strikingly well squared, with walls of faggots and a roof of rafters thatched with straw, all very proper to look at, a big and sumptuous abode, thought Gest, even for men.

And here Skur milked her cows.

Gest was silent while this went on; he expressed no astonishment but looked on and took note of what he saw, he was always ready to learn. So she squeezed the milk out of the cows with her hands, and why not? — adroitly catching the jets in a pail; he could scarcely control his curiosity about the pail, which was not made in one piece but built up of several staves, with a hoop of withies round it, an extraordinarily neat piece of handiwork. The cows willingly let themselves be milked, they stood chewing the cud and puffing, warm and fragrant, the whole house was full of twilight and the sweet smell of milk. When Skur had filled her first pail, with her forehead pressed against the cow's belly and seated on a three-legged stool, she rose and put the pail to Gest's mouth; he drank the foaming drink, full of vital warmth, shyly and with deep emotion.

Skur poured the milk of all the cows, many pails full, into shallow round tubs which she put up on shelves in the cowhouse, and when she had finished she came into the doorway, where there was still daylight, with a cake and began cutting bread.

Gest tasted and ate, quite incapable by now of grasping any more. A food made of kernels, he could tell that, baked into a lump and sweet, and while he was still eating and thinking he had never tasted anything so delicious, she put a new food into his hand, cheese — ?? — he looked at it, smelt it, ate and shook his head with the deepest gratification. But then the knife — the knife; what was it that cut such thin slices and was so narrow? The knife was of bronze. Gest sighed, the riddles overwhelmed him, there were too many of them. Wait a bit, let us see, let us think. Much wisdom was required to penetrate so many hidden things at once!

And indeed it took Gest a long time to get quite familiar with the way things were. The place he had come to was his native valley, but everything was changed. He must have been away a very long time, a thousand years or so; he had left in the grey Stone Age and had come home in the middle of the Bronze Age. All those who had shared his wanderings had remained at the same stage while they were on the way, with them motion had taken the place of growth; here, where people had been sitting still, they had become different men. Gest was a long time finding out merely wherein the difference lay, but he never felt at home with it.

They were the same people as they had always been, but new generations, without the smallest recollection of the past which Gest shared with them; and they had multiplied, the valley was inhabited from the coast up along the fjord and the river and far inland. Gest never associated with any but Skur, the first he had met.

Amongst all the other things that were new to him Gest discovered that Skur was unfree, that is to say she was owned by a man in one of the homesteads of the valley who could put her to any work he chose and in all else disposed over her lot. In Gest's day there had been only one kind of folk, now there were two, masters and thralls, and to the latter class Skur belonged.

She was living alone in the woods when Gest found her, tending the cows and making cheese from the milk while the summer lasted; she slept in the pen with the cattle, and nobody asked any more of her. For the sake of her working efficiency care was taken that she was left in peace; girls that were to run after the cattle had to be kept apart, like those that were set to tend the fire, one thing at a time; they were decent people at the homestead she belonged to. On her own account she kept a cudgel just inside the door in case any hunters or young fellows might be prowling round at night. But she was no hater of men, and now without much reflection she had given herself to this strange guest, because he wanted it so badly and it was to be he. They shared the light nights, and Skur's springtime came to her.

It was Dart and yet not Dart. She had Dart's loving mouth but not her slender form, and her hair was not fair, nor black either; red it could not be called, it was something like the colour of peat; but for that matter she had hardly any, it had been blown off her, she said. But for the shortness of her hair she made up in the length of her fidelity, a warm dumb soul that swelled once for all with gratitude for being loved. Heavily built she was, looking almost dangerous in her strength of limb, but with a blameless heart, a fountain of generosity and cheerful withal, full of latent tenderness and happiness if only the sun would shine on her.

Gest saw handsomer and grander women later on, for the daughters of the free men of the valley were dazzlingly beautiful, flocks of tall, fair, sprightly maidens, with a sea of hair flowing down their backs and a wealth of ornaments, flashing new bronze rings on arm and neck, sometimes gold, and a bronze sun in the middle of the pliant tunic, not too great an ornament for a slender girl's waist; they were garbed in costly homespun, thick, heavy woollens that had taken masses of yarn, a fortune in themselves and beyond question burdensome in summer, but they had to be worn; to make up for it they naturally had nothing on underneath. The latest fashion was not to gather the skirt together with the belt, as was the natural thing to do when it had been thrown round the body, but to fasten one end high above the other, so that there was a pleated edge in front, like a basket of folds in which they carried their proud breasts, decently concealed but with outlines that could not be hidden, beneath the smooth woollen bodice; this was the custom of the valley and every one followed it. On the head, when their hair was not fluttering free, they wore a little network cap, full of the golden hair which hung imprisoned therein like a heavy lump of light weighing upon the neck.

A sight not to be forgotten was to see the young daughters of the freemen being driven in bronze-mounted cars from one homestead to another by their stately sword-bearing fathers, behind little shaggy snorting steeds and followed by a cavalcade of young mounted spearmen.

But Gest kept to the homely bondwoman who had appeared to

him in the glory of a goddess when he saw her for the first time
and who had since enriched his heart in simple human wise.

Not only were the people changed and their way of life quite
different, but the country itself had undergone great changes in
the time Gest had been away.

The first thing he looked for was the spring up in the valley
where Dart and he had lived. It was there still but did not give
much water, and the deep source itself was overgrown, the greensward had closed over it; the mirror and what Gest and Dart had
seen therein was no more. Now the source came out of a wilderness of weeds on the ground, many little springs that trickled and
ran together to form a thin stream. And the river where it ran
out was now nothing but a brook.

The big deep river which ran with a swift current up to the
top of its banks had shrunk and lost itself in winding intricacy
through the meadows, choked with water-plants and vegetation;
the meadows themselves were drained and cleared by human
hands, and up towards the sides of the valley he came upon large
open spaces of purely arable land, glades in the forest which had
been cleared and made fit for agriculture; here the crops of the
year grew in green wind-stirred plains, like the wild grasses Gest
had known inland, but here was all the same kind of grass which
was cultivated for the sake of its seed. And in the midst of the green
clearings stood the homesteads.

Elsewhere the forest remained the same, where no gaps had been
broken in it, extending dense and pathless into the interior, and the
game was as before, though scarcer and more timid, as Gest
learned by experience.

Only the bisons had vanished from the forest; some of their
blood had passed into the tame bulls, who resembled them but were
much smaller. But deer and wild pig were still there. Now tame
swine were kept on the farms, besides horses, sheep and other
domestic animals that were not indigenous to the country; the migration of domestic animals was an obscure saga in itself. The disappearance of the bisons made the woods quieter, the great roar to
greet the sun was no longer heard in the valley. But a memory of
it was preserved in the shrill note of the *lur*, the great bronze horn
which was heard now and then in the valley and meant either a
sacrificial solemnity or war, some sanguinary encounter between

lords of the soil who could not agree and marched against one another at the head of their men.

People were more relentless now than they used to be; then they had been full of threats, noisily calling down slaughter for a week or so, without bloodshed; now they stabbed and then without a word, they had lengthened their knives; nobody now seemed to feel the smart in his own breast at the bare thought of wounding his neighbour. So when the lurs woke echoes in the valleys there was blood in their note. It was as though the bisons' mad onslaught at pairing time still haunted the air. In their very curves the lurs recalled the bisons' horns, which had been blown before they were imitated in metal; but that was so long ago that even the population of the valley had forgotten all about it; so long had Gest been away.

But if the voice of the primitive bull had passed into the signals with which the free owners of the soil called each other to single combat over disputed land, the primitive cow reappeared in the tame cattle which grazed in the woods and shared their peaceable disposition with the quiet folk who owned nothing and were set to tend the beasts and till the ground. If the thralls had been asked whence they came they would have answered that they were born to it. And where were they born? Probably in the turf-pit or the pigsty where they lived. But for that matter they never showed any discontent. Thus the life of the valley had assorted itself.

And it was populous, restless both to the eye and the ear, a bustling traffic along both the roads which ran from the coast inland, one on each side of the valley; hardly a day passed that one did not meet some man on horseback or driving along at breathless speed; and it was not as in old days some man one knew and whose business one could guess by the look of him, tell what he was hunting; now they were all strange faces, nothing was to be read in them, and their errands might be of the most various kinds; life was a complicated affair now, it was impossible to survey it any more.

Besides people flying along the roads a thrall might often be seen at work in the fields, or a herdsman; the wild animals had of course fled from the valley but in their place you saw the tame ones. An everlasting sound of men and their companions came from the valley, the barking of dogs from every side, the neighing of horses and distant cries, the shriek from the hub of an

ungreased barrow, crowing of cocks – foreign birds that spread
their feathers here and grew thick-voiced and impudent; tame
geese that shot their necks at a wayfarer and wanted to bite, poor
wretched poultry, now bound to earth and fat of throat, robbed
of the music of the clouds as in the days when they were birds.
From the homesteads, from the women's quarters, stole the cat,
another foreigner, creeping on tiger's paws in the dewy grass with
its snake's eyes, on the hunt for the innocent native field-mouse.
There was always some movement, always some buzz of sound
in the old valleys, once so silent, if it was only the hum of the
children's toy mills which they stuck up in the breeze on the pal-
ings. Yes, wealth and life had come into the valley.

Gest preferred to keep to the forest. At the top of the valley,
round about the source, it was fairly untouched but was not the
same forest, even the oldest trees were other than Gest had known;
the tall old ash by the spring was gone and in its stead there grew
a little grove of many smaller ash-trees, perhaps ground shoots of
the big tree in which Gest and Dart had once had their nest. Of
the house in the ground where they had lived there was not the
smallest trace, turf many centuries old covered the spot. The
forest murmured, but with a different murmur from the old.

And what of the settlement on the bay inside the fjord? Not a
soul lived there nor had done for generations, there was not a
trace of human habitation; only a long low ledge above the beach,
overgrown with wild plants, showed where the settlement had
been. There were still fishermen, but they lived out on the coast
in quite different conditions and had no traditions about there ever
having been a fishing station inside the fjord. They had clincher-
built boats and went sea-fishing in the Belt.

In a harbour in the fjord, by the beginnings of a town, lay great
sailing craft, so big that the canoe, which had sunk into a dinghy,
looked like a tiny baby beside them, as it lay made fast by the
painter. Yes, those were ships, and Gest hung about them a long
while at a distance, studied them almost in fear, circling round
before he ventured little by little to approach, the wonder of them
was too much for him all at once.

They came and went between foreign lands! Some of them
were so big that they could take twelve or twenty men, besides
cargo! They expanded the soul with immense vague ideas of the
distant realms they came from, entirely different regions from

those in which Gest had lost himself; they were the mysterious countries from which all this wealth had come to the valley, the metals, the domestic animals and the knowledge of agriculture — and Gest kept silence, said nothing even to himself if he could help it; had not life cheated him after all, in spite of his travels and all that he had seen?

This traveller and discoverer might now turn and begin again, travelling and discovering in his own home, so had time slipped from him. Was there any part for him in this entirely new world on the old soil?

The valley and all the conditions of life in it gave him a silent answer, as he gradually made his way into things and learned to understand them. The homesteads were closed to him. They spoke with their open green cornfields, but they were fenced in, the husbandman owned the land together with his family, and the woodland around they owned in common with other families, up to the boundaries where other ownerships began, other groups of families in other valleys beyond the forest; everywhere the whole island was as thickly populated throughout its valleys as here. The boundaries only met in the midst of wide uninhabited forests, but on every hand the right of proprietorship was vindicated, whence it was that the lur spoke now and again and the long stabbing sword sat so loosely in its scabbard. So there was no chance of Gest getting any land, since he had no kin.

The landowners lived on their estates in log houses of heavy timber, many different houses grouped together and fenced in; they did not object to visits, they were armed and feared nobody; how to get past the shaggy bandog that foamed and danced round itself by the yard gate was the wayfarer's own business; the master of the house was gracious enough to a wanderer, especially if he had some stories and could tell them or was gifted as a bard. He was liberally treated and offered shelter, in the loft or in an outhouse, according to his appearance, but next day it was understood, quite reasonably, that the wayfarer must move on.

Gest for his part soon found his place. Who he was and where he came from nobody knew or cared, and he never touched on that himself; but it had got about that it was he who had taken up with Skur the cow-maid in the woods; nobody took him to task for it, but still people seemed to recoil a little stiffly when they saw him. For, apart from the fact that as a stranger he had involuntarily chosen his own position, he had begun by committing a little breach of the law, a depreciation of the girl's value, not yet visible but presumably to be expected before long, to the injury of another man's property.

They were not mistaken. Towards the end of the summer Skur began to lose her breath when she had to run after the cows. By that time Gest had also made up his mind about his position and seen that there was no place for him here. At first a certain curiosity made him quite favourably received at the homesteads, for he played the harp remarkably well. The fine freemen's daughters were carried away by the waves of an undreamt-of world rushing over them in his music, but their dilated eyes went beyond him, they had visions but saw him not. And if they did see him their eyes froze up and their nose gave a jerk as though it caught the smell of the cowshed.

Gest did not envy the lords of the land. They lived amid a wealth of which greed for more made them unaware. Dry bread was no longer good enough, they cried for added delicacies; supporting one's self alone in the woods, as men had been able to do in old time, was a lost art; even the thralls talked about being hungry if they hadn't a loaf in their fists, and that in a mast year!

Gest could easily have made a living, if they had but allowed him room. He would willingly have been a fisherman, but found that his catch would be taxed and he would have to pay rent to the owner of the shore rights, and that was not to his liking. Within the fjord where the ships lay a number of unattached people had taken up their abode, owning no land but supporting themselves in various ways; here, for instance, dwelt the bronze-smith who made all the fine weapons and ornaments of metal. After watching his work a few times Gest caught on to the handicraft and had a taste for it, but when he had made himself a good ax and a knife his inclination was exhausted: working for others, even for pay, seemed to him an ignoble lot. Wherever he turned it was obvious that he would be dependent on others.

So for the present he took to the woods with Skur, thus making his crime complete. As a robber he was free as a bird, as he had been once before.

But this time things were not so easy. No doubt he could live as a hunter in the forest, but in the long run it would be hard to keep in hiding, even in the thickest and most remote parts of the island. Swineherds passed through, or other hunters came prying about; a fixed dwelling was not to be thought of, and without one you could live in summer but not in winter.

So Gest once more fashioned himself a craft on Sealand's shore, in an out-of-the-way place where he could escape discovery for the time, and when the birds of passage began their flight he too set out and sailed with Skur to other shores.

X

IN SWEDEN

THE COUPLE felt by no means poor and abandoned as they left the coast of Sealand behind and steered for the unknown. Gest had fish-hooks and bow with him as he always had, and as to the bronze knife and ax, he had to go and hide himself in order to enjoy these possessions to the full. To him they represented his share in all the glories of the rich native valley he was now leaving. Perfectly astonishing it was what these new implements could accomplish. And he had well noted what it meant: the fine big log houses that were closed to him might be made real elsewhere and bring him the right to the ground whereon they stood; he too would become a landowner and had made a note in his head of all that pertained thereto.

He laughed again and again as he told Skur of his good fortune with the two bronze things. He had himself cast and forged them to gain a knowledge of the nature of the metal, and he had paid for his instruction, everything had to be paid for; but he had also paid for the metal, and that was dear, there was a lot of weight in the ax, and what did she think he had given for it all? A stone, just a little bright stone that he had picked up once on his travels and kept because it was red; that bronze man's eyes were like hot coals when he saw it and he would have loaded him with more metal than he could carry simply to get it — well, some people were fools. And Gest roared with laughter over the crazy fellow who had handed over an ax and a knife of bronze for a little stone!

But Skur was not devoid of possessions either when she left the country, for she had in the boat a little bag of seedcorn which she guarded as her dearest treasure; it was to rise again as a cornfield in her new home, if the Spirits of the soil were willing and Heaven gave its blessing; and in her arms she held two young kids, a pair, they were hers, and she took them with her when she ran away. She would have liked to take her cows too, but they were not hers, and besides there was no room for them in the boat. The kids gave her trouble enough, they were afraid of the water and wanted to jump overboard, and at last she had to tie their feet together and lay them down where they could do no harm.

It was not long however before they could land on another coast and let the kids have ground under their feet for a little while every day, and afterwards they got their sea legs and stood up in the boat without having to be looked after. Gest left Sealand on the side opposite to his valley, over against the great land of Sweden which he knew of but had never before visited. He crossed the Sound in its narrowest part, in fair weather, nothing even for a heavily laden canoe, and when he was across he turned northward along the coast in the direction of the low mountain chain that lay like an outpost in the sea; it was his object to look for a river that might lead him up into the country. Southward he did not go, since he knew that the whole of Skoane and the coast towards the Baltic were well populated, and, as in all his travels, it was not men he sought for.

Wherever along the coast they saw smoke or other sign of habitation they passed by, if they could, or lay concealed till nightfall; they entered the first river of any size they came to after rounding the promontory and found its banks apparently uninhabited, but after travelling up it for a couple of days they saw entrails drifting with the stream and turned, seeing that there were men higher up. In the next, which ran out farther north along the coast, they again found men; they came unexpectedly upon a skin boat in a creek among rocks where they themselves had put in to hide, but the people in the boat were more frightened than they, shamming death and lying immovable at the bottom of their boat so long as they looked at them, with the whites of their eyes showing and their mouths wide open. They were little people, there were two of them, with coarse black hair; their mouths were long and pink at the corners, they were very greasy, had salmon in their boat and were evidently fishermen. None of their gear was of metal. Gest decided not to go up that river either.

But the next again, which was a big, fairly rapid stream, did not look much frequented; great fallen trees lay rotting and untouched everywhere along the banks, few if any landed and lighted fires here, that was easy to see, and up this waterway they voyaged for many days, deeper and deeper into the country, among a maze of forests, no lofty trees, but slender, light and open woods, mostly birch, with bogs and glades between, rocky ground with scattered blocks as high as houses, and here and there firm rock. The country was wide and open but with stretches of valley and turns and heights which gave a view, a paradise for game, and in primeval stillness, entirely after Gest's heart. He felt that here nature was younger, here he would stay.

Far up the country, where the river narrowed but still abounded in fish and where there were tracks of elk on the bank, they sought a lodging one night under some huge rocks which projected one above the other so that they formed a shelter; here they stayed, and this was their first house in the new country. The kids climbed the rocks as soon as they were put ashore, clambered up as high as they could come above the house and seemed happy, they too felt attracted by the country. Gest began to look about him in the forest with his bow and felled trees for a dwelling when he was at home; matchless his new ax was; Skur found a level space near with a soil of mould which could be made useful for a crop when the worst of the stones were cleared, and she went to work at it without delay, with her giantess's strength, carrying off big and small stones and building a fence with them round the cleared space; it was a couple of score of paces each way and neither round nor square; that was their first farm.

The forest was uninhabited on every side for many miles around; on his long hunting expeditions Gest made sure that he had that part of the country to himself. At a distance the forest was bounded in one direction by great lakes, which he had not examined closely; in another, many days' journey away, the land ran up into long, low, rounded hills, masked by snow late in the year — the cold corner of the country; from that quarter he fetched a reindeer when he wanted one.

The elk was found in the forest in his immediate neighbourhood, the broad scoops of its horns, like immense hands with outspread fingers, showed among the foliage in the wet, low-lying forest swamps. He did not scare them, they should be allowed to live undisturbed by the bark of dogs; Gest hunted without a dog and usually went about the forest as quietly as the other animals. Once or twice a year he took a bull, when it was necessary, and as a rule without its knowing anything about it; the lightning struck, it had the shaft in its body and fell, without so much as having time to feel sick; one had to live but not to do harm. Therefore Gest never had to go far for food.

At home he was a carpenter and raised a fine log hut under the lee of the great rocks where they had first made their camp. He learned husbandry from Skur, and in the course of years they extended the farm with many small fields, all well fenced with the stones they had cleared off them; in time they grew more corn than they could consume. The pair of goats became a herd. They themselves had a flock of children.

Gest was at home here. Above his head the wind passed through the wide forests, came far away with a rustle of the trees, tore along and lost itself far away in other rustling trees: the birches straightened themselves, shook all their leaves and were at rest again when he had gone by; it was the Wind God who was abroad, invisible, the cold one, the never-resting. But Gest stayed.

Over his head stood rowan-trees bathed in sunlight. Here was work for him to do; he carved wooden spoons for all the mouths there were to feed as time went on, fashioned wooden bowls for Skur of gnarled birch roots, enough to keep him busy most of the winter. Everything they possessed was made by themselves.

Gest thought he might almost call himself a lord of the soil, when a few years had gone by and they had houses and outhouses round the yard, with not a few fields about it, irregular in shape and up and down according to the lie of the land, with big rocks in the middle of the corn, but productive and always capable of extension. Of domestic animals they still had nothing but goats, and for years Skur sighed for cows, to say nothing of sheep, for goats' hair is not the same thing as wool; a pair of horses was Gest's constant dream; but all this came of itself when the children were grown up.

Skur's children, red-haired, freckled and hardy every one, were born here in the hut under the great rocks; outside its door the world displayed itself to them, a stone-fenced plot with many little houses where they took their first steps in the open and made playmates of the kids; afterwards the world expanded to the tilled fields, and then came the river and the forest; they were not very big when they began to roam on explorations as far as they dared go.

The heather received them and spread rough couches for them to lie on in summer days, with a scent of spice and the revelation of a bird's nest, well-hidden, mossy and wadded; the raspberry brake took them into its sunny cover where only their red shocks of hair showed up, whortleberry and bilberry offered them banquets in the rocky glades with fallen trees and cushions of soft moss, and here they annexed land, like the little men they were already, taking possession with a broad gesture of a tuft or a stump with lots of berries on it, if they had found it first; on such occasions no regard was paid even to kinship and the right of the first comer was always respected.

All things that crept upon the earth crossed their path and each received its own welcome: the ant, that little creature so murderous for its size, the choleric bee, the caterpillar, furry and arched as it crept its little way, the spider cunningly hoisting itself from thread to thread in its web, the black slugs that left a trail of slime and shortened themselves when touched; they learned to know the birds and greeted friends wherever they went in the forest, each tree received them with its living soul.

And the seasons changed about them, the hard winters, darkness and snow piled against their doors to the height of a man and barring the forest; but even this taught them delights, they dashed downhill on an improvised sleigh and went hunting with long strips of wood under their feet, made short work of the wolf, which sank to the bottom in the new-fallen snow, while the hunters gaily slid along the top.

Then spring came upon them with its marvel of the thaw, the bright sun, that great wooer, and the humble trees that received his k sses and began to swell with buds; song of birds and warm nights; then the long sweet summer days with the goats in the woods and the love-smitten cry of the cuckoo in the valleys with the impudent laughter that followed it, like a frivolous forest divinity; the short light nights that buried a treasure, never fully known, in the soul and every year added a new treasure to it. The harvest, when they garnered in reverence the ripe corn on their little irregular fields and chased the fox out of its last corner; the autumn's great time of nuts and berries and the wild apples which deceitfully tempted, red on one side, but were as sour as a kick in the mouth. Most things in this world they tasted and made a wise choice, wherefore they grew — and so they were grown up, at one end of the line, while the last were still small.

They were hale and strong as giants, the boys with shoulders that they had to turn sideways to the doors, not to mention ducking their heads, but then that was the only thing they bent the neck to, Father's and Mother's house door.

These tall fellows sat still as mice, wooden spoon in hand, around the supper dish, waiting decorously while Father made his usual little speech about the wonder of the corn and its unrivalled blessing; but then they fell to with a ring of the spoons on their sound teeth; down went the groats, bruised corn boiled in water, and they were nice enough partly to conceal their greediness, did not encroach on their neighbour's lawful section of the dish but met in the middle like well-bred children, until there was nothing left.

And the girls grew strong, swung the quern wherein the corn was bruised to groats, and sang a quern song, in the summer scent of the sweet grinding carn; they got a powerful swing and grew rich in bestowing nourishment and receiving intense joys.

Gest's and Skur's children put an end to their solitude and isolation in the forest; strong as had been their parents' desire to be alone, the young people's yearning for the world outside and the society of their fellows was a natural force equally irresistible.

The sons found their way through pathless forests, a journey of days and days, to inhabited places, where they appeared in the new-created majesty of primeval men to tame women who in *their* eyes were altogether too desirable and delicate to tread the earth; they simply *carried* them off, after tearing down the maiden's bowers where they were kept and thrashing those who had the keeping of them. They came home in transports with bedraggled maids and were either allowed to keep them or went off sulkily to clear a space for a new home in the neighbourhood, if the maiden was too ragged-looking and did not find favour with the family; in this way one or two new farms sprang up as offshoots of the old one.

Skur's daughters looked after their goats capitally in the woods, but were negligent of their own personal security; they met rovers who had tracked *them* from afar, gods to look at, young swains who did not beat about the bush; and then there was more offspring about the place, of which no more was to be said but that they came and Grandfather had to make a wooden spoon for another mouth. But some of the rovers didn't let the girls go when once they had had their arms round them; they became sons-in-law and perhaps got a pair of goats as a dowry with the marvel of a freckle-nosed girl who had captivated them in the woods, with help to clear a farm near Gest the Old. Thus with the years a whole hamlet arose where before had been nothing but wild forest.

The sons, who had used their eyes and pried right down to the rich inhabited tracts to the east and south, had thoughts of improving their way of life. They had grown up from childhood on Mother's hearth cakes and goat's milk cheese, dried elk's legs hung in the smoke over their beds, and there was always porridge, better food was not to be had and there was always enough of it, but variety has its charms and what one sees other people enjoying one would like to share; the boys made long trading expeditions, since they had to fill up their spare time, and brought home new domestic animals, not without great difficulty; they were several weeks conveying a couple of fowls up into the wastes from inhabited places, awkward poultry to keep alive on the way, for they couldn't walk all that distance and when carried they scratched and were apt to peck nasty holes in one's hands.

When after a great deal of trouble they got them home and went and looked under them, they were rewarded by crowing instead of eggs; the chickens grew into cocks with spurs and combs, they had been taken in and sold cocks instead of hens! Well, well, then they would have cockcrow about the place, that was the proper thing in the morning, the same as other folks; and on another journey they brought hens and were careful not to complain about being fooled the first time; no need to expose one's weakness, but they looked more carefully this time. So now the cock spread his plumage on *their* midden, and pancakes were going when Mother was kind.

One year the boys came home after long wanderings afoot, dusty and tired but happy, with a couple of sheep at their heels. This time they had taken care not to be cheated the other way about; one of the sheep was to be a ram, and a ram it was. The women could depend upon getting wool now. And there stood the sheep, docile and used to the tether, far-travelled, with yellow eyes in which a black worm seemed to be alive, dumbly chewing when given anything to eat. A new note was heard in the forest, the baaing of the ewe as she stood in the wind alone, the ram's *molm, molm, molm,* like a bitter soliloquy that was not meant to be heard but could not be kept entirely to himself. Next spring the bleating of tender lambs was heard in the yard about the houses.

Little by little all tame animals found their way there. Gest himself saw to the bees, caught the wild swarms and made hives for them, protecting them in winter with roofs of straw; their summer hum resounded deep in his soul. Soon the beehives took an important place on the farms; they were given a sheltered nook behind the houses, the beginning of a kailyard.

A great event it was when at last the first cow arrived. They had waited a long time for that, many preparations had to be made; first payment had to be got together, in skins, the hunting of many winters. The sons had gradually become experienced traders and had an idea of prices; if they were tricked now and then it was always a question who came off best in the end. People might take liberties on the sly with these shaggy, innocent country lads from the backwoods, in the far-advanced places down country where they traded; thus they were once persuaded to give a whole stack of squirrel fur for a sewing needle, just one needle, of bronze, with an eye in the middle; but the boys dashed home rejoicing through the forest, many days' run, with the needle, and in spite of the price they delighted the women with their find. Even Father Gest's eyes brightened when he saw it; his own priceless treasures, the ax and the knife, had not propagated, and this little thin baby of a needle was after all bronze.

But at last they had collected skins enough to buy the cow, a load, for many men and many journeys forth and back; it took the whole summer to complete the bargain and it was late in the autumn when they got home with the cow. She moved slowly and got sore hoofs, so that they had to let her lie down before evening; she had to graze rather a long time every day; they had to go a long way about where the forest was impenetrable; it was a tedious journey, the cow's forehead was wrinkled with fatigue, but home they came with her.

It was worth all the trouble to witness Mother Skur's joy when the cow arrived at last. It could be seen that she was getting old now, she fell to trembling when after missing them for years she again for the first time took hold of Sister's warm horns.

But with this one cow they could not go very far. A bull was wanted if they were to have calves and milk, and the outspoken sons of Gest let fall a remark about the duties of sons-in-law . . . and well it was that they had them, for this was a time for united effort, for saving and getting up betimes in the morning to scrape together all the furs and corn a bull would cost. But when they had got it, at an unmerciful price, a perfectly unreasonable profit to the seller, they nevertheless thought they had done well and that it was the seller who was the fool, for with those two beasts they had bought not merely two head of cattle but the whole world of live stock at once, calves and their byres full of as many cattle as they wanted for all future time.

In a similar way they got horses. The whole place was in a fever the day they were expecting the two who had been sent out for them. They came riding home, proudly, with legs tucked in, for their steeds were small and they were tall fellows, but the display had its effect. The womenfolk were out with barley-bread in their hands to receive the dainty animals and put them in good humour. But out with their bits first, shouted the boys to their ignorant sisters; a nice thing to go and spoil their teeth through not knowing any better!

And there they were, the shaggy little nags, standing with their legs together and getting restive, well broken in eating bread with their gentle, short muzzles and covered with harness to the eyes; now they too had come. The children stared wide-mouthed; the tales of the grown-ups about the strength and speed of horses had led them to imagine that they must be as big as houses and provided with wings. But the reality soon made up for their dreams.

On the other hand the grown-ups suffered a certain disillusion; it turned out that they had had another little trick played on them, not as regards sex, that was right enough, only one of the horses was not satisfied with grass alone but ate wood till the splinters flew, was quite capable of chewing up a whole log-house starting at one corner, if he was allowed to go on; and the two men who were responsible for the bargain went about looking glum with vexation, for how could they tell by the look of him that the horse ate houses? But they would get their own back; if such tricks were transmitted they would have many a vicious crib-biter to bring to market in return, be sure of that!

Now the family at Gestthorp had all that a husbandman could desire. Swine they had long ago driven in from the forest and put into sties, the bandog foamed at the yard gate, and geese plucked at the grass with curly necks down by the pond. With the coming of the horses they had reached the summit of their ambitions, the mark of freemen, they had attained the dignity of horsemen and had it in their power to drive. Hour after hour the sound of chopping, broken by pauses of reflection, was heard from the workshop of one of the sons; he was engaged in building a car, balancing on the horns of the difficult problem of making a wheel round.

All the boys had inherited skill in different kinds of handicraft from the old man, to which title Gest now had to submit; one worked cleverly in wood, another became an inventive smith; hunters and powerful bowmen they all were. But from their mother they had the innermost secrets of agriculture and cattle-breeding.

Work on the farms became distributed entirely of itself. Strangely enough Gest the Old, who by nature had been a hunter and a passionate carpenter, came in time to drop these occupations, which he left to the others, while he kept to fishing which he had more and more to himself.

He loved to lie out in the river alone in his old canoe, the same one that had brought him and Skur into the country, in a dawn of the ages which their children and grandchildren knew not.

And in it he left the country. Alone, working his double paddle, with his back towards them and facing ahead, his kindred saw him one day set out to fish, as was his custom. But he never returned. His sons searched for him and came home sorrowful; they had found neither the canoe nor the old man.

The river had taken him, he had gone into the current which bore him along, out of the country, towards the sea. Now they were orphans.

For Skur was dead.

A few weeks before the young people of the thorp had lost their mother.

One day she turned pale; for the first time in her life the old woman felt ill and took to her bed, still without assistance, leaning on the table and the solid stools as she made her way through the room, but when she had put herself to bed she found she was more helpless than any of her babes had ever been. The heavy body which had given life to so many could no longer keep itself alive. She smiled calmly upon the room, searching for her husband with her eyes, but he happened not to be in; she felt for him with feeble hand, turned her face to the roof and grew paler; she was dead when they fetched Gest. They had been inseparable, living in concord all their life, and yet she was to die alone.

Gest made his beloved's last bed of a tree from the forest, a great living green tree which was to share death with her, their souls should fare together. He hollowed it out like a boat, with a melancholy fancy of the stream of time — towards what shore? — and laid her in a mound with all that had been hers, that it might remain with her. Skur's best cow and a pair of goats were given her in the grave, and beside her pillow Gest laid a little bag of seedcorn; as she had come, so should she go. When the tree in whose stem she was buried turned green again, its evergreen leaves should wave over her beasts and over a cornfield.

The young families of the thorp had lost their venerable mother, the mother of them all. But to Gest it was a young maid who had died, he never remembered her otherwise than as she was in her warm youth. He could no longer live in the spot which she had left, she had gone and he set forth after her.

Downstream — ah, an easy task — he glided with the swiftly rushing river, away from the brief life which he had built up through so fair an adversity, the only thing that endures.

XI

THE ISLAND OF THE DEAD

A ND then again he sought new shores, old but not aged, serious but unbroken, with a great empty place in his soul, severed from life's import but with a world before him in which to find it again.

He was alone, torn out of all that had been nature to him, only himself on his wanderings, alone with the ancient eternal solitary things, the waves, the blind stare of mountains and lands, the clouds that look down without a face, the trees that hold their peace, and the backs of the dumb, downward-working rivers.

He passed along the Baltic coasts in his old single-handed craft, found the great rivers and fished his way on as once before, with no joy of recognition; and when they could carry him no farther he landed and turned hunter, concealed himself in the densest forests and took to the mountains to gain the source of new rivers on their farther side. But this time he was not bound for the East, towards the sunrise, the morning path of all beginnings, where he had been before; he would go down to the south, to the noonday shores, and see how time went there.

A vague hope drove him on, the hope of finding again what he had lost. But neither was sheer curiosity quenched within him, he still thirsted with the soul of the primitive man after making the world's last promontory and last billow his own.

For it had not escaped his observation that while he had been away for thousands of years in the East and to the south of it, beyond the ken of the old world, that world had made vast strides in arts and forms of life; he had left home as a hunter and come back as a hunter but found the people he had left behind enriched and supported by the land where they had remained settled in the interval, with tame animals and agriculture in full bloom, no longer a few scattered tribes but a numerous, prospering and vigorous people. And yet it soon became plain to him that this was only a Northern, secondhand expansion of a progress which must be still richer elsewhere, whence it had come. Nobody in Sealand was at all clear about where they had their bronze, their corn and their domestic animals from, but they knew that all these glorious things came from the South and had their origin in southern lands; from that quarter they still derived all that they could not produce themselves, a constant stream of new things and new views of things, so that must be where the mountain of wealth stood, from which all gifts proceeded. Towards the same quarter the birds of passage migrated in autumn; it was said to be always summer there.

Some even asserted that death was altogether unknown there, not only did the natives enjoy perpetual life, but it was thought possible that all the dead, even from other parts, assembled there, a spacious thought which it was not given to every man to grasp. Far up in the North were found folk with southern influences who were so convinced of this that they no longer buried their dead according to old custom, but burned them upon a pyre, in the faith that they would come to the sun's coast if they were committed to the fire and the path of the sun. Sometimes they gave them some birds of passage on the pyre that they might show the soul the way.

To all this Gest did not know what to say. For his own part he had been content to lay Skur in an oak canoe, for that was a well-tried mode of travelling, even though it might take longer. This about the soul having first to pass through fire and then up into the path of the air was a thing his mind refused to understand, though he could not reject its possibility. Gest's own immortality gave him hard and fast ground to stand on; as regards dying he shared his former Stone Age contemporaries' direct conviction that of course a man continued to live for all eternity, unless he had the misfortune to be killed or bewitched by wicked people or fell into a sickness that was not to be driven out; such things unhappily befell every one, an exception was hardly known, but for all that it was just as certain that a man would keep his life for ever if the causes that threatened it were removed. And Gest himself was a case in point. But what was the explanation of other people's death, whether as some said it was a transition to further existence of another kind or in other realms, was not at all clear to him. So what else was there to do but to visit the coast they talked of and see with his own eyes what there was to see?

Gest found the countries in the interior of Europe very populous, but he avoided inhabited places, leading the life of an outlaw and making his way unobserved through many realms to the mountains in the centre of Europe. In lakes among the mountains he came upon people who lived in houses standing upon piles, whole towns on the water; they did not seem to wish for visitors, the bridges to their towns were carefully hauled up; so much the better, they would have to be longsighted if they noticed *him*.

Few men ever saw Gest while he was travelling. There were his tracks, big tracks and far between, he was as long-legged as the elk, but he himself was seldom seen, he was already a long way in front when his tracks were made out. Up over the eternal snow on the mountains, immense slanting snowfields which went right into the region of clouds, where vultures hung, his tracks lost themselves, and no one who traced them could tell where he had gone; downward they turned on the other side, no one could tell where they came from.

Once down on the other side Gest built himself a boat in a lonely mountain wood near a watercourse that promised to become a river, and if any one heard him at work he may have thought it was a supernaturally large woodpecker hacking away, the bird of Time; but when it ceased Gest had vanished without a trace down streams that marked his passage with a wake and blotted it out again.

He lost his way in the mountains and came into bypaths that did not lead directly to the South; a tributary of the Danube caught him up, and from that he came out into that great old winding river, a highway in antiquity; here was much navigation in many kinds of craft, and a great diversity of people, a traffic beyond compare, not a day but one saw a vessel or was seen by one; so much the better, where the whole world scraped sides, one toiling up stream, another riding easily down, nobody took notice of an extra nutshell; so many a greybeard dropped his lines in the Danube.

The more unseen from the very fact that they saw him, Gest swept on alone, a bearded face closed to the world; he drank of the river, a fresh and muddy, tepid drink, rich with the many lands it had soaked up on its way; he made his frugal little fire ashore among the rushes and broiled his fish, different creatures here from those in the North, some with sensitive feelers around their mouths, others powerfully protected with armour on their skin, but like all fish they swallowed the hook and by their greediness made a

meal for others. Thoughtfully eating Gest looked towards the sunset with sober eyes, like many another numbed old fisherman.

And if a harp was noticed in his boat that was nothing to be
surprised at; what seaman does not divert himself on board with
some melodious plaint, borne upon the wind, profound homesickness when he is in foreign seas, restlessness incurable when he is
at home and misses the waves so sorely?

Thus Gest fished at his ease through outlandish realms, caught
glimpses of horsemen in kirtles of violent colours with horses' tails
and feathers on their heads, clad as it were in galloping fire and
crested with folly, and he heard them shout; deeper he plunged
his oar into the Danube and swept on, came out into the Black Sea
and paddled about there, landed in Asia Minor and became a
poacher, wandered in the desert and found river sources again,
this time the Euphrates, and came into a cedar-wood boat down
into Mesopotamia, where he dwelt for many generations and
witnessed great and marvellous things.

Then he went down into the Persian Gulf, round the south of
Arabia and into the Red Sea; turned westward, through deserts
once more, and took to the Nile, came down into Egypt and remained there for many ages.

At last he drifted out into the Mediterranean, visited all its
shores and islands, from shore to shore and from island to island,
all round the sea. Every sign told him that he was now on the coasts
of the Sun, and he stayed there until they had no more secrets
for him.

They were rich countries. No misty legend in the misty North
gave any real idea of how blue the sky was here, ever blue, it was
a boon merely to be alive, and in a bountiful climate there flourished one happy and industrious people after the other. Gest
watched them go their way through the light and filled his heart
with their destiny.

He had seen the powerful people, delighting in the chase, in
the country between the rivers, their ruthlessness in war and their
enterprise, all their abundant irrigation works to make the corn
grow; he saw the same thing in Egypt, and now he knew where
corn came from.

Bull-worshippers they were on the Nile, as they were in Crete,
all domestic animals had their home here or had been tamed in
these luxuriant lands; and from here the sheep had tramped, teth-

ered by men, all the way north, till they were penned in a mud hut beneath snowdrifts through the long winter and had to yield their wool to clothe the hairless Northerners; that is why the ram mutters through his nostrils in the evening breeze, complaining of his treatment. The goat lived on the mountains in the Mediterranean lands, therefore he still climbs every knoll amid level ground in the North, gathering all his feet, as though on the world's highest summit, and looks about him without giddiness.

And what these first creative people had founded, Gest saw carried further and raised in richer fulness and greater freedom by the happy Greeks; nothing they could not do, no bounds to their joy.

Long ago on his way south Gest had chanced upon arts and objects that were still quite unknown in the North; things that were but tentative fragments there he found as complete and already ancient civilizations in the South, so slow was the spread of the new on its way from South to North. They had iron in everyday use while those in the North still kept to bronze; they built marble temples and adorned them with perfect statues of the human form, at the time when the Danes poured blood upon black idols, a block of wood with a hint of a head, in smoky huts of turf.

And yet they were the same people, at root the same race. As Gest had followed the early Forest Folk, pre-glacial man, on its Stone Age trail eastward to the uttermost seas of the earth, so he was now taking part in the migration of the Ice Folk, only so far behind that they had become changed in the meantime, a richer and happier folk, unrecognizable. They were the descendants of those the cold had hardened, Carl's and Mam's people, White Bear's and May's people, who had gone south in waves, one generation after another, while the rest of their kin stayed behind in the North; and from these first great joyous seafarers, who left behind them marvellous skipper's yarns among the Greek islands, were descended the Greek Gods and Heroes.

For that which in the North is held fast by cold, rigour, adversity, bursts into flower in the South and grows into happiness and liberal arts. And as the wave, dashing against the shore, sends back many little waves, from land, so did a rebound of the emigrants' fortune reach the North arousing others there, who made for the South with new fettered forces and souls in bud ready to burst into flower. Thus culture came from South to North, where after all it had its tap-root.

Other conditions helped, more favourable than in any other part of the world or in any other age; in the Mediterranean countries the peoples of three continents were intermixed; from Europe the Northerner came down to blossom out, from the East the Asiatic, Wolf's and Tchu's people, to settle instead of wandering, from Africa the warm primitive folk seeking coolness, and coming together they released each other's forces and flourished in common, in a beauty which found expression in Greek sculpture and has never been surpassed since; in memory of a happy people on a happy shore there stands for ever the human figure in its marble nudity against a blue background, the Greek beneath his sky. So powerful was the expansion that it outlived the age, persisting in the spirit even after the conditions that had supported it had ceased to be.

Gest saw the sun of Rome traverse the heavens; he lay in the Tiber as a poor, unknown fisherman while the great imperial galleys passed in and out like overweening monsters lording it with three tiers of oars one above the other, marching back and forth in perfect time like so many legs, a fettered slave at each, such was the power of discipline; and out of the Tiber he slipped in his old canoe when the mob roared in the streets and Rome began to crumble.

Now he would soon have accomplished his mission, for which he had travelled so far and so long.

It had not turned out according to his hopes. No, his mission gradually faded away, as he came farther and farther on.

What he had set out to find was the Land of the Dead, and he found long summers, dwelling-places beautiful as those men had dreamt of, a nature imperishable, but nowhere did he find the dead.

The most likely place, it seemed to him, for them to dwell in would be an island, a place surrounded by the sea where every one could not come to them; he therefore sought out with special diligence all the islands of the Mediterranean, and they were many; but the inhabitants of all of them were natives, people lately born and with a pronounced stamp of the soil. Not everywhere was a man equally well received; on far-away islands where the natives were deficient in decency you could see them a long way off coming down to the beach, sharpening their knives on the rock, their home seeming to serve them as a whetstone; this showed no great development of wit, since they give a stranger a chance of becoming suspicious and turning back in time. Now Gest had not exactly expected the dead to appear as spirits or to behave in a particularly amiable way, they would be as they had always been; nobody doubted that the dead might be dangerous and voracious, but one thing was certain, they did not slap themselves on the back and make rude gestures at a seafarer in their disappointment at his turning away instead of coming in to them. These were men, entirely unpurged by death.

The same might be said of the inhabitants of the great populous islands who had more civility, they were all new, hearty people, open-mouthed, thirsting for tales, themselves overflowing with loquacity, eager for chaffering, with a fancy for female slaves; they were alive enough here, this was not the Isle of the Dead.

Finally, at the very last Gest found a little insignificant islet, far out in the sea and uninhabited; it was not the one he was looking for, but it was the last, there were no more to fix his hopes on; and here he stayed, settled down with all his memories.

It lay in the midst of the blue sea, the top of a sunken mountain, with the beautiful ever-blue sky above it; at its highest point it had a sort of shallow cracked bowl, a dead crater, overgrown with a heath of lavender, where grasshoppers played in airy solitude. Somewhere in a rocky valley grew a thicket of laurel and myrtle, a grove of carob-trees flourished by a little spring, on their fruit Gest lived; a rock close by canopied a sheltered nook, here he slept. Lizards sported upon the stones in the sunshine, they were his delight. On the steep cliffs sea-birds brooded and wrangled the day long; it sounded like a note of music, and the sea lay about the island like a harp. A sail might rise into sight far out, but only to turn off and sink into the sea farther away. The porpoise gambolled in the deep clear water just under the island, scratched itself on projecting rocks far down, blew voluptuously on the surface and plunged down again. Otherwise the island was still. Gest talked little to himself, shook his head from time to time. This was good.

In the face of the rock Gest hollowed out a little vaulted niche with portico and ornamental pediment, like a tiny temple, the work of several years, but he had time enough; and in the temple he set up a little idol he possessed, a piece of Greek work, the figure of a woman, the only one he had loved on these shores.

Wonderful were the Greek girls, whether they shone in holy calm, with all the folds of their clothing falling quietly to the ground, or whether in noble frenzy they kicked a leg free of the chiton and made a hook of it to catch the Wine God; of all things they might be guilty, save only of the one crime: lack of grace. Gest had looked upon them all with desire, they had been his delight; but only one had he loved and she was not alive, she was made of baked clay and less than a hand in height; it was she who now stood within the rock above his dwelling and received his daily prayer, ever and deathlessly the same. She was a tall and slight young maiden with strong and slender legs, perfectly nude, with her clothing laid beside her on a vase, and her hands were in her hair, tying it fast before she ran, for she was a racer, swift, swift as a flame, as the wind; she was the wind, she was in the air, she was woman, she was youth!

With such worship did Gest refresh his heart. It was not laid to rest thereby. When he had lived here for some ages, listening to what sea and sky said and listening inwardly to what he might have to say to himself after long undisturbed contemplation, it resulted in this, that he had indeed chosen solitude, but not altogether of his own will; it was rather solitude that had chosen him. He had been left alone because the others had gone from him. But was it not true that he had once himself fled from the place where he should have stayed?

Ay, that was the sum of life: first one is in advance, then one is left behind. As a young hunter he ran from life, and when he became mature and was rooted in existence, it ran from him.

He had lived long enough. Of what use was immortality if it could not be shared with others?

So, after calm reflection Gest lighted his candle for the second time in his life, in order to die. He had no wish to live when life had lost its savour.

There was only a stump left, the length of a finger, and it burned quickly. Gest felt himself aging as the candle burned, and that set him free from pain.

It was day when he lighted the candle, but it filled the whole world with a yet more powerful, unearthly light, he was in light, and with him was all he had lived, all ages returned and rested in the moment; with him were Dart and Skur as though in one person, the same love-dazzled smile; with him was the wise Mother Gro, herself the essence of all love, and all his children; time and distance did not divide them, he was his childhood, youth and manhood again in one, in the same light; he had lost none, was not alone, only in his being was there truth, it was immaterial and untrue that he had gone away, not reality, he was again at home — and then the love of life returned, it was still too soon to die, a good stump of the candle was left, quickly he bent forward and extinguished it.

He was sitting in darkness when it had gone out and noticed already that he was in a different air, colder, refreshing to the soul; instead of the hum of the sea there was another hum over his head, from great trees; he heard birds, but they were not the same.

Slowly the darkness gave way and instead of the rocky island in the blue Mediterranean he saw trees about him, rowan-trees; he was in a forest of lofty blowing trees, above them the sky hung low like a continuous roof of grey chasing clouds.

He was in Sealand, it was autumn, in the thin foliage of the trees the storm tore with a mighty, open note, and the falling leaves swept like a fire up and out of the forest; rooks and crows were pressing up against the wind with tempestuous cries, scattered flights of plovers came down and tried to collect where slopes gave them a lee. It was one of the year's flitting days, the birds were being blown out of the country, the woods were groaning, cold jets of wind poured into the chambers of the forest among the open trees. Nature's harsh breath fell like a great, chilly streaming body upon exposed, light-forsaken Denmark. In their passage the clouds opened a rent and let through a cold streak of sunlight, the pale afternoon gleam of a frightened and freezing day, looking backward in its flight.

Ah! Gest blends his freshened sigh with the blast, with an autumn heart; now he is at home. The wind is on the way, and it draws on to winter, but he will stay — he will stay, he too will draw on to winter.

XII

THE WANDERING SCALD

ON winter evenings a strange tangled clang was heard, blending with the whistling in the doorways and the blast without — music — Norna Gest? — and if the outer door was thrown wide, he stood there, in the light of the hearth fire, against a background of raven-black darkness, tall and stooping, as though he bore the night on his back, with swathed legs and wrapped in skins, his harp in his hands. Norna Gest was come.

He had but to pluck the strings once, it sounded like suns and stars, and the whole homestead came to life, the young people filled the doorways in a glow of expectation, and even the goodman of the house, whose dignity bade him stay within, could not restrain himself but came forward with eyes dilated and fair words on his lips; Gest was come!

And then the old man's long, heavy wanderer's pikestaff was placed to rest behind the door, and he himself was led up to the high table next to the master, together with his harp. Tales and the outer world made their entry into the hall that evening and stayed there many evenings, so long as with fair words, full mead-horns and downy beds they could make the scald comfortable and persuade him to stay.

But they knew they could never get him to rest quietly for more than so many days, even though they sent the children to beg it of him. His wanderer's staff knocked in its corner at night and was getting quite bent from wanting to go, he would say; they could look and see if it wasn't really bent; Gest would have to go and walk it straight again. Thus he jested, but one day he took his leave, and they saw the tall form with the harp on its back swing out of the yard gate; he walked slowly, with a swing, gave himself time, but it was surprising how quickly he got over the ground. Gest was gone.

Half a year or a whole year after, they heard him playing outside their doors again. He came and went just as inconstantly and just as surely as the seasons.

Gest had taken to roving, he was always on the road like the sibyls, he was a traveller, with no hearth of his own; this had come about of itself when he returned to his native land, there was no longer a home for him, but he was the friend of the homes, and as he could not be in all of them at once he had to divide himself among them all and go visiting from one to another. All the year round he was travelling through Sealand, but there were also years when he did not show himself at all; then he was down in the South in foreign lands, or his wanderings took him up into Sweden or Norway; and when after a lapse of years he showed himself again, the sound of his harp was more varied than before and there was no end to the tales he could tell. He was homeless, but all the world's lays and legends had their home in his memory.

When Gest came home from his long journey to the South, where he had sought in vain the Island of the Dead, he was very lonely; no laughing young herdswoman waked him and asked who he was, he found himself alone in the forest, and when he made his way out into the valley he scarcely knew it, and not a soul knew him. It was his native valley, but it was greatly changed.

A thousand years or more had passed over it since Gest had been here last; even the oldest secular oaks were not even acorns when he left, no trees were the same. The clans were different, with no living memory of the clans from which they were descended, and yet they were the same people; the big red fishers of the Stone Age as well as the sturdy husbandmen of the Bronze Age lived again in them, but their tradition did not even go back as far as the Bronze Age, they were now living in the Iron Age and had no conception of men ever having lived another sort of life.

They knew not who they were who reposed in the great stone-set chamber graves of the Stone Age, and yet they were their own earliest ancestors; giants had raised these stones, it was thought, or they were the home of the elves. They themselves still buried their dead in mounds, but without burning them as in the Bronze Age; they no longer believed in fire but had other complicated ideas about the Powers, no longer seeing them directly in Nature; they had become gods, persons, not very unlike the doughty sons of men who worshipped them; they made images of them, just as if they were to be seen, and regardless of the fact that by doing so they exposed their impotence. Gest never became an adherent of Odin, but he believed, as he had always done, in the weather.

Their ideas about the realm of death were not clear to him; they appeared to imagine two, one good and one bad, and you didn't enter into the good one, as might have been supposed, by assuring to yourself a long life with possible continuation beyond the grave, but by an abrupt conclusion of it; you had to get killed, to fall in battle, then you were sure of being admitted to the good country, of whose whereabouts they had only a general, embellished idea, no definite directions for the journey being available. But they still gave the dead a few important possessions when they buried them, so the early belief in immortality seemed to persist, though only in their customs; the belief Gest shared, namely that there was no inherent necessity for dying, and that one was there so long as one *was* there.

The new faith had a sanguinary effect on the morals of the valley; they fought more, human life had fallen in value, since the proper end of it was presumed to lie beyond the grave, albeit nobody had ever come back and confirmed this presumption; but as the noble life one was to enter demanded a noble death they slew one another with the utmost cheerfulness and hoped to meet on the other side for renewed mutual slaughter and resurrection. Frequent death evidently meant happiness and glory to the majority, whereas an unviolent end was associated with shame and gave admittance to the other kingdom they believed in, a dark and mournful one. Longevity, which one would have imagined to be the thing aspired to, was thus a questionable fate, and Gest never sought an opportunity of mentioning his age, which for that matter concerned nobody but himself. He was no confirmed adherent of the bellicose Northerners' religion but was glad to add it to his scald's repertory.

Human nature is undeniably a queer thing: although the valiant Northerners took special delight in exposing themselves to death, in the hope of a speedy sequel, they nevertheless did everything humanly possible to prevent their being killed, surrounding themselves with armour, whole shirts made of iron rings, impenetrable to cuts and stabs alike, helmets to cover their heads and great shields; they made it quite an art to get through to their vitals. And this art never rested; as fast as the protection grew strong, the weapons got sharper and more mercilessly ingenious; they went for one another with big sharp iron axes and tempered swords, as though they would cut down trees; a battle was a noisy affair, the clash of iron against iron could be heard far and wide.

And their numbers were great, fearfully great, no longer a few bands of franklins who went out and settled a dispute — they still did that; but by the side of this ancient form of warfare a new one had grown up which threw that of the franklins into the shade, a different body from that of the actual landowners — the *Army*. But this was all a part of other great changes which had taken place in Sealand.

At bottom they were to be traced to one main cause, the increase of the population. Gest's native valley alone was so thickly inhabited that you could go through it all the way from the coast into the heart of the country, the best part of a day's journey, and never be out of sight of human beings, whether that was a comfort to you or gave you a headache.

This increase of the population had naturally taken place in the first instance at the expense of the forest: as human beings became thicker, so it was thinned out. In the Bronze Age the clearings had eaten their way on both sides of the valley as great open spaces; now the case was reversed, the forest only showed in as many patches as there had formerly been clearings, and the rest was all open cultivated land, neatly divided into fields by fences and dikes of the stones taken off the ground and crowned at the top by the sharp, bare ridges on which stood the barrows of many generations.

Not till one had gone a long way up the country did the edge of the forest present a closed wall, and from here it still extended as a vast connected whole towards the interior of the island. But even far within the forest there were open glades with clearings and green fields; settlers who had started farming on their own account in a strange place and there laid the foundation of a new thorp. The old scattered homesteads in the valley had become villages with common cultivation among many distantly related families.

Just inside the entrance of the fjord lay a town, with a harbour full of longships. It was not a big town, only a street of thatched houses, but its inhabitants lived a life of their own, were neither husbandmen nor warriors but were allowed to carry on some kind of trade or handicraft; quiet, cautious folk who offended no one, liberated thralls or strangers from foreign parts, useful and unobserved; they had dived into their town and waited for what might befall them.

Up at the end of the valley, opposite the town, dwelt the Earl. Who was he? If you asked the franklins, then his importance was shown merely by the respectful tone in which the free men spoke of him. He was Earl. A freeholder was of course a freeholder here in the valley, but somebody must be acknowledged as a superior, somebody there must be to lead them in war and to take the tax from them in peace time, which was due for the use of the land — to whom?

To the King presumably. The King lived on the Roskilde Fjord and so could not personally manage the whole island, though a contribution was due to him from every homestead; he appointed the Earl to administer his rights, and there were many earls in the island, one for each district. In their origin they too were franklins, but on a large scale; they were descended from families which had early seized upon much land and had brought great estates under cultivation; thereby they acquired the means of keeping a great body of men who might secure them in the possession of what they had taken and add more to it. From one of the oldest and most powerful families of earls the King himself was descended.

The Earl at the head of the valley owned all the broad meadows there, a great tract of forest and many farms. On the largest of these he lived himself, with his retinue of armed warriors, whose only work was fighting and who were bold, impudent fellows, juggling with their sharp swords and certain of escaping the garners of a straw death. Where did they come from? Well, they were the surplus of the homesteads, the many sons who could not all have land; they took the Earl's pay, entered the King's service or banded themselves together under a leader and sailed abroad in ships after land wherever it was to be found and could be had cheap — after the death of the owners, which they saw to. That was the Host.

The earls did not cultivate their land themselves, for that they had churls, the peasants who occupied their farms and had become dependent on them; they themselves were taken up with the King's warlike affairs, and they spent their time in pomp and prodigality after the fashion of foreign countries, heaping silver upon their women, who were always fair and lovely.

At other times when there was no slaughter on hand they hunted in their woods, not for subsistence but for the sake of hunting, for the graces of the sport, on horseback; they were horse-lovers and trained hounds to set upon the game, they blew horns and filled the forest with noisy alarms, the galloping of steeds, the many-voiced baying of the pack, hallos, with the whacking of trees and shouting of a whole countryside pressed into the service as beaters. Their handsome ladies galloped with them, sitting side-ways as though they could not bestride a horse, in flowing robes of silk and linen, falcon on hand; the whole hunt a proud spectacle for the eye and a joyous uproar in the woods, but enough to make an old food-hunter shake his head, one who had been used to steal about alone with the utmost quietness, losing himself in the forest stillness, when he wanted to bring home a head of game. The stag was there to be hunter, true enough, but hunting and noise — ! Several score of people raising a din, and many of them on horse-back, all after a single scared beast in the forest — it was not a thing to say aloud, for the Earl was a mighty lord, but the old man shook his head that evening over his supper of dried pork; he could not understand the world any more.

And amid all this pomp the King's hunt was the most magnifi-cent. He had the right of hunting in *every* forest. At the King's court was assembled the greatest host, the pick of the freemen's sons from the whole island, and if he called to arms all the earls had to join him without delay with the host they commanded and with the muster of the freemen whom the King had at his dis-posal. This was when war was on foot and other lands with other franklins were to be brought under the King's tribute. All the waters of the realm, the channels between the islands, were in the power of the King; here he passed with his fleet, holding his lands together or making raids on foreign shores, when raids on his own were to be avenged.

Even the connection formerly existing between the individual and the Powers had been taken over by the mighty lords. The sanctuary stood in the Earl's burgh, he was the priest and received offerings to the gods on behalf of all. But the King again was supreme among the priests; in the eyes of the vulgar it would al-most seem that he was the god and the gods in his own almighty person.

Thus then the population had increased and spontaneously ar-ranged itself in layers, one above the other. In the middle were still the free tillers of the soil, but they were not what they had been;

they ruled with an unrestricted hand over their thralls, who in their turn visited the cattle with human oppression or mercy according to their humour. Above the franklins stood the Earl, and his tolls were willingly paid for the sake of keeping his friendship. But if you saw the Earl and the King together — they were indeed two peers, but one of the peers was nevertheless so much the greater. The Earl's eyes were raised high, but never higher than the King's chin; over his head the King looked out upon the whole realm. That is how things were.

But among them all moved Gest the Old, equally welcome everywhere, and felt as much at home with one as with the other. He arrived on his wanderings at the town on the fjord and was greeted with joyful recognition, like the stork in springtime, by the humble folk there; and Gest poured of his music and of his visions into their souls in return for his good reception, slept in their houses and found honesty, the treasure of life, in their inquisitive children. He went about with them in their workshops and lent an observant eye to their trade, the work of shipbuilders, which had absorbed the cunning of so many generations, a craft he could never tire of keeping pace with; he blew the smith's bellows for him and kept it going with its puff and sigh, heard the fire roar with its blue abysses and watched the smith toss the slag from the iron before he began to shape it on the anvil. The cooper's work fascinated him, and hard it was to leave the joiner and the refreshing smell of wood in his workshop. The wares of the small tradesmen had many things to say to him.

Gest would stray in the thralls' mud huts behind the homesteads and stay there the whole day, to the astonishment of the people of the house. They discovered that he stood and watched the girls at the quern and sometimes helped them, adding the power of his stiff arms to the supple turn of their young heifers' strength on the same handle; he saw the malt run into the quern and fly from the stones as flour; he traced the sunny fragrance of the corn which yields its summer as it is crushed, a sweet, bewildering odour of sunshine; and then maybe the old man would sing over the quern, a song of malt and sunshine which was afterwards handed down and preserved the thoughts that had moved his heart.

He was seen in the byre with the milkmaids, where he listened to the splash in the pail and might be offered a drink straight from the cow; there were some comments on the old man hiding in the dusk of the quern-house with the maids or among the cows, but Gest took the joke in good part, he knew what men and women were but he knew too what he was. Ah, the kindly striding fairies of the outhouses might every one of them be his daughters!

From the despised dwellings of the thralls Gest betook himself to the hall and was a freeman among freemen, talked farming and helped himself from the porridge bowl with the sons of the house; at the Earl's he held himself erect and looked the Earl in the face, fell to with his children and held the hand of the smallest in his own, feeling the warmth of the young blood communicating itself to his veins and there too meeting life; to the King's hall he came as a kinsman, increased his stature as a scald, a natural thing where all was great; much honour had he from the King, and weightier than gold were the strophes Gest laid in the scales of time to the King's honour. Where would Rolf Krake's fame have been without his scalds? Gest had been with him and with all the kings of story, with Charlemagne and with the Varangians in Russia, with the sons of Gunhild too, he was at all the courts of Europe with his story-telling and his harp.

None saw him grow old or remarked his age, for he lived longer than memory lasted from one generation to another. So long as the North was Northern he was there.

Of course every one could see that the old man was very old. He had habits of his own, which no one within remembered time could have taught him. The old vagabond did not care to be indoors, even in the most magnificent houses; when there was a chance he preferred to go outside, even on cold days, and there was the curious thing about him that instead of staying by the great hearth the old man would be seen lighting his own little lonely fire out in the open, where he sat and warmed his hands over it. In food he preserved the simple taste of a vanished age, was well satisfied with a handful of raw grain and a drink of water; he was clever with his hands but strangely enough disinclined to use better tools than an old worn sheath-knife; often he would pick up the first stone that came and use it when he had anything to scrape or cut.

His harp was of his own making; it was very handsomely ornamented with carving and was a strong harp, suited for travelling in every kind of weather. It was made of a moderately thick block of wood with a branch growing out of it at right angles; between this and the stem, which was hollowed out, the strings were stretched, a good number of them, each with its soul of music, every one a world in itself. If he did but strike the strings in order, from the deepest up to the very shortest of all, it was like flying up the stairs of heaven, the rainbow in music, blissful to listen to; but he had a magical power of playing about among the strings, up and down, and coaxing all the secret worlds of the soul out of his hearers thereby; he was practised in the most fugitive and tangled mysteries of the heart, which music sets free. Beloved and almost feared was Gest's harp.

The favourites among his songs were those which treated of the Volsungs, the wild obscure lays of the Migrations, which Norna Gest's Saga puts into his mouth; but the Migrations and Gest's part therein form a story of their own, which shall here be related.

The first men followed the game as hunters and fishers, and in that way spread themselves over the earth. Then as cattle-breeders they were still nomads, moving from one pasture to another; only when they took to agriculture were they bound to settle and stay where their corn grew, the plough and the ox-team, back and forth along the furrow, became the measure of their life; if the world had a message for them it had to come to them, they were the boors, the dwellers on the soil; the flower of their life came in the last part of the Stone Age and the Bronze Age — the family, the homestead, the rich quiet valleys hidden in the forests.

But then came Iron, the forest fell before its thin, greedy axes, and the country was laid open; the fields gave nourishment until the people became so numerous that there were no longer fields for all; and then the iron turned not only against the forest but against one's neighbour; blood was sown and the harvest was war, the sword took the place of the plough, and faces which before had turned inland towards the heart of the country were now directed outward, like a ring of ripples running into a crest in the centre and then spreading out again in new rings. The world had come to the husbandman, but the warrior went out to meet the world. And then the Migration began again. The viking raids of the Northerners rushed out like a dammed-up wave and made for the South.

In the centuries following the fall of Rome all the Germanic tribes of Europe began to arise from the soil, which had made them strong, and go adrift, pressing upon one another and working their way above and below, like the flow of the ice in spring; this was the great Migration, of which history has preserved accounts, meagre and half unreal, and yet nothing was more destructive and real than it.

We are told that the initiative of the great rising was provided by Attila, king of the Huns, when he broke into Europe from Asia, and that the thrust communicated itself from one people to another till none kept its place; the cause lay deeper and was of older date, but *it* gave Attila the chance of bringing Asia and Europe together in a maelstrom, the great wreck of the gods at the opening of the Middle Ages, the cleavage of races; and of this wild drama Norna Gest was a witness.

In the midst of the Migrations Gest walked like a man in a whirlwind, saw forces spend themselves in a storm before his eyes, while he himself stood in a calm; he had absorbed all wanderings and all movements, the elements, into his being and there laid them to rest; he was North and South, East and West, the soul of all change, just as he was the world of childhood and had penetrated all old age. Himself no longer in ferment, a force proceeded from him made up of all the forces he had collected and balanced in himself; this was his force as a scald. And as a scald it was that he aroused Attila.

He had come to his court, far away in the uttermost confines of Asia, and had sung before him, had been made to tell all he knew of Europe and its princes, and to all this the Mongol King had listened inquisitively but callously, unfeelingly. Then Gest had sung to him of the Northern woman. That brought him in danger of his life. The more the Asiatic heard of the tall, fair, free-born women of Europe the wilder he grew, setting off at a gallop, shouting to his myrmidons to take off the singer's head; it was intolerable to him to think that any other man should even have seen and be able to describe what Gest described; but he took him into favour again and waved off his guards, for he wanted to hear more; and he heard the rest of the song, and galloped off, steaming, with flaming eyes like a stallion, altogether beyond control.

And his gallop infected the hosts, the myriads of Asia, they poured in from the steppes and overthrew kingdoms everywhere in Europe; Attila would possess all Northern women, he had the daughters of freemen brought before him, hosts of captured women, bright and fair; but their fairness was not for him. He made them his wives by force, loaded them with crowns and rings of wrought gold, as thick and heavy as their rich maiden plaits; he had them killed when they were cold and would not smile, though he knew that their soul was all warmth and smiles when they loved; and at last he saw that they would not love him. They hardened in adversity, white and dumb, took their fate with indifference, as they would have borne a sickness or a hardship, despising life itself but never yielding, just like their tall and hated men who laughed at the swarthy weakling when he had overpowered them, twenty to one, and had them flayed alive; he could get the better of them but never bend them.

And there the despot found his limit. He could take hundreds of Northern women but did not get a single one, for they would not have him. But to be such that a single one would have him, he would have had to be another, and then he would not have been Attila. Therefore he went like an avenging scourge over Europe, burning everything down, since he could not become other than he was. Until a wise and penetrating woman, Ildico the Burgundian daughter, hatched his ruin, pretended she would be his, the first sign of willingness he had found, and strangled the happy bridegroom on the wedding night.

It was long before the ground swell left by the storm of passion the Hun King had raised came to rest. New tragic factors were added, for waves from Asia and Europe had now dashed together and could not quiver down to rest until they had broken and mixed and had become themselves again, though changed in their nature. The great, complete, tragic natures perished. The power of *gold* wore out the ties of friendship and blood, the Nibelungs' *Hoard;* grasping men, and women whose unkindness was a heritage from bloodthirsty fathers, extirpated each other, as the Edda laments:

> Brother bringeth
> brother his bane,
> cousin with cousin
> breaketh kinship.
> Never a man
> spareth another.
> Hard grows the world.
> Whoredom prevaileth,

> ax-time and sword-time
> — shattering shields —
> wind-time and wolf-time,
> ere the world waneth.

Yes, even in those days they expected the destruction of the world!

Through the bloody storms of the Migrations strode Norna Gest. The memory thereof lived in the Volsung lays, like the night howling in the doorways, when all the living voices of the day are silenced.

Norna Gest's death is recorded here as it is told in his Saga. When Christianity appeared it was time for him to go.

But he dwelt in the memory of man and there continued his long life.

Therefore after his death there is more to be told of him: how he lived among the Cimbrians and followed them on their disastrous raid against Rome.

And still later he appears as Quetzalcoatl.

How?

In this way. Long before *Leif the Lucky* "discovered" America men of Northern origin had been there. Yes, and among them Gest. He sought the Island of the Dead in the West also, on one of his immensely long voyages, and came to a strange people, to whom he appeared no less strange; in the book of "Christopher Columbus" this myth will be told.

The last years of his life Norna Gest spent in Norway. There existence seemed to him younger. The fresh life of young herbs on the ancient black mountains appealed to his soul, it was as though his childhood was brought nearer to him in his extreme age.

He lived in his memories and with them he grew dim, sank into himself and was scarcely more conscious of his being than a tree in winter which bears scars where all its leaves have been. So distant was the summer, so distant the days of his youth.

His most delightful memories, belonging to the morning of his life when he and his companion, the first human couple, had shared a tree with the squirrel, were blended in his mind with the myths of other races, races which had wandered as far from their early home as he and preserved an early memory as clouded as his, the myth of Ygdrasil, the great world-tree, the origin of all life.

For memory is a tree, it grows in time and with time it becomes ever greater and richer. The older we are and the greater the expansion of our souls, the fuller will be the light which is reflected upon our beginning. Therefore our longing ever returns to what we have possessed in life without having soul enough to prize it, when we have grown sufficiently to possess it in the spirit; but then it has passed beyond our power of experience.

We learn from Norna Gest's Saga how he come to Olav Trygvason and was christened in his presence, shortly before his death. It gives one a thrill to see King Olav on this occasion, at a moment when he seems to stand still in his career, viewed from the past and by one who is to die before him; he was still like a glorious sun at noonday, and the Battle of Svolder far off; how far from us are the hero and Svolder now!

Norna Gest received baptism because King Olav counselled him thereto, and because he found that what the clerk who confessed him said about the future life seemed reasonable enough. Gest in the course of his long life had sought it upon earth, but from what he understood it was not to be sought so far away, it was close at hand, just over him, only death separated him from it. And indeed the time was not far off when the Kingdom of God was expected to come on the earth itself, the millennium was near, and then it was believed that the Kingdom would be established. Then all warfare and strife would be at an end, no more manslaughter, no pool of blood beneath the one while the other ran off with his arm-ring, no rapes of women, nor any hate, nor want and affliction for the less well-armed; all would be peace and righteousness.

To all this Gest nodded, nodded with his chin upon his breast and dim, wise eyes; ay, was it not all he had hoped for? Easy was it to die, with the promise of so good a land, both above and below.

And when he had taken his candle out of the harp, where he kept it, and given it to the King that he might light it, he lay back and clasped his hands, as well as he could manage it according to the clerk's instruction, and prepared to depart.

Only a little stump of the candle was left, and it burned quickly. To those present in the hall it looked like an ordinary candle, nothing but a tiny drop of light in the great room, drowned in the glare of the fire which blazed upon the floor and filled the beams of the roof with shadows and smoke.

But when the wick sank and the candle was on the point of going out it struck them that the hall grew darker and colder, some began to shiver. Then Gest was cold and his hands numb. And when the candle went out he was dead.

They had noticed that the dying man's eyes were widened, as though he saw other worlds, mightier and more dazzling than the sun; the old man smiled, as one who meets his dear ones again. It was as though he was already in eternity, in the brief space his candle was burning out; many would fain have seen what Norna Gest saw.

A shudder fell upon all these sturdy young warriors when death approached Gest, a creeping at the roots of their hair; they were to have the same sensation once again, when they went overboard from the *Long Serpent* and the sea closed over their heads.

The King ordered wood to be thrown upon the fire, he had himself grown cold; the ashes were raked off between the logs, and in the light of clear flames and a shower of sparks the banquet was resumed.

XIII

FROM NORNA GEST'S LAYS

THE QUERN SONG

Maids at the quern
Their young strength straining;
The golden gift of the field
Gushes out glorious.

Sweet smells the malt
Like flowers of the summer,
Milling goes merrily
In a cloud of grain.

So do the sun, moon and stars
Grind out the gloom,
As meal from a rocking quern,
Worked by the warmth of woman.

Tell me not any
Can give nourishment
As the churning woman;
In sun's arts is she skilful.

I sang o'er the quern
To woman's honour
And felt me a captive
For ever of the fair one.

While yet is bread
The food of bairns,
I'll love the humble
Peasant mothers.

THE NORTHERN WOMAN

(*Fragment*)

In the morning of time,
When Man and Maid were born,
The world knew not death.
Then folly begat slaying.

Of wolf Man learned murder,
And a bloody bane had he.
But in her bower sat Maid
Giving bairns the breast.

Among fragrant cows
Moved franklin's daughters,
Fair and mild were they,
With milky hands.

In rain-cooled forests
She grew erect.
Like rain and the dog-rose
Is the taste of her cheek.

Blue are her eyes
As limpid lakes,
Never found frankness
A fairer speech.

Nay, I swore in my soul,
When she turned them upon me,
Such blue simplicity
Never should suffer.

Rich is her hair
As fountains of light;
I sought to be snared
In thy braided tresses.

The wild foal's whinny
On springtime pastures
Recalls thy laughter;
Never was gladder mouth.

A maidenly joy
Was the Norns' gift to thee;
For this have I found — that beauty
Is ever akin to mirth.

As the growing wort
Discloses a wonder,
So flashes thy wit.
Whence hast thou it, Woman?

An ocean of kindness
Thy heart encloses!
All the world's warmth
Dwells in thee, darling.

Here I confess it —
Ne'er saw I a woman
But the hot blood mounted
To my lusting heart.

Yet was life too short,
Even with its nights added,
To learn to the full
The love of one only.

Thy fair arms held me
A prisoner for ever,
So lovely was thy being,
So lasting thy beauty.

In rain-cooled forests
I find thy soul anew;
In the dewy dog-rose,
There art thou, my darling.

Ah, in the hazel thicket
'Twas more than nuts we plucked;
Sweeter than leafy booths
Was the bower I found there.

Let me ever wander
In kindly woods.
Close thine arms about me,
Dewy-cool Denmark!

BOOK TWO: THE CIMBRIANS

PART I: IN JUTLAND

I

DARKEST JUTLAND

Up through Jutland came a tall old man on foot, with his harp on his back and in long, loosehanging clothes, a staff in his hand as a third leg; he walked with long, slow strides and a great swing, like an elk, covering many miles between morning and evening; this was Norna Gest, the wandering scald, on his way from the South up into the parts of Jutland.

He held a mid-course through the land, following the high ground and the watershed, from an old predilection for a free view on every side; he took the roads when there were any and they suited him, but just as often he left them for paths and tracks he knew of and shared with the retiring creatures that used them, or went straight across country, through tangled forests and over heaths, the way the land pointed, in the northerly direction for which he was bound.

He had his own landmarks, on a great scale, the fjords of Jutland's east coast which cut into the land like so many deep pockets, one to the north of the other, from the foot of the peninsula facing the Baltic, through the Middelfart Sound with the coasts of Fyn opposite, to those which opened out towards the Cattegat, right up to the Limfjord. How many there were he did not count, but he knew them every one, they were like living beings to him, each with its mirror; they turned as he passed them like long gateways to the sea; and between the gaps lay the landscapes of East Jutland, a mighty undulation of hills and woods. Here the population was dense, with many wapentakes; the rich valleys showed at a distance their clearings, green and chequered on the floor of the dale, townlands with open home-fields and pastures running up the slopes and meadows beside the watercourses towards the fjord; all framed and protected by the wild, ancient forests with their hunting grounds, miles of swamps and commons lying outside as belts between the hundreds. Far away above the trees rose smoke from hidden dwellings, and in the fjords were craft among the bays and headlands, great masted vessels; beyond lay the sea-fog, the way out of the country. Here in the fjords and along the coast the population was still thickest, and here it was in communication with the outside world.

Few folk dwelt towards the centre of the country, where Norna Gest walked. Now and then the decorated gable-end of a newly built, freshly tarred house showed up in an opening of the forest, surrounded by newly cleared fields with the tree-stumps still standing and great stones scattered over the ground; the wooden bell of a cow moving about the yard was heard, a whiff of spicy smoke came from the settler's hearth, the bark of a dog, and Norna Gest made a wider circuit, he was not one to encroach upon other people's domains. He kept to the confines dividing inhabited districts and outlying settlers, on free ground and outside the law but with less chance of meeting people; though Norna Gest knew homesteads enough where he would be welcome, he kept to himself, he would not tarry, his way lay farther north this time.

A man could go through forest from one end of Jutland to the other and remain unseen the whole way if he wished, meeting no other creatures than deer or wild swine. Norna Gest had no need to hide but preferred to travel undisturbed; if he wanted to look about him he made for open country, and if now and then he came across herdsmen, hunters or other wayfarers, they usually knew him at once and did not delay him, unless he chose to stop and talk; they could see a long way off that it was Norna Gest.

Caution was the habit of wayfarers; if a man on coming out of the forest became aware of the presence of an unknown in the open, it was entertaining to watch the way their movements were influenced thereby. In a sidelong, constrained fashion each held the other fast, as it were, and tried to get away from him; a long-sighted observer could guess by their motions that the bow was being strung and the quiver shifted to the front; sometimes they vanished, crouching on the ground behind the shield, or else there was nothing to be seen but bushes, until the two seemed to grow out of the earth again, increasing the distance between them, with their backs to each other but heads turned, until they were out of sight. For people from different districts, separated by a fjord, a river or an impassable swamp, had no business outside their own territory and if they met on the dividing line it was not as friends; on the contrary, they warned each other in time, the border rangers kept an eye on each other, and if a couple of men rose out of the brushwood on one side of the river, another couple instantly appeared on the other side; with drawn bows and brandishing of long spears both sides struck fear into their neighbours and declared their intentions — no ambush here, come forward with bared chest if you have any message!

Jutland had many districts which thus blockaded each other, as many as the fjords by which the people had once come into the country, and on which they had grown into several mutually independent tribes — others again on the west coast side — with a prescriptive right to their territory; a whole number of peoples with different names for themselves and their neighbours, some forgotten later or changed, others long remembered, not a few nameless but by no means negligible if their frontiers were invaded. These tribes were made up of small clans, originally scattered at great distances from each other and on a mutually hostile footing but derived from the same root. Their continually strained relations kept them in arms, they had no more dangerous adversaries than each other; but when circumstances stronger than the perpetual border skirmishes forced them together, they had no difficulty in uniting, and this fusion might lead to the sudden appearance of great hosts, which instead of holding each other in check were set in simultaneous motion beyond their borders against a common enemy, or perhaps clean out of the country to face new destinies, if their star so willed it. Many such composite hordes, unexpectedly appearing elsewhere in the light of a foreign tradition, had Jutland produced in prehistoric times, more than were remembered in Jutland itself, and many more she was yet to produce.

It was in the pause before Nature prepared one of these fusions of forces, while relations between the districts were strained to the utmost and the hundreds, nay, even the individual homesteads, were armed to the teeth in a state of equilibrium, that Norna Gest was on his way through Jutland to visit the Cimbrians, up in the out-of-the-way tracts on the Limfjord.

Everywhere along his track Norna Gest came upon traces of a state of war and picked up news here and there from some herdsmen or outlaw of cattle raids up country by men of the fjords, always a favourite way of rapidly increasing one's stock; of franklins who had burnt other franklins in their houses and had been burnt in their own in return; of levies and set battles with varying fortune; of sacrificial banquets out of the common, single combats much discussed, love affairs, scurrilous lays, everything that a district hums with when you come to close quarters, no matter how far out of the world it may seem. Norna Gest listened and added to his experience.

He liked to come to Jutland; here, the farther north he went, he still met with old times which were declining elsewhere, in the islands that were his home; in certain things he could feel transported right back to the first ages he had passed through with the early immigrants who settled in the country; here they still honoured the same things between heaven and earth that his origin had taught him to respect. Often he saw faces which seemed familiar to him among the hearty folk of the fjords, features that had been handed down from ancestors with whom he had walked upon earth in a morning of the ages of which no one retained the faintest idea.

It was Norna Gest's habit to visit Jutland in springtime, he came from the south where it had already burst out, and followed it, keeping pace with the birds of passage; he wished as it were, to see it arrive time after time, a show of permanence that delighted an aged wanderer. Besides, it was his secret joy to be himself received, through no merit of his own, as integral part of spring wherever he went. In Jutland they used to say that he and the stork came at the same time and were equally welcome; indeed, some were courteous enough to hint that it was through him and his powers spring came at all. In few parts did he meet with such happy faces as among the hard Cimbrians; here they knew how to value spring and held great festivities in honour of its return, the ancient grateful customs which Norna Gest loved; when he had long been dwelling with folk who waited on him with dressed food and closed beds he yearned for simple, coarse fare and nights under the open sky; thus it was that he chose to visit the Cimbrians in springtime.

Up in Mid-Jutland Norna Gest lost sight of the coasts and went over the broad inland hills which close in here, with the biggest timber of the peninsula, the great ridges clad in woods and heather with a ring of lakes at their feet. Here the land rides highest, and in the spaciousness on every side one seems to feel the whole extent of Jutland, the foot of the peninsula on the south and the ragged east coast, far away the backbone of the country towards the North Sea, and behind receding horizons, like one ring within another, North Jutland with a distant glimpse of an arm of the Limfjord, and the country beyond that again, with the neck of the peninsula, and farthest up the two seas that break against The Skaw as against the spike of a helmet.

Here the country already had a wilder look, with great lonely, far-stretching woods in the hollows between the heights, which gathered as though about a centre of gravity that the whole country rested upon. From here the lines ran out on every side; from sources rising in these furrowed hills the brooks parted to form the great streams of Mid-Jutland, some westward on their long winding way to the North Sea, others through tortuous valleys, spreading out league after league, to the broad east country and out into the Cattegat; waste land much of it here, with the population still collected down in the warmer valleys, and the forest was tangled and wild; the deer were bigger here than elsewhere and stood quiet when a wayfarer passed by, many of the beasts had never seen a man before. The stag showed his head with furry swelling burrs, the new growth of antler which was coming on.

Signs of spring on every hand; the trees, dripping wet, were swelling in the bark and stretched twigs and buds up into the clean-washed air; there was a sparkling high and low, the sun clear but not yet hot, like a sisterly light in the sky, the daylight penetrating to the bottom of the shadowless woods, the stems a gem-like green, a twittering and calling of birds as in great empty chambers where they were to move in, but soon there would be settling and building. Away over the open plains hung the lark in a dazzling noonday glory of sunlight.

And Norna Gest followed the lark into the open country, continued northward over the heights, with broad horizons lying beneath him, a sheet of water far away, fjord or lake, clouds and sky in a mighty expanse above his head.

On the highest points of the long naked heather-clad ridges he found the charred remains of bonfires, local sanctuaries where the people of neighbouring hundreds assembled on the high days of the year to kindle their fires and perform their worship of the sun. The loneliness and might of the high places appealed to a heritage in their minds, the view threw open the traditions of the race, obscure to most of them, but Norna Gest, who acted as their memory, knew what it meant: from here they saw the way they had come into the country, which had been forgotten, it was a look into the past — the old tracks, the rivers, the fjords, farthest out the sea, which perhaps the inland dweller had never seen, but from which he had come; what was swallowed up in the everyday life of the valley became revealed as a great memorial up here in the face of heaven. With this feeling they sacrificed to the sun, made fire in its likeness and symbolically bound it to its course. This was to be done on high places, for fire had come from the mountain; even those who had never seen a mountain and knew nothing of it performed the rite from ancient and obscure but hallowed custom, a root in their origin as men which was not to be pulled up. For the solstices there were sacrifices, summer and winter; but thanksgiving festivals were also held for the spring, the reawakening of Nature, the bursting of the leaves and the warm days; this was the gift of the sun, and as the sun was beyond their reach they betook themselves to his kinsman, fire, with gifts and honours according to their means. Soon the spring bonfires would blaze on the heights throughout Jutland; this was what Norna Gest wanted to witness, and this time among the Cimbrians, who laid special stress on the spring festivals, perhaps because they lived farther north and were poorer than the rest.

He took his time on the way up, paused when the spring paused, and started on again when it made a step forward; stayed for weeks in this place or that, in quiet corners of the forest or by a water-course that tempted him to tarry.

At night he slept out. The air, so early in the year, was still wintry when the sun had gone down, and he sought shelter among rocks or in a thicket, with a big tree at his back and a fire burning in front of him; here he nodded the whole night long and passed from one doze into another, but heard every movement of bird or of footstep, far or near. The night was long.

But towards its end, in the hour before dawn when all living things fall into a trance, Nature's death-like truce, then Norna Gest too fell into a deep, heavy sleep, wrapt in skins to the chin and with his head bent low, like a sack beside the fire; and the flames died down, while rime covered the grass in the cold still dawn.

When he awoke he did not know at first where he was; he was stiff in the face with cold, chilled to his soul; only with difficulty, as though after a swoon, could he crawl out of his skins and stretch his limbs. It was like a dead man coming to life, a man without a face, inconceivably old; feebly the arms straightened themselves as though the joints belonged to a shadowy creature; he stirred up the ashes, plunged his lifeless hands into them and found warmth, an ember that was still alive, and he burned himself on it, gleefully, it went right into his veins; he laid on sticks, the smallest and thinnest he could find, as though he could lift no more, lay down and blew the fire with weak puffs that might have been his last, but the fire blazed up and soon he had high, clear flames. He rose, staggering, but recovered his strength, grew as the fire grew and got back his vital warmth.

Then he turned to the day and his vision came back: the dawn beleaguered all the sky, the sun was still below ground, but its outposts were advancing, crimson spears in the east. And lo! the forest came to life, the ancient oaks stepped forth from the dawning, created perfect from root to twig, marvellously full of being, the frosted slopes bent and received the light, the land threw open wide its gates, in a hushed and holy pause of frost the earth was reborn, while the horned moon sailed high and paled into the sky above the tree-tops.

A faint twittering of birds was heard, like a creaking in the trees, nothing more, and the sun rose, red and all-powerful. Norna Gest drew himself up before it, and his features became so clear and still; with a shake of the head he received the marvel, the old revelation.

In the morning hour the forest steamed as the rime passed from it, and Norna Gest saw how big, wet and tense the buds were; he recognized the spring in the volume of light, flocks of birds passed airily above his head, a distant, shivering music came as though from the clouds, the wild geese on their way north, and an irresistible impulse seized him to resume his wandering.

But first he went to the nearest water and uncoiled his fishingline; turned over a stone, the roof of the worm's house, and found it there, just ready to be taken. He caught a meal of fish, with life must life be supported, and broke fast by the fire, chewing and looking before him with absent eyes, and many calm thoughts were his companions while he ate. Then he followed the sound of a spring and drank: strong springs here, they forced their way up from the greensward under the slopes in cold, clear, domed fountains, as though striving to reach a mouth; they tasted fresh of the earth's sweetness and quenched him to the very marrow. In drinking them he gained the freedom of the land, and they mirrored the sun; he drank in them the morning hour, the thaw and the air of spring, and in return he knelt and kissed them.

Then Norna Gest made ready to leave, shouldered his burdens and plucked up his staff, which he had planted by his restingplace; it had not taken root.

The beasts, who had risen in the valleys, heard some one clear his throat, a man, a strong hollow cough among the woods; an old solitary male striding along by himself; the echo resounded answering among the slopes, and the deer twitched their ears forward and twitched them back, and made off without more noise; no one could know what a man meant by clearing his throat so loudly. They went their way and Norna Gest his; rested and rejuvenated by the morning he strode northward with another day's travel before him. A lay of thankfulness took shape in his mind, after he had gone a little way and turned his back as though on a cast slough:

Praised in my heart
be the light of the world,
the risen sun
and the gift of sight!
From sparks in the ashes
the fire is rekindled.

Ever o'erwhelms me
the daily marvel.

Where is refreshment
like springs in the wild?
Happy who laps from
the veins of the land.
Open heaven
is hope's sure anchor.
Homeless wanderer,
worship the dust!

Now the country changed, becoming lower and spreading into
wide expanses, plains and wastes with sparse vegetation, heaths so
extensive that one forgot every other kind of country while crossing them, which took days; and then one was a lonely man, poor
as the heather, closed in by drear horizons, with no other company than the birds of the heath, which ran in front and chirped
in a queer distress, as though they did not know who they were
and were asking the stranger about it. One feared the face of the
sky and heard the throbbing of one's own blood in the stillness; a
chastening of the soul it was to cross the heath.

But even endlessness has an end, transient it is in reality; though
he had lost his way Norna Gest made for the north in good heart;
he had his landmarks on the left hand to guide him in the direction he knew Vebjerg [1] to lie, and the black horizons in front told
him that now he was beginning to approach the Cimbrians' land.

All thoughts of the seas on both sides, the free coasts of the
peninsula, had now receded; this was an island tract, as though no
coasts existed, not even the Limfjord was yet in sight. Otherwise
the country was well enough watered in itself, difficult of approach from the south when one was on foot; the track led over
swamps and streams running from east to west; a long-legged man
had trouble to ford them even in the shallowest places, in their
swollen springtime condition, and when across them he did not
reach dry ground, for floods and bogs barred the way for miles, his
feet sank in and he had to make long circuits.

Here was a great assemblage of birds, waders that had just arrived, ducks in swift flocks, which filled the air, alighted everywhere and tried the water, taking headers, glad to find it open again

[1] Vebjerg — the Mount of Sacrifice. Now Viborg, where a Christian cathedral has taken the place of a sanctuary of the old religion. — Tr.

after the winter ice. They gambolled on the surface as though caressing it, flung up the precious element with snake-like neck and got drops on their feathers; twisted round and wriggled their tails so that the water powdered them with a fine rain and flashed a rainbow over the spots on their wings, quacking loudly all the while, and by the tone it could be heard that the drake was amorous, breeding-time was in the air. Away on lakes made unapproachable by banks of mud and quaking swamps white flocks of swans merged in the fiery reflection of the sunlight; the wind brought music from them, tones and light and distance blended together. Everywhere water, and the water was blue, the sky was blue, the air cold and clear, the meadows still bare, but catkins and shining white osier buds were on the bushes. The wanderer found the earliest birds' eggs lying before his foot in the marsh, the lapwing's exposed nest, and slipped a couple into his mouth, whole and with the shells on, full of their brooding warmth; thus he tasted the country's welcome.

The slightly higher land between the marshes was covered for miles with scrub and brushwood, osier bushes, tufts of grass and great stones, furrowed by sluggish watercourses and stagnant pools; it was a wild tract, a home for the wolf. That the country lay off the beaten track could be guessed by his showing himself in broad daylight, slinking from one thicket into another; a man might come face to face with him, but only for a moment; he dropped his eyes at once, shook his long jaws and sneezed when he had gone by — an unpleasant thing to exchange glances with a man, ugh, who wore a tanned wolfskin coat on his back! The thought of an old account crossed his mind, but he did not follow it up. The eagle was slow in leaving his tree, long after one had come within range: an innocent, undisturbed region, where the beasts kept their old habits, and Norna Gest did not hurry here, meeting many a creature that he seldom had the luck to see; it was clear that men did not often visit these wide border lands.

Spring tarried long in these parts, as though it could not get across. In the morning the bogs were frozen, the floods covered with thin ice, and the ducks sat on top of their element with their webbed feet on the cold floor. As the day went on the ice cracked under the sun and was slobbered up by blue waves in the fresh breeze; then it snowed, and the whole land lay as though smitten with snow for miles, when the shower had passed and the view cleared again, a relapse into winter. The noonday sun took away the snow, and once more the earth was black and newborn as far as the eye could reach; the withered grass was steaming, and the sky was like a bowl with immense abysses of cloud and shining peaks rising to the topmost roof of blue.

But by degrees the nights grew milder, the ditches brought forth toads that wallowed in water and sunshine, yellow flowers burst out, with their roots in the mud and their faces turned to the sun, all gold and growth.

And at last one day came the first pair of storks, gliding around each other up under the clouds, in great circles, like a solemn symbol of dedication over the land. Then Norna Gest travelled on.

The country now became more hilly again, with long, broad heights between the marshes, and traces of habitation began, pillars of smoke from clearings in the forest, and he prepared to meet the natives.

The heart of the Cimbrians' land was a highland, wide plains exposed to the wind, broken up on west and north, between the centre and the Limfjord, by many clefts and hollows, the beds of ancient fjords, now watercourses and marshes. Everywhere woods, but scattered and checked in their growth by the weather; bushy and impenetrable in the valleys, crouching and, as it were, thatched by the wind on the level ground. But in its highest parts the country was open, with a series of long, bare ridges running across the land from east to west which showed black outlines at a distance; covered with high-lying heaths; they stood out from the bushy country like bald pates, and along their crests long rows of burial mounds stood sharply against the sky, built in a yet older age by the forefathers of the Cimbrians, who had taken land here and bequeathed their taste for it, incomprehensible to others who had had the good fortune to occupy better regions, as a heritage to their descendants.

At a distance the first impression of life was the graves of the ancients. *Their* eyes had seen the long, strict lines in which the land was laid out, like a vast, black, storm-swept roof, these had been the frame of their existence, and the tearing winds that passed over the country were soul of their soul.

But if the heights and horizons were given over to departed generations, the living dwelt down in the valleys, in hereditary homesteads lying far apart, with extensive surroundings of wood and pasture; the wilds in the interior were for common use and were divided among the clans. The Cimbrians were great cattle-breeders, for half the year they moved about with their herds, and in winter they stayed at home on their farms, where they carried on agriculture.

The first people Norna Gest met were two young men, whom he surprised by a beck where they were setting snares; one of them snatched up a spear to fling at the stranger, but dropped it in time when he saw it was Norna Gest.

They were a pair of very big fellows, immensely strong and active, free in their movements, showing that they had spent their whole lives out of doors in hunting and on horseback; they were weatherbeaten and perfectly blue, bilberry-blue, in the face, even their lips were blistered by wind and weather, their ears black and notched at the edge from old frostbites, with little eyes almost closed under a heavy growth of eyelashes, shunning the light behind their keen brows; their hair grew far down over the forehead and was tied together at the top, forming a long tail. They were lightly clad for hunting in leather breeches and jerkins; one of them had a freshly killed otter hanging at his belt.

Norna Gest's appearance seemed to cause them a certain excitement, which however did not find vent in words or work itself up into any play of the features; their thick lips were expressionless as before and their foreheads, puckered by nature, showed no fresh puckers; but they slung their shields on their backs again in silence, the defensive attitude was of course superfluous, and they looked at the scald and at his harp, exchanging a mutual glance, unnoticeable, but signifying fairly strong emotion: music and marvels came with Norna Gest, that was evident; for they had known him from their childhood, as far back as they could remember.

But then it turned out, by a wonderful piece of luck, that the scald was on his way to visit the man Tole, chief franklin in these parts. Did they know him? Both nodded at once, decidedly, and saw the whole thing, privately winking to each other. Then the elder went off and returned with a pair of shaggy horses that had been standing among the reeds; he looked at Norna Gest and at the horses, looked in the direction of Tole's homestead and wet his lips, but did not commit himself to words; though the offer was plain enough, it was the stranger's part and not his to make known his intentions. Norna Gest understood very well what was proposed: that he should mount and have company the rest of the way; and he gladly accepted. Without their having said so he concluded from the look of things that the two young hunters, obviously brothers, belonged to the very homestead he had enquired for; they might even be sons of Tole, though they were too polite to call any attention to themselves.

Before starting the elder of the brothers took his scrip from his horse, opened it and spread it out on the ground. It was a skin with holes round the edge through which ran a thong; the skin could be gathered up into a bag or laid completely open; it proved to contain curdled milk in clotted lumps; the man offered it with the idea that a traveller who perhaps came from afar might be hungry and in need of a bite before they reached home — all in a casual way and as a matter of course, one didn't want to lay any stress on one's power of doing a man a trifling service; anyhow, there was food. And Norna Gest, who understood the language of the country, took a handful of the curds. It tasted of smoke, from smoky houses, and like sweat, of cows, of women, of children, all creatures with a healthy skin; and an old man, who had walked alone for weeks, felt that now he was approaching human haunts again. The two men also helped themselves, after the old man had had what he wanted, but tried to conceal the movements of their lips, for their guest was so much their senior.

They washed it down with a draught of water from the beck. Norna Gest produced a big shell he used to drink out of, a coloured foreign conch, sky-blue with a rainbow sheen, flesh-coloured inside, which he had picked up once in the South; and the two young men were fascinated when they saw it, their eyes clung to the irresistible thing, without of course their showing the slightest curiosity; on the contrary, they screwed up their eyes and put on a hard look so as not to fall into temptation. Norna Gest did what he always did when any one marvelled at his shell, held it to his ear; and then he seemed to hear the beating of the waves on the far, far distant crater island in the Mediterranean, on whose shore he had found it; then he handed it to the men, and they put it to their ears in turn and listened; sat with frowning looks and absent eyes, shaking their heads; and they laughed inwardly, their gaze expanded, never had they heard anything so mysterious. Without their knowing it they sighed and their faces fell as though a sun had set, when Norna Gest took back the marvellous thing.

When Norna Gest was mounted the men joined him, one on each side, obviously regarding themselves as his escort; the little meal they had partaken of meant more than refreshment, it admitted the stranger to the country's protection.

The road to the homestead, a league or so, was covered in silence. The brothers took it in turn to ride, one running while the other had the horse. Uphill, when the strain on the horse's shoulders became too great, the rider would swing a leg over the neck of his mount, slip to the ground without halting and run by its side, with a hand in its mane.

And thus Norna Gest came riding in.

II

IN TOLE'S HOME

A T the top of one of the valleys which led into the country, towards the high land and the watershed, — a natural centre with streams communicating both northward and westward with the Limfjord — dwelt Tole. He was Thing-leader for the common people, and priest at the same time; a much venerated sanctuary stood on his land.

The homestead was more like a little town, consisting of many scattered dwelling-houses and outhouses along the foot of the slope and bordering on the marsh, most of them of earth, hollowed in the ground, others of wattle and daub, and a few more substantial buildings of timber. Round about were paddocks and cornfields, framed by the woods which filled the rest of the valley. Above were heaths and wastes.

Other homesteads of the same kind lay farther down the valley, hereditary properties whose occupants were more or less nearly related to one another and to Tole. Besides the master the whole family lived on the homestead, the sons and their offspring, the daughters and theirs, three generations at the same time; besides many other people who belonged to the place, the bondservants too, the thralls, if you counted them; altogether, with the domestic animals, an extensive settlement, to which were added outlying huts among the pastures, chiefly for use in summer, when the herds were not driven home.

To a man coming from uninhabited tracts the place was positively bustling; at any moment he saw people by the score and a busy traffic, deeply worn paths in the greensward between the houses and countless tracks of men and beasts; a profusion of women and children, the houses were full of them and the wailing of infants came as though from the earth itself; the houses smoked, not only from the smoke-hole but through the roof of heather and from every pore, as though warmth and well-being were oozing out of them; often the house-door stood open with the smoke pouring up over the eaves; the season and the long days were beginning to make themselves felt, children sunned themselves outside the doors, shielding their eyes from the strong light. On the stones in front of the storehouses lay bondswomen bruising corn, on all fours with a promontory in the air, the attitude of grinding, and with their hair down over their eyes, blinded with toil; but a memory in their souls made even them seek the light and take their work out into the open air.

Sheep were shorn by a pool, a thing as regular and familiar at the season as the peculiar refraction of the light in the cold, clear ponds or as the appearance of the first short-stalked daisies in the meadow; it could be seen by the women shearers that spring had come, they sat with their kerchief pulled down as far as possible to screen their eyes from the sun. Cold for the sheep, which were first ducked in the pool with their feet tied together and afterwards released despoiled of their wool, disfigured and skinny, in the still biting air. Some of them already had lambs, which were staggering about on four unpractised pins, clumsy as footstools, and bleating with thin voices; ah, the young, tender year had come too early, but it had come.

From the smithy came the clang of the anvil, there too was strength and industry; a bellowing of cattle outdoors and in, the noise of dogs that seemed possessed, the tramping in and out of horsemen at a sharp trot on their fresh little horses, for which the riders were all too big; elsewhere archery practice with a shield for target, the whirr of the bowstring and the smack of the arrow when it hit; a couple of lads wrestling in a field, with long, slow grips, gasping, well-matched in strength, first one on top, then the other; pig-killing, with the carcase hung up on a tree and a woman on a ladder with her bare arms in the pig's inside; everywhere life and activity, a whole little community, restless and agitated, but dependent, on old, fixed custom, influenced and made yet more restless by the season.

Out in the yard stood Tole, with both hands resting on the handle of his ax, clad in furs down to his feet, viewing his cattle.

They had not yet been driven into the pastures, as there was not enough for them to live on, but were allowed to stretch their legs and get some fresh air outside their narrow stalls for a while every day. The cows, many of them in calf, moved about licking the short grass; horsemen and dogs kept together the herd, which took up some space, a whole field of cattle to look at, brindled, black and white, and dun, a mass of horns and blazed foreheads, a splendid sight in the sunshine and a joy to listen to: cracking of whips and shouting of men driving back stragglers, for the sun had put heart into the cows and they wanted to go their own way, attempting a gallop; the heifers were quite out of control, feeling the call of the wild pastures; but their hour of freedom had not yet struck. Tole had his sun-marks; the shadows were still too long, and the woods too backward. When everything tallied, when omens and spring sacrifices had opened the year in regular fashion, they would get out. It was high time, for this year there was only just enough hay and fodder left to last out.

In a place by himself stood the bull, with a special guard of honour of two men, who watched his movements at a distance. But he was quite quiet; he stood in the sunshine, which made him sleepy, and enjoyed its far-away warmth, in noble animal calm, planted on all fours and dozing lightly.

He was a mighty beast, shaggy, with something in his build of both of the aurochs and of the bison from which he was descended, with deep forequarters and enormous horns, doubly strengthened at the root like stakes going right through the head, only slightly bent upward and blunt at the ends; his way was not to pierce, he attacked as though with a pair of battering rams; no rapier play when *he* gored, everything was pulverized before there was time to make a hole!

Now, and as a general rule, he was docility itself, with slumbering forces; slowly he turned his huge angular head and made the sign of calm above it with his horns; he was heavy and drowsy about the eyes, all swollen and stupefied with latent vigour, curly-haired on the forehead with the whirling *star* in the middle, the mark of the bull with which he confronted his cows and which he turned towards his enemy. Hair and brows veiled the dark misty eyeballs, which gave no sign of intelligence but showed a white bloodshot ring when he turned them: power and rage ready to break out on occasion.

Ah, when he is wild! A terrible gallop dwells in his hindquarters and massive high shoulders, his forehead is bent forward from the thick, deep, fleshy neck and projects with its mass of bone and the roots of the horns, with these he charges, flying through the air with all his immense weight and impetus put into the blow; then a sweep of the horns, and what they have not destroyed he lays under him, with all his weight in the hoofs, each leg a battering-ram, and tramples it out of recognition; that is his way when he is mad.

But now the bull stands quietly reposing in his power, so still that the steam and vapour of his vital warmth, billowing from his shaggy flanks, rises straight up above him like a column in the cold air. Only now and then does he make his voice heard as in a half-awakening, some foggy bull's idea arising in his forehead; from deep down in the belly of him comes a muffled bellowing, gloomy and subterranean, with a strange intensity; it sounds like a light touch of a drum and vibrates in the air long after — what then is he like when he rages and all his vital spirits roar through his nostrils!

From time to time it is as though a dream of another kind arises in his angular consciousness, buried beneath horn and hair and bony structure; then he stretches his neck and sniffs the breeze with wet and beady muzzle and the white ring shows in his eyes; this is when a breath of air from the cows reaches him. But here again the year is still asleep, the time has not yet come; the veil falls again and he sinks back into himself, under the distant power of the sunbeams.

As he stands thus he is the root symbol of the state of nature from which he and those who have tamed him have proceeded. A long way they had travelled together, man and the ox, and they were to be companions longer yet. But the primitive state which the bull had inherited from vanished ancestors who once inhabited these forests, was not so very far away, and the savagery of the ancients, who had seen the aurochs in these same valleys, might turn to savagery again among their descendants, to whom they had bequeathed the tame ox.

When the cattle had been driven back into the byres Tole had all the horses collected; the men too, all his troop of horsemen, could come and be reviewed at the same time.

And they came, sons and sons-in-law, all the dreaded clan of Tollings, tall upright fellows, and many of them; *how* many sons Tole had nobody knew exactly, such things were not counted or gone into very deeply, for decency's sake, but there was a host of them and they struck awe when assembled together in one spot, with almost the same look, every one, like the formidable appearance of one and the same man repeated again and again; all aggressive in their bearing with their hair in a horsetail carried high above the head, and all with Tole's features, Tole's red face which reappeared in all his progeny, the daughters too; but they were a pale pink, for they were less in the open air; the sons were bright red, shading into blue, from the wind of Jutland. Such were Tole's sons.

The sons-in-law showed more variety, from different families in other valleys, but they were no starvelings either; to be accepted as a son-in-law of Tole's meant fighting one's way through the sons first; it was only stout adventurous gallants that won through to the girls, and then came the question of pleasing *them*. So it was something of a sight and it made the earth shake when all the Tollings trooped past at once.

If Tole gloated over his cattle with a broad, religious joy of possession, which he concealed — since it is not wise to boast of one's strength before the Powers to whom one owes it all; they might change their minds, such things have happened — it was impossible for him to restrain his pride when the horses and the lads rode into the yard and paraded before him. The horses were the apple of his eye, he had bred them through many generations, from excellent mares and the choicest stallions; there was not a single animal of his that he could not remember, all through his long life; now they were as he wanted them, all pretty much the same like his sons, derived from the stock which was common to all the breeders in Jutland but yet with an imperceptible strain which a judge's eye could detect: that's one of Tole's, you might hear far and wide, when one of the stud was seen.

They were small, short in the legs but with a big head and fairly long in the back, shaggy, with a reddish hue, and could easily stand being kept out in the winter; they had big, spreading hoofs, so that they could carry a man on boggy ground without sinking in, were frugal and could be fed on straw alone with their big jaws, and were equally good for heavy draught work, for riding or driving. Tole himself had given up riding and always drove, but it was his delight to see the youngsters on horseback.

Every man was the friend of his charger and had trained it to tricks which they kept to themselves, only they two fully understood one another. The weight of the riders and the whole aptitude of the horses had resulted in their developing into trotters, and in this they were quick, sure and untiring; they broke into a gallop when the rider eased them of his weight and ran by their side with a hand in the horse's mane; by aiding each other in this way they got over any kind of ground and more quickly in the long run than much bigger coursers would have done it. Now off and now on the horse, that was the man's training, shooting in full career with arrow or lance; their stratagem was to hang on to the horse's side at a gallop so as to be covered by it, but with the shield protecting the horse's exposed flank; or to lie dead, both invisible on the ground, or again they stood upright on the horse's back at full gallop, stood on their heads even; all these tricks they were masters of, more or less, and Tole was full of glee while horses and riders disported themselves on the sward, and laughed his great laugh, ho, ho, ho, which told people at a distance that the master was enjoying himself, whenever one of the boys took the grass.

This was only a foretaste of what they were looking forward to before long, horse-races and stallion fights which would take place at the spring festival, with the horsemen in all their finery and fully armed; besides all the other attractions, the great bull chase, which was the men's keenest sport, for it meant risking life and limb; and then there would be the lur-blowers to put fire into horse and man; all this was in prospect and was drawing near.

The din and galloping in the yard brought the women out of their houses; they stood at a distance with pink faces, dazzled by sunshine and wonder: marvellous what daring fellows they were! They too promised themselves golden days to come; more than one girlish heart swelled at the thought of what *her* share would be when suns and Powers and swains and sorcery all joined forces and fell upon the female sex with a terrific rush. Oh, they felt so defenceless in their clothes and began to shiver; yes, it was really cold, they ought to go in, but all the same they stood there and could not take their girls' eyes off the men, who whirled about on their horses in perfect mastery, belonging more to the air than to the earth.

But far in the background dark heads appeared, half concealed by the outhouses, in the holes leading to the earth cellars they lived in — the thralls, who had nothing to look forward to, nothing to expect of the spring but the work it brought. The doings they witnessed in the yard did not belong to their world at all, it was the world of the free, a glorious world that seemed bound up with the sun and the air, they were the air and the daytime, the freemen, while the thralls crept upon the earth, with stooping back and bent knee, in a gait like a perpetual fall; and they were the night, it smouldered in their tarry eyes, they carried it with them in their black bushy hair. The newborn sun came on them like an itch and they wriggled in their coats of skin, without any thought of the great glow in the sky; their twilight souls gave birth to ideas only as worms are bred in muddy depths. The horsemen's performance set them staring. From the turbary in the bog black figures rose like turf of the turf and turned a listless gaze towards the homestead, where the young men were at play, their long hair like a halo of sunlight round their heads. Even the horses seemed ablaze with manes and tails; Tole's horses were all chestnuts, with a pink, human colour about the muzzle; one would think they were brothers to the men. The whole place was like a wheel of light.

Up on the slopes was a man ploughing, with great trough-like wooden shoes on his feet and his head on his chest; he stopped his wooden plough for a moment and let the bullocks get their breath, while he looked through filmy eyes at what was going on in the yard without being able to make it out, for he was dull of apprehension, slobbered on his beard and stared: at their riding tricks again, were they? well, they'd break their necks at it one day or the other! But *he* was going to get their fields ploughed. And he started his bullocks again and crawled along his clayey furrow. A couple of short, broad creatures in skirts, girls from the byre, were spreading dung; they stood still betweenwhiles, steaming and looking towards the homestead through the trellis of their ragged hair. They squinted up at the sun: would it be long to dinner-time?

The centre of observation, the one who attracted every eye, was of course Tole, standing in a raised place, leaning on the handle of his ax and with his long thin white hair flowing out from his marten-skin cap.

He was an old man, thick-necked and stout, big-boned and heavy-limbed, with a slight tremble; the rims of his eyes turned out, red and watery, but there was power in his glance and it rested steadily on the person he was addressing. A peculiar intensified power came into Tole's eyes when it was a woman they fixed upon, as though they exerted an influence from a distance, and the women became uneasy under the master's glance, friendly though it was.

Another reason for staring at the yard was the tall stranger who stood by Tole's side, in whose honour the feats of horsemanship had been performed, Norna Gest, who had arrived and was staying at the homestead. Expectation was focussed upon him, it always meant something above the ordinary when he came.

Tole and the scald had much to talk about, they could be seen turning to each other and growing animated; Tole started back as though he would fall at something he heard, it must be great news; but not a soul could hear what they were talking about, the distance was too great for any one to catch a word of it. It was known from former years that the two were on very intimate terms, and things that had influenced the fate of many could be pointed out as the result of Norna Gest's visits to Tole. The very thralls looked at him, knowing that when it suited him he would visit them in their caves; things which even their owners did not know about them were known to him, he could share their world too. Those who had begun as captives and who had memories of another home found a release from their heaviness when they could confide in Norna Gest, it would be strange indeed if he had not been where they came from.

When the riding was over the two mighty ones were seen to make their way from the yard up the slope behind the homestead — hush! now they were going into the grove, the holy place, hu!

to look at the stone of sacrifice, and conjure, and perhaps make magic broth, and meddle with the heavenly bodies!

It was broad daylight, one *dared* approach the grove, and a few daredevil boys followed in the wake of the two elders, the inquisitive train that is never noticed but sees everything.

And they saw them go through the fences into the little wood, which lay by itself like an island outside the forest, thick and closed round the edge by small trees and bushes, higher with big trees in the middle, where there was a source and a pond, the whole place unapproachably holy, to say nothing of the consecrated houses which stood on the open space and scattered among the trees; grim houses, the abode of the weird, and uncanniest of all the temple, the great timber house where was the holy of holies and the banquetting hall in which the men ate the offerings on the great high days of sacrifice. The trees, which were also uncanny, old, gnarled and with dead branches, were full of hanging skeletons, carcases of beasts, frontal bones and horns of slaughtered cattle, not a few men either, old stiff black corpses dried on to the bones; others had fallen and lay under the trees, there was a whole bone-yard in there. The ravens took wing as men entered the enclosure, big, lazy, bloated birds, almost tame; they settled on the trees again at once, with a knowing croak, obviously of recognition, when they saw who was coming.

The corpses and the smell were nothing to the boys, they were pretty well used to the sight of dead bodies and to all kinds of smells; it was the terror of the sanctuaries and their hidden contents that attracted them so irresistibly. They knew a little about them but not nearly enough, and they lay with their eyes glued to cracks in the wattle fence, trying to penetrate what was going on inside. So long as Tole and Norna Gest were walking about among the houses they could follow them; yes, there they were by the stone of sacrifice, and Tole laid his hand on it, whatever that might mean; but when they went into the houses the boys lost sight of them, could only guess and were in sore distress. But when at last they saw the two great initiates prepare to enter the temple, the holy of holies, the boys' hair stood on end and they took their eyes from the crack, looked out into the wide world as though to call it to witness, with round, terror-struck eyes and open mouth: now they were going right in to the gods, ye gods! and would be blinded; for that was the only thing they knew about the Awful Thing in there, that you were struck blind if you looked at it. They could stand no more, creeping and crawling they worked themselves out of cover, away from the perilous region, until they were well out on the fields, then jumped to their feet and tore down to the house to announce to playmates and mothers that Grandfather and the tall old stranger had just gone right into the bogey place!

Tole and Norna Gest, however, felt no particular emotion as they entered the temple, ducking their heads in the doorway and taking a long step down, for the interior was half under ground and extended a long way, with no other opening for light but the door; a fire was burning on the floor, they passed from day-light into gloom, only half penetrated by the light of the fire; the corners and the background lay in shadow. An aged woman rose and came towards them; she was all bent forward, crippled with rheumatism, but brisk enough, chattering like a magpie with her toothless mouth; she had dirty red eyes and wrinkles full of soot, her tiny head perfectly bald and her claw black and scorched from tending the fire. It could never be allowed to go out, for it was the hearth of the whole country, on that account alone it was kept up all the year round and solemnly renewed at the sun festivals; the priestesses were responsible for it, besides their other sacred duties.

There were several of them, living close by in huts within the enclosure and relieving each other, and there were younger ones among them, even down to newly initiated little girls who were taught by the old ones and would learn all their arts by degrees, how to slay a victim and take omens from the entrails, how to make incantations and brew magic broth, and whatever other deeds of darkness a sibyl is expected to know. Once inside the fence there was no return; the women who were dedicated to the service of Heaven could not go back to life.

It happened sometime that the young initiates grew up into bonny lasses whose fame spread beyond the sanctuary, and then the young men had a taste of sorrow: in their eyes much desirable intercourse, said to be reserved for Heaven, regrettably went beg-ging. What the maidens thought about it never came outside the enclosure, any more than they did themselves. But however fair they may have been in their youth, they all ended like the old priestesses, if they lived long enough.

The priestesses were virgins; in some respects life and death remained a closed world to them, in others a long life gave them a grisly experience, they ceased to be human without having even the simplicity of animals; of all creatures the priestesses were the most cruel.

Tole greeted the old woman who was on duty and went about the sanctuary with Norna Gest, took the ring from the sacred raised place in the background of the crypt; the *ring*, of solid gold and so heavy that you could kill a man with it; Tole laid it in Norna Gest's hand, no small mark of confidence, for nobody but the priest himself was allowed to take it, it was death at the stake simply to touch it by accident, it pledged its victim to the fire. On holy occasions it might be done, but then it involved heavy obligations; covenants made with an oath on the ring were inviolable, and young couples were wedded by laying their hands on it. For the ring was the sun, the golden circle, by touching which one came under the ban of Heaven, but also under its protection if one was true to one's oath. Norna Gest weighed the ring in his hand, nodded and nodded again, and Tole nodded as he put it back in its place.

In front of the high place stood the huge sacrificial bowl, of pure silver richly embossed with figures, the most intimate symbols of the Cimbrians buried as it were in hieroglyphics, only to be interpreted by the initiated; it was now cleansed and bright, but on the great days of fate it reeked with the blood of the victims, when priest and priestesses performed the solemn rites that maintained the order of the universe. Its mighty swelling form witnessed by its bulk alone the powers that were set in motion when it was full of blood; at once clear and mysterious the figures stared out upon the gloomy crypt, the silver catching the red light of the fire.

But at the top of the high place there was as it were a house within the house with a door. Tole opened it and exposed the god.

There was a mewing by his side from the old priestess who was jealously following his movements and gave him angry looks. But he pushed her away with his elbow, put his hand into the shrine, the holy of holies, and took out the god.

He and Norna Gest put their heads together, did not say much but exchanged many wise nods and emphatic winks. Behind them the bent old crone shuffled about, making dull sounds of anxiety in her chest; she strewed something on the fire, as though to atone for what was taking place, and a spicy scent of gum filled the cave. One finger she put into the fire till it began to smell, then started cackling like a bird and smacked herself in the face; more than that could not be done.

But the two superinitiates were not doing anything to the god, only looking at it. It was a smallish god to look at, scarcely two spans high, a sort of embryo, made of wood roughly carved, not much more than a round billet with an indication of a head, no arms, but divided at its lower end by a slit, like the beginning of a pair of legs. The wood was black with age and saturated with grease; the mouth of the image, indicated by a slit across the head — nose and eyes were wanting — was newly smeared with butter. The god ate on the day of the summer solstice; then the rays of the sun fell into the temple through the doorway, right into the holy of holies and melted the butter on the god's mouth; that gave it food for the whole year. Ay, ay. It was she; Tole pointed a rude finger at the sex, saying nothing but giving a grunt. He turned her over; no art had been used on her back, she was not to be seen from behind. But all over its body, both in front and behind, the image was covered with holes, black and charred at the bottom, like those produced by drilling fire; and in fact the god was an old firestick, how old nobody could say, but at any rate as old as the Cimbrians themselves. It had *always*, from the very creation, been in their possession, and in more definite tradition it had been handed down from father to son in Tole's family; it was the most sacred thing in the country. Everybody knew that from the beginning of the world the lightning had dwelt in it, that was why it struck any one blind who looked at it. In the popular imagination all kinds of monstrous and supernatural ideas were formed about it.

Tole put the image back in the shrine and closed the door on it. Muttering to each other with many pertinent nods the two experts then betook themselves again to the daylight and left the fussy old priestess to smoke the place out after them; they still had the rest of the sacred gear to see and went into the house specially built for the *car*, the god's holy car which was used on behalf of the whole country on the most solemn occasions and which was a masterpiece, lavishly ornamented with costly mountings, a thing beyond all price. Tole's thoughts, however, were more concerned with the team; on certain occasions the car was drawn by heifers, on others by stallions, in both cases Tole took care that they were the best to be had. Whatever the team might be composed of, it almost gave the impression of being a kind of transformed human being that drew the car in honour of the god; Tole bred his animals with a view to pink flesh tints; his own taste lay that way.

The car then was found to be in order and it was refreshing to see it again, many memories were connected with it, such as the rolling of time; but the car was ready to roll once more, there would soon be use for it. Yes, so long as it carried the Cimbrians' sacred traditions about the country for the solace of the people, so long would they and their cattle multiply and the produce of their fields be assured.

Norna Gest was to be shown Tole's treasures, his store of weapons and valuables; but first they made for the smithy, and Tole was excited about something which they stopped to discuss on the way.

It was a plan that had been matured between them years before and which Tole was now carrying out; he was going to cast an image in the likeness of a bull. Norna Gest, who had advised the smith about a silver bowl — a work inspired with secrets that only a travelled man had the key to — had also promised his help in the matter of the bull.

The idea was that the ancient inviolable god which was kept in the holy of holies should be enclosed in the interior of the bull and thus be insured for ever against being seen; its sanctity would then naturally pass to the bull, and the image would take the place in the temple now occupied by the god and would be borne on the car in the sacred processions, a far more striking object to the eye than the receptacle, insignificant in itself, in which the god was now conveyed; this was the scheme the two wise old men had hatched together, and now it was approaching realization. For two years Tole had been collecting brass for the image, including a number of old bronze swords, greatly valued as heirlooms but surpassed as weapons by the iron swords now used; they were to go into the making of the bull, and thus their ancestors' most precious possessions would be applied to a holy purpose.

The work was now so far forward that the casting could soon be taken in hand; it was the biggest piece of work that had ever been undertaken in these parts and was much talked about; its success was considered by no means certain. A pit and a furnace for the casting had been constructed on a hitherto unknown scale and many preparations had been made; a whole staff were employed on the work, among them many freemen, kinsmen of Tole, besides himself; the rest were trained thralls.

The smith, a good man, was Tole's friend and distant kinsman, a skilful armourer who also worked in precious metals; under his direction the image of the bull had been set up in clay. Then it was moulded in wax on the inner core, another coating of clay was to be applied outside, and then the whole thing would be fired and the wax melted out; finally the metal would be poured into the mould, an elaborate and doubtful operation which might come to grief on many a snag in its course.

The image was practically finished in its wax stage when Tole and Norna Gest came to see its progress. It was modelled in the round, not fully life-size but over half, and it looked remarkably lifelike in the hut where it stood, like a creature that had appeared there, clay and nothing else, but still alive.

The likeness of the bull had been astonishingly caught, it stood defiantly planted on its feet, rather squarely built, but so it should be, lifelike about the head, and Norna Gest saw at a glance that a hand unknown to him had been at work here, the smith had not made it alone; and involuntarily he looked about for its creator.

The smith, who saw the meaning of his glance, pointed with his thumb to one of the thralls in the background, and from further explanation it appeared that this man had disclosed special abilities while the work was in progress; he alone had carried out most of the final moulding in wax, which would be reproduced in the metal, assuming that first the firing and then the casting were successful. Yes, he was clever, could get it to look as it really looked; and if he was in doubt about the image he went straight and looked at the thing itself, took the bull by the horns so to speak; that was more than would have occurred to other people who thought they had seen enough to make an image out of their head. Of course they had humoured the thrall in every way for the sake of the result, as soon as his gifts declared themselves; they had even brought the bull down to the hut so that he might look at it without leaving his work. Evidently he was held in high esteem.

They called him "the Squirrel" for want of other name, not having been able to understand a word of his language or what he was called; now he was beginning to pick up a little human speech. He had not been long in the smithy; Tole had bought him of a Baltic skipper at the fair on the Limfjord, and by all appearances he came from a distant country; he was dark-haired and well sunned, with a skin like gold, and must have passed through many hands before he came so far as this. His name of "Squirrel" had been given him because he was small and agile, with big front teeth; he had gleaming eyes, looked like a handsome boy and in fact was not much more; quite young, but in spite of that he possessed this very valuable talent. It was a lucky thing he had been sent to the smithy, for which at first glance he did not seem fitted; if he had been put to peat-digging, well, then he would no doubt have turned out uncommonly shapely peats, but it would have been a pity. As it was he gave satisfaction and was unreservedly appreciated.

The Squirrel smiled when he was noticed and talked about. Nobody was readier to smile than he, with a bright, shining smile incomprehensible to the men about him, they could see no cause for his joy. The women had noticed it; they sometimes passed by the smithy to see the young thrall smile through his soot. He had curly hair which many a one might envy, and this too attracted the women's attention. Though small he was well built and there was charm in his gestures; without a doubt he was of gentle birth and through some misfortune had been sold as a slave, who could tell where? But perhaps Norna Gest was the very man to clear up the mystery.

Norna Gest took him in hand; to every one's surprise and deepest awe it appeared that the scald was able to address the foreigner in his own language, and they saw the thrall's eyes fill with tears.

It turned out that he was a Greek, a piece of information which did not convey much to some of those present; most of them only gathered with a shake of the head that it was a question of an immensely distant country, somewhere down in the Welsh parts [1] or perhaps even farther off, and they regarded the Squirrel with correspondingly vague feelings.

Tole vouchsafed him the full broadside of his attention for a moment, with head thrown back: so he was a Greek, was he? — whereupon he turned to some other subject.

But after that Norna Gest had several talks with the thrall and

[1] I. e. Italy. — Tr.

was able from his story to picture to himself a remarkable destiny, in which what seemed to be only the workings of chance were nevertheless fate. Five years before the thrall, whose real name was Cheiron, had been carried off by pirates from his home in the Greek archipelago, had been sold until by roundabout ways he reached the Black Sea, thence he passed from hand to hand along the trading routes of the Danube, still farther north and down other rivers, and it always seemed that there was no abiding place for him, whoever had bought him had sold him again, whether because he was too feeble or for some other reason. Finally his last sale had landed him in a place the situation of which he still could scarcely guess, though he believed that if he had his freedom he would be able to find the whole long way back, he had taken note of it. But now it looked as if he would stay here for good, since it had been discovered that he was of some use.

He did not complain of his lot; on the contrary, he was better off here than anywhere else he had been. His owners took no notice of him beyond his duties. With his fellow-thralls he did not get on so well since he had begun to be important; they dared not do him any injury, but secretly put filth into his food; at night he slept chained together with them in a sty, there was no help for that. But in the daytime he was happy; work, which to other thralls meant sighs and groans, was his delight. And now he was even gladdening his owners with it. Things could not have gone better with him. But . . .

Thus had fate dealt with a young Southerner, a friendly being, cut off entirely from his kin, who was not yet twenty. What things he had seen!

Every day Norna Gest went to the workshops to see how things were going, and he always found the Greek thrall cheerfully busy with his work on the image, to the obvious admiration of his master the smith, while others regarded him with lurking feelings of resentment. He was rather lame for a day or two, one of the thralls having chanced to drop a heavy pair of pincers on one of his feet, but even a limp became him.

Norna Gest was not the only one interested in the great bronze casting, every one who could or dared found an excuse to pass the smithy and see how it was getting on. Even the women, who were not supposed to know anything about smith's work and who as a rule tactfully avoided places where bulls or anything in the likeness of bulls attracted people — remarks unfit for their ears were liable to be heard in such places — even they could not keep away. But this was something quite out of the ordinary, which kept every one in suspense, and the women shared in the interest, strolling by in little groups, feeling strengthened by numbers after the way of women; but their courage was very half-hearted, they were really going somewhere else and just dawdled for a moment outside the door to have a peep at the men's dangerous arts. The Greek happened to be very busy, surveying his difficulties with a flashing eye, with all his fingers on his work; or perhaps his glance fell as though absently upon the crowd of girls, a glance deep as a well, impossible to plumb; or he limped over the floor with wonderful grace, or they just caught sight of his back and shoulders, which he carried in a way they had never seen in any other man.

Inge, Tole's young kinswoman, the daughter of one of his nephews and closely connected with his household, often found a pretext for visiting the smithy and came down there alone, to call the master or see if he was there, walked straight into the workshops with her fair head bare and stood there breathless an instant, looking about her — and then the Greek was always the quickest to give her an answer, he stepped forward and made an obeisance, his whole being in one long look, and said in his melodious foreign accent, No, the master was not there. Blushing like the wild rose Inge then went elsewhere to seek him, and they saw her vanish, erect and supple and rounded like a young shoot of the willow, with her heavy pale yellow plaits hanging down her back.

At evening too, now the evenings were so light, the Lady Inge went out without escort, not anywhere near the thralls' quarters, but an attentive observer would see a figure like a statue standing in the clear air in that direction, the Greek reposing apart after the day's work and gazing at the stars; not a sign, not the slightest connection between the two figures in the evening light, and more than the distance divided them, an absolutely impassable gulf lay between. But they happened to be there at the same time, and if one went in the other soon disappeared, like two stars which are placed far from each other in the sky but set together.

Norna Gest took note of things of this sort, but scarcely any one else; he had a sharp eye and nothing to occupy him but watching the growth of others' destiny. Ah, the others were too much taken up with their own affairs to have eyes for any but their own partner: everywhere in the twilight was a secret attraction, the young people would not sleep and stayed out till they could not see each other any more, could only glimpse a dewy face in the moonlight and feel the nearness of a marvel.

The moon, the spring moon was waxing. Far and wide from the marshes came a mating song in the coolness of the evening, frogs and all living things witnessing of the earth's increase. The lapwing cried in the darkness, the cry of a mother, the ever-wakeful, a soul in the vast wild chamber beneath the moon. From the woods came hollow sighs, ghostly sounds and echoes, the beasts were restless.

And an uproar was heard behind the closed doors of the cattle-sheds, restive cows hammering at their stalls, the milkmaid in tears, and much bellowing, deep and aggrieved; the cows were in an angry mood — now they *would* go out to grass, what was the Master waiting for?

All at once and from every side welled up forces which were not to be controlled.

Now the Greek would surely be quite beside himself with homesickness, and Norna Gest chatted with him to see how this might be; but the Greek was not exactly longing for his home any more, he said, and Norna Gest nodded. In his own mind he added the explanation of the young thrall staying so short a time in all the places he had been: the men must have quietly come to the conclusion that the best thing to do was to sell him again. Was he likely to be long here either?

But of the Lady Inge Norna Gest knew that, without her having an inkling of it, she had been chosen for the May Bride of the year; it had been decided at a recent council at which he had been present. Every one was agreed that she was the fairest of all the girls of seventeen in the whole country on whom the choice could fall.

III

THE STRANGER MAID

THE TREES were late in coming out that year, but at last they burst into leaf. The herald of spring came to Cimberland.

Much had been whispered about it beforehand. A surprise of course ought to come as a surprise, but you could not prevent at any rate those who were making all the preparations from knowing what would happen. Where the May Bride, the Stranger Maid, was coming from was known in this case among the Tollings. It had been so arranged that she should visit the other districts first, where nobody knew her, and come home to Tollingthorp last of all; there the May wedding was to be held, after the bridegroom had come to meet her.

On a certain day Inge vanished from her usual place; some asserted that they had seen her taken into the sanctuary, where she was to be made ready and adorned. A few of the irrepressibly curious who sacrificed their night's rest for the scent of a piece of news were able to relate that the sacred car with its escort had left there early one morning, long before sunrise, without attracting any notice, *that* of course was not to come until the procession began visiting the homesteads. Others had heard that horsemen, swains and bridesmaids from other parts of the country were to meet the bridal car at a certain spot in the forest, and when the procession was complete it would come forth in broad daylight and visit the haunts of men; a procession that made a show of coming from the forest, decked out in all the gifts of the woods, and was now to bring summer to every home.

Putting ourselves in the place of the people of some outlying homestead where they had heard nothing but guessed what was coming, the spring procession had all the appearance of a revelation; they knew of course that it was mummery but had soul enough to take the visit seriously.

First of all they heard the music of lurs, as though there was war in the land; but this was not war, the notes were those of spring, easily recognized. In the morning, at sunrise, they might have heard distant lur notes brought on the wind from the forest, as though something was being born there, a sign for which all had longed; for now the cattle must be blessed or they would be too late, the woods were in leaf, it was full moon, all the signs agreed — so then summer *had* arrived!

Then old and young coming out, their souls already fired by the music, saw the approach of the May pageant, at a distance a bright green troop on horseback and on foot, surrounding something that looked like a swaying tree, a little wood in motion, when it came nearer a car bedecked and canopied with fresh green boughs.

The car moved slowly, decorously, drawn by a pair of heifers which were almost perfectly matched in their markings, white with a few splashes of dun, with white horns and hoofs like clouded amber, pale pink around the eyes and yellow downy udders; that they were Tole's cattle any child could see. They were very quiet and broken to driving, but still a girl walked by the head of each for the sake of security and spectacular effect. Beside the car walked all the bridesmaids with wreaths on their heads and green branches in their hands, and outside them was a guard of horsemen, young swains in their best finery but unarmed, bearing only white peeled hazel wands, the inviolable sign of peace, resting like lances on their thighs.

One thing was not mummery but solemn and awe-inspiring enough: the car bore the god, hidden from all eyes in the holy chest. No one had the slightest idea of its nature or appearance, but all knew of its boundless power both for good and evil. As the quintessence of all fertility it was the real heart of the procession; the mere fact that the car carried it over the land was enough to ensure the crops. Its power was diffused over the whole pageant.

In the straw at the bottom of the car behind the sacred object sat two sibyls, the oldest and most dignified to be found, both bald as eggs, swathed in white pipe-clayed cloaks which were tied under the chin, looking like two bags of bones with a death's-head on top, nose and chin meeting with age, shunning the light and annoyed by the sunshine, being accustomed to live underground, but turning their beaks hither and thither, watchful as hawks.

But in front of them, high up on the car in a transparent tent of foliage, sat the Stranger Maid, with flowing hair like a mantle of light, still a child but full-grown in her loveliness, of a wonderful freshness, as though she had become a woman that very morning:

blushing, smiling, she was the morning, the sunshine, the Spring in person!

She came from the wood, she was the wood, in her hand she held a branch of fresh foliage, the unpretending symbol of her power. But it was a magic wand; she held it out towards the wood before her and it burst into light green domes, new-born in the sunshine, like the wood she came from; she stretched it out over the fields, and look, you could see them grow green; she strewed wild flowers from her car, and all the meadows were full of blossoms as far as the eye could reach.

Those who had been blind to the springtime, to them she gave sight. For she was the Stranger Maid who brought new vision with her. And yet she was the soul of all familiar things and gave to each its soul again. As she was bright the sky was bright, the clear daylight was in her eyes and the sun on her brow, cloudless was her soul. As the blue of heaven merging into the blue fjords where rivers run out, sky and sea and sunshine blended into one union, so blue were her eyes, so open. She was warm as the breeze was warm, but with a cool breath from the forest, hot blood and sweet cool cheeks like wild roses still bedewed. She was laden with all the gifts of the land and gave them back with both hands, re-animated with her soul.

And the May song was sung:

> May, the mildest
> Maid, is coming!
> Crowned she goes
> to every home.
>> Bringing leaf
>> and bringing life,
>> to Man and Maid
>> so bountiful —
>> colt and cattle,
>> calf and kid,
>> fairest flowers
>> and children fair —
>> She, the fairest
>> young Midsummer!

> Bless our shores,
> ye southern breezes!
> Gentle Lady,
> bless our soil!

Bringing leaf
and bringing life,
to Man and Maid
so bountiful —
colt and cattle,
calf and kid,
fairest flowers
and children fair —
She, the fairest
young Midsummer!

Light the bonfire,
call the clansmen,
show our Lady
honor due!
Bringing leaf
and bringing life,
to Man and Maid
so bountiful —
colt and cattle,
calf and kid,
fairest flowers
and children fair —
She, the fairest
young Midsummer!

And while the May Bride stayed in her high seat on the car, the bridesmaids went into the homestead waving fertility to everything and everybody; they entered the houses, touching beds and benches with their wands, the stables, blessing the cattle; they blessed the whole place, even the old grandfather lying wrapt in his skins, never to rise again, saw a vision approach and strike his bedclothes with fresh leaves, a message from the woods which made him speechless, staring with wide-open eyes.

But the people of the place crowded about the wonderful car, which shone with its newly polished bronze mountings as though made all of gold, and tried to touch it for luck, the wheels, the symbols of the sun, the tail of the car, the innocent heifers, if possible the Bride herself, or but the fringe of her garment; they kissed their fingers to her that she might give them a flower or even a single leaf which they might keep to bring luck to the house.

But nobody ventured to touch the holy coffer, they knelt before it at a respectful distance and made a sign on their foreheads with clay; if any one came too near, the two old birds on guard at the back of the car shrieked and opened a toothless chasm in their faces; terrible boys who *could* not behave themselves got a stroke on the neck from the white wands of the escort.

Then the trumpeters blew their lurs again and took their places at the head of the procession as it passed on to the next farm. But it had not gone far before it became quite superfluous to visit them all; the people came of themselves, pouring from every side to meet the Spring pageant.

The sound of lurs was heard far and wide: first came people running at full speed, then men on horseback galloping from place to place, with the earth flying from their horses' hoofs as they thundered over the heath-mould, shouting and making signals to each other at a distance . . . before midday the whole of Cimberland knew that the May Bride had come that morning, and people from the valleys began to flock up towards the high central land, the heaths, the wastes and the forests, where they knew the procession would pass.

Before evening they were all home again bringing a green bough fresh from the May Bride's hand, hallowed by her touch; the messengers' lips crusted with their exertions, their eyes ringed round with sweat, their lungs at the last gasp, but they triumphed, holding the green bough high in the air; and before the sun went down every single home in Cimberland and all its fields were blessed. The cattle had now to be passed through the fire, then they could be let out and the open air life would begin. Not a soul thought of living indoors any more.

In the evening bonfires were lighted on all the beacon hills, as though all the hearths of the country had been moved out into the open. Everywhere people trooped up to the long heath-covered ridges, which gave a free view over the country so that they could see each other's fires, row upon row of fires all round the horizon as far as one could see; and they knew every place, knew whose fire each one was, some blazing up fiercely, others only a distant dying spark in the glimmering moonlit night. All the clans and families of Cimberland were in communication through the fires on the heights; it was as though they could read each other's thoughts from place to place.

And everywhere the same picture, if you approached the bonfire, the height and a ring around it illuminated by the great blaze which burned straight up in the still air, sending up a pillar of smoke; shadows like the cogs of a wheel thrown outward from the top of the hill, with the fire like a hub in the middle; and the wheel turned, for the shadows were those of men going hand in hand about the fire, the sun dance, the symbol of the year and its course, the joyful return.

Now all fires were put out in every house in the country, the old, used-up winter fire, and new fire was kindled on the heights from the friction of wood brought from the temple and consecrated there. But in the sanctuary it was known that tonight Tole the priest would renew the sacred temple fire on behalf of the whole country, and tonight and the following nights great sacrifices would seal the covenant. Brands from the new fire were carried to every home to light the hearth again, the cattle were blessed by being driven through the smoke of a fire in the open, and then the summer had begun.

Nobody went to bed that night, they were all up and out of doors, at the bonfires and on the heights, to see the sun rise and rejoice over it. With the deepest interest they observed and recognized the fires all round the country; such and such a one was burning low, another burned brightly, and they thought of the farm and its owner, took omens and sent each other all good wishes.

Tonight too they felt a certain connection with strangers, in foreign parts, they could see the fires beyond the borders of the country, right over on the other side of the fjord both on the west and on the north; there too they kept the festival, the rude men of Salling, the savages of Thy, ignorant they were in many ways and needed a drubbing on occasion, yet they scarcely deserved to lose their sight like the mole, since they still acknowledged the sun and honoured it with new fire when it was new. Far to the southward they could see great fires and guessed them to be in the neighbourhood of Vebjerg; of course there would be a big festival at the temple there, though this was not a gathering of the whole country. At still greater festivals, with intervals of years, they assembled there for sacrifices, Cimbrians, Aaboers, and Harders, a levy of the whole of Jutland; but the Spring celebration was the affair of each district. Hereabouts it was Tollingthorp that took the lead.

And there a mighty fire was seen; but it looked as if there were two! People shook their heads and could not understand it; they

knew the position of the bonfire on the slopes above the homestead, and that they could recognize, but there was another burning below, apparently in the homestead itself, and it was even
bigger — the place could not be on fire?

No, the place was not on fire, though it looked very much
like it: the hut which contained the great image of the bull was
burning. But this was no accident. The clay mould was ready and
the firing was to be attempted; they had then decided to sacrifice
the hut to avoid moving the image; they had filled it with firewood
and turves and set fire to the hut at the same time as the Spring
bonfire was kindled; this had been thought out beforehand as
auguring a fortunate result.

One thing promised good luck, a fateful coincidence: on that
very day the bull himself, who had served as model for the image,
had been sacrificed.

It had to be. The bull was the chiefest and most honourable offering with which the sacrifices were inaugurated, as the being
who was accounted nearest to the supreme deity, in an obscure
sense almost the god himself, a mystery associated with sun and
moon, secrets of which only a few initiates had the key; but for
laymen it was enough that the bull was sacrificed, it was to be given
to the fire and its horns hung on the sacred ash in the sanctuary.
There could be no greater mark of distinction. The bull had had
his time, younger bulls were to take his place and to fight their
way in the course of the summer to the leadership of the herd. It
was as though the old year was sacrificed for the benefit of the
new, the accomplishment of the very order of the universe.

The sacrifice was carried out with special rites, an entertainment
with sacred significance: the death of the bull was the culmination
of a hunt by the young men of the district.

On the same day as the Spring pageant left the woods and revealed itself to the inhabitants young men from all parts of the
country assembled on horseback at the home of the Tollings, all
those who desired to take part in the chasing of the bull and believed themselves equal to the encounter.

They were the doughtiest lads of the neighbouring hundreds,
horsemen and runners if any there were, experts in the art of
slaughter, great rough, reckless fellows, who spent their whole
lives in hunting, manly exercises and sporting contests; in every-

thing they were pretty equally balanced, and here was a chance of proving which of them was the smartest. It was a game where they risked their skins; so much the better.

A hot-headed crowd while they were waiting to start, all on choice prancing horses with fire in their nostrils, and each with a leash of hounds, which all flew furiously at each other's throats until the chase should give them other work to do. The hunters were armed with swords only, for the fight would be at close quarters; all carried their heads thrown back intrepidly, rolling their hazy blue eyes, with their hair tied together on the top of the head and waving in a tail. There was not a young warrior in all these parts who did not wear his hair thus, it was the latest fashion and the idea was based on utility: as each one hoped to get a handy grip of his foe's hair when he was severing his head from his body, so he would oblige *him* with something to take hold of — when and where he wished! As they curbed their unmanageable horses the lads' patience, of which they had but little, ebbed, their eyes were wild, their foreheads frowning: when was it coming off? If they were not given something to contend for, a death to face, a life to take, why, it wouldn't be many minutes before they began to devour each other!

But their quarry had been prepared. At last Tole came out, clad in the sacrificial robe he would wear all day, with his sacred staff in his hand, and announced to the crowd that the bull they were demanding had already been let loose early in the morning in the wastes; *where*, it was their affair to find out. Tole hoped the bull would be properly mad when they came across him — good morning!

The men flung their horses around, all of them together, and the sudden tramp of many horses sounded like a landslide, a drumming on the turf as the united band dashed across the yard and out of the homestead, all their straight backs swinging up and down, all their tails of hair waving, a rain of earth and pebbles flying from their horses' hoofs. On reaching the fields the band divided and scattered in every direction, seeking cover, each with his own plan, not to be spied on by the rest; in a moment they were all swallowed up by thicket, wood, heath or bog, and only the distant baying of hounds was heard from every point of the compass.

Some, the more methodical, cast about for the trail, taking their time; others made at once for the highest ground to get a view; a number trusted to instinct and galloped straight ahead, one way or another, only at full speed; it was by no means all who could be in at the finish.

The bull had gone far, several leagues to the eastward towards the moorland, and was found on a wooded slope surrounded by a ring of hounds, whose terrific howls proclaimed the place. The horseman who had been first on the scene was found by the next who rode up following the sound; he lay dead together with his horse, mashed into a confused heap on the ground, with a huge rent in his body as though the whole bull had gone right through him. More hounds came up, with a baying that smote the sky, more and more of the hunters; those who had not heard the din scented where the bull was found, by tracking instinct, dots seen in the landscape, twitching of the limbs, anyhow they were there, a score or more of horsemen who were fortunate enough to be on that side of the country; so they shared in the chase and were in at the death.

But first the bull was to be driven back all the way home, a stiff piece of work but not to be avoided; the slaughter had to take place in the neighbourhood of the sanctuary, and it was to be *seen*, witnesses and spectators were waiting for it.

It was late in the day when they reached home with their quarry, after a breakneck ride and many fears, pursuing the bull and letting him pursue them, in the right direction, loss of horses and hounds and several men badly hurt. The bull was visibly fainter, could not be expected to be at the top of his fury all the time, only now and then he turned on the dogs, and you could see him shooting white jets from his nostrils, challenging them; a hound or two would fly into the air from his horns, but he could never get at the whole pack. He seemed to know the last part of the way and to want to get home, went of his own accord, and they let him recover his strength, so that the game might be more equal when it came to the last round.

He was brought to bay in the paddock between the homestead and the sanctuary, and hundreds of people had collected to see the tussle, the greatest of their public amusements, not one of the elder men but had taken part in bull hunts in his young days, and all the younger ones were in a state of excitement, eager to learn against the day when their turn would come. In an age which none of those present had known but of which they had traditions, it was the wild aurochs, now extinct in the country, that was hunted; this trial of manhood was an ancient and holy institution, an inherited passion in the blood of every man.

The struggle was short but fierce and bloody; for the last time the bull was incited to a full display of rage; the men attacked from every side without thought of life or limb, and in this merciless charge the beast went down. To look at it was a whirlwind of men and horses with the bull in the middle, scooping up black streams of earth with his forefeet, his muzzle to the ground, roaring with all the force of his lungs, a sound not unlike the bursting of ice in winter, and lashing his tail; the hunters could be seen flying in the air above him with legs and arms free, leaping in the nick of time before the attacking horns, horses crumpled up on the ground in front of the bull, trampled down; fresh attacks by the men, leaping over the raging beast, a creaking of hoofs and joints, horses rearing straight up in air as though they would jump to heaven — and then an instant when the whole immense uproar subsided all at once . . . a silence in which was heard a long *Oh* from the women, who had witnessed the wild scene from a distance, sheltered behind the men: the bull had received his death-blow.

No more than *one* wound must be found on the slain victim, and that had been dealt.

The men all aimed at the chest with their sharp two-edged swords as the shortest way to the heart; the plan was to ride up as close as was safe, then throw one's self off one's horse and receive the bull's charge; if there was no chance of a thrust, take a leap lengthways over the beast and land behind it, a dangerous jump with a drawn sword in the hand, as a rule they rolled over many times on the ground after it, but that they thought nothing of, up again and another try!

But the man who had dealt the lucky stroke had discovered entirely new tactics. They saw him jump, but not in front of the bull; it was a running leap from the side, such as the men practised when jumping on their horses in full career, and he landed with perfect sureness *astride the bull*. In breathless suspense the spectators watched him ride a short distance as in a swing, the bull now on his forelegs and now on his hindlegs, shaking himself in the wildest frenzy; but the man kept his seat, and they saw him aim his blade, throw himself forward and put his whole weight on it, and the beast sank on its knees under him. It was all over. From above he had pierced right through the lung to the heart. Immense relief of the spectators, which found vent in shouts, hurrahs, transports of joy: a fairer sacrifice could not have been accomplished.

The priestesses with kilted skirts ran with buckets of the warm blood across the fields to the sacred grove and poured it into the sacrificial bowl in the temple; it covered the bull's image at the bottom of the bowl, where the hunt was pictured, both its course and its finish: the stricken bull lying down, surrounded by dogs, and the hunter in a flying leap above it with a drawn sword in his hand. It was as though the image appealed to be hidden; when a sea of blood swam above it its summons had not been in vain.

But the hunter who had achieved the victory was led in triumph with his horse; the others who had taken part in the hunt surrounded him and formed his escort; he was their chief, all loved him for his supreme achievement, their joy on his account knew no bounds.

And now he was to be escorted to his wedding! For he who laid the bull low was by that very deed chosen as the May Bridegroom, to be wedded to the May Bride before the bonfires were kindled.

Ah, yes, the prize of victory was such that every single young swain in the country had dreams of it that put him in a fever, and one would have thought they would *all* be present at the bull hunt. The number of those who came, however, was not so overwhelmingly great: as many as had seen Inge had also seen the Tolling bull! And those who did not show themselves might hope to remain in their obscurity.

But the competitors were the flower of the first families of Cimberland, the hardiest and most dreaded of all the dare-devil youths in the land. And he who proved himself Number One among them all was the most reckless, he had the most splendid top-knot of straw-coloured hair, the lightest, fiercest and haziest eyes, an eagle tattooed on each cheek and a serpent — the lightning — on his forehead. He was so young that his beard was as yet scarcely a down of bog-cotton on his lip. Boierik was his name.

If the May Bride had driven out with heifers at a most orderly walk, so that even a child could keep up, she was brought home at the fastest gallop a pair of horses, white stallions, could flash out of the ground, the bridesmen in a ring round the car with their green boughs flying like banners in the air, Boierik seated nobly beside the Bride in the high seat, and two old sibyls nodding and smacking their gums behind with their sacred charge.

Both it and they came near being shaken out of the straw, for the driving was so reckless, road or no road, scrub or bog, that at times the car flew through the air with not more than one wheel or none at all touching the ground; and it is certain that if they had driven slower they *would* have been upset, but at the pace the car was going it could not overbalance. It was the kind of driving that meant life or death, wedding or childbirth; there was laughter in the banqueting hall when the young people arrived and they saw what haste they had made.

Thus the Stranger Maid came back and made her final entry at her own home, and it really seemed as if her familiars scarcely knew her, they thought she had grown in the course of that one day, taller, more beautiful, with bluer eyes, as though the sky and the sounds she had seen lay in them, with the wonderful first freshness of the woods over all her being. And yet, the shadows were long when she came home, the day was sinking, and was there not something like a shadow on the May Bride's brow? She might well be tired after such a day. All were agreed that no better matched bridal couple than Boierik and Inge had been seen in any year.

The May Bride was led by her maidens to the women's quarters to rest and be prepared for her wedding.

But the car with its sacred burden and the two sibyls drove back into the sanctuary. Here the holy coffer was put in its place in the temple, with the door of its shrine open, so that the god might enjoy the smell of the bull's blood in the great bowl. The heart was roasting at the sacred fire before the high place, filling the whole temple with sweet fumes, and the two sibyls cackled with delight at being home again, sheltered underground from the hated daylight. Much labour awaited them during the coming night and day, sacrificial duties, and they began to make themselves ready, pipe-claying not only their clothes but their faces and scalps, sharpening knives against one another, old slaughtering knives, pliable in the back, that had been ground so often that there was only a thin strip of blade left, regular women's knives, but they could depend upon them for their work. And their gums were on the go;

ugh, they had been listening to the song of birds the whole long disgusting day; this song, *hwee, hwee,* the song of knife against knife, that was better.

Meanwhile the bridegroom was received by Tole and conducted into the men's circle, for the first time in his life, with a certain ostentation on Tole's part, while Boierik took pains to conceal his feelings, as though it were an everyday affair; but something in his walk betrayed him, the honour was too great. Happy friends followed him in the background and saw the great old franklins, chiefs of neighbouring clans, offer him their hands.

They had arrived in the course of the afternoon to be Tole's guests at the sacrificial feast. If the bridal pair had driven smartly there were some of the visitors who had not spared their horses either; those who were going the same way had raced each other so that the stones flew; some of their cars were muddy to the hubs, they seemed to have driven over peat-bogs and everything, a few upsets there had been too. Now they were out in the yard in the evening twilight, looking over each other's teams. Every one of them had a matchless pair of horses, trotters that could not be beaten if you searched the world over, the owner offered to bet any odds, and the teams should be tried against one another in the morning! All kinds and all colours were there, it was not everybody who swore by Tole's brood mare with the maidenly hue; there were brown horses of every shade, down to raven black; there were roans and mouse-coloured nags, but otherwise all were pretty much alike in their build, long-haired, with bony heads and spreading hoofs, made to swim with, the Jutland ideal and the first point looked for in any horse one saw.

And Boierik took his part in the horse talk, as his friends in the background could see, he was not at a loss among all these knowing ones; they saw him lay his hand on an animal's flank, feel its leg lightly down to the pastern and give his opinion, and the wise old franklins nodded in a ring round him, yes, yes, that's so; the friends in the background laughed aloud in their excitement and gratitude at the solemn way Boierik behaved, with impenetrable features, going straight to the heart of the matter when he spoke. He was so obviously at home in the men's circle, without any effort, but at the same time as though he had taken twenty years at a single leap.

IV

THE WEDDING

THERE were no heroics about Boierik when he afterwards accompanied the elder men to the sanctuary to take part in the sacrificial repast, where the bull was to be served up: with toes turned in and swinging stride he marched with the others, whose precedence was part of the nature of things.

And here his friends lost sight of him, within the sanctuary they could not follow him. Perhaps he missed *them* a little in his great new dignity; now they would be amusing themselves with bathing in the stream and other pastimes that belong to spring, before the bonfires were lighted.

Washing and purification were part of the inauguration of the new season, for it was impossible to pass into springtime unpurged of the winter; when smoking out the old season it was fitting to scrub one's old self and put on a new one. The houses were aired; they were lined with soot from the winter and not fit to be seen in the strong light which now poured in through the doors; people had been living and breathing in an atmosphere of lamp-black for the last few months without noticing it and the daylight exposed this horrible state of things. The old bed-straw was carried out and burnt, with all its mice's nests and fungus; some made straw men of it and burned winter in effigy, replacing it by fresh grass. But few of them hoped to sleep indoors again for the next half year.

Men and women visited the bath-house and had themselves steamed, well and long. And after the bath they put on entirely new clothes, linen and light frieze; their winter skins were put away if they were fit to wear again, otherwise offered to the fire, and a fine blaze they made, smoking and crackling; what is nastier than an old cast slough?

The young unmarried people preferred the stream to the bathhouse, boys and girls together, a whole swarm of them down in the meadows below the homestead, in full view of all; you could tell the boys from the girls at a distance, the latter were pinker and more compact in figure, with excrescences before and behind, they kept to the ground when running, as though they couldn't take their feet from it; the boys were up in the air, and they were bony and dead white, with a mother-of-pearl tint of muscles and joints under their thin skin. The water was evidently cold and the air coolish, they raced for their lives to reach their clothes, shirts and linen smocks fluttered over their heads and were pulled down over wet bodies.

Home they came fresh and carefree, blue about the lips, in new clothes from head to foot, dressed for the feast and ready for the evening ceremony. In getting into their clothes they had the unconscious feeling of having shed a state of nature and put on a better man, washed and renewed, in this as in other ways keeping pace with the year and its resurrection.

The supper was a festival one, and now Mother and her flesh-pots came into their own; the band of young people mingled with women and children from the homes around, who were taking their meal in the open air for the first time of the year, at open smoking fireplaces on the grass, crowding round the cauldrons with wooden spoons in readiness. Holiday fare it was: barley groats boiled in sweet milk, dried mutton-ham and smoked pork, cheese as much as they wanted; bread only for favourites, for Mother was sparing of her loaf, there was not much of last year's corn left and the new harvest was a long way off. On the other hand mast-bread was passed round freely, but at the mention of it the young people politely said, thank you, they *had* finished. Their meal was only a hurried affair, the whole band wanted to be up on the heath as quickly as possible, the heights and the night were calling. Thirst was quenched, a big wooden bowl of whey went round, without further ceremony than that the bowl was of maple with handles carved in the form of horses' heads, and that one or other of the young fellows cleverly managed to drink just after some particular girl. What feeling she put into it as she handed him the drink!

Dusk fell, their souls felt the power of the long evening twilight, they sought each other with wider eyes. Up rose the moon.

But at sunset a shower had veiled the blue sky, before it turned red, and a few cold drops had fallen, still with the bitterness of winter, but no more came. The women who were dressing the Bride remarked at the same time that she wept and was distressed; they read in it an omen of abundant rain in the coming season.

Up in the sanctuary meanwhile the men were assembled in the banqueting hall, as the guests of the god, in whose honour they partook of the repast; for though the Bull was an offering to the fire, it was to be eaten in order that the sacrifice might be consummated and all might share in the sanctification.

Not every one could explain wherein this consisted, it was the secret of Tole and the holy women. But that the Bull and the Sun and the Moon had something to do with each other, were to a certain extent one and the same Power, was comprehensible even to a layman. The Bull was absorbed into the Sun when it was sacrificed, and that renewed the year, so much at any rate one could understand. Therefore in eating of it one of course shared in its resurrection. Anyhow it was Tole who had the responsibility of maintaining the Sun and the year, and they could trust to him. He and the sibyls had searched the bull's heart and reins and drawn omens from them for the year, uncommonly good, it was said; so there was nothing more to be done but to see how the beef tasted.

All the partakers had spots and splashes of blood on their faces, which were left to dry and might not be wiped off; it was the blood of the Bull wherewith the oldest and most reverend of the sibyls had besprinkled the congregation; by this act they had been washed of the old year and their old selves in the blood of the Bull and were made partakers in the Sun and its renewal; all felt like new men.

Reddest of all was Boierik, splashed to the elbows and with a mask of clotted blood over his face; he had received a jet of blood as he plunged his sword into the bull, a sanctification which ought to be of some use. The greater part of the bull's strength had passed into him, whether the others liked it or not. Ah, he was a lucky man, all privileges had fallen to him in one day. Outside the temple door the bull's pizzle was now hanging to dry; he had a right to it for a riding-whip and sign of authority; oh yes, he was in luck!

The hall in which they sat was a low room, half under ground, with walls of earth and stone and roofed with timber; an open fire burned on the floor — the god himself, present in a tamed, domestic form. Round about the fire sat the men as the god's immediate guests and took their meal; the tender beef went down without much previous preparation, each man did his own cooking and could roast it to please himself, holding it in the fire on the end of a stick or contenting himself with rubbing it a little in the glowing embers. Horns went round, but the drink was neither ale nor mead at this time of the year, everything of that sort had been drunk up at Yule; they had spring water, the best thirst-quencher after meat, as the wolf knows, and it was not any ordinary water, it came from the spring in the sacred grove and had powers which there was no fathoming. True, it kept them sober; but with sunshine and summer coming on nobody needs a spur to his vital spirits.

And sober things were discussed, sowing time, border questions, strained relations with neighbouring tribes, all which things, however, would not be taken seriously in hand until the day when the Thing was called together on the Thing mound. Horses were talked about again, a subject not to be avoided, and they had a taste of those which had lost their lives on the bull's horns, bits of kidney and tongue; the regular sacrifice where horseflesh was the chief dish came later. Hunting was discussed: not many deer nowadays, compared with what every one could remember; on the other hand wild boars were too plentiful, they rooted up the cornfields and ought to be hunted more often. The wolf had been fierce this winter, in one place it had killed eleven sheep, *in* the pen; such and such a man had lost his grandmother one winter evening on her way from one house to the other and had had only half of her to burn, a shameful business. The ice had taken some people this year; the fjord opened its mouth in broad daylight and swallowed four men spearing eels, and that in spite of its having been given a thrall at the proper time. Oh, ay.

The death of the bull was gone over again, with kindly glances at Boierik, who sat feeling hot and swollen about the head, snuffling violently and with eyes quite drowned in moisture from the strangeness of finding himself in a room; his nose ran and he felt as if he had had a blow on the head when he came under a roof, it was much tougher work for him to sit at table than to jump sixteen times over the bull; but he stood it manfully, did not move a muscle of his face when assailed by praises and modestly changed the subject when they grew too strong. His behaviour greatly pleased the elders, who had been quietly trying him.

But the culminating point of the feast came when Norna Gest was asked to touch the harp and perhaps reveal some of his treasures of song or story; they knew that he came from afar this year, from travels beyond all known bounds, so far as to baffle the

imagination of most of those present. With repletion came a desire
for spiritual expansion. They had eaten the second course, soup
with the meat boiled in it; after that black puddings, with smug-
gled bits of pork in them, not belonging to the bull (swine had
their turn at other solemn festivals), and finally came the dainties
and sweet things, bread, of which there was no lack in this company, long slices like the soles of one's foot, cut from the broad
loaf and spread with butter; with this they drank a native wine
made from cranberries and whortleberries, sweetened with honey
and spiced with bog myrtle; oh yes, they knew how to live.

And now they were disposed for fable and approached Norna
Gest with respectful questions, seeking knowledge. One wanted
to know if he had seen the World's Pillars, and whether one could
be sure that they would hold, so much depended on them; another asked if it was really true that there were animals as big as
peat stacks with their nose hanging down between their tusks and
provided with a sort of hand at the end. Just imagine, taking hold
of things with your nose! They were said to be quite invulnerable,
covered with iron all over the body and with plates of it on their
heads, born in armour. Well, one was told all sorts of things, and
of course there were pictures on the sacrificial bowl which everybody could see, not only of the snouted beast but of many other
supernatural creatures. One wasn't altogether ignorant either, and
even if there were no such wonders here at home, the pictures
of them proved at any rate that one knew the gods and recognized
their omnipotence in the diversity of created forms. Truly there
were more marvels under the sun and more Powers than any one
had an idea of. And that had been in the smith's mind, when he
and his mates in all reverence had made the great silver bowl, the
work of many years, to the glory of Heaven and all the gods. In
it were honoured all the gods they had heard of, with their attri-
butes: the god of Valland,[1] who had hart's horns on his head, the
ring of oaths in one hand and a serpent with a ram's head, the
lightning-stroke, in the other; he ruled the thunder in Valland and
was a god worthy of fear. Besides him there were many others,
some of the female sex, every Power under the sun to whom they
owed deference and sacrifice; therefore they were all symbolically
present on the sacrificial bowl to be remembered every time blood
flowed into it. Ay, was it not a strange world — you even heard

[1] Gaul. — Tr.

talk of invisible gods now, and they were said to be the most powerful of all; but they could be left to such folks as believed in them, here they preferred to keep to those they could see, Sun and Moon, oh yes, that was their way.

At the time the smith was fashioning the bowl and ornamenting it with all kinds of symbols and animals it was known that he had questioned none other than Norna Gest, who had been to the world's end, and been instructed by him — of course, here was a witness who had seen the things with his own eyes. How did these wonders look in reality? The griffin now, did that fly about everywhere, like eagles or cranes here, or was it a rare bird? Did it fly with a car up in the sky and help to draw the sun? Then it would have to be fireproof — but of course there were other creatures that were that, the dragon both ate and vomited fire, as every one knew. Did it dazzle you much to see a griffin? As to horses, no doubt they were very different in other lands, they had winged horses for use in the air and horses with finned tails that swam in the sea. How did one manage to ride on whales in Serkland?[1] There was no denying that the means of getting about had reached a high development in the South, in this the Welsh were ahead of the Northern farmer, sure enough. But weren't they unsafe countries to live in, didn't you have to fight monsters and defend yourself all the time? The wild beasts — there were some of them that had curved swords or sickles on all four feet and mowed everything down with them, regularly cropped their way through every living thing. And the women in the South were said to be so beautiful that you were quite bewitched and crippled if you looked at them. Were there really females with a score of breasts? All these things and more they wanted to know.

Boierik joined in, modestly as became the youngest, but clearly, straight to the point, and the old men nodded, yes, he would turn out well. It was a technical point; young as he was Boierik was collecting military knowledge and wished to hear something about the castles in the South, both in Valland and elsewhere. About Valland he was fairly well informed and always made a point of interrogating the merchants and travellers who came into the fjord to trade. But Norna Gest no doubt would have special information. What they understood here by a castle was one of the long earthen ramparts which they threw up on high ground or deep

[1] Syria. — Tr.

in the forest, and to which they withdrew with their cattle in time of trouble; but he had heard that in the South there were fortresses entirely of stone, each stone cut into a square, with chambers high up, one above the other, and constructed on such a scale that a whole population could live inside. How then did you take them? They said that you could sling stones, so big that one man could not lift them, to a distance of more than three or four bowshots; how much truth was there in all this? And what about their arms generally?

Norna Gest looked at each man who questioned him, Boierik too, as though storing their enquiries in his memory, but he did not answer at once, nor was his answer a direct one. He, the scald and story-teller, was the most silent of men. What he knew or had seen he kept to himself, until it turned to images; the clearest speech, he knew, was but an image. What he gave them should have form, terseness, his language should be coloured by the world and by his being. He began to think.

He placed the harp between his knees and began to play, a simple twanging of its few strings, with no great display of skill, more tones than melody; but at once it had a strange effect, in this murky house half under ground, upon his wild audience. It seized upon their features, as though in distress they looked towards the harper and turned cold, what was it? A faint and distant world streamed from his strings, difficult to catch, and it possessed their hearts, they became so heavy, with burning eyes.

And while he thus held them spellbound the old man was meditating, with his chin sunk on his breast and with no light in his eyes; long he meditated, as one who was far, far away. At last he rose and recited a lay, only one, obscure and, as it seemed, of deep symbolic meaning. He stood at his full height and recited, after the manner of a scald, slowly, in a full and penetrating voice:

> A stronghold stands
> in southern clime,
> its walls a hundred leagues;
> countless its roofs
> of icy peaks
> that strive toward the stars.

> Upon that roof
> ranges the goat,
> and over it the eagle.

The dizzy eaves
drip into dales,
whence run the mighty rivers.

Dismal pine-trees,
sadly sighing,
close its northern portal.
Southward opening,
sunny gateways
show their azure arches.

Two worlds confront
the castle walls:
misty and murk the one side.
Brightness and blue
in sky and shore,
these are the other's portion.

Lonely the white bear
floats on his iceberg,
sniffing the waves for seal.
Limber the reindeer
runs in the ghost-light,
fleet-footed captive of cold.

Elsewhere the elephant
trumpets in plenty,
tramping beneath the palms.
Sun-hued lion
leaves to the vulture
bones of a naked black.

He who has built
so firm a fortress,
he willed that it should stand.
Eternally,
unshakeably,
to sever North and South.

May be the marmot
chooses the midway,
building his house between;
seeks not the South,
nor haunts the North;
better a boundless view.

Creep over, ant,
and mole, crawl under!
Fly over, fowls of the air:

none may o'erthrow
so old a bulwark.
Still firm that wall shall stand.

Man of the North,
be hope thy nurture!
Better is soul than sunshine.
What will the sons
of Nile in the North?
No rover gathers riches.

The dun hyena,
nor dog nor lion,
laughs ever at the luckless.
Full oft I found
noble the native,
and poor the newcome stranger.

Wisdom it is
that sundered worlds
seek not their place to change.
Respect a rampart
of ancient rearing:
still firm the wall shall stand!

Norna Gest ceased, and there was silence. All had a deferential
sense of having received instruction, and each one seemed to find
a hint of an answer to his own questions. In particular the lay had
much to tell of animals they had never heard of before. Undoubtedly it was a good lay, and the feast was much honoured
thereby. Boierik flushed; he could see before him the castle he had
asked about, towering to the sky with its ice-blue walls! So faithful was his memory that it retained the once-heard lay and it came
back to him word for word, years later, when its meaning became
clear to him.

The thralls who had been in attendance now brought water for
the guests to wash their hands, and the feast was at an end. As they
held the basins the thralls stole glances at the heap of bones in the
corner: it looked like a lavish heap; that was their portion.

Yes, behind the outhouses and middens, in the thralls' quarters,
preparations were going on for another festival supper. They
were to have bone broth and were strengthening it with toads and
other creeping things from the marsh which they could manage
to catch; the black cauldron was stirred with a great shin-bone, as

the mouths of all watered in expectation. Here too a lay accompanied the feast; when the pot boiled over and hissed in the fire they put their heads together and sang right down in their stomachs this ventriloquial song:

> Hubble bubble
> Pooh!
> Sweet smells our broth!
> But bones and fat,
> They'll breed you bantlings!
> Gorge yourselves,
> Swill it down,
> Fill your guts!
> Hubble bubble.
> Brew a broth for your masters,
> Scorch 'em and scald 'em,
> We'll rifle the robbers!
> Hubble bubble.
> Pooh!

They were in high spirits, those who were cooking the supper, for on them the lot had not fallen that morning, *they* were not to be sacrificed. That was the fate of twelve others of their band, seven of whom were now sitting apart in the condemned cage, where they had been left to their meditations the whole day long; they were not to be sacrificed till midnight. The other five had got it over; they were the ones who were taken out to wash the sacred car when it returned to the sanctuary; they had to follow it up to the grove, and you could hear their shrieks a mile away, no doubt when they were washing the god, which it was supposed they would have to do, and that of course would blind them and scorch them. They did not shriek long. The last that was heard of them was a loud roar of hydrophobia; no doubt they ended by being drowned in the pond. Quite different was the fate of those who were boiling broth. Without the least effort on their part they had had a lucky day.

Among the seven victims who were still awaiting their fate was one from the smithy, the man they called the Squirrel. He danced no more. That toady! Now he could see the result of making his mark! He'd tried to rub shoulders with the masters, and now he'd get rubbed the wrong way. Doubled up with delight, lusting with malice, they gave the pot a good stir at the thought.

But the Greek sat behind the bars, keeping quiet the whole day.

The other six had begun by howling, had then subsided into lethargy and were now pretty nearly out of their wits. But the Greek was at work; yes, to the no small surprise of the Tollings who happened to pass the cage they found him occupied; he had got some clay and spent the whole day modelling a figure. And they simply could not take their eyes off what he was doing; it was extraordinary, a woman to the life, not full size of course, but otherwise exactly as if you saw a girl, with nothing on, perfectly lovely, they had never seen anything like it or imagined that such a thing could be.

Not a few of the Tollings thought it rather hard luck on the Greek, no small loss either, a useful man like that; but what was there to be said, they had themselves seen Tole throw the wands, split sticks of which the bark side meant freedom, the white side death; he had flung them up to heaven and it was heaven's decision when they came down; who could change it? Others expressed no opinion and maybe had harsh looks for the handsome Greek, when they noticed in the course of the day that the women walked by the cage just as they had been in the habit of passing the smithy. However that might be, he was now handed over to the priestesses.

By evening the Greek had finished his image, and they saw him smile as he gazed at it. Then a thing happened which saddened the onlookers; he destroyed the figure, hastily kneading it together in his hands and throwing the lump of clay to the ground. But many who had seen the image never forgot it, it remained alive in their memories as long as they lived.

The rest of the time the Greek sat idle, silent, and very, very sorry for himself; yes, there was no concealing it. He sat looking through the bars and could see the meadows and the stream; he stretched his neck when the young people were bathing.

Sunset turned the meadows green as fire; a mist rose from the stream.

He watched the shower as it came and went. And he looked upon it all as one who saw it for the last time.

From the sanctuary came a sound of lurs, shrill and harsh, the signal for the evening festival.

All fires were extinguished, all arms, everything of iron hidden away. God's gifts were to be received again as new, that men might value them rightly. The only light that burned above the earth was the moon; deepening in colour its full orb climbed in the sky.

The homestead lay in stillness, all whose legs could carry them were ready to move up to the heath; but first the fire was to be born. This most momentous and holy act was taking place within the sanctuary; not a sound came from thence, enclosed in its gloom the grove was like an island of darkness among the fields, and all eyes were turned towards it.

Some there were who knew, what they were not supposed to know, that as one part of the secret deeds of darkness now going forward in the grove the old priestesses would ride on sticks round the newly kindled fire as soon as the first spark was seen; a strange and revolting ride, whatever its meaning might have been, whether it was to show that they fetched the fire, had been away and come home again, or was a magic circle which they drew about the fire; many insisted that certain smoky and ardent Powers of a dangerous kind were conjured up by the ceremony. Many sinister acts were performed. But the birth of the fire announced itself to outsiders by being seen at a distance, when the hag's dance was over, and by the blaring of lurs. That was what they were waiting for.

Then the lurs brayed, tu, tu, tu, tu, a triumphant flourish, tu-h, long notes of deliverance, and they saw the fire among the trees, more fire, flickering up all at once, many torches; the procession left the grove with Tole at its head, all bearing torches, turned off towards the heath, and all the people joined it, lighting their torches from the others, a whole migration of torch-bearers from the houses up to the heath.

Behind Tole came the bridal couple, Boierik and Inge, festively adorned, now wedded, since they had joined hands upon the ring.

At the highest spot of the heath the bonfire was lighted, a regular timber stack, and a minute after it had blazed up, all the fires began to show for miles around, as far as the eye could reach.

The newly married pair were then sent away, in a covered cart like those used in the fields in summer, with a tent and all the gear required for living out of doors. Many hundreds of the same kind would leave the homesteads on the morrow and take to the pastures with the cattle, the beginning of the free summer life; the young couple were the first, they were to initiate the move. It was their first journey together; to begin with they could drive where they pleased and spend the night in any part of the woods.

The young people accompanied the cart for some distance, in happy envy. Lucky couple! In the morning they would return to the homestead to be honoured and placed at the high table at a banquet, and would receive gifts, and look beautiful and mysterious, and be admitted to all the privileges of the elders, lucky people! Shouts of joy followed them as they disappeared in the moonshine which blended with the beginning of the night-long twilight, and many a merry cry from swains who ran by the side of the cart and permitted themselves some liberty of speech; but it drove all the faster and they were left behind with their good advice and rank laughter. Thus the bridal pair went off.

Oh! The half-grown girls signed and groaned and stamped their feet; when *would* they come to that, when *would* they be grown up!

While the dance was in full swing round the bonfire Tole betook himself to his father's grave-mound, alone, as was his custom.

In his absence the dance assumed a less sacred character, the solemn circling degenerated somewhat in the direction of a hop, and a game was started which was the privilege of the young and to their minds the most attractive part of the feast — the races between boys and girls.

It began almost of itself, through some young couple breaking out of the ranks on a secret instigation, hidden threads that pass between the young and bind them two and two together; for it was usually the fact that the pair who broke out and took to flight as though in sudden disagreement had agreed upon it beforehand or had just discovered that they were of one mind; for many of them a connection that lasted for life would begin in this game of catch. However that might be, the girl took to flight, and the man after her. As a rule she was soon caught and brought back to the ranks, happy to be overpowered; sweet was the flight, but sweeter to be fetched back with gentle compulsion.

Yet the girl did not always allow herself to be caught as a matter of course. Though she ran as though glued to the ground, like the hedgehog, her sticks kept going under her all the time, and she could not get tired, had incredible tricks of twisting and turning and slipping from her pursuer at the last moment, so that it might take all the wind of a hardy, vaulting young hunter to overtake her.

The game spread from the height far over the heath and away to the woods, and sometimes a couple would disappear from view among bushes and undergrowth in the distant twilight. If the man then caught the girl he was liable to be heated and take hold of her roughly, but if she asked it she was given quarter; the game was not to have a painful ending, it was not for that these big, boisterous youths had their strength, and they could not associate love with injury. Any dog can pull down a weaker opponent. They would be friends first. Hand in hand the reconciled pair came back to their companions.

This racing, though not many knew it, was no doubt originally a symbol, obscurely connected with the movements of the heavenly bodies, the sun and moon pursuing one another. A dangerous third element comes in, in the form of a rival who tries to separate the two racers and to force himself in between them to the detriment of one; this leads to a doubly exciting chase, but in the end the right ones come together and the order of the universe is re-established.

Occasionally the game takes a violent turn, through some outstanding quarrel among three which here comes to a head. There are two men in pursuit and the girl runs for her life, in earnest as it seems; she is hampered by her skirt and you can see her unfasten it as she runs, stand still a second and let it fall; she jumps out of it in her shift and flies on; that too is in the way, and she pulls it up to her waist, running on with her dazzling bare legs, and if her pursuers were not leaping high before they do so now. The girl disappears into the wood, with a good start, for in the middle distance the men are seen to rush at one another suddenly and roll over on the ground. After a short, sharp wrestling-bout one of them is left lying there, to get up presently and hobble away. But the other is up again and on the track of the fugitive into the wood; and that pair is seen no more. Their companions comfort themselves with the thought that if the man hasn't caught the girl he is hunting her still!

With dancing and chasing and all kinds of games the hours went by till past midnight; the fires all round were burning low and sunrise was not far off.

About midnight the lurs were heard sounding from the neighbourhood of the temple, long discordant notes, intentionally false, which seemed to rasp against each other, death-notes, and they knew what was happening: now they were being dispatched, the seven wretches who had been chosen to satisfy the harsh gods; the fire craved life in return for giving its warmth and holding back lightning and destruction, the sun and stars demanded an offering for maintaining the course of the year. But nobody liked the business, except perhaps the priestesses. Any who had ever seen it — the priestesses by the stone of sacrifice with sleeves rolled up over their shrunken, wiry forearms, the grove lit up by torches, with skeletons and corpses hanging about on the trees like walls of horror, the moon above — he would see it all again and shudder; any one who had been near and *heard* it — ugh! But the young people did not give much thought to the sacrifice, it was a ceremony of the elders, a manifestation of stony-hearted necessity, the order of the universe and that kind of thing, it did not weigh on their shoulders yet!

By degrees as the night wore on the groups round the fire dissolved, some would see the sun rise and dance before it in the wood, others stayed; one group had a fancy for the fjord, which glistened a couple of leagues away in the hazy moonshine and slumbering half-light of the night; they felt a longing for salt water and a briny smell and would bathe at sunrise; others stretched themselves behind the bushes and would doze an hour or so; the groups went their several ways, to reassemble after sunrise for driving out the cattle, whose summer life was also to begin.

The fires died out; only smoke was to be seen far away on many heights; the dawn asserted itself and the country recovered its distances. The moon paled and faded out in the sky.

Over the moorland rose the lark, that herald of the birth of light, infinitely small as he sang in the sky, with the immense wide plains beneath him.

But the forest is closed within its leaves, with all its curtains drawn, a stagnant air as of a bedchamber, heavy with fragrance. Light begins to break through the leafy roof, golden green, and now the birds awaken. One after another they chirp, hidden beneath the foliage, from a thousand nests, a tiny, sleepy note full of the warmth of brooding; soon it is taken up and swells into a vast united many-voiced chorus through the woods.

And the sun rises, as a deep glow on the edge of the wood, rays of fire shooting up between the trunks, a dazzling world of light that merges trees and a whole quarter of the heavens in a ring of fire in which the sun moves, climbing free of the forest; like a ship of fire it casts off from the earth and sails into the open blue. Light and dew and morning stillness over all creation!

Misty forms rise from the grass, twirl as though picking up a trailing garment, and disappear. Spirits drift as borne upon a gust towards the trees of the forest and are merged in them, become one with the fresh light-green foliage; they are the souls of the trees returning home with the daylight.

But they leave a trace behind them even at high noon, a mysterious nakedness in the woods; the trees seem bewitched, with swelling, rounded limbs, forked limbs, like creatures standing on their heads with legs in the air; forked trees everywhere, with scars like mouths in their bark, and their foliage trembles as long hanging hair, blue eyes open, the sky opens among the leaves, the forest is as though wrapt in the silent presence of woman.

And deep in the wooded dales the cuckoo, that mischievous wag, sounds his note that echoes between the slopes, with a flighty laughter to follow, ha, ga, ga, ga! Nothing that he does not know, and never will he keep silence!

V

CIMBERLAND'S BULL

An hour or two after sunrise, those who were up on the high ground could trace, if their ears were fine enough, a change in the tone of the whole country: the song of birds, the wind in the reeds and a chance human voice were not the only prevailing sounds, but from every quarter came the lowing of cattle, far and near, an impetuous, oft-repeated bellowing from the valleys below, and in the distance a sort of tissue of subtle, high-pitched sound which blended with the horizon and the sunshine. All over the land the cattle were being driven into the fields and greeted the pastures with the roar of enthusiasm that was their own.

And they came in sight; just below the Tolling cattle moved

in a great straggling herd up to the wastes, with horsemen and dogs swarming in a ring outside them; farther off were motley cattle from other homesteads, all the fens dotted and dun-coloured with cattle; such would be the appearance of the country for the coming months. Behind the herds covered carts were seen crawling, bringing the tents and household goods, last of all whole loads of leather bags that would be returned in the course of the summer full of cheese.

But back to Tollingthorp came in the course of the day all the men who could be spared from the herds, from the whole country; now was the real beginning of the feast.

From early morning interest was centred on the smithy, where all preparations were being made for the final casting of the bull.

The firing of the mould had been successful — so far as could be judged. The outer crust was burnt red and crisp, here and there it had run, the heat had been as much as it could bear; what the core was like was not easy to say, but it did not rattle about inside; every trace of wax had naturally evaporated. Now they would chance it and make the casting, however it might turn out; and so impatient was the smith that he had already begun to heat the furnace the evening before and had kept the fire going all night. The metal lay like a flowing, crackling lake of fire in the white-hot furnace; the mould had been lowered into the pit, all was ready, with eyes weary with watching and sore from the fire and scorched fingers every one was waiting for a sign from Tole.

At the last moment Tole threw something into the furnace, no one knew what, and a green, immensely hot flame rose from the fiery lake in its interior. Then the smith with his own hands hammered away the fireproof stone from the outlet of the furnace, and the metal ran in a smooth bubbling stream into the mould, until it was full and the metal spurted over the side, spitting and flaming; quickly the smith plunged a spade into the stream and turned it off by another channel into a hole where the superfluous metal cooled and solidified.

The suspense was extreme while waiting for the bronze to harden and cool sufficiently to be approached; the smith stood by with furrowed face and deep-sunk eyes, worn out by weeks of doubting.

With tackles and winches the mould was hoisted up and brought into position above the pit, the smith seized a heavy wooden mal-iet and attacked it: even if he was knocking away the ground under his own feet, he went at it! The clay crust split and rang, he had aimed his blow at the bull's forehead, down rained the sherds and the bull's head was revealed as if by magic, newly cast and reflecting all the colours of fire, perfect and whole, even to the tips of the horns! But the smith hammered on, as though in anger, along the flanks, down the back, the hindquarters, the legs, and the chips hailed down like a vestment falling off: everywhere the image came out, whole and complete in the casting from head to foot!

Then the smith smiled, through soot and sweat and cinders, wrinkles and beard the smith smiled with all his white teeth like a child. Tole raised his broad hand high over his shoulder and brought it down in the smith's: Well done and thanks!

And the enthusiasm was general, for it was the finest sight that could be seen, the bull risen again, alive in the flashing, iridescent metal, like a bull of gold and sunshine; yesterday mortal and gone the way of all bulls; today reborn for eternity!

And that it was an event for the whole country was clear to all, a new sacred sign of union had here been created, an image which would gather all to worship. Ah, a fateful figure it would prove!

The smith walked round the image, a mirror of joy, bright and new-made like itself; it was still too hot to touch but he looked at it here, stooped down to examine it there, and nodded: the casting had come out in the smallest details, every trace on the surface of the wax was shown in the metal, even to the prints of fingers; yes, it was true, a finger-print, the finest possible thing was made imperishable.

And the smith shook his head, a shadow passed over his face: what a pity the Greek could not see it! For properly speaking the whole thing was his work: the mould, the figure of the bull was his. The casting and all its troubles, the responsibility and hard work had been borne by others, but the spirit was his. Yes, that the smith would say.

Artists are touchy people, who either complain when others, as they allege, steal their ideas, or else energetically refuse rewards in favour of a superior; degrees of merit too rare and personal for the attention of the ordinary man. Here, of course, between a freeman and a thrall, no comparison was possible. The Greek — he would be well on his way to the South by now, and they would like to know how he would chisel his way through the forests all alone. . . .

What was that? Not everybody was so well informed. The Greek, the "Squirrel," hadn't he been slaughtered with the other six last night?

Well no, it seemed he'd got away. He was missing in the cage when the others were fetched, however he had managed to get out, and it had been no use setting the dogs on his trail, he was too far off, a start of several hours; naturally a horse was missing too. So they had pulled a substitute out of the turf huts, of somewhere about the same size, and sacrificed him instead.

That was all that was known, and it was all forgotten before many days were past. But, in certain circles, women's circles, there was a buzz of rumours which had a longer life. No complete story was ever pieced together, some knew one thing, others said it was all wrong, as true as they were alive and standing there; so what was the truth?

That it was Norna Gest who had set the captive free and let him run seemed to be a fixed point that nobody could get away from; it had happened at dusk when every one was up at the bonfire, and had not been discovered till several hours later. But what could have been the scald's motive? Here it was that one particular woman with a shrill voice and not very pleasant-looking eyes declared roundly that it was Inge, the young newly wedded wife, that had been behind the scald, for the two had been seen together up on the heath and Inge had had her arms on the old man's neck and had certainly whispered something to him, and she had been weeping and quite beside herself! Some boys had seen this, but the woman who told the story hoped it would never come to the ears of Boierik. . . .

Nor did it, for the things which the women discussed at great length among themselves and which were meat and drink to them, never went any further; the men had a thousand other things to think about. And besides, it is said that men's senses are too coarse to catch the higher and finer tones, such as the chirping of grasshoppers.

In any case the wedding feast went off without the slightest discord. The young couple received costly gifts, especially the bride, clasps and stuffs and dresses to the value of many score of cattle, for their familes on both sides were among the first in the land; it was not often that a Spring Bridal occurred so near the top.

From Norna Gest she received a gift on which many cast envious eyes, in spite of its being the smallest of all her gifts, but it was a gem from the South, to be worn on the neck, possessing undoubtedly the greatest powers for bringing luck. The old heads of families took it between their big fingers like an insect, held it at arm's length before them, without being able to make out quite what it was. But it was really an insect, very like a beetle, of highly polished black stone, with a hole through it for the string; on the flat under-surface a tiny picture was engraved, almost invisible, the head of a woman. Probably it was a very powerful divinity under whose protection the wearer of this jewel would come. It did not escape the notice of some that the young wife showed sings of emotion on receiving the gift.

Inge now sat among the women and wore her hair gathered up and hidden under the little married woman's cap, it would never again flow freely, and its light was quenched; to make up for it she had a heavy band of gold on her head.

The banquet took place in the open air, and this time the women took part in it; they had driven in from all parts of the country, stout mothers of families hung round with amber beads, with their children and grandchildren; great family gatherings there were, cooking and eating their food in the open under the great trees round the homestead; provisions had been brought and everything necessary for camping out. For that matter the feast might have lasted all the summer; they carried everything with them wherever they went, and the summer life was as a feast in itself.

But this was a special opportunity of meeting and seeing one another. Families were introduced, the offspring of the years exhibited, proud mothers pushed their children into the foreground and held them there with a hard grip until they had been admired, for the children did not like coming forward.

The matrons put Inge through her paces and talked to her about washing, and Inge came off in housemotherly fashion, answering with all she knew about washing. In brewing she also passed, came fairly well through a long examination in weaving, but with the bright tears twinkling on her eyelashes, the matrons were so strict. Well, well, they would let her go, and the women rolled off somewhere else to hold another matron's council there and dazzle one another with amber beads as big as fists and rattle them and turn the broad side of their arm-rings outward and smile sweetly to one another, showing a lot of teeth.

The young people took stock of each other in their own way, with the unavoidable glance young people have, the unconscious power of the first impression — a pair of seven-year-olds looking at each other! Ah, many were the looks that their souls recorded on *that* fine May Day.

If the wedding was an event on account of the two great families, the best known in the country, which thereby united their branches, it gained in importance from the consecration of the great image of the Bull, which took place at the same time and provided a background; in the popular chronology the year was afterwards known as that in which Boierik and Inge were married and Cimberland's Bull taken into the sanctuary.

It happened the same day. The image was actually finished, only the supports which had separated the nucleus from the outer crust had to be removed, otherwise the figure was whole, cast in one piece with its pedestal, faultless in every way and imperishable.

With particular joy and awe Tole gazed at the Bull's forehead; here, just where the " star " should be, the sacred symbol of rotation had been inserted, looking like a glittering little golden sun in the freshly cast metal. Some years before the smith had punched out the same sign on the Bull's forehead in the figure at the base of the great silver bowl, by order of Tole, and it was seen at the end of the pole of the sacred car; it was the symbol of coming to life, which connected the innermost centre of life with the secret of the fire's conception and the course of the heavenly bodies.

Tole ordained that the laying of hands upon the Bull's forehead and the ancient symbol should be decisive for every Cimbrian; no man *could* be unfaithful to the obligations and destiny thus assumed.

The sacred car was brought and the image set up in it, with great solemnity and in the presence of the chiefs of all the clans in the country. The effect of it was excellent when standing in the car, as though cast in one piece with it; thus it would be driven in future round the hundreds at the great festivals; and every one could see that in this Tole had added both to the sacred import and to the splendour of the country's worship, when the holiest of all symbols, whose nature was only known to the priest and the priestesses, was enclosed within the image, as was intended. That the image exercised immediate power could already be seen: the women and the common folk, whose presence in the direct vicinity of the car was of course not permitted, spontaneously made signs of submission at a distance, putting earth on their foreheads, when they saw the gleaming Bull being driven up to the sacred grove to the music of lurs.

The transference of the holy of holies took place at midnight, only Tole and the priestesses attending to the important and uncanny ceremonies connected therewith.

Here a conflict arose; the ancient sibyls were not pleased with Tole's new dispositions and would not have the god moved from his house to the belly of a bull, they raised a disturbance like a lot of cats, and Tole was obliged to use a stick on them before he could carry out his purpose. It came to a positively scandalous scene when Tole wanted to take the fire god out and put it in the hollow prepared in the Bull, closing with a door; the priestesses held on to the god and Tole had to wrest it from them and hit them over the fingers and on the skull with it; and that hurt, for it was a hard god, but it made them give in.

Fortunately this scene remained one of the inner secrets which never came outside the temple; only Norna Gest, who was present as Tole's confidential friend, had any inkling of it; and perhaps the old ravens of the grove who were so tame that they wriggled their way right into the houses and said How d'ye do and blinked the whites of their eyes.

They were having a good time, all day long and for half the light night they could be heard chattering in the trees and presumably exchanging observations about the new fruits the trees were bearing for them: such and such a one was good, but the one over there was superlatively excellent; thus it was once more proved that many a man's merits are not fully manifested until he is dead.

Other great flocks of birds came and hovered in swarms circling like great wheels above the grove, crows, jackdaws, even eagles; but they had not been invited and were chased away with loud croaks and screams by the ravens, the rightful owners; great battles were fought in the air and the feathers flew above the sacred grove.

The Spring Wedding and the consecration of the Bull God were celebrated during the following days with great driving matches, horse-races, tournaments and ball games.

But first the spring sowing was consecrated, a holy act accomplished on behalf of the whole country by Tole, who sowed the spring seed in a field, alone in the presence of earth and sun; thus the covenant was observed, and the rest could be left to the thralls. The sowing fell late this year, as Tole had not been able to get the solar signs to agree before.

In the driving races a franklin from the west came off victorious with a pair of mares that were not much to look at but good goers; the distances were greater where he came from and the nags of those parts simply had to stretch their legs. In the riding races a certain thin, vicious animal was successful, as was expected. Of course it was the quality of the animals that was here decided; of the riders neither the strongest nor the nimblest could count on winning, but the lightest, and of these again the most expert.

The interest and excitement were extraordinary; women were admitted to this sport and brightened the green turf with their spick and span-new spring dresses, heavy-footed, each with a perceptible weight of jewelry about her, silver chains, clasps, amber, bronze and gold, all the family treasures.

The dress was the same for all, though with very slight differences which showed from what part of the country they came. Their clothing was composed of two pieces, smock and skirt. Foot-gear, none. The foot trod the ground with delight in the direct contact with earth and the free passage of air about the legs under the skirt; the wooing of spring was felt to the waist. Over the smock a sleeveless bodice was born, in bright colours and very varied patterns; it was here that the taste of each separate district showed itself, and critical were the glances bestowed upon anything new and seen for the first time, without the slightest notice of the wearer; the dress was examined with a pursing of the mouth: no, that was really too much; and a note was made to copy it. Finally a cloak, worn either over the shoulders and fastened with a splendid brooch, or over the arm, completed the costume. No display of furs, squirrel or marten, could be made, it was too warm for that. Herbs were carried in the hand, the head was bare, the matrons wearing thin grey pigtails under their circlets of gold.

The men's passion for gambling was aroused and many bets were made, the horses that competed changed hands again and again, and sometimes more went with them; bargaining flourished and few came home with the same team which they had set out; a love of bartering and change had seized on the franklins, who coveted their neighbour's jade as violently as they suddenly despised their own precious colt. But however much the nags changed hands, they remained in the clans.

In the evening there was great feasting, men and women affectionately together, sitting in each other's laps and sipping lovingly at the same bowl, offering their sweethearts nuts from lip to lip.

Somehow or other, though the feast began with spring water, it ended with old ale, first a single keg, discovered in the straw of one of the carts, then another, several more, as though the kegs were breeding; and as the night wore on there were sounds of exuberant song from the yard and the surrounding groves where the leather tents were pitched, a joyous howling and roaring as of many wild beasts, screams of delight and loud cacklings, songs of praise and warm bursts of laughter, a general uproar of satisfaction.

Nobody slept, the night was too good for that; on the other hand there was much scurrying of bare legs among the tents and flapping of flying smocks, as when birds are on the move, cuckoo-cries and hide-and-seek, a carefree rapture through the long, blessed night, with a blush in the northern sky and the meadows full of elves. The moon sailed high, pale with watching; only with sunrise and the song of birds did the tents fall silent little by little.

All in the most profound peace and harmony. Only a single unpleasant incident happened: a couple of young fellows who flew at each other over a girl, one much bigger and stronger than the other, so it was rather unfair when he doubled up his opponent and made fun of him into the bargain. All weapons had been laid aside; the smaller man dashed at his conqueror and killed him with a nail; instantly he was seized — dastard's deed! no fair fight! no challenge made! The men dragged him to a tree, and with a voluptuous feeling the sinner went to his punishment, conscious of his shame but not regretting it; to die would be a relief! But he shed salt tears and held his breath when the noose was round his neck, not from fear but in order to die more quickly, so unbearable was the thought that, though he had spoilt the other man's prospects — in a cowardly way, yes, but still the swine was dead — he would not after all get the girl he had set his heart on! The two fighting-cocks were burnt together and their ashes deposited in the same grave, with razor and tatooing-needle; it was to be hoped they would get on better hereafter, beyond the fire.

On the second day the feast took on a more scattered character. The women did their cooking on the turf between the tents, all the country's families like one great family, smoke and the smell of food wherever you went, and everywhere the gossip of women, more and more intimate as they got into each other's confidence. Ah yes, all their troubles and trials, but a good deal of merriment besides; they laughed and laughed, with tight-shut lips and inward chuckling, their stomachs dancing, over some of the things they heard — *men!*

Meanwhile these same men were up on the heath, holding the Thing; they could be seen sitting the best part of the day within the circle of white wands, discussing serious matters, and the ears of the neighbouring peoples would no doubt be tingling; perhaps it was historic decisions that were being made, plans for invading the land of the Aaboers and laying it waste, or a raid into Salling with burning of houses and lifting of cattle; they were said to have good steers in that part. Everyday conditions had returned to the extent that the men were armed again, which made a certain difference in their bearing; every man saw the long spear in his neighbour's hand, and joking seemed to have been dropped. Show rides in full armour, with the animal-crested helmet, formed part of the day's amusements. It seemed as though there was a longing for a taste of warfare and manslaughter after so much softness.

Afterwards some went hunting, spearing the wild boar in the marshes, with much merriment, or followed the deer on horseback halfway across the country with hounds and hallooing; while mummeries and masked dances by torchlight were prepared in the deepest secrecy for the evening.

Others betook themselves to the river, where a fair was being held; several traders had come sailing up as far as their light craft could go and had spread out their wares in tents upon the meadows; the women especially went that way. Betrothed couples who had met during the nights of the festival, two hearts with one beat, came hand in hand to tie the knot for ever with clasps and chains and pendants, the handsomest the trader might have to show.

It turned their heads, like the revelation of the starry sky, to look into the booths and the opened chests of wares that had travelled a thousand miles, from the shores of the sunrise, through all the kingdoms of the world, till they had finally arrived at the very head of a narrow river to dazzle the eyes of the fresh-faced countrymen: burnished bronze mirrors from the south, the finest glass beads, golden trinkets of incredibly delicate filigree work, stuffs with woven figures of birds, so fine that you could not see the threads, clinging to the finger-tips like cob-webs; pins, the costliest pins, and finger-rings whose stones had magic powers over the soul.

Bartering was brisk and long, the buyers with flushed cheeks, unable to resist their desires, bidding too much simply to satisfy them quickly; the trader impenetrable, with dark eyes in which nothing was to be read. When the fair was over the foreign merchants took a whole fleet of prams down the river, laden to the water's edge with the wares received in barter, furs, hides and wool, which were now to travel southward the way all the finery had come.

With the third and fourth days the Spring festival ebbed out. One covered cart after another was loaded with tents and cooking-pots, youngsters and puppies, the bullocks were put in and it rocked out of the yard towards that part of the country where the owner's herds were to be found.

Norna Gest wandered off one day; they saw his back disappearing to the southward, his long staff measuring the ground as he walked. Then all knew that the holiday was at an end.

VI

VEDIS

T HE SUMMER passed, in self-forgetfulness, like all summers. The birds hatched the spring's eggs into young, the calves became heifers, the lambs grew big and fat, boisterous from a whole summer's sporting and galloping about.

Summer narrows the mental vision; men live in the moment, with the animals that know nothing of time. All through the long summer the families moved from place to place in the moors together with their herds, staying a while now here, now there, in tents or huts but mostly under the open sky, and often for weeks they had nothing but sour milk, even hunting did not tempt them; and for the rest they lived on the wind, on song, light nights and each other's company, few thoughts and much fellowship. The heat of midsummer was exhausting, they sought shade and dozed among green leaves. The sheep hid their heads under each other's bodies in search of coolness.

The bees swarmed, it was their hour of being, you could see how they were born of the sun, great hot hosts of them came out of the sun's fire in the dazzling noonday sky and flung themselves down to find a hollow tree to live in; and men noticed where they settled so as to take their honey from them in the autumn.

And as the honey stored up sun, fragrance and summer, they entered upon autumn with a reserve of warmth in the blood, sunburnt and saturated with light. The long dark months that followed took away the sunburn and transformed the red blood into memories and visions. Then it snowed for the first time, and to many it was as though summer had never been. Winter, ay, that is our life, it blots out all summers.

But in autumn the spring lived again with its fruit. The brief infatuation, the blossoming, life's fleeting touch, all soul and perfume, this now begins to grow and gather weight; the sun's smile over the corn is forgotten, but the grain is there.

In the depth of winter's most hopeless night hope was reborn: Inge, the May Bride, gave birth to her firstborn, a spring of the

springtime, a star in the midwinter night. The new life appeared
and grew together with the solstice.

It was a girl; the young father's first glance was not for the child
but for its mother, when the women called him in; had it been
a boy it was usually the other way about. She was given to the
mother and was called Vedis. Her destiny was fixed at birth, she
was devoted to Heaven and was to be a vestal and a sibyl; as soon
as she was five winters old she would be given to the priestesses
to be educated in her duties.

But so long as her mother could keep her, she was her joy. She
who herself had so lately been a child continued her childhood in
her daughter; it might almost be said that she played with her first-
born like a doll.

She was fair like both her parents, the lightest creature that had
ever been seen, a double fairness, with eyes like the milky blue
sky of early spring, and a skin so white that it suggested snow and
moonlight, almost greenish in the shadows, like the white shoots
that grow in caves and never see the sun. But as she was fair and
pure so was she cheerful, healthy and round, a rarely happy child,
bubbling over with joy as soon as she could distinguish one thing
from another.

Life began for her like a great darkness from which the world
emerged, a world within a world. They were two in it, when her
first memories began, one smaller than herself, but it was a boy, a
little fat thing that tottered about and copied all she did, was silent
and sleepy, but wanted everything he saw. To those two life appeared as a series of important discoveries, every day some new
wonder or other revealed itself to them. Even while they had
scarcely been outside the narrow room in which they were born
the world came to them, in fragmentary fashion but so that they
could never afterwards forget it.

The winters were long, it seemed to be always winter and the
memory of any other state of things was lost; they were indoors
for all eternity, on the floor between their little bed and their
stool; the grown-ups towered in a world above them, to which
they looked up with head bent back. Above them was the roof
with its beams and hanging shapes of soot, a primeval world that
had always existed; and at the top of all was the smoke-hole, a
glimmering well leading to outer space, always coloured by the

smoke of the fire, but at night when the room was cold showing clear right up to the stars, which swam a little in the warm breath that rose through the hole. They were always the same stars, although they were so many; they only saw them now and then when they woke at night and were alone with the immense darkness, and it seemed as if the cold that fell upon their faces came from them. Then when they cried they heard their mother's voice close by in the darkness and felt her hand on the bed until they fell asleep again.

Wonderful messages came from the world outside. In the doorway, where was the threshold which might not be passed, strangely disguised forms appeared, wrapt to the nose in cloths, and brought in peats and heather, letting in icy air with them, so that the floor was cold for a long time. And the heather seemed to be wrapt round with cold, it held snow and the bundles were frozen together, with little icicles that quickly thawed and wetted the fingers and tasted freshly of earth.

What a scent the heather had, as soon as it came into the warmth! A strong, violent scent, like the emanation of a being, the heather's being; it filled the room and penetrated into every corner, spicy, sweet and astringent, a smell that got into the nose, into the throat, into the forehead; and as it smelled, so it tasted, hot and bitter, cooled by ice-water, like a hot world that had concealed and concentrated itself in the tiny green needles of the heather.

The children made their first and greatest discoveries in the bundles of heather by the sloppy door, they pulled out the prettiest plants from them and busied themselves all day long with evergreen whortleberry, whose small hollowed leaves tasted so strong; with twigs of bearberry, which looked almost the same but greyer, with berries most attractively red but a disappointment to the tooth, only pulp with no taste — they spat them out again and wiped their tongue on their sleeve; bog myrtle, with lovely little cones, not fit to eat, sharp as certain insects they had chanced to get into their mouths, but valuable things to collect and keep; crowberries, of which the grown-ups cleverly made brooms to sweep the floor, but they were the best of all, they might have blackberries on them, even in winter time, they were dark-red and watery inside, had felt the frost, tasted of rain with a sluggish sweetness and a bitter bracing aftertaste from the little pips in the fruit. Moss they picked out of the heather and long, branching green stalks of club-moss; a dreadful bug they came upon which made their fingers smell; the heather revealed a whole world to the two children of winter.

Even stronger was the scent of the heather's soul when it came into the fire; then it crackled and sweated white smoke and gave out a burnt, hot breath; the twigs popped and sputtered before they burst into flame, shrank up as they burned and shrivelled into little worms of fire that had a charred smell and fell into ashes.

The fire was a world in itself, glowing and unapproachable. It was only to be looked at from a distance — you're not to play with *that*, their mother warned them — and the little ones stood away from it and watched the heather burn, felt the radiant heat on their faces and were lighted up by the fire, with serious, puzzled looks, such as the fire always holds with its enchantment. In its hot places they thought they could see into infinite abysses of fire, the infinity of light.

Between these two abysses, the sky above the smoke-hole and the fire, the little ones lived, these were their Up and Down. In space they were cramped, but they lived in presentiments; the house-door shut out the world, and through its cracks the fine drift-snow found its way, an icy cold powder shaped into little tongues by the draught. The timber of the walls had cracks in it, deep black mysterious slits, through which cold came; these were the children's caves, in which they hid their fir-cones, pebbles and other treasures.

Glum was the name of the little brother with whom Vedis shared the world; his tongue soon found its freedom and a little language of their own sprang up between the two.

Later on a new voice was heard in the room, a being for the present invisible, but seemingly a powerful being, for it upset the peace of the whole world; the two were banished from the room and from Mother in charge of other, unknown grown-ups; their existence was thrown into confusion and was never the same again.

No, only once again did they see the room where their world had begun, and then it was completely cleared, the beds and everything taken away, leaving nothing but the four bare timber walls; the fire on the floor was extinguished and a thick carpet of juniper twigs laid in its place. And in the middle of the empty room lay

Mother, a long white form with only the face to be seen, and it was whiter than the white snow.

Some one joined their hands and led them to the bier, and then they saw that Mother's cheeks were frozen, there were flowers of ice on them and on her forehead, fine stars and spraying fronds, as when the water freezes at night. The room was colder than the coldest night, everywhere the walls were glistening with rime and threads of ice, water that had trickled down over the timber and frozen.

The dead woman was so young, they had given her a wreath of the evergreen whortleberry leaves on her head. And in her hands they had placed the orchis, not its stalk and leaves, which were not to be found now, but the roots, which they had dug up under the snow; two roots, one black, the other white: the old year and the new, death and resurrection.

Daylight fell upon the bier through the smoke-hole, which was no longer discoloured nor disturbed, the air above it was quite clear and still, with a light as of ice from heaven, the bitter, blinding frost-glare outside.

And then, another day, the two little ones were led outside, where they had to be carried, and shown a mighty fire blazing with white flames in the wintry sunshine, a little way off in the midst of the snow. Many grown-up people were passing round it to the sound of lurs and throwing clothes and other things into the fire. And when Mother never showed herself again and they asked for her, they were told that she had gone to the home of the Sun.

BOOK THREE: THE RAID

I

THE FLOODS

GAIN Vedis's world widened, there were now three of them in it, a new little fat brother who tottered about and took Glum's things and had to have them wrested out of his hands by the offended Glum; his name was Ingvar and for a time he only expressed himself in shrieks, but afterwards he mastered their language and the three got on well together, so long as Vedis maintained peace and no disturbing interference on the part of the grown-ups took place.

They were now in another house, in the not very sympathetic charge of women who chased them away from the fire and from the door, but had no compensation to offer for all the things they prohibited. The three then shut themselves up in their own world, which nobody took from them, since nobody had any inkling of it.

But, alas, they were parted; the day arrived when Vedis was taken from her brothers and led away to her duties, at the age of five. She was brought before a number of hunchbacked old women who smelt of mice and had bristly hair on their chins, they felt her over, without a smile, and turned her round between their bony fists, croaking to each other the while. Then she was placed under the care of one of the younger sibyls and had to begin looking on when the fire was tended, but was still too young to take a turn herself. She was led into the holy of holies, and there she saw the bronze Bull, big and shining like a creature of light, and she was taught to make the sign of submission with her forehead to the ground.

On the whole she was well treated; they put her to sleep in a house with two young girls who were also to be sibyls and who received her kindly; they played together on the sly and knew a way of laughing heartily without a sound being heard. Their house was round, made of wattlework plastered with clay, and at the top was a smoke-hole, through which Vedis could see the same stars as she knew from the house she came from, soon to be forgotten.

If she woke at night she thought of her mother, whom she no longer remembered except as she had seen her for the last time, the long white form under the light from the smoke-hole. And then she was always reminded of the glittering cold motes in the air, like the finest powdered ice, which descended into the room from the smoke-hole, stars that sank down and were so cold and rested upon Mother's frozen face. But when she awoke and was afraid in her loneliness she felt at her neck where she had a chain that could not be taken off, with a holy protecting object on it, a little black beetle; this her mother had given her, kissing it again and again on her breast, as though to kiss it fast there; little as she was she understood that it was her protector.

But Glum and Ingvar were always in her thoughts and for the first few weeks she was dumb with grief at being taken away from them. And afterwards, when she had to live without them, the loss was enshrined within her heart in a grave of pain; never, never did she cease to regret them.

Later on she saw them now and then, when she was occasionally allowed to leave the sanctuary; but they had quickly grown into boys and their feelings for Sister were different from those she had for them. They soon became aware that they were sons of Boierik and aspired with all their might to the world of men, began to talk horses even before they could pronounce their words properly and were always in the open air near the young men. Nor were they themselves unnoticed, their father made them their first toy bows with his own hands; the popularity of the two lads reached even Tole himself and the old man was often seen leading his great-nieces' sons by the hand; of all the innumerable offshoots of his family who swarmed about the place he seemed to be specially fond of these two.

But although her brothers were always there, Vedis could only half approach them. Her father she seldom saw, his eyes were always kind when he looked at her, but it was only a flying glance as he went by on horseback; more than that he never gave any one. So Vedis's eyes followed her father and brothers as a greatness she loved but which always escaped her; the sense of her loss buried itself more deeply in her soul, the loss of a world which vanished in a world. Never, never would she cease to regret.

Within the fence surrounding the sanctuary Vedis had a secret hiding-place to which she could steal unseen and spy out through the bushes towards the homestead and the world of men. She watched the wonderful young braves tearing over the ground, now on their horse and now off, flying in the air, now with their arms on the horse's neck, now with a hand in its mane, inseparable, a galloping friendship; she heard a shower of stones from the impetuous hoofs, and she loved them, loved them, horses and men, the terrible, magnificent, rough and nimble heroes!

None of them knew that a watcher sat within the sanctuary yearning for those who durst not approach it; the inviolable one who dreamed of great transgressors, in unselfish worship, soulful and fervid, all emotion and nothing else, as only a child's heart with a budding woman within can love.

She became a woman, grew and was grown-up, and alas, her heart grew with her; with love and anguish she looked upon the warriors from *her* world, the world of the vestals, the lifelong virgins; and heard the clamour of their iron accoutrements and grating shields, when the horsemen rode past and the fierce fellows all jingled together, with a wave swinging over them of heads and shoulders going up and down, the splendid, splendid butchers!

But then it was no longer from the sanctuary that she watched them, but always from the travelling waggon, always on the road towards new lands, new worlds, with the homeland almost forgotten as the years passed since they all broke up and migrated and existence became quite, quite changed.

Yes, the Cimbrians had left their country. It had come about through great disasters, threatening all with destruction and drowning; flocking together of people in one place as though all the men and women alive sought each other's company, a crowd that hid the green grass from view, of wrathful men and silent women; and so they had left.

Their misfortunes went as far back as Vedis could remember, they were a part of her life, she had never known anything else. As early as the year of her birth the waters were high in all Cimberland, and over the whole of Jutland, as they learned; the thaw was followed by floods that put all the meadows and low-lands under water, the fjords rose above their banks, the rivers swelled and were stemmed so that they filled the valleys far up the country, the broad ancient valleys through which the waters of the Ice Age had once found an outlet, they were now full again.

In summer the waters subsided, but every autumn opened with storms and rain, the sea rose and made itself felt far up the fjords like a strong, violent pulse, and outside it was black, with high, steep waves; the frost bound the water like an armour upon the land, snow piled itself above, and in the spring when the ice was gone and the lowlands dried at last, the floods had left seaweed high up on the fields, the ground was white with salt, and that year no corn was sown.

For five years in succession the floods returned and rose higher from year to year. Nobody could doubt that the sea aimed at the conquest of the land and every year sent down new waves so as finally to be strong enough to lay it low.

Every attempt was made to propitiate the humid Powers by sacrifices, direct appeals; cattle were driven in hosts into the sea, and the poor horned beasts floated back on to the land with bellies distended and hoofs in the air; the sea would not accept the peace offering.

The whole country was summoned to meet at the Vebjerg, in the midst of Jutland, Harders and Aaboers from the south, even the men of Salling and Thy were there, all ancient quarrels set aside for the time, for the floods threatened the whole of Jutland;

and when all the country's leaders and chiefs of clans were assembled a high Thing was solemnly proclaimed and the sea was arraigned before it.

Yes, all the great franklins in their united wisdom dug up ancient prescriptive rights and asserted the claims of justice: the land was theirs, thus far and no farther; they denounced the conduct of the sea as robbery and aggression! And the sea actually accepted the summons, made its appearance in the country that same year with heaving black waters and spewed up a whale which rotted and stank in the fields the whole summer, not so far from the Vebjerg itself but that it could be seen from there. The sea had declined to be governed by the judgment of the assembled franklins: to remain outside their coasts. Powerless their court and sentence!

Some of the younger men, who found the ways of legal chicanery too slow, formed themselves into a mixed body from many districts, with Boierik, as was to be expected, at their head, and made an armed attack on the sea, rode in full harness and in serried ranks eastward to the Cattegat and challenged the blue sea, pressed on and pierced it with their spears; as far as the outer shoals they carried their charge, scoffing the waves; but then they had to turn again, the sea only yawned and made the warriors wet; their campaign was a failure.

The same year Boierik disappeared together with a troop of Cimbrians of the same spirit as himself, southward, it was said; and, flood or no flood, his absence was felt almost as a welcome change of weather in his usual haunts, the thralls hugged themselves, got the wounds of his whip healed and scratched their backs as far as they could reach, with sounds that were something like song; among the freemen too many a young fellow held up his crest and took up more room in the landscape. But good manners returned and the thralls dropped their singing when Boierik came back a few months later.

Secret meetings and discussions followed; it leaked out that Boierik had been far down in the South, all the way to Valland, to spy out the lands, and was now for leaving the country in a body and seeking fresh pastures where pastures were to be had. He was keener than ever and appeared in a foreign helmet which was closed all round, nothing but iron to be seen, and he never took it off, as far as he was concerned a state of war had begun and would last for ever; if the country turned beggarly then out of it!

Finally came the last grievous year, when both seas attacked the land at the same time, fjords and rivers swollen, rain as from opened sluices, foaming lakes rushing in from every quarter; then they thought their doom was near.

It was springtime after the thaw and the previous year had ended with high water and the valleys filled to the brim, masses of snow on the high ground which melted and added to the flood, rain in torrents, and a north-westerly gale which brought in the North Sea on the back of the land and packed the Cattegat with spring tides that flooded all the fjords of the east coast.

This drove the inhabitants of Cimberland out of the valleys and up to the high ground with their cattle, horses and poultry, all that they could save; but much was lost, including many hundred human lives. Houses and dwellings were flooded, the earth huts filled and were washed out, the timber houses floated away, and that was the last sight the fugitives saw, house and home floating down the fjord and out to sea, while they themselves with children in their arms and their shivering, bellowing cattle in front sought safety in the interior, wading in mud and sodden turf, battered with rain and blasts, in half darkness at high noon: would they live through the day?

Waggons and possessions were saved, life was saved, and then they formed camp up on the moors as they were used to do in in summer; but alas, it was not summer, and it looked as though it would never be summer again.

Here on the heaths and in the wind-scourged woods the clans and families met from every quarter of Cimberland, all who bore the name of Cimbrian, the whole people in their thousands, an immense concourse of victims, a meeting as in the face of death. As one great family they had once entered the country and had spread and increased in the good days; now that disaster was upon them they assembled again and their numbers were great, immensely great; was this the end, or was it a new beginning?

Origin and destruction had met, even the dumb beasts felt that and it overcame lesser fears; stags could be seen amongst the cattle, they were banished from the dales; wolves and wild boars made for the dry land, shook themselves and looked with the eyes of sinners upon all these men, who on their side were too miserable to do anything to the wet creatures of sorrow. Even the horses did not snort and lose their wits as usual when the scent of wolves reached their nostrils; they stooped in herds with head down and tail in the air, the wet forelock hanging over the eye, coughing in their throats with jaw awry and teeth bared, throwing their dejected heads backward, quite old all of them with rain and adversity, rumbling in their empty bellies but with no appetite for the withered winter grass that was stuck to the ground with rain; they lowered their muzzles and sniffed at it, but brought them up again and sighed, in the way of horses, very composedly, and scraped the ground with numbed feet as though to find some other destiny.

Here then were men and beasts driven together as on an island, with floods and waters on every hand, exposed to cold downpours and hail-showers, the earth wet, the heather wet, the woods another bath of rain if they sought shelter there, their waggons and skins wet, the fire smouldering in musty leather tents with wood too wet to burn, everything red with rust, even the swords in their sheaths, straps and clothes swollen with water, men's skins blotched and denumbed, their backs wet, their brows full of raindrops — and no one knew how long.

The storm increased, blasts of rain came on in hosts like one wet wall behind another over the wild country, pressing down the woods, low and bent already, raising a cold fog of lashed and vapourized drops from the heather, creasing the surface of pools and floods, as though all the water would forcibly tear itself free and go the way the wind went. It blew so that big strong men leaned forward on the wind beyond their balance, to keep their feet; with hand to mouth they shouted to each other to be heard; it made every man feel alone with his thoughts and the cold roots of his hair.

Terrible tidings arrived, messengers who returned half senseless and blinded by riding in rain and against the wind; the men drove them in under a bluff, behind big stones, where there was shelter so that they could be heard, and the ring closed about them to keep the news from going further, but a rumour of it reached the crowd and madness was stamped on the women's faces: the North Sea had come a league into the land!

From people who came from Salling, where they had it from Mors, news just arrived from Thy, it had been heard that the sea was riding in upon the neck of Jutland with waves that stood on each other's shoulders; the sea was raging madly, perfectly white with flying foam and scum, the waves chewed up great rocks, sand-dunes and cornfields disappeared, the sea came round behind, broke through and surrounded whole districts, islands lay out in the surging deep, remains of the mainland that had gone bit by bit into the billows!

From the fjords on the east news came that almost every tract was gone already, and from far to the south vague rumours found their way that the sea was swallowing the root of Jutland, many leagues of land and thousands of human beings had gone beneath the waves.

Then there was weeping in the Cimbrians' camp, the women sat over their children and wailed, put their wet plaits of hair to their eyes and wept into them, making them wetter still: Alas, their poor country! Far and near was the sound of sniffing and suppressed sighs, the weeping of the women which blended like another stray gust with the gale and the rain and made the men turn pale.

Three days the storm lasted, and for all that time semi-darkness brooded over the homeless, with rain, hail and snow succeeding each other; short commons prevailed in waggons and tents, bread was unknown, milk scarce at this time of the year, the herds were thinned, to slaughter meant making one's self poorer. If the danger of drowning should pass the spectre of famine arose behind it.

The Elders waited and waited, letting the storm pass over their heads; there was nothing else to be done. But the young men took it in a strange way, with mad passion; it seemed as though the storm fired them with new, inconceivable joys, they rode out at night into the tempest, galloping and roaring with the mighty Breather; shaking their heads the Elders saw that if the rude, dark Lord of the Storm continued to rage the young men would end by making friends with him. And indeed that actually happened.

Boierik was out in the tempest, and his following grew greater and greater; assemblies to which half Cimberland flocked, with Boierik's rusty helmet always towering in the middle, and from it came speeches that swept with the force of the storm; men armed themselves noisily, revolt was in the air, and great decisions.

And the decision came the first time the sun appeared. It was a mighty moment. One forenoon it was, and the sun was only out a short time, the clouds opened in wings of fire from heaven to earth with an immense hole between, full of a welter of light, blue abysses and in the midst the sun, with the clearness of spring but cold; it sent a passing smile over the country, swift as the wind light and shadow hurried across the woods like a ray of hope. And then an extraordinary thing happened: *it hailed in sunshine*, from the height of that vast fiery door, which was black as pitch on one side and white as fire on the other, a hail-shower came down to earth like thousands of fiery arrows; *the rainbow stretched in glowing colours across the chasm of the sky, and right through it flashed the lightning!* A thunderclap was heard in storm and light; then the hail-shower shut out the sun again, and in the whirling gloom every man bowed his head, trembling at the revelation of Heaven.

But in the moment when the sun was out, the lot was cast which decided the fate of the Cimbrians.

Boierik cast it, and he was terrible to behold as he did it, fierce on behalf of all his people, in a ferment of fatefulness. He flung the cleft ash-stick towards heaven more in sign of challenge than as a devout appeal for a decision affecting himself and his followers. The stick did not go very high; the wind took it and twirled it round several times before it fell some way off; twelve men, the witnesses, approached and picked it up, brought it back to the Thing and gave their testimony: the white, split side was uppermost. That meant leaving the country.

Swords flew from their scabbards in the hailstorm and thundered upon shields; a loud war-cry sounded in unison: Accept the omen! The act took place on a mound with all legal forms, a duly constituted Thing and all the necessary sacrifices; they had only waited to see the sun's face before casting the lot; now it had been done.

But the court was entirely self-established; the young men with Boierik at their head had simply taken matters into their own hands without consulting the Elders; they had been their own Thing, and now the step was taken there was no going back, they had challenged a decision from Heaven and intended to stand by it.

Before this nobody but Tole could take omens, but he had not been asked. Nor had he made any objection; when he heard what the young men had done and all that depended on it, he simply shook his head or nodded; but nowadays Tole was always nodding and shaking his head.

It was never said in so many words, nor was there any need to say it, but everybody knew that in recent years Tole's rule had not maintained any favourable relations with the Powers, whether it was that his sacrifices had not been acceptable or, still more unfortunate, that he had mistaken the Powers to whom he ought to have applied. Many dark hints were dropped that the old man had made too much of the Sun, with poor return, seeing that it became clearer year by year that storm and cloud were more powerful. It would surely have been wiser to have some thoughts for the Blusterer as well, perhaps even more than the others, considering the power unmistakably exercised in heaven and in the life of men by tempest and night.

Boierik's idea in casting the lot was that the Sun should see it, but it was the wind that turned the lot and he accepted the result as far as he was concerned more as a pact with the Speedy One than with the Sun. The younger men had no fear of associating with the Powers of Darkness when the old sources of Light failed them. Waiting for things to grow . . . if they would grow no more the only thing was to get up and follow the way of the wind!

A new era announced itself in this abandonment of an ancient pact, the transition from direct confidence in the endurance of Light to a worship of the dangerous Powers connected with doubt. But even if they were to be called confederates of the Enemy of Light, they would make trial of the God of Storm and see how far *his* power extended; so thought the young in their harshness. No abiding place for them either! War for war's sake! New gods! In this turning of the soul away from their father's relations of gratitude to Heaven lay the germ of the later conception of the weather and war god's restless being.

And what objection could be made when the young men openly professed the worship of the Light's antagonist? A flight, Tole considered it; they would have been more courageous to stay, to accept their lot as their fathers had accepted it, so he might have spoken to Boierik and his men; but Tole held his peace. For causes he could not understand the Sun had failed him, he was no longer a man whose words claimed attention.

So the Cimbrians set out. Almost the whole people followed Boierik.

Scarcely was their decision made when the storm subsided, as though it had its will. It fell dead calm, and the morning after the Cimbrians had committed themselves to the migration they were aware, as they stood on the high ground, of a mighty inexplicable, seemingly subterranean thunder, they hardly knew whether it was as a sound or a shaking that went through the very foundations of the country. It came in long-drawn beats like the distant breath of an immense being embracing the earth; and at last they grasped that it was the North Sea, many, many leagues away, which few of them had seen and which had never before made its surf heard so far inland; they could plainly hear each separate wave as it thundered upon the shore.

In the clear cold air they saw the valleys below full of water, the country seemed surrounded by water, black and still after the storm, with all things doubled in the mirror of its surface, floating trees with their roots in the air, drowned cattle, wooden houses tilted by the current with their floor-timbers uppermost. The quiet morning was like a weary pause in the tempest, the sky was threatening and leaden, holding the world in a narrow compass; before noon snow was falling. And it should have been spring . . .

Nobody would stay any longer, the hair of the strongest stood on end when they felt the earth rumbling beneath the attacks of the distant ocean which they could not see. They turned to put their waggons in order, or to build new ones. A month later the country was emptied.

Tole stayed behind. He would not leave the neighbourhood of his father's grave-mound. But he voluntarily gave over his authority and all the signs of it to Boierik before they parted.

The sacred car with the image of the Bull and the ring of covenant were to be taken on the march; they were sacred things inseparable from the Cimbrians as a people; where they went their sacred things should go. In this Boierik agreed with him; whatever heavenly Power they placed their trust in, the Bull should always be the expression of the Cimbrians' inmost nature and of their earthly fortunes.

And when in the course of the spring the ground became passable and the expedition started — an endless line of waggons on the way south — a shining speck of gold could be seen miles off at its head: this was the Bull set up in the open on the sacred car and led before the emigrants. It was accompanied by priestesses and sibyls with all their secret arts for maintaining the sacred fire.

The country was not entirely depopulated; besides Tole many of the other old heads of families, men and women, stayed in their homesteads, with a few cows and horses, the remains of the great herds that were driven away with the expedition. Some odds and ends of the thralls were also left behind, such as had been overlooked underground or in the turbaries, where they escaped notice on account of their colour. Tole kept a stallion and a couple of mares; though he had not long to live he could not bear that the marking whereby every one could tell his horses should die out in the country. He had asked to be allowed to keep the youngest of Boierik's sons, Ingvar, who was still only a child, so that the privileges of the clan might one day pass to him, and his request had been granted.

From what was thus left behind new possessors of the soil were to grow up. The manhood was gone, the effete and the budding were left.

Empty and unused the temple outlived Tole, the sacred grove uncared for and overgrown. No perpetual fire burned there any longer, only the night brooded there at night-time, and there was a rustling as of a thousand spirits in the high, creaking trees, wind and weather had resumed their sway, the elements had returned untamed.

In a mud hut on the site of his home, which the flood had destroyed, shivering by a big fire, Norna Gest found the old chief, one spring when the scald's steps brought him back to the land of the Cimbrians. The nation itself he had met far down in Europe and could give Tole all the information he desired about them; the two old men put their heads together and exchanged wise words as they had so often done before, but Tole's was a broken wisdom, the wondering of a lonely, melancholy old man over all that had forsaken him.

A last sacrificial act Tole had performed in silence, as Norna Gest learned, shortly after the expedition set out; he had taken the great silver bowl, which had been left behind, into the moors, broken it in pieces, that it might never again be used by men, and had left it in the open, in a certain waste place, feared and avoided by the common people from time immemorial, a damp marshy hole buried in a gloomy, unwholesome thicket full of hedgehogs and weasels, the home of shrikes and hawks, forbidding in its loneliness.

An old heap of bones on the ground showed that this had once been a place of sacrifice, at a time when their ancestors had only vague notions of divinity and worshipped cruelty in this wild and remote spot. Here children had been given to the grim spirits.

Nowhere else were so many adders seen; on sunny days the grass round the swamp seemed alive with them, whole bunches and knots of them lived in the earth; at a distance you could hear their hissing and scaly gliding through bushes and heather — not a place to come near. All the more important had the men of old thought it to maintain a good footing with the reptiles. They had gone so far as forcing young girls to go naked into this pen of serpents, which they surrounded with dogs, until a scream from within convinced them that the victim had been bitten.

Tole remembered that his grandfather had sacrificed in this weird spot, secretly, as though ashamed of it, but firm as a rock in his belief in its necessity, shaking his head over the young men of his day who thought otherwise, as — ay, just as Tole shook his head over the young men of his time.

Sacrificing to the adders, there was no sense in that, even though the men of old were right in looking upon them as in some supernatural way an embodiment of the lightning. But Tole had never been able to interpret such things otherwise than as symbols. Certain people kept snakes in their houses, under their beds even, and fed them in the hope that they would keep off lightning-strokes, and there could be no harm in that; but if an enlightened man wanted to be on good terms with the Thunderer he went to the fountainhead, the Powers in heaven itself, with his head erect, not staring in the dust. But nevertheless the silver bowl should stay there, as long as it lasted, abandoned to whatever horror there was left in the place, even if the local gods had had their time. This was a fit place for it, since it too was out of use, belonged to the past.

It had been seen that the Power in heaven to whom so much had been sacrificed in the sacred bowl had not accepted the offerings. Had there been no strength in them, or had the Powers proved powerless? The images on the bowl, which represented the trust and the fear of the Cimbrians, were they but images? Was anything more?

As nothing was certain Tole had committed the things and their images to each other, in the face of Heaven. It was for Heaven to regard the wreckage it had wrought and to preserve it or let it perish as Heaven pleased.

Yes, Norna Gest had met the Cimbrians and it was a consolation to Tole to hear that they fared well, so far as Norna Gest could give news of them.

He had come across them down in the south of the Frisians' land; they formed camps of their waggons for safety's sake, though they had fairly empty tracts on all sides, forest and moor, much that they were accustomed to at home, only farther to the south. Their herds could range undisturbed, though of course a guard of horsemen had to be always in the field to keep off the nearest strangers, who were not very friendly disposed; but that they were also used to at home. The country was not suited for agriculture, so the talk was of breaking up and moving on with all speed. Probably they were already much farther south.

They had suffered no misfortune or perceptible loss of life; on the contrary, they were much more numerous than when they set out. On its way through Jutland the expedition had absorbed a multitude of the various tribes who had also suffered from the inundations and preferred to emigrate; they had had to lay their hands on the Bull's forehead and swear obedience to Boierik; and Tole nodded, shutting his eyes, when he heard it; that pleased him, it was right and proper. Trouble they had met with, of course; not every tribe was content with their bringing a whole country's cattle to graze off their land, even if they kept to the common lands in the middle of the country, they grazed there themselves; but Boierik had used force where leave was not given and had thrashed the men sent to order him away. Not without the noise and tumult of arms had they come out of the peninsula; the border folk had sent the arrow round to call every man to arms; a battle and a rapidly concluded peace were the result, and when Boierik marched on he had incorporated a number of them in his army, by their own consent, the rest he packed off home. One of the hostile leaders, who had shown himself particularly stubborn and who fell into Boierik's hands, was harnessed with other bullocks to a waggon when the march was resumed. . . .

Ho, ho, ho! Then Tole roared, with something of his old horse-laugh in his voice. Was that true? Ho, ho!

He wanted to hear all details of the action, his face clouded on hearing of the enemy's impudence, scowled when Boierik prepared to meet and chastise them, and glowed, with a young look on his big, pale features, when the braggarts were sent about their business and their leader put in harness. Oh yes, now he knew his lads!

How were they getting on in other ways, what about the women, how did they take the change? How did they get through the winters? Could they manage altogether without corn? If they had no chance of sowing any of their own, there must be other people's fields here and there? The horses, were they looked after and not shamefully overridden on the long marches? And the *Bull* — did it hold its own under a foreign sky, did it inspire respect wherever it went?

Strange, strange, they had hardly cast and consecrated the great image before it became a sign which united all the men in longing to leave the country! Assuredly that had not been Tole's thought in setting up the Bull; on the contrary, he had hoped it would bind its worshippers for ever to the place where it stood. But he was glad they had wanted to take it with them, since they had to go; he was glad of that, yes he was.

And Tole was lost in thought. As he listened to news of his sons and his clan and all the other countrymen whose chief he had been, it seemed that they and all the old, happy state of things were still present to him. But soon reality asserted itself again; they were all gone, for him existence had gone to pieces. He pondered, could not yet grasp it.

He raised his head and turned a candid look on Norna Gest, in dismay . . . what could it mean? That it should happen to him: the whole, whole country gone, leaving him utterly alone with his thoughts! His youth, his years, his whole life gone at a stroke!

Gently Norna Gest reminded him that such things had happened before. Fathers and sons! Even a whole race turning its back at once on its traditions and its land had been seen before. It might happen at such long intervals that neither the emigrants nor they that stayed behind preserved any memory of it. But *he* had once before seen the population break up and pour out of Jutland, the same line of waggons, as though foreboding another migration, or the next as a ghost of the old. The waggons were rougher in former times, the wheels scarcely round, but they too covered the ground; their axes were of stone, but they cleared a place for them. Now the old forgotten march of their ancestors was repeating itself — and it would repeat itself again more than once in the future!

Did he mean that? Tole dropped his voice deferentially and thought over it, shaking his head feebly; did he really mean that! Those were omniscient words. But for his own part the pain remained the same. He placed his two big useless hands in one another and pondered, rocking to and fro, and his eyes grew dim. At last he looked up again, in another train of thought, with features in which tears were working:

Then Echo is dead.

Norna Gest was silent, with a questioning, wondering look.

Yes, Echo was dead, Tole explained in grief and fear. He never heard voices now either on the slopes or in the woods. Nothing answered him any more. The spirits of the land were dead.

That was the last time Norna Gest saw Tole. He left Jutland on a sea voyage and was away a long time.

II

NEW VISION

ONCE more he exchanged the staff for the oar and made ready a craft on the shore of the Limfjord, thence made his way to the Baltic and lost himself on its rivers, moving southward towards the countries of the Mediterranean.

When the rivers became mountain streams he landed and hid himself in the depths of old pine forests he knew, in the mountains where the sources of the great rivers of Europe lay not far from each other; wrapped himself in perfect solitude and became like the ancient pines, like the deepest shadow beneath them among the granite boulders, like Time, which announces itself in the falling pine-needles or the long dark sighing of the trees.

Legends went abroad among the mountains of a great forest spirit some thought they had seen, woodcutters and herdsmen; and it was long ere they recovered of the sight, though the spirit had no air of wishing them ill.

A lonely old wanderer was set upon by robbers in a desert place in the mountains, they threw a spear through him, but in that instant he was not there, it was a cloud that lashed them about the ears with hailstones; and when it cleared they saw the wanderer step out of a shred of cloud farther off and continue his way: with fierce howls the robbers were turned into a pack of wolves and tore each other to pieces. That was Norna Gest.

But when the legends had formed and remained behind, *he* was gone, had hollowed out a boat of a pine-tree by the Danube's source and committed himself to the stream, appeared as an old fisherman, with nothing odd about him, floating in a trough that would carry a thin man but no more; like many another old angler who has had enough of society and keeps to the water, because its disposition is retiring and the fish are taciturn.

So he fished his way down the stream, drank the good water of the river and hauled up his food from its depths, river fish, sheatfish, whose swollen spiky faces he had seen before. The river was rapid and bustling to begin with; afterwards it took to itself tributaries and became broad, entered the low country and spread itself, comfortably and strong, with much running hither and thither, exactly like a man; Gest became one with it, while vessels from countries far apart sailed up and down it and life approached its banks; animals coming to lap their morning drink at sunrise, when the moon's watch was relieved; women at their eternal washing, who knelt to the river here as elsewhere and dipped their arms in the stream. . . .

And who were those he saw jogging down to the watering-places on brisk little nags, long-legged riders out of all proportion to their horses, with crests of fair hair waving from their heads; who were they but the Cimbrians, astray in the wide world!

There they were, living on the south bank of the river, which they had crossed not long before, slowly drawing to the southward, not much faster than their herds could graze their way.

They were now a vast swarm, double many times over since they left their home; they filled whole countries as they passed, spread beyond the range of vision when they were divided into many small camps with their cattle, the smoke of their hearths rising far and wide with miles between, like a whole settled country, which the next day might have vanished beyond the horizon; and like a town of many, many thousand inhabitants when they were in hostile parts and collected behind their waggons and entrenchments. Thus it was that Norna Gest found them, in an attitude of expectation, while the country in front was being reconnoitred; prepared for peace or war with the next nation they intended to pass through or round.

The Cimbrians were no longer alone in their raid, they were accompanied by other young nations from the North who were also looking for new homes and made common cause with them, on equal terms, but each forming a troop by itself. For that matter they might all have been brothers, since they were all big, fair fellows, distinguishable from each other by a slightly different fashion of wearing the hair and other small matters; a difference of dialect no greater than that they understood each other quite well; their ideas were the same, their prospects the same, the world was open to them and in one respect they were united — in the intention to conquer it as soon as possible.

A strange, overpowering town it was to come into; for Norna Gest was recognized at once and joyfully admitted. But the way to Boierik's presence had more stages than before; it meant passing from the hands of one high commander to another's — ranks had come about of themselves — and in the centre of the circle being brought before Boierik, who sat on a raised chair in a decorated tent, in armour except for his helmet. With closed lips, cold and weary, he received the stranger, but smiled like a boy when he saw who it was, the sun of remembrance rising between the two; he was still himself, but the intervening years had drawn lines in his young face like a map of all the countries he had already forced his way through.

News was exchanged, greetings from Tole given; but Boierik was absent-minded and broke in with cross-questions, wanting information about other things which he thought the travelled scald would be able to give him; it was easy to hear that his plans could never for a moment be driven from his head. Had Norna Gest been in Rome? Not lately, but earlier . . . and Boierik questioned him about its situation, defence, the course of the Tiber, the heights round about, the nature of the surrounding country — things which the much-seeing Gest had to admit he had not noticed exactly, but it appeared nevertheless that in a roundabout way Boierik gained information from his answers.

He had learnt an astonishing amount in these years of exile, knew as much as Norna Gest about the countries of the South, in some respects more, but extracted from it all a special dry score of knowledge which he kept within himself without disclosing its purpose. He expressed no wonder at all the new worlds that had opened before him, he had simply absorbed them and at the same time had become another man. But when the conversation offered no further advantage and he accompanied Norna Gest to the tent-door, he smiled again, with a glance of the rare sun of Cimberland, and the old man left him with the feeling that a wild young soul had vanished and given place to a maturity which, come what might, pursued uncommon ends.

The other young men of the camp had not changed in so striking a way. Their eyes indeed showed that they had seen a good deal of the world. The old, becoming respect which had distinguished them at home was a thing they no longer had time for; they laughed on every occasion, were quick to fly into a passion, their features had grown harder, they made a noise in the camp like a pack of hounds. But they were splendid to look at, hardened by wind and weather, the acme of manly strength, bursting with reckless courage. The many thousands of them gathered in one place made the strongest impression, a mighty natural force, as yet uncertain of its object, but terrible if it should be aimed in one direction.

It did not escape observation that the ancient, highly developed nations to the south of the Alps, whom they were approaching but had not yet seen, had already set their mark on their behaviour, without their knowing it; the influence had encountered them on the way and could be seen in the clothes and trinkets they wore, plundered from people they had come in contact with; the influence had even wormed its way into their language with a few Latin words which they already used as their own without troubling where they had them from.

Everything they had heard about the Romans occupied them

and was their constant topic of conversation; lately they had seen the first watermills and were much intrigued by them; a smart invention that, it made you laugh but was worth copying, getting a wheel to go round and round and do the work without your having to move a muscle. But what had the river to say to it? It was pretty cool treatment of the river spirit to harness him to a mill like that. It would mean plenty of sacrifices, one would think. Treadmills they had also heard about, but not yet seen; another Roman idea, wheels that they filled with slaves, making them climb up and up the whole time, driving the wheel round; enough to kill you with laughter, one of the best things ever heard! Ah, no doubt they'd see some fine things when they got right down and had a talk with the Romans, who had taught people all these tricks.

As might be expected, it was in their dress that the women showed signs of the change. They had collected colours wherever they went, giving the camp a motley look. It was noticeable that the distance between them and the men was less pronounced, the women had a freer look and took part in the talk; their travels and what they had accomplished on the route had evidently added to their prestige; but they were not merry. Of children there were countless hordes, noisy as birds; what with them and the cattle and all, the camp was one great roar.

Of unalloyed beauty was the impression made by the young girls, those who were still children when the raid began and who had become women on the march, had grown up walking, so to speak, with new souls, new eyes, a generation cast in the same mould, all of them upright, strong, sunburnt maids, hosts of them, all light-hearted and gentle, robust young women, the good spirits of the camp; a more vigorous breed of girls had never been seen, so many and so much alike, collected in one place.

The incessant rough attentions of the young men swathed the girls in an atmosphere of desire, as they were swathed in sun and wind, the whole day long. With a cow on one side and the big, sure hands of a deceitful swain on the other, a woman was always hard pressed. A great deal of equivocal laughter and play, suppressed giggling, hide-and-seek and mock wrestling took place between the sexes; there was no thought but of love. But shy feelings lay beneath the surface, bashfulness wearing a coarse mask, and no two lovers were united in earnest unless they felt a secret sweetness in the blood, and a deep, kind warming of soul to soul. Ah, the young couple's subtlest art was to adopt the naughty tone in fashion among the youthful crowd, while concealing the deep emotion and craving for compassion which united them for ever. Not before they wished it, but early, the young women became mothers.

But however free and powerful were the manifestations and achievements of love, however sensitive and beautiful it might be at heart, its inmost yearnings remained unsatisfied. A desire that was all soul, longing personified as woman, sought an object in vain, and Norna Gest had not lived long in the camp before he discovered the quarter to which the worship of the young men was directed. For it was worship, and it was centred, unuttered but with the strength of a natural force, upon a single woman, still scarce a woman, half a child — the vestal Vedis.

If the relations between the sexes within the camp were a continual state of siege in which the finest expansion of the soul was lost, this higher feeling was focussed in a blameless devotion to her, an enthusiasm which all shared and all held holy. She had become a young maiden on the march, not yet grown up but on the border between child and woman, a tall and lovely girl, a revelation as it were of all the strong young girls of the camp in one person, but more graceful, delicate and fair than all of them together.

In the middle of the camp, surrounded by an additional rampart of waggons, a great and roomy leather pavilion was raised, besides the tent of the leader Boierik; in it stood the sacred car when not on the march, and here burned the ancestral fire, which might never go out. In tents around lived the sibyls and their assistants, women young and old dedicated to the fire, and youngest among them Vedis.

By birth alone she was the highest, as the daughter of Boierik himself, but that was not the chief cause of her renown; she was the most beautiful creature that had ever been seen among the Cimbrian nation, the flower of their dreams, the perfect realization of all they loved piece-meal in many others lavished upon a single woman, the finest picture of the race in one person.

With all their force and all their wiles the men secretly sought to be entrusted with some trifling message to headquarters, merely in the hope of seeing her, of catching a glimpse of her fair form with her hair flowing down her back, either among the tents or by the fire in the holy of holies, where she sat among old cinder-smeared sibyls, like Beauty herself caught and caged among vultures, a sight never to be forgotten.

The luck of perhaps being seen by her was the men's happiness; she smiled, a wonderful smile, at once like a child, a maiden and a mother; she smiled on all the men, and her face shone upon a sinner, no one had seen so bright a face as hers; hardened warriors were melted and came back with its reflection, as though they had seen a marvel; the others knew what they had seen and envied them, but were not spiteful; a heart that is touched is not to be meddled with, and they were all affected in the same way. More than the sanctuary itself, in whose precincts she moved, was she worshipped and loved.

When the host was on the march the sacred car was uncovered and driven at its head surrounded by horsemen, and then the sacred bronze Bull was exposed to all eyes, green rusted with the weather now, with head and horns turned in the direction of the march, the solar sign on its forehead facing the sun, towards uncertain landmarks: mountains ahead, with horns raised to the sky, but the Bull bent his forehead to the new horizon, horn against horn, and every man was staunch in the trust that he would open a path. Charge, thrust and raise a dust in the world, they would be with him!

Scouts and scattered troops looked from afar for the familiar sign at the head of the column, the Bull's horns like a sickle turned against the world; but more often their eyes sought a possible glimpse of the fair girl's head on the car, which would catch the sun and shine to a great distance, itself a little sun on earth.

If the Bull led them into all the kingdoms of the world, then they were leading her! She was the luck of the raid. They felt that what her eyes rested on came out in a richer, fairer, sweeter light. She was a living treasure the host carried with it, a precious centre about which all gathered. Their hearts beat faster and they gripped their lances with a firmer hold when they marched with her; they rode up closer to the car and jostled each other, a wall of horsemen about the car and her.

With buried passion they regarded her, who was inviolable and to remain so; never would a man's eyes rest on her otherwise than as a child and a virgin; as such she shone upon their path, and a host armed to the teeth surrounded her.

Even the inarticulate thralls in charge of the bullocks and wag-gons kept their eyes on a bright head in front of the column, a ray therefrom penetrated even their darkness, but she was a crea-ture not of their world; unearthly they thought her, a spirit of Heaven's grace, and they threw themselves beneath the wheels, let themselves be crushed to death, if the idea entered their thick skulls that they might thereby serve her.

From afar the warriors saw their fairy driving on, like a little fire in the daylight which they knew to be she, in the midst of a strange world; and they loved the countries they passed through, stock and stone, rivers and foreign skies, because she was in the midst of them. So mightily did a maiden shine upon the host that everything their eyes rested upon was made beautiful in her name.

Up and down went Norna Gest, not losing sight of the Cim-brians; of so strange a destiny as that he foresaw awaiting them he would fain be a witness.

It would scarcely be their fate to find land somewhere and settle down on it, as was the intention with which they had set out and of which they still talked; but they were already a changed peo-ple. The plough had not yet found soil, would it ever find it? What they had gone through on the way had made them more warriors than husbandmen, they were now rather an army than a nation.

This could be seen in the horses; they were fresher than ever, but ungroomed, trained to the utmost as war-horses, but no longer showing crests and plaited manes as in the days when their masters were at home and had nothing to do; the raid had taught them to dispense with the unnecessary, to use up a horse for what there was in him.

The cattle could not be dispensed with, it was what the people lived on, their whole fortune, but the tending of the beasts was left entirely to women and children and the household servants; the men's old delight in their cattle seemed to find expression exclu-sively in the bronze Bull, the symbol carried at the head of the column; as for the rest, they thought only of their warlike equip-ment. They had good arms, fashioned in a rough and ready way with an eye to use alone; great single-edged swords that looked like scythes, and indeed came in as such now and then, in another man's fields; but it was for a different harvest they were meant.

The past years had been one long campaign, ever since they

fought their way through kinsfolk and out of Jutland, extricated themselves from many fierce tribes in the densely wooded inland tracts, covered their rear with the rivers and had trouble in crossing them, with many sacrifices, now to the rivers, now to the woods; then war with formidable antagonists still farther inland, conciliation with some, others taken into their company, but nowhere an abiding place, wherever they came the land was occupied or unsuitable; they were many, no small country was required to contain them and provide pasture and arable land sufficient to secure their future.

Hitherto the peoples with whom they had come into collision had been of a Northern type like themselves, with characteristics of their own but not very different in nature, nor in hardness; the Cimbrians had doubtless looked on them as foreigners, since the distant kinship did not happen to strike their eye. But very soon they were to meet people who were foreign in earnest, an entirely opposite world.

They entered the countries between the Danube and the Eastern Alps. Norna Gest followed them as far as their first collision with the Romans, the battle of Noreia, a name till then unknown but destined to ring, as all the names of places and peoples involved in the Raid would ring. It echoed through the world. And a more stirring sound was to follow.

The external destiny of the Cimbrians, when from an obscure past they entered the light of annals, is a theme which extends from that time to all times, the ghost-world of history; henceforth it is this we follow in following them.

Great was the derision of the Cimbrians when for the first time they made the chance acquaintance of writing. They were shown a couple of scribes who performed great exploits, so it was said, by sitting and scratching with a bodkin on a coated tablet, the trail of a worm in wax; no, now they must really be excused, and they went into fits of laughter, killing funny it was, this galloping of lice; what was the idea? — to see who pricked best, who could fill up his tablet first? Could you bet on it? The clowns did not know what ignorance was, for runes were still unknown to the North, the wizardry of writing had not yet occurred to them. But it was by this scratching that their posthumous fame would be kept alive.

The tablet hangs on the wall of History, with all the Cimbrians' exploits, not omitting their fall. But the new vision of their blue eyes looked upon a world which was on the verge of growing old, and never more could it remain the same.

To rehearse the chronicle in brief: the power of Rome had shot a tentacle up to the north of the Eastern Alps, the province of Noricum, and to this the Cimbrians came, after having been a good way down the Balkan peninsula, which had returned them — a foolish people down there and thick as fleas, no chance of getting through; the Cimbrians then turned about and went northward again to knock at the door of the Norici, a prosperous mountain people, whose villages they emptied of corn and other movable goods. Up came the Romans and pronounced an interdict, under their proconsul Gnæus Papirius Carbo: palaver of the leaders, bringing face to face for the first time men of widely different horizons and degrees of culture; the Romans condescending, the savages innocent, — without the slightest ill intention had happened to remove property which they could not possibly know to be owned by the Romans . . . as a matter of fact they were bound for Valland and had taken the wrong turning among the three big promontories in which they knew Europe ended on the south, had struck the easternmost, but if they were given guides they would quickly disappear. Guides they were given for Gaul, and Gnæus Papirius Carbo smartly took advantage of their innocence to entice them into a dangerous mountain region, where he then fell upon them unawares with his legions. Unexpected result: Gnæus Papirius Carbo and his army cut to pieces.

At Noreia the Cimbrians learned some of their first Latin. The highly developed military organization of the Romans, which they had heard so much of and honestly feared, had failed before them at the first shock.

If Boierik's plans aimed at an immediate advance on Rome, the way was now open across the passes of the Alps. But it rested with the first collision for the present, whether Boierik's plans were not yet mature or the omens were against following up the victory; in any case the Cimbrians actually drew off to the westward along the northern edge of the Alps in the direction of Gaul.

The Romans had also extended their experience. Wise men in Rome took advantage of the barbarians' absence to make preparations for the event of their return.

But when Norna Gest had seen the result of Noreia and guessed that nothing very important would happen for the time being, he parted for a while from the Cimbrians and went south as they went west.

For his own part Gest had a journey in mind which he had begun before but not yet brought to an end, the weightiest of all his journeys — to the Land of the Dead.

He had looked for it, we know, in all the islands that lay towards the sun, in the Mediterranean and in the East, in vain, as is related in his book; now he intended to go farther south, through Africa; he would try the Nile.

He had been up it before but had had misgivings about penetrating farther than to the boundaries of Egypt; now a hope urged him to try again, farther south this time if possible; so far as the river went he must be able to sail. When one considered it, where did the Nile come from? Nobody knew, therefore nobody could know what a voyage up the whole length of its course would lead to, before it was tried.

So he made for the Mediterranean, rowed round its coasts, a grey old fisherman of whom nobody took notice, many coasts, and came to the Nile, smelt once more its muddy smell of bodily warmth, as of infants in swaddling-clothes, the smell of life's beginning, dung and vinegar, the salve of Mother Earth; here began the warmth, at whose source, which none had seen, the ancient life-giving river was born — where?

With the sun always facing him Gest rowed through Egypt, past temple-cities and pyramids, the fabulous works of the ancients which reduce a man to silence and take away his cheerfulness: the efforts of generations, so great a bulwark against time and so long ago ready! But *one* step towards heaven, and that already in ruins!

From the desert a face, the ruin of a face, looks out upon the desert, so great that it seems a part of the earth, the land itself stretching its neck to look; and indeed so it is, a piece of living rock shaped by the hand of man, like a lion below, drifted over and buried in sand; above, a head with the features of an Egyptian: the emblem of a riddle, but no other riddle than that the symbols which gave rise to so imperishable a work are forgotten.

Norna Gest rowed past, and it was as though the head first turned its full face towards him, then its low profile. Slowly he left Egypt behind him, took all the windings of the Nile, going almost north again for a long while, then south once more, through Nubia, with the crocodile and hippopotamus for company, flocks of screeching birds over his head and familiar notes among them now and then, the birds of passage from the North making for the South with him. They called up meaningless memories of a coolness which was now so far away, in these burning lands where sunshine lay upon the boat like a bonfire close at hand and the surface of the water flashed lazy lightnings in his eyes. Gest clothed himself in grass and green leaves, rowed, rowed, and the heat increased; in the fierce light of the sun on the river, framed in primeval forest on both sides, he and his boat disappeared.

Seven years later he came back, still alone; for he had not found the Land of the Dead nor the dead he looked for, the ever-dead; ah no, their abode was not in that quarter either.

He had gone deep into the continent, into immense hot countries, the home of beasts; in flocks they moved beside each other, zebra, lion and giraffe, as in the morning of creation, but not for friendship's sake, only because they were many, the lot of earth. The lion struck down a beast when he was thirsty, he was the murderer; afterwards the vultures invited themselves and plucked at the carrion, and last came the hyena in the foul darkness of night and cleaned up the bones: the partition of the ruminant! The elephant tramped down to the drinking-places, pumped his trunk full and blew it into his mouth, flapping his big muddy ears with pleasure and squirting water over his back. Out on the farthest branches over the river came the apes, hanging out of dark chambers under the leaves, and showed their teeth, dazzled by the light into an ugly grin. Man could be seen, in the depths of the steaming swamps of the forest where it was always dark like a sombre underworld, skinny and shy, stark-naked snivelling dwarfs like children out of their wits, a vermin that haunted the accursed woods.

But at last Gest had gone so far that he had the sun behind him; and then he saw his voyage was in vain and turned back.

Back he came down the Nile, with the stream now, but poorer by a hope; the man of the desert showed him his profile when he came in sight again, then his full face, then the opposite profile; to swing past him was like swinging round Time.

Up on the skirts of the desert Gest found caves with ancient hearths, once inhabited — who could tell by whom? — and deserted again; here he took up his abode and digested his journey, training himself to entertain no more desires.

But when he had been absorbed long enough and penetrated with calm, had brought Time to rest in himself, he felt a new craving to mirror himself in the perishable and to share time with the living. Refreshing were the nights of Egypt, the stars lavishly great and brilliant, as though all suns, but for whom was this peacock's tail in heaven displayed?

Hardened and disappointed Gest felt that a man is alone, even with a god's glory over his head, when he is alone.

For domestic animals and for company he had procured himself poultry, but when the cock embittered his hours with its crowing, he wrung its neck. The wretched bird mounted his meagre scrap-heap and filled the world with crowing, flapped his wings as though it was he who waved permission to the dawn each morning: now it might begin down in the valley of the Nile and Numidia and Mauritania; one would think a cockadoodle had produced the world, could anybody stand it?

After that Gest had peace, a perfectly dead stillness in heaven and earth, stars and sand staring at each other like corpses. Then Gest retired within himself and put his thought into words:

> Hate-filled I fed on
> the heart of the cock.
> Now is the dawn like death
> without his crowing.

> Much may a man
> achieve with a knife:
> yet never raised he
> life in a worm.

> Ill has befallen
> the feathered one's foe.
> Who cares not for cackling
> were best in his coffin!

Gest then turned his back on the desert and rowed with all his might towards the thronged and motley cities of Egypt, the great towns of the Mediterranean, Alexandria, and from there, when the season was calm, he set out direct for Rome.

III

THE BULL AND THE SHE–WOLF

Up the Tiber he rowed one morning and saw at a great distance the wide-spread cloud of smoke and dust which hung over Rome, clinging to the land; white pinnacles and columns towered above it like the mirage of a marble city, but it was real, the high-placed temples of the Capitol, and the flaming things that caught the light and floated like golden eyes in the haze were gilded statues crowning terraces and pediments. The voice of the city was heard, a distant surf-like sound, as of a sea within the land.

The river traffic already proclaimed the great city; the winding course was covered with ships, outward-bound and up-stream, heavy-laden cargo-boats and transports from every corner of the Mediterranean, fleets bringing tribute to Rome from subject countries, great corn-boats from Africa and Sicily, Greek ships, ships all the way from Asia with sacks piled high above their bulwarks, fruit-boats like floating cornucopias, long barges from Egypt laden with onions — who could eat all those onions! — salt-ships, oil-ships, cattle-ships, wool-ships with bulky cargo — all for the insatiable city yonder.

And down from it in the opposite direction came Rome's galleys bound for the provinces, fitted out for war; long, black hulls with castles fore and aft, ballistas and catapults on the superstructure, the ram frothing the yellow water at the stem like the trident of a sea-giant; sweeping down the stream with all the force of their oars, the helmsman and a helmeted commander on the poop, the clash of cymbals, a ringing word of command and a quicker beat running along the two and three banks of oars which all swung at the same time and caught the water at the same time like gigantic fins; Rome's eagles and ensigns raised over file upon file of colonial troops: it was the power of Rome and the obedience of the tributary countries that met here at the entrance to the capital of the world!

For a man floating low in the water in a canoe it was not so easy to keep clear of all these high bluff bows; Norna Gest and others with him cautiously gave way and made for the bank, where it was shallow. But in another respect he could feel easy, for he remained unnoticed; among so many vessels great and small he disappeared completely like a magnitude invisible to the eye.

Unseen as though wrapt in a cloak of invisibility, Gest rowed into Rome, and entirely unnoticed he came alongside under the bridge by the island outside the walls, where so many other fishermen had their quarters; made fast to an old ring in the quay-side, where he had tied up before, and made ready in all modesty to become a nameless Roman among Romans.

He did not abandon his boat; he slept in it at night and awoke when the rumble of waggons and many feet passing above his head announced that early market-carts and traders were coming into town; in the evening he fell asleep with the secure feeling of having the bridge above him for a roof, no small convenience to a man accustomed to sleep under the open sky. The place was of bad repute, the Tiber fisherman being notorious for not taking more account of life than of the fish he caught; even thieves and murderers preferred to give it a wide berth rather than get a knife in the gizzard; one could therefore find perfect peace there, when once adopted into the circle of the simple fishermen.

The street-sellers filled Rome's mornings with their melodious cries, a sunrise chorus which embraced the whole city and which many a Roman never heard except in his sleep; by the time citizens were up the costermonger had long ago passed through the street and bargained with the kitchen slaves and brought in fresh things for the first meal; other kinds came by and sang their song, until in the course of the day the chorus was swallowed up in the general uproar. There was the poultry man who went up street and down street with his bunch of hens quietly tied together by the feet with their heads hanging down, alive, for they had to last until they were sold; the fruit-seller who bawled in the narrow slums, with pigs in the gutter and stuffy air that you could cut with a knife, between houses of eight or ten stories; the snail-woman with her basket and her song, constantly interrupted while she picked a snail out of its shell with a hairpin and fortified herself on her round; and others of all sorts, indistinguishable from the sunny streets of Rome, with their smallwares and their cries of self-preservation, which had turned to song.

And Gest mingled among them, a man with a sturgeon who was seen and not seen about the city; he did not call his fish, it spoke for him, and sometimes it was bought of him, but just as often he came home with his fish dried and curled up by the day's sunshine.

Or he was a porter, took a cord over his shoulder and placed himself by the riverside among the other porters, was then one of them and went up and down the city on all kinds of errands, in and out of all sorts of houses.

Between whiles he was a harper in some place of resort, outside the circus or the theatre, by the look of him some Thracian or Scythian vagabond; few took any notice of him, there were so many foreigners in Rome; but he saw the world. Often he would have a sesterce put into his hand by a high-born matron, stola-clad and with hair freshly oiled, large, fine, plum-coloured eyes; and he did not forget it of her that they had been bedewed for him, if only for an instant.

Gest would sit the whole day long in the Forum in the sunshine, only a greybeard and a bundle of rags among the beggars and idlers who drank up the sunshine from Rome's paving-stones as with suckers; and his eyes were busy, without moving he observed the world, for here it was collected, Europe, Asia and Africa, all complexions, all languages, all kinds of eyes, and just as many souls, widely different; the old and new races of the Mediter-ranean countries were here in an epitome, irreconcilable contra-dictions, but agreed in meeting at Rome, the refuge of the world.

In the sun-haze, the perpetual summer, above the Forum at the top of the steps leading to the Capitol gleamed a metallic green-rusted form which every one knew and understood: the She-Wolf with the founders of Rome under her paps, guarding the city and showing her teeth at its enemies. Under this symbol they all loved to live, from the beggar to the corpulent senator swinging across the Forum in his litter on the way to the Curia; the slaves groan-ing under the weight of him had other dangerous desires but not that of living outside the territory guarded by the She-Wolf; the old native noble families and the latest arrivals, all alike looked up to the She-Wolf with the same confidence.

For she was Nature that had fostered Rome, ravenous but free, the Mother who took all sucklings to herself, even young of a totally different kind from her own. She tolerated every foreigner who found shelter within Rome's walls, but turned savagely to-wards the frontiers: no one should violate the Roman peace! No

more motley world existed than that she embraced under her
protection and with her motto: Leave for all! Every one his own
soul!

In the Forum, the ear-drum of the world where rumours
buzzed, there was also a place for Gest, room to sit down on the
steps of a temple, among the arcades where Rome's business men
and politicians met and all news was spread; near to a cooling fountain in whose basin the children of Rome played with toy tri-
remes; he sat somewhere or other among the statues, himself a
mute person but following the vibrations of the place in his distant way.

Talking to anybody was not to Gest's liking; but what cannot a man see, undrowned by his own voice; what does he not
find out about men at last, when he draws from other sources
than their speech?

So it was not long before the old observer was familiar with
all that had happened recently in Rome and in a great part of the
world, what took place daily and what would take place, as
though he had been a tablet reflecting the shadow-play of humanity, vanished almost before it came to life, image upon image
rolling up and passing over into time, as everything passes over
into time. He too looked up with wonder at the She-Wolf, in
whose sign all the generations of Rome were as though summed
up, an imperishable symbol of which changing symbols were
formed; what would live, what would endure?

Posterity receives scant written fragments, not much more than
the names, which as ever figure in place of the things; but what
is not written, what is in the air, that remains for ever in the air;
the distant years when Cimberland's Bull drew near to Rome and
the She-Wolf, with all four legs stubbornly planted to shield her
young, turned her jaws to the frontiers to receive it — they live
a shadow-life for all time.

Full of an overpowering anxiety were the years when "the
Cimbrian Terror" spread and reached its culmination in Rome.

After Noreia the Cimbrians had made their long march to Gaul,
gathering in more allies as they went, a Helvetian tribe, the Tigu-
rini; and when next heard of they had grown together with the
Teutons and Ambrones into a multitude beyond all ideas of
number, hundreds of thousands, warriors, women and children,

cattle and baggage, a swarm that poured onward like an element, demanding land, room for expansion; and they were to learn that nothing is more difficult to get, when the seekers themselves bring congestion with them.

They tried several years in Western Europe, pressed in vain upon the Belgic tribes in the north and were pressed back by them, as they had been repulsed by Boii and Scordisci, they ate up the lands in Gaul and kept the population invested in their fortified towns, pressed them so hard that the unfortunate Celts were forced by famine to eat each other; they made a wry mouth, the Celts: ill is the taste of one's own kin. But the Celts held out. And now the swarm had turned to the southward and for the second time fell foul of the Roman power, in Provence, the Gallic Province of the Romans.

By degrees the rumour reached the Forum, in vague and incomplete forms, as when one hears of a tempest brewing far away, which darkens the sky but is not yet imminent; beyond the Alps, up in the more or less unknown parts, where barbarians of one kind or another made shift to live and now and then ran together into packs. And the Roman took his late perfumed bath and was carried to the theatre, in an ebony litter covered with horsehair and borne by Ethiopian slaves, all for the colour, and saw the "Sufferings of Orestes," successfully stimulated a craving for the emotional and tragic which everyday life could not satisfy, and got an appetite, lay late at table with Greek-speaking friends and handsome boys, all crowned with vine-leaves: the golden age of innocence, imagined at home in Arcady, which the fashionable world regretted and imitated at great expense. The man of the people gaped in the Circus over gladiatorial games, a tightly packed ring of idlers, toothless from sweet food, but still capable of being gladdened by the sight of murder.

The Republic was in its flower, its prosperity and might still on the increase, the great protracted wars with Carthage concluded, the She-Wolf vanquishing the Elephant, Africa subjected. The Commons of Rome had come out of the duel rich and with absolute power, the great generals and statesmen stood in marble in the Forum, the Republic was irresistible. But its timbers were already worm-eaten. Dissolution had already begun to show itself during the recent Numidian war — the She-Wolf against the Horse, Jugurtha's dangerous cavalry, and the Horse brought low

— the austere Roman Knights had clearly sold themselves a little in the Forum and had come near selling the whole Republic too. They had grown too rich, others did their work for them; and Rome's peasants had become an urban mob, the Republic a kept community which lived on the tributes of dependent nations. But at least the predatory instinct was still vigorous, and when Jugurtha had been ignominiously made cold in the Tullian dog-hole, the people breathed freely, as though it was he who was the thief and justice had at last been done.

All this had been done with just as the tempest beyond the Alps began to gather and send forth lightnings. This same Numidian war had brought the name of Marius to the fore, a vulgar person, but not for sale. It would be seen that, when Rome was threatened by an element, she had recourse to elementary Roman qualities in order to meet it.

To begin with the savage strangers did not offer the Romans battle, when they came in contact with their frontiers in the south of Gaul; they asked for land to settle on, a request often repeated at the doors of Europe, and generously offered an alliance; nay, they would take military service under Rome, if they could agree upon the destruction of some third party or other; the Romans gave them a refusal.

On this occasion an embassy was in Rome, consisting of both Cimbrians and Teutons, the only time negotiations took place; and now the parties were able to take stock of each other. We hear nothing of any difference between Teutons and Cimbrians, the Northerners were in general tall, fair, coarse people, coldly regarded by the Romans as phenomenal: an un-Romanly exaggeration of stature, but many negroes were just as tall. Fair they were, of course, with a sheath of straw for hair, like all the rude peoples of the North one had heard about, who lived their lives in forests and eternal shadow and on that account had lost their colour.

Howbeit these fellows of superhuman size were apparently of docile and merry disposition; they smiled from their height upon the little Romans and showed an unreserved delight in all Rome's marvels.

The streets with their shops and taverns fascinated them, they walked in the middle to avoid knocking anything down, planted their big feet cautiously, trying not to smash the paving-stones and mosaics; they looked up and they looked down, wrinkling their foreheads like bulls — by Jupiter, these were the clodhoppers come to town! The simplest things seemed new to them; in the Forum they gaped at the fountains and one of them drank straight out of the basin like an ox. Pipes for the water to come through — wonderful: even the springs were tamed and shut up in iron here! Their hair simply bristled with inspiration when it dawned on them that the *whole* of Rome was paved, miles of slabs, each one of which was worth taking away for a good grindstone — incredible! And the statues, the naked figures; Oh, they were good; the men pretended to cast down their eyes and check themselves, but couldn't keep it in, had to snigger or they would have died. And the laughter came, in huge open roars, as they held each other so as not to fall: nothing concealed here, of either sex!

But the biggest success, almost, was when they caught sight of a donkey with a nosebag on. Evidently the use of nosebags was unknown in the countries these big, clumsy, straggling creatures of innocence came from, for they fell into immoderate transports, stopped and laughed till they roared, shoving each other off their feet: no, this was a bit too much, what would they think of next? There was no getting them away until they had fallen on the ass's neck, finding a brother at last, and kissed it and shown that they could carry it; and the centurion who was showing them through the city got bored and shrugged his shoulders: and these were the fellows that were going before the Senate! Pretty green, weren't they? born yesterday, me Hercule!

Here in the Forum it was that a certain Teuton put his foot in it and found a place for ever in history; the man who was shown a much admired piece of sculpture representing an old herdsman and asked how much he thought it was worth: even if he was alive the Teuton wouldn't give anything for such a useless old slave, was the answer. So much for the ambassadors' knowledge of art — acorn-eating bumpkins!

They showed themselves not altogether without manners when they were brought before the full assembly of the Senate, up in the Capitol, holding themselves very properly and putting aside their laughter for the time being; but of course these illiterates could not express themselves in language; an interpreter had to be sent for, an old seaman or loafer from the riverside who spoke Hyperborean and whom the strangers seemed to know and hold in respect, whoever he might be, from their own coasts perhaps; through him the envoys submitted their case and boldly looked the assembly up and down while it was being translated, like a troop of big thumping boys who had proposed a game and confidently expected the other party to accept with pleasure.

One or other of them gave a sigh and shifted his weight on to the other leg: it was a long way up, they had been taken up thousands of steps, a mountain of steps, right into the sky, through one dizzy pillared court after another; it seemed you had to pass through many chambers before reaching the kernel of Rome. But now at last they were there and could survey the assembly, a whole lot of little old men, surrounded by much marble and themselves frozen in the face, bald, most of them, with polished scalps, the hair all gone; the whole council oppressively still, though there were so many of them, all seated, with one bare shrivelled arm outside the toga and the other in its folds — what could they be hiding in it?

One spoke at a time while the negotiations were going on, not loudly but so that all could hear; on the other hand it was extraordinary to see how the speaker used his hands, moulded his meaning in the air with them, twined his fingers at a difficult point, and flipped himself on the teeth, strewed out invisible things and clutched at his chest, hammered like a smith with one hand on the other, the picture of passion all of it, but without the speaker getting the least excited. Nobody addressed the strangers, nor even the interpreter; the assembly discussed the proposal amongst themselves, not at any great length, and announced the decision through an attendant when it had been arrived at.

The end of it was, then, that the embassy was sent down all those steps again, in and out but down all the time, with a view as they went of all the glories of Rome spread out beneath them. The little old men all sat in silence, relapsed into complete frigidity, after they had drawn up their answer and the petitioners had been dismissed with nothing but a No for their trouble and their journey. One of the old men had taken his left hand out of his toga, and then those of the strangers who had been inquisitive as to what he concealed in it — a knife perhaps, something sharp? — had a chance of seeing before they left that it was a long ivory claw, with which the old man scratched himself. Ah yes, and now he had used it to rake them off him!

So there they stood in the Forum again and could stretch their heads back and look up at the high place where they had been given audience, that and another high place farther to one side, the Arx, the strong citadel of Rome, towering with its sheer walls and its temple on the highest summit like a closed unapproachable shrine. With contempt for any information the spying eyes of the strangers might pick up, their guides had chosen to bring them face to face with Rome's strongholds; now they might go home and tell of what they had seen!

Crestfallen they were, and many a Roman dryly relished the disproportion between the size of the braves and their importance, when they turned their backs — and what backs! — and took the road out of the city carrying with them nothing but a certificate of their own insignificance. Oh yes, the nosebag, no doubt they would introduce that when they came home. *Habeant!*

The Roman women looked after them with other eyes, the eyes of curiosity; a pity they were going before there was a chance of knowing a little of each other: the old lawless look which implies the warning that a woman is ready to go over to the enemy at any time, if he proves himself the stronger. But were not the Roman ladies descended from raped Sabine women?

The doughty champions on their side had not shown themselves devoid of feeling; they nudged each other when they saw a pretty woman in the street, drinking in the lines of her figure, the robe tightly drawn over the breast and stomach, and turned when she had passed, tightly drawn at the back too; and they gave each other a forcible look, as though calling to witness: were such things possible, could one trust one's eyes, so much voluptuousness, a child of Heaven out for a walk! But could it be the thing — by herself among male men, slaves and blackamoors of every kind! How was it she wasn't devoured in broad daylight, why didn't everybody smash in everybody's else's skull so as to get her for himself and snatch the blankets out of a house to wrap her in and carry her off! And with a shake of the head they hunched up their giants' shoulders, bearing a load of renunciation, and walked on, unable to conceal a certain smacking of the lips.

Somewhat bowed down under all their disappointments they made their way out of Rome.

Here they were forgotten in a day for other things.

But they can scarcely have reached their own people again before the information came to Rome from Gaul that the Consul of the year, Marcus Junius Silanus, had joined battle with the Barbarians and had been beaten with his whole army.

This was the Romans' second defeat and again the Barbarians might have crossed the Alps, this time from the western end, and invaded the plains of Italy, which lay unprotected. Instead of that they stayed in Gaul and pillaged the countries there to the very bone; and later, when they had inflicted on the Romans their last decisive defeat at Arausio, they turned towards Spain and played havoc there for a time, though without making much impression on the warlike inhabitants, while the Romans recovered and collected their forces in the meantime.

Why did they not strike when they could have struck? Were their leaders in disagreement? Were their plans more far-reaching? Was it the omens? It was Boierik's custom to seek important decisions for himself and the hundreds of thousands who depended on him by sharpening a splinter of wood in the form of an arrow and throwing it up into the wind; the way the arrow pointed when it came down was the way he took, for that was the will of the winds; had not the arrow yet pointed towards Rome?

The time came when it did so. After Silanus's disaster the Romans sent fresh armies to Gaul under the Consul Lucius Cassius; he engaged in several actions with the united tribes, but ended in being defeated and himself killed; the remnant of his army was forced to accept peace at the hands of the victors on humiliating terms.

One of the captured officers who was brought before Boierik warned him, with all the authority of Rome in his bearing, against approaching Italy; Rome was not to be attacked, even Hannibal had not ventured it. For answer Boierik cut him down: if the man fell, then the inviolability fell with him!

Finally, at Arausio, in the neighbourhood of the Rhone, the defeat was crushing. This time two generals led the Roman forces, Cneus Manlius and Servilius Cæpio, and they were jealous of each other, Cæpio a man stained by the corruption of Rome; they divided their forces and the Barbarians overcame them in detail. The double defeat is said to have cost the Romans over a hundred thousand men.

In this battle as in the previous ones the Romans were literally howled down by the savages, the legions first scared half out of their lives by the bestial Cimbrian howls and then mowed down. The barbarians acted upon the eye simply by their appearance, horrid bodies leaping high in the air, flesh, tatooing and iron, two-pronged spears like forks, long, heavy one-edged swords like scythes; their slaughter was a piece of harvesting, the enemy pitchforked into the air and laid in swaths; noise was their tactics, suddenness their plan of battle: the whole terrible yelling horde charging at once! And thus the legions were paralysed, the hardy little Roman soldier was disarmed by panic, even before, true to his wont, he had taken his stand and begun to plane away the enemy.

The Cimbrian howls were heard as far as Rome, even in the bedchambers; many lay awake at night after the mournful news had been received. The extent of the disaster was intensified by what was heard of the Barbarians' treatment of the vanquished; horrible, horrible tidings.

It seems as though these peasants had been seized with malevolence after the murderous battle of Arausio; Cæpio's tricks and untrustworthiness had made them disgusted with Rome; the defeated should be punished and at the same time the old, cruel gods honoured with a sacrifice that would be remembered: the prisoners were dispatched, some of them hanged as offerings to the Wind God, the fruit of the Hell tree, others slaughtered as a human sacrifice to their fathers' ancient, greedy Gods of Fire: miserable stripped Romans by the thousand, a repulsive night work left to the sibyls.

Fires and the smell of blood ascending to heaven, the sacred Bull towering in the midst of a reeking abomination, the moon red and swollen overhead like a mass of entrails in the sky! In festal robes the terrible old women stood upon the shrine, barefooted and in white, heads smeared with chalk, and drew the knife across the throats of the victims who were passed up to them; quickly, next man up — while the blood collected below in the immense sacrificial bowl and ran over. In cackling voices they prophesied from the signs they found in hearts and entrails, good signs, repeated a thousand times, no doubt of it, the more omens of that kind the worse it looked for the enemies of the Bull!

Not even the booty would the victors keep, it had been promised in advance to the gods of the country, in the knowledge that the battle was a hazardous one. All the silver and gold was given to the Rhone, which had shown them favour, together with all the captured arms, armours and ensigns, and the horses of the Romans; all was sunk in the river and devoted to the River God. Many rivers had they passed, and many yet awaited them; with them above all they wished to be on a good footing.

Let it be seen whether the Romans could offer the local gods more than they had now given them! And truly, they could afford it; there was not a man in the host who was not already carrying about a pig's weight in gold, besides waggon-loads of treasure, bronze vessels and mountings, chains and jewels, all taken by cautious violence, to avoid breakage, from the many peoples whose countries they had passed through.

The battle of Arausio was the first round of the duel, when the Bull had taken the She-Wolf on his horns and tossed her to the sky in such a sweep that she was likely to be fixed there as a constellation.

But she came down again and remained whole; she would come again with a sharp fang.

In Rome the news from the seat of war called to life all the old steady defensive spirit of the Republic. Every sensible man said to himself that the threat to Rome's existence was now imminent, if this human avalanche poured down from the Alps over Italy.

To begin with the gods gave them a respite; the sinful city had looked to its own profit but had never neglected to sacrifice to the gods, and *they* too had revenues to lose. Rome breathed again when the tempest, with a tempest's opulence and absence of plan, drew off elsewhere, clouding the sky of Spain for a couple of years; in the meantime the Romans were busy. When the pause was over, the Cimbrians and Teutons again on the march and on their way to the Alps, it was known that this time they would cross them. But in the meantime Marius had been getting ready for them.

In the hour of need Rome had recourse to the man with the simple, certain instincts, Marius the man of the people, in whom no refined or complex line of thought checked initiative. The old gentlemen of the Senate were wise enough to set aside their own feelings in order to choose a nature repellant, openly hostile, to

themselves, to do the work of saving Rome; you do not grasp
the scorpion with bare hands.

The occasion was an extraordinary one; since Hannibal crossed
the Alps Rome had not been in such serious peril, and he was
after all an enlightened man who knew bounds; this time it was
boundlessness itself that was coming, the Senators were clear
about that and showed considerable active disinterestedness; all
considerations but that of meeting the danger were swept aside;
straight to the goal: Marius at the head of the State! He was
elected Consul out of the ordinary course, and re-elected year
by year contrary to law, until the campaign was concluded.

Afterwards they would be able to wash themselves free of him.
A strong smell of stables clung about him, he bragged of having
the habits of a common soldier, after his unquestionably useful
service in Africa, and he was insolent and scornful about the
hereditary nobility: hadn't they risen from the ranks in the beginning, like himself, he would like to know? He couldn't keep
his mouth shut and shouted in the popular assembly about the
venality of the Senators, as though everybody didn't know it, and
thus secured the votes of the mob; of course he was himself in-
corruptible, never took money for political purposes, *he* bribed!
He was brutal, put down vice without regard for the pet sins of
many; while he himself was so ugly that he had to take his
caresses to women of the coarsest type, preferably in the dark,
and pay them well; no Greek graces of face and limb or amiability
about that man! No, few were less Greek than he, for he did
not speak the language of the gods, like Rome's men about town,
and is even said to have boasted of it, certain of the applause of
the ignorant, and to have declared that he scouted a learning derived from libertines and slaves. A soul like his was an offence to
Rome, but now he would have to be used, there was need of a
rasp.

Marius's frank primitiveness makes one think of that Teuton
who was shown the statue and his remark about it; in reality a
judgment on decadent Rome, the peasant leaving art for nature,
back to the beginning! For Marius was the old strict agrarian
spirit of the Republic over again; instinctively Rome summoned
her lower orders to meet an outbreak of nature from beyond her
bounds. A bust which is said to represent Marius, and is in any
case a portrait of a citizen of the Republican period, seems to con-

ceal in its rough-hewn features the memory of a woman buried
beneath them: the mother, the harsh Roman woman, practised in
self-sacrifice, who brought him up and kept order in the home
he came from, with the taste of a working woman and a dog's
fidelity to her race, one of the mothers of the Republic: the devotion and the ferocity of the She-Wolf!

And it looked as though the memory of ancient discipline, an
almost forgotten rod of punishment, reformed the morality of
Rome for the time; the nobility could do nothing themselves but
they knew what energy was. And intrigue they were skilled in,
concocting a plan, and fear goaded them on, they were afraid,
a delicate flush suffused the cheeks of enfeebled old Senators; they
worked, the Senate sat day and night. The city buzzed about
their ears in an audible panic, clients came up to them as they left
the council chamber, wringing their hands: the big business men
were in a fever, the brokers glowed like copper with a green
sweat, could not keep their food down, terror and doubt upsetting their stomachs: should they be bulls or bears? The wealthy
freedmen looked petrified, like the statues in the Forum: what
about the interest on their capital, their house property, villas,
the mausoleum they had built on the Appian Way, would they
have a use for it too soon? Or would some unworthy outsider
get buried in their marble instead of them? Was the government
taking the right line for them? Had the Senate made the right
choice? Ought they to go to a common person to save the country? Yes, a common man was just what was wanted. The language
itself would be all the better for a change of values.

Everywhere the terror was general and was never afterwards
forgotten. Augurs and soothsayers were quite wrinkled in the
forehead from worrying over entrails and the flight of birds; up
on the Arx, Rome's ancient look-out round the horizon, the universe was studied early and late: what was to be read in the stars?
Rome's householders dared scarcely put their foot over the
threshold when they came out of the atrium in the morning with
slaves bearing rolls and documents behind them; what would they
meet, would they stumble, what kind of birds were in the air?

The braying of an ass, earthworms above ground, the sight of
a hare, even in a poulterer's shop, all were interpreted as fateful
omens. Rumours of portents flew from one end of the city to the
other; a gulp had been heard in the Cloaca Maxima underneath

Rome, a weeping in the city's foundations — ah, drivers and water-carriers told each other of it in the street, shivering in the middle of the summer day. Never had the air been so charged with fate; almost tangibly, in a woman's shape, the destiny sent from above was felt leaning over the city.

The Roman ladies, the defenceless ones, shuddered. Would it really befall them to be dragged off by the big, hairy savages? They remembered that the envoys they had seen had a thick golden nap on the back of their hands, like bears walking on their hind-legs; a wantonness as of new-born gods sported in their locks; and the Roman ladies sank into their chairs like hens all rumpled at the thought. Who could read what was in their minds? What omens did *they* take, when the legions marched out of Rome for the seat of war, the compact little Romans in full marching order with their packs on their shoulders, braced up, hardy as ants, our own brave fellows — but didn't one know them in and out, down to the very birthmarks on their bodies? Hush! And the Roman lady went home to her mirrors and her women slaves; it was obvious that whoever it was that came back, she would keep herself anointed and dainty, all ready for the triumph. The apprehensions of the Roman ladies were divided, when Marius set out with his army *versus septentrionem.*

But they regained their balance and showed the correct attitude, as ever before, towards the vanquished, when Marius had annihilated the Barbarians; first the Teutons at Aquæ Sextiæ, then the Cimbrians in the Raudian plains.

IV

THE BATTLE

THE HORDE had agreed to divide itself: the advantage the Romans had given them at Arausio by dividing their forces, they now resigned to their enemies.

The object of it was dangerous enough; the plan was to hem in the root of the peninsula, when each body had crossed the Alps at its own end: the Bull closing on Rome with a horn on each side. But the upshot was that Marius broke off first one horn, then the other.

The whole horde at once he could scarcely have mastered; each half by itself gave him plenty of work.

At the very beginning he applied the technical methods of Rome, the science of war first, then war itself; he put in hand elaborate engineering works on the Rhone, the gateway towards Rome where the enemy was expected on his return from Spain; and when he arrived he found Marius entrenched in an impregnable camp, while at the same time he had regulated the outlet of the Rhone, dug canals and assured his transports and supplies, an immense piece of work at which he kept his troops to drive the idle habits of Rome out of them.

They were a new military material which he could shape as he pleased, the population of Rome drafted into the army irrespective of class, not as before exclusively the old free citizen class to whom war was a privilege. Marius introduced recruiting, a far-reaching measure which affected both the aristocracy and the common people, downward on one side, up on the other, and which contained the germ of the autocracy to come: the army increased in power and at its summit the dictatorship. A year or two after these events a child was born who was to grow into a man and give his name to this apex: Cæsar. Begun as a roping-in of the people, the establishment of the new army ended in placing the yoke of a single man on the necks of all classes in Rome and of a great part of the world; few men have disposed of the life of so many generations as the remorseless Marius.

Besides turning his troops into diggers, doubtless not without a sinister hint as to who was going to be buried, he trained them with an iron hand in obedience and discipline, taught them to suffer, made them artisans of war; he thought out a nasty improvement of their arm, the *pilum*, the Roman lance, the nails of which he had taken out, so that the head might stick fast like a harpoon and eat its way in better. He took methodical steps to accustom his soldiers to the appearance and howls of the barbarous warriors, arranging a sort of school or theatre where, from the ramparts of the camp, the men were daily confronted with the enemy, themselves under cover for the present, and thus got the panic gradually rubbed out of their eyes.

And the Barbarians, without knowing it, lent him a hand, were quite pleased to show themselves; it was their amusement to ride up to the ramparts and challenge the Romans — poor little souls

who shut themselves in so carefully and shunned the open field!
It was not *their* way to take advantage of a better position than
their opponents', an equal chance was reckoned among them as
one of the rules of war. Shouldn't they have a little fighting these
fine days?

The plain was black with their hundreds of thousands, and the
Romans' blood began to boil at being unable to stop their ravaging the country and at their boastfulness; they could quite well
stand the look of the enemy now and were hardened to the
yelling. Skirmishes took place before the ramparts, the Romans
were blooded and wanted to fight, railed against their general,
were not inclined to sit still and be laughed at. And Marius nodded
to himself in his tent, now they would soon be right.

But he did not accept the Barbarians' challenge. First he waited
till they had divided themselves into two hosts and the Cimbrians
had left at last to march over to their position on the eastern side
of the Alps, where the other Consul, Catulus, was posted to meet
them. And then he still waited while the remainder, the Teutons
and Ambrones, in their own words grew old and regarded the
idea of fighting as a distant improbable legend. Marius waited and
played the coward for weeks and months; the Teutons rode up
every morning to ask after his health, yawning like big tired
dogs, crying out with boredom; and the Roman soldiers' bile was
stirred.

At last the Barbarians lost patience, since it was evident that
the Romans had settled for life in this entrenched camp, the soil
within the ramparts must have an attraction for them; well, they
might squat there till they were over head and ears in their own
filth, the Teutons were bound for Rome — ridiculous that they
hadn't gone on at once, all they had to do was to march past the
Roman fortifications!

And they did so. As their braves rode up to the ramparts for
the last time on their way to the Alps they gave the Romans
the benefit of their high spirits and asked if they had no messages
to send home to their wives, for they would soon be seeing them.
It was an ill-advised thing to shout, and the Romans had no re-
tort; with pale lips they followed the march of the multitude,
towards the Alps, towards Rome.

The march past lasted six days. For six days the vast mob was
moving past, infantry and cavalry, carts and baggage-waggons,

cattle, women, thralls and children, slowly advancing, the heavy oxen with their heads bent down by the yoke, the wheels bumping behind them in the dust, a sluggish river of waggons; but on it moved, irresistibly, beyond the horizon, like the thread from a spindle in the inexhaustible camps of the Barbarians. Finally the last column of waggons disappeared and the horde left behind it a broad ploughed-up track under a veil of dust, as though a landslide had passed over the country; the last crack of the whip, the last shout died away. For six days the earth had trembled beneath this black human stream; the Romans looked after it, in silence, speechless from what they had seen.

But now Marius broke camp and followed the horde: across the Alps they should not pass. Cautiously, always in fortified camps at strategically favourable points, he followed at their heels, until reaching Aquæ Sextiæ, the place of hot springs near the foot of the Alps. Here, half by chance, but a chance utilized by Marius with careful calculation, it came to a fight. The accounts give details, the sum of which is that Marius won a complete victory, by good luck, by the fact that the enemy was again divided, and by surprise tactics skilfully carried out.

The Ambrones were beaten first, and as the Romans pursued them to their waggon-camps they came upon howling women, we are told, who with axes and swords attacked not only their own men in flight but the pursuing Romans, grasping their naked swords barehanded and " abiding with an invincible courage to be hacked and mangled with their swords." [1]

Plutarch gives the account. After the defeat of the Ambrones the Romans passed a critical night; they still had the Teutons to deal with, in immense numbers, and the camp was unfortified. All night long they heard the Teutons uttering " loud cries, which were nothing like men's lamentations and sighs, but rather like wild beasts' bellowing and roaring. So that the bellowing of such a great multitude of beastly people, mingled together with threats and wailings, made the mountains thereabouts and the running river to rebound again of the sound and echo of their cries marvellously: by reason whereof, all the valley that lay between both, thundered to hear the horrible and fearful trembling. This made the Roman soldiers afeard, and Marius himself in some doubt: be-

---

[1] The quotations from Plutarch are here given in North's translation. — Tr.

cause they looked to have been fought withal the same night, being altogether troubled and out of order."

But the Teutons let the opportunity slip, and Marius had time to lay his ambush. It was significant of the Barbarians' ideas of warfare that the Teutons' leader, Teutobod, offered to fight Marius in single combat, a duel between the two strongest was to decide the matter on behalf of the armies. Teutobod was about seven feet high and according to tradition could leap over six horses. Marius declined his offer. When at last the armies came to close quarters the Teutons in their rage threw away an advantage and charged from the plain against the higher ground occupied by Marius; an outflanking division of the Romans took them in rear, and it was all over with them.

Teutobod fell into the hands of the Romans alive. All the tents and waggons, the whole property of the migratory people, were captured, the Teutons wiped out as a nation, killed or taken prisoner.

So many fell that the inhabitants of the region afterwards fenced their vineyards with the bones of the slain, as Plutarch relates in his Life of Marius, adding that the soil became so fertile from the putrefying bodies and from the heavy rain of the following winter that in the spring it gave an extraordinarily rich crop. The chronicler does not vouch for the excellence of human manure, though it is asserted by the Greek poet Archilochus; he quotes other who claim to have observed " that of ordinary after great battles there falleth great store of rain. Either it is by means of some god that pouring down pure rain doth purify, wash, and cleanse the ground, defiled and polluted with man's blood: or else it happeneth by natural cause. For that the overthrow of so many dead bodies, and of the blood spilt, engendreth a moist, gross, and heavy vapour, which doth thicken the air. . . ." He thus leaves it undecided whether the carrion or the rain benefits the soil. However this may be, wine grew of the Barbarians' bodies, sweetness of slaughter.

While Marius was occupied in arranging a sacrificial pyre of the shields and spears of the vanquished, a messenger arrived announcing that he had been elected Consul for the fifth year. A few days later news reached him from the eastern theatre of war: Catulus had guarded his passes so half-heartedly that the Cimbrians *had* crossed the Alps and were now in Italy. Marius then postponed his entry into Rome and was afterwards able to turn two triumphs into one.

Plutarch's ancient prose sounds like a fairy tale of giants and goblins, a piece of early Gothic viewed with the amazed eyes of the sober classical historian: "Now, these barbarous people had such a glory in themselves, and disdained their enemies so much, that more to show their force and boldness, than of any necessity that compelled them, or for any benefit they got by it: they suffered it to snow upon them being stark naked, and did climb up to the top of the mountains, through great heaps of ice and snow. And when they were at the very top of all, they laid their long broad targets under their bodies, and lay all along upon them, sliding down the steep high rocks that had certain hangings over of an infinite height."

Clearly enough glad winter memories of home had had a refreshing effect on the spirits of the Cimbrians, oppressed by the heat of the South, and they could not resist a boyish desire to roll in the drifts and sledge down the steep snow-slopes of the Alps. Like a band of noisy lads they came sliding down the roof of heaven into Italy!

Catulus had taken up a position behind a river, the Adige, with the intention of checking them there. And then the Cimbrians "came to camp near unto the Romans by the river side, and considered how they might pass it over: and began to fill it up, tearing down (like giants) great hills of earth which they found thereabouts, brought thither great trees which they pulled up whole by the roots, threw great pieces of rocks which they brake, and whole towers of earth after them, to stop and break the course of the river. But besides all this, they threw great timber into the river, which being carried down the stream, came with such a force, and hit against the post of the bridge so violently, that they shaked the Romans' bridge marvellously."

Catulus was forced back from the Adige and evacuated the country as far as the Po. The first encounter, moreover, had been accompanied by all the courtesies of war; the Cimbrians had taken prisoners but generously set them free again, and so good was the impression the Romans made on them that they confirmed the safe conduct they gave them by oaths and laying of hands on the sacred Bull. Possibly another alliance might have been offered, in all amity, if they had had only Catulus to deal with.

For the present they spread over the plains between the Adige and the Po, occupied the land as if it was their own and liked it well: plenty of room, if the people who lived there already squeezed up a little; excellent arable land, kept in very good order by the natives, who could go on with that and bring the corn as tribute; on the whole a tempting place to stay in.

During this breathing-space Norna Gest saw them. He appeared one day at their camp with his swinging, unhurried gait, and was recognized by the Cimbrians and well received; but he had no long talk with any one of them, they were too restless for that; for news from the North, where they might imagine Gest to have been, they never asked; they were full of their own affairs and had been too long away. But they were glad to see the old man and let him go about the camp as long as he liked and where he liked.

But this time he had no audience of Boierik. You now had to pass through three ramparts of waggons, one inside the other, to reach his tent, which showed up in the middle with crimson trappings and a long banner waving from the top; but Gest got no farther than the first.

The ranks had become higher of necessity; true, all were equal as members of free and equal tribes, but the Cimbrians, who formed the core of the avalanche and had given it their name, preserved a central position, and their leaders had become dukes, Boierik a prince. He lived in the innermost ring, and admittance to him was gained through the mediation of the dukes, who occupied the second; they could be approached, though with difficulty, by one who had good connections in the outer ring, where the Cimbrians' trusted chiefs of clans and most valiant champions were gathered together; beyond them Norna Gest did not succeed in penetrating during the time he stayed in the camp.

Now and then he saw the leader of the army ride past, but at a distance, the body of horsemen who formed his escort were so thick about him that only a helmet was to be seen towering above the rest, apparently of gold with a huge crest of fiery red feathers. He rode at a smart pace, and the escort with him; a thunder shook the ground and they were gone in an instant, every man silent, with wild boars or gaping beasts on their helmets, the two-pronged spears lowered at the charge, and the whole troop moved like one body, with a drumming in the horses' bellies and a blowing in their throats.

These were the same little horses they had ridden from home, but the next generation; for about a horse's age they had been on the move, Gest reckoned, and the men he had known as lads of twenty would soon be elderly; children that had watched the start from their mothers' arms were now grown up. Many, many had been born on the trail and had known nothing but travel. They had grown into quite another people than that which had set out. Even those who had been mature before the migration had greatly changed. Well, what is it they expect, thought Gest, if they are no longer the same on reaching their journey's end!

The tone of the camp was still set by the braves, the young crowd which was constantly being renewed from below as the boys passed into the men's circle. Their intercourse was marked by the transitional age, the rough tone, the grating laugh, coarseness and a bold front, heat and impatience; but the tone had become coarser under the influence of the life they had led and the knowledge acquired by contact with all kinds of people.

It was extraordinary to see the fellows' vanity and contempt for death, which had reached a pitch of fanaticism. If they counted the lives of others no higher than their own, then Woe to the rest of the world! So highly did they rate themselves that they threw away what one would have expected them to cling to, life itself; no one, not even the gods, should have the power to give them anything! They shed each other's blood without cause; a quarrel came of what was hardly a difference of opinion, the ghost of a suspicion that a man was capable of fear, and they went for each other like fighting-cocks, death for one or both of them, hale young fellows bursting with life hacking at each other; and the stricken one laughed, could not help it, with the blood gushing from his mortal wound as from a vat, died on his feet and laughed, a hearty laugh, was still laughing as he lay, till his gums turned white and he groped blindly in the air. So dear to them was honour, though when all was said and done it was only based on a weakness for what others thought. But then their lives were their own.

The men drank. They had taken to it inevitably in the wine-producing countries they had scoured. The cellars were the first thing when they stormed and sacked a town, and they were in such a hurry to get drunk that they kicked in the great earthen jars and slobbered up the wine from the floor. Their old Northern habits were forgotten, as their homes were forgotten, spring water was no longer a gift of the gods, curds, herring and barley were no longer their staple food, they had acquired a taste for seasoned dishes, frowned upon any fare but rarest dainties and paid for their luxury with toothache. Men who had once stood winter nights in the open under a cowhide now slept in the South behind hangings in fringed tents.

Gest was scandalized. He turned his eyes to the women; they could hardly have grown womanly! They were more outspoken and headstrong than before, hardened by the hard field life and marked by the precariousness of their existence; the mothers dried-up and lean, but blazing with courage. The young girls were handsome as before, even handsomer; a wild new generation had grown up that had known nothing but a wandering life, limber young heifers with the creak of the wilds in their joints, blue-eyed and blithe, strong, powerfully built and upright; flocks of them, a wonderful breed fostered by the open air, with all the gentle capability of the race in reserve. What a future they bore within them for a nation!

But chiefest and most beautiful among all was the priestess Vedis. She was now in the flower of her age, at the summit of exuberant womanly maturity, very tall, and the brightest being any one had ever seen. She was like the rosy blush of love, but was never to see her own blood repeated in a new generation; she was love itself for all generations. She was to remain alone and shine upon all as their hearts' most beautiful dream.

Strange it was to see with what sacred feelings she was regarded; all the young men, every one of them, looked up to her with unmixed reverence, nay solemnity; their grimaces vanished as soon as they saw her or even heard her name. They retired into themselves, found their real self in the radiance of her being. They worshipped her as a soul, without earthly thought, but deep down within them they were aflame for her; how could they help it! And she, she loved them all. She was betrothed to all these wild lovers, dedicated to her people, but was never to become a mother.

This could be seen in her; she was in the radiance of her youth but shone alone, like the morning star; a motherly light was on her maidenly features, she felt for all her big distracted erring children; she had become the protectress of the camp, to whom all looked for spiritual comfort; but she was alone.

And the most fervent wish of every warrior was to protect her, to surround and bear her in a ring of steel safe and untouched for ever through the world!

Not long could the Cimbrians rejoice in the good pastures of the plains of the Po and the fair prospects they offered to a settled agricultural population. Just as they were beginning to get on quite well with the worthy Catulus, Marius arrived with his troops from Gaul.

He did not come to hobnob with them or get a testimonial from them; the grim Marius cared nothing for what others thought of him, did not even trouble about his fame with posterity. Nor had the army he had trained any intention of marrying the enemy. Whether they showed bravery or covered themselves with honour was all one to them, so long as they got their knife in before the other man and could get back to the circuses and shady quarters of Rome. They were long since hardened to the sight of the monsters, even to indifference; their *moral* had almost passed to the other extreme, contempt. They had swallowed the Teutons, now for a dish of Cimbrians!

But the Cimbrians avoided battle with the combined forces of the Consuls, showing deliberation for once; better after all to wait till the Teutons came! They were touchy about taking an advantage — a thing a warrior *could* not do — all the same there was no sense in exposing one's self with half one's forces when it was just as easy to wait for the other half to come up. In the mean time they sent envoys to Marius and asked leave to remain on the land they had taken, or to be allotted other lands broad enough for themselves and their brothers. Refrain: land.

Marius: What brothers?

The envoys: The Teutons, of course. (Aside: The density of these Romans!)

At this all present began to laugh, like the entrance of the Chorus in the ancient tragedies. But Marius replied that they need not trouble about their brothers the Teutons; they had already got as much earth as would lie upon them.

The envoys then saw that they were being made fools of and

became rude: this should be avenged, it was an insult to the majesty of the Cimbrians as well as the Teutons; the Romans should smart for it as soon as the Teutons came.

Marius: They are here *now*.

And on a sign from him Teutobod and the other Teuton chieftains were brought forward in chains.

Dumb show, a few words exchanged in undertones between the Barbarians in their own tongue, and the prisoners nodded, mournful as the grave, like messengers from the realms below; yes, it was true, they were all dead.

Then the flap fell in front of Marius' tent-door, the Cimbrian envoys were gone, and the laughter of the Chorus broke out behind them in a peal.

Then the Cimbrians offered instant battle, advancing in battle array and challenging the Romans.

Marius stayed in his camp, disregarding the sneers at his cautiousness. But it was now that he had the pins taken out of his soldiers' lance-heads, so that they might stick faster in the enemy's bodies.

As Marius did not leave his camp, the Barbarian Prince, Boierik, rode up to it in person and challenged him to name his own time and place for a fight which was to decide which of them should possess the land.

So then they had a chance of seeing him, and terrifying was the look of his person, tall and huge as a tree, with his feet almost touching the ground as he sat on his horse, which however was only of moderate size, his breadth of shoulder almost eclipsing his height; on his head he wore a helmet with bull's horns and above it a crest of red cock's feathers, but his face was bare, fierce with the murderous red moustache on his lip, an unwonted sight to the clean-shaven Romans; scowling eyes of icy blue and cruel brows drawn over them, his whole expression full of wrath, head thrown back; and his dread arms completed the picture, a sword of super-human size at his side and the fork in his hand; a drastic weapon, but was it not apt to defeat itself by penetrating no farther than the length of the prongs? His shield was not strikingly large, for in this particular courage showed itself in a neglect of protection; it was white, as though chalked, and could be seen a long way off; its bearer did not seek invisibility in battle!

Boierik was accompanied only by a few horsemen, an insane exposure of a man on whose life the fate of hundreds of thousands depended. Marius could have had him seized and hanged, and the Barbarian knew it, but the Roman let him ride back unharmed, crowned with his savage halo; if the whole welfare of the hostile army was bound up with this one man who acted for them all, Marius may sarcastically have thought, then he should surely live!

He accepted the challenge, not without taunting the Barbarian with the un-Roman form in which it had been delivered, and the battle was fixed for the third day following, the place the Raudian plains near Vercellæ. Here, then, the Cimbrians were chastised at the time and place they had themselves proposed.

The sun and the heat of the day were the chief cause of the fall of the Cimbrian nation. In a literal sense the sun fought on the side of the Romans; Marius had taken care that the position gave him this advantage; and even if he had not thought of it, the Barbarians would certainly have yielded it to him, in their anxiety to avoid the reproach of a lack of bravery.

In Plutarch's words: " The heat and the sun which was full in the Cimbre's faces, did the Romans marvellous pleasure at that time. For the barbarous people being very hard brought up to away with cold (because they were born and bred in a cold country, shadowed altogether with woods and trees) were to the contrary very tender against the heat, and did melt with sweating against the sun, and gaped straight for breath, putting their targets before their faces: for it was also in the heat of summer, about the seven and twenty day of the month of July, that this battle was given, and this dust also made the Romans the bolder, and kept them that they could not see the innumerable multitude of their enemies far from them. And every man running to set upon them that came against them, they were joined together in fight, before that the sight of their enemies could make them afraid. And furthermore, they were so good soldiers, and so able to take pains, that how extreme soever the heat was, no man was seen sweat nor blow."

Another writer uses the mythical expression that the Barbarians dissolved like snow in the midday heat; the right image, that of the Ice King who had ventured south of his own dominions and melted away.

Before the attack, when the two armies were drawn up in front of each other like vast human tidal waves conjured up on the plain — the united armies of the Consuls to the number of over fifty thousand, that of the Cimbrians unnumbered, but their order of the battle, which was in the form of a square, is said to have measured three miles each way — Marius performed his devotions, as Plutarch witnesses: " Marius having washed his hands, and lifting them up to heaven promised and vowed a solemn sacrifice unto the gods of a hundred oxen. . . ."

What a moment! On earth the armies, drawing towards each other with their infinite tramp, the plain spread out on every side, fair and open in its verdure and dotted with the homes of men, and above it in the north the long snow chain of the Alps hovering like a mirage in the sky, the rampart which the invaders had scaled; but above armies and earth and heaven-seeking mountains the eternal, unapproachable heaven itself, the *day* — and then this snarling pitiless Roman raising his hands in all simplicity to Heaven, like a child begging its mother to be lifted up, a gesture whereby the very sternest seeks to escape from the earth, whose pollution is near. . . .

And then the armies begin to get in touch with one another, tuba and lur roar with hoarse throats against each other — the She-Wolf and the Bull! The wild predatory howl of the She-Wolf when she sits on her haunches and fills the night with her blood-song before going out to hunt for her young, that is the note the long, straight tuba sends to every part of the horizon; the roar of the rutting aurochs in boundless echoing forests is heard again in the curved neck of the lur. Slaughter and destruction hang over the world.

From the compact masses a flight as of swarming bees shoots obliquely into the air and down again in an arch, with a thousand flashes of steel as it goes, the first volleys of arrows let off at once, hosts of barbs falling upon the hosts, and a great raw reek from one army meets its fellow from the other, sweat and stench given off by the charging masses in the immense crush and heat of the day.

And the war-cry is raised from the stormy sea of the Cimbrians, the howl with which they strike the enemy's soul before they reach him and excite themselves, the vast roaring of a host.

And with high leaps in the air the warriors can be seen charging on, already in the blazing delirious frenzy which possesses

them in battle and makes them insensible to wounds, superior to
life and death, thrilled through with a terrible form of soulfulness,
like the element of fire.

On thunders the cavalry in scattered swarms, each acting for
itself, the horsemen leaping on and off their horses, as is their
tactics.

But the Roman cohorts stood close and firm as walls; with cool
head the soldier muttered to himself the instructions he had been
given, like a lesson he would be heard in, grasped his *pilum* and
sniffed quietly.

A cloud of dust hid the hand-to-hand fighting, like a curtain
heaven drew before its face, so thick that men lost their way in
it, whole divisions roamed about without being able to find each
other. Beneath this curtain the slaughter was accomplished. Marvels of valour were performed by the Cimbrians, a fire dance, the
topmost pitch of crazy joy, and in that they died. Their long
heavy swords they used like artists, and now and then succeeded
in cleaving a Roman soldier to the groins, but nearly always they
were brought down first; the lithe little marten of a Roman went
in under his shield and made two, three and four thrusts with his
short, two-edged *gladius* while the scythe was in the air; he
worked.

Boierik came on, his bull's crest foremost amongst the fighters,
blowing from his nostrils like a bull, all his mad animal forces
flashing from his heavy sword; he was now in the fire his terrible
heart desired, and in it he would be consumed. As a warrior he
knew no bounds, he would have gone against the Roman army
quite alone, mowed it down with his own hand, going up and
down among the swaths till the field was bare. But the Romans
stung, he did not feel that one lance after another struck him,
breaking in the shaft, while the point bent and hung in him like
an anchor; at last he was heavy with anchors whose barbs ate into
his flesh; as in a fog he dragged himself on with all the crooked
irons in him, sweeping the air with his weary scythe, and his
shoulders sank, the bull's horns went down like the sickle of the
moon in a sea of fighting-men and weapons. A howl closed over
him. Howling the remnant of his army rushed to their death.

Plutarch: "So were the most part of the barbarous people, and
specially of the best soldiers, slain in the field. And because they
should not open or break their ranks, the foremost ranks were all

tied and bound together with girdles, leather thongs, and long chains of iron: and they that fled, were chased and followed into their camp by the Romans, where they met with horrible and fearful things to behold. For their wives being upon the top of their carts, apparelled all in black, slew all those that fled, without regard of persons: some their fathers, other their husbands or their brethren, and strangling the little young babes with their own hands, they cast them under the cart wheels, and between the horses' legs, and afterwards slew themselves. And they say, that there was a woman hanged at the end of a cart ladder, having hanged up two of her children by the necks at her heels. And that the men also, for lack of a tree to hang themselves on, tied slipping halters about their necks, unto the horns and feet of the oxen, and that they did prick them afterwards with goads to make them fling and leap so long, that dragging them all about, and treading them under feet, at the length they killed them. Now, though numbers were slain by this means, yet were there three score thousand of them taken prisoners, and the number of them that were slain came to twice as many more.

The Romans must have been fighting against odds of about three to one, and when it is considered that their enemies as individuals were both bigger and stronger, they might claim to have used their other advantages with honour.

Roman training and technical skill had asserted themselves *splendide* against the overpowering physical gifts of a primitive people. But had they not been forced by these same people to return to ancient Roman virtues, and had not the vigorous invaders learnt slackness of them, amongst other things?

The sun went down over the Raudian plains after the battle, red and round like a bloody shield from the dust which still hung in the air as after a volcanic eruption, and crows and birds of prey were already beginning to glide down from every quarter of the sky in the cool twilight — what a battlefield! Far and wide lay thousands and thousands of young warriors who had risen hale and rosy-cheeked the same morning, Romans and Cimbrians in confusion, some in each other's embrace, and now stiff corpses every one!

The evening was more than still, after the immense war-cries of the day were silenced, and the shrieks of the women had died away, shrieks of despair, shrill and penetrating like the birth-cries with which they had once brought into the world all those who were now dead. Still was the evening after all the shouting, as still as the surviving women when they were led away to captivity and humiliation.

But when the sun had gone down and dusk had fallen, the chain of the Alps still glowed with a distant unearthly glory. A shadow from the battlefield turned towards it — Norna Gest, the Lonely, the Long-lived, who was here with his sorrow, always among the dead!

Before now he had seen vigorous new peoples come down over the Alps, and none of them ever returned. When would the next wave come? How long would the conflict last, before the combining power of Rome and Northern nature, more pristine but as yet undeveloped, were merged in productive unity?

The battlefield lay with all its dead, and among them Boierik, a prostrate form among the rest — yes, it was the Bull that had fallen. The She-Wolf had got her teeth into his entrails from below and torn them out. And now the Bull lay with broken horns and crushed limbs upon the ground.

V

VÆ VICTIS!

IMMEDIATELY before Marius took the field against the Cimbrians and Teutons he had concluded the Numidian war and celebrated his triumph by a solemn entry into Rome and a pageant of booty and chained prisoners along the Via Sacra to the Forum and Capitol. Of this Plutarch records:

He showed "that to the Romans which they thought never to have seen: and that was, King Jugurthe prisoner, who was so subtil a man, and could so well frame himself unto his fortune, and with all his craft and subtility was of so great courage besides, that none of his enemies ever hoped to have had him alive. But it is said, that after he was led in this triumph, he fell mad straight upon it. And the pomp of triumph being ended, he was carried into prison, where the sergeants for haste to have the spoil of him, tare his apparel by force from off his back: and because they would take away his rich gold ear-rings that hung at his ears, they pulled away with them the tip of his ear, and then cast him naked to the bottom of a deep dungeon, his wits being altogether troubled. Yet when they did throw him down, laughing he said: *O Hercules, how cold are your stoves!* He lived there yet six days, fighting with hunger, and desiring always to prolong his miserable life unto the last hour: the which was a just deserved punishment for his wicked life."

As it befell the Kabyle, so should it befall Teutobod and the other Barbarian chiefs; they decorated Marius's triumph; afterwards the chronicle is silent about them, the only mercy that was shown them.

Did the Romans consider the rank of the vanquished and the extent of their misfortunes, were they generous towards their enemy, did they measure their magnanimity by the bravery of a worthy opponent? Oh no. On the contrary. All the deeper, all the more perceptible was his degradation. But had not the vanquished themselves, when they were powerful, slaughtered Romans after the battle of Arausio?

The vanquished lost not merely life and liberty, they lost their character; this was in the hands of the victor, posterity sees it in the mirror of revenge, unless it has the means of going behind this. The posthumous fame of the Barbarians became part of the Romans' stock of abuse, lost itself in proverbial phrases, a few striking traits engraved in the memory of the people: a Teuton was a furious person, a Cimbrian a yelling one. With their names they created a notion, as Cæsar afterwards made absolute power synonymous with his name for all future time, when the name of King was too small to fit him; but Cimbrians' and Teutons' names were used to debase the notion of their report, they explored a new dimension for contempt. The synonym for bogey-man, ogre and tosspot was an Ambronian, but then it was notorious that the Ambronians had been drunk at the battle of Aquæ Sextiæ. Certain bestial ideas were associated with all three names, so that the verdict of history could be summed up in a *graffito* on the street corners of Rome:

Teutons raging
Cimbrians howling   } Swine.
Ambronians foaming

You Cimbrian! was the cry in Rome's taverns, when one fuddled slave abused another over their cups, and the man turned pale; you Teuton! and he was on his feet; Ambronian you are! and the limit was reached, the slave felt degraded, a box on the ears rang out, and a scuffle followed. When feared images fall the mud gets to them at last.

So much for their fame; in their lifetime the vanquished, all the thousands of prisoners, were punished as severely as a Roman overseer, most likely a freedman who had been a slave himself and *learnt* ill-treatment, could lay it on.

First the shame and spiritual torment of having to walk the Via Sacra in front of Marius's triumphal car, barefoot and loaded with chains, between two living walls of the Roman mob, who with drooping eyelids aped the nobles' way of looking at this human scum and in their greasy togas shrugged their shoulders in the most superior style, when they did not give way to their own instincts and fling dirt in the faces of the bound captives.

Colder than ice upon the mountains was the chill with which Knights and Senators looked down on the procession from their litters or from the balustrades of the Capitol; these noble gentlemen had made no mistake in mobilizing the Plebs; you want rabble to keep down rabble. (Later, there was no end to the trouble they had with Marius, whom they had spoilt.)

The ladies of Rome watched the procession, wrapt in grace and distinction from top to toe, showing no more cruelty than was becoming, with the sweetest look of disgust and a silvery laugh at the sight of the fettered brutes; for them of course the pageant was a chance of being seen.

It might be that here and there a glance fell on the big red bristly fellows, recalling a memory of having seen the captive before: the hairy back of the hand, the bold, powerful carriage — but now it was broken; and the Roman lady's eyes shifted from the prisoner to the little Roman soldiers who were marching with wreaths on their brows, armed to look after the fettered captives, noses in the air; strange how it struck her that they had grown broad, compact, strong, campaigning life had almost made strangers of them, though she knew them so well; and her finger went up to her mouth, and she threw them a hasty kiss, while her great dewy eyes gleamed and filled with tears.

With the red bear she had an account to settle, and when the prisoners were sold and she had got one of them in her house as water-carrier, and he appeared in the bath-room with his yoke, strong as a bull and useful, she was just undressed, but took no notice of his presence — what did it matter to a lady if a slave saw her naked, his eyes were nobody's; but with her sense that nothing escaped she felt that the slave was shaking with agitation, his bellows stopped blowing and water splashed on the mosaic floor; he was allowed to go without so much as a fibre of her Aphrodite's body betraying the fact that he existed. The Roman lady could never forgive a Barbarian for having been, in a moment of vertigo, the object of her desire, when he was free.

But worse things, inconceivable things, are at work in her feline soul. A long, carefully calculated look at the water-carrier, on a ripe opportunity, and he draws himself up, she has *seen* him; an occasional meditative look at him, a pensive sigh, and he grows bold, for he was once a free man and worshipped beauty; and if one day an exclamation escapes him, a homage not to be re-strained, but distant, the joy of the child of nature in loveliness — why, then she breathes lightly through her nose, looks round and beckons to the slavemaster, points, and the gigantic Nubian hur-ries in fuming; and then the leaded scourge whistles over the back of the unfortunate water-carrier. He smiles, holds himself erect under the blows, he has been misunderstood, and he smiles again; but then the negro seizes his yoke and knocks his teeth down his throat, more hurry in and he is held and bound, ten men are not too many, two or three for each limb. With hands and feet tied together he is given a dose of the cat on the floor; the Roman lady looks on with little pensive eyes; then she turns and retires to her apartments.

Some other day when she has forced him to shed tears, though it takes long, she will perhaps take him into her alcove and enjoy his crippled body.

Sure enough, the young Cimbrians' superfluous laughter, both their frank merriment and their loutish larking, was turned to groans; they were kept up to the collar and felt the lash.

Some of them went to the treadmill, which they had thought so funny the first time they saw it; that was from the outside, inside it meant aching feet and a gradual brutalization.

Others had work in the fields; that was in the open air, but under supervision, with frequent blows from a man of lower worth than they had been; chained at night in cellars together with other rabble, their food all kinds of offal.

But the toughest customers were sent to the gladiatorial schools and trained to manslaughter. They thought they knew all about it but had a lot to learn, all the airs and graces and dexterity, the various tricks, according as they were put to fighting with helmet and dagger and called a Thracian, or were sent naked into the ring with a net and a fork, like a merman, with the name of *retiarius*, or again whether they had to face lions in the arena or were expected to slay each other. They had to learn Latin and say *puls* for porridge and *aqua*, like a croaking frog, when they meant water.

They were condemned to bodily torment, from the day the red-hot iron branded them with the mark of the school and they smelt their own roast flesh, until they were turned out as finished bruisers and had had most of the bones in their faces broken and mended again; they were brought up to nothing else but death. A round-about death, of course, full of artistry and long drawn-out; and when it came there was form to be studied, a fine gesture, one should breathe one's last to a burst of clapping. More than one of them, when he had murdered a brother, tasted the applause of the amphitheatre's connoisseurs. Occasionally, from certain considerations, they were spared, since it would not do to exterminate the gladiators all at once, there would be none left.

Thus they found their places, as men do who have left the land of their childhood and are no longer boys, have entered a regulated community and are harnessed to some calling or other, in which they are to die.

The Bronze Bull was captured at Vercellæ, and Catulus is said to have had it set up at his villa.

But on the day of the triumph it naturally formed part of the procession, rocking on its strange barbaric car, on which it had been brought from Thule through thousands of miles of Hercynian forest and across the wildest mountains along the Via Sacra towards the heart of Rome — but it was not thus that its entry into Rome had been imagined by the captured chieftains, some of whom were driven in cages in the procession, gone mad from grief and ill-treatment, with festering sores on their limbs from the fetters, and teased like apes by the Roman boys who prodded them through the bars with sticks.

Then from the sunny haze surrounding the Capitol the She-Wolf could look down at the Forum, where the Bull was being driven up amid the scoffing of a happy mob.

The pontiffs versed in the mysteries and service of the gods afterwards examined it from curiosity: barbaric workmanship, yet marked in certain details in a striking way by enlightened taste. The solar sign on its forehead puzzled them, not its interpretation, but the fact that a barbarous people had got hold of this highly-developed symbol. Had the light of Rome really penetrated so far to the North? A stolen Southern work, some thought, the whole image had been carried off with sacred signs and all. But concealed in a chamber in the interior of the Bull they found an ancient idol, certain features of which reminded them of the most holy image both of Rome and Greece, transmitted through the ages, which only the highest initiates had ever seen, for it would strike ordinary mortals with blindness, though the augurs retained their sight, the Palladium itself — was it not strange? The same fire at the very bottom of the sacred conceptions of all peoples? The worship of Vesta; and what had they been told about the fire-priestesses of the foreign barbarians? Yes, it was strange.

In Catulus' garden the Cimbrians' Bull was soon forgotten. And afterwards it disappeared entirely. The She-Wolf was preserved to posterity, but of the Bull nothing is known; doubtless it ended as old metal and went into the melting-pot again, the best thing that could happen; it had been a failure, and new rallying-signs would be found for the forces of which it was a symbol.

And as the Bull was lost in oblivion, so were the Cimbrians. Of the terror a memory was preserved in Rome, but the terror itself was worn away, like so much else, in the mills of Rome; the Civil Wars and the days of the Empire raised many other bug-bears.

When the Roman mother wanted to get her little son to bed in the evening and he took his stand in his scant shirt a long way from the door and would not come in, she had once been used to say, Now the Cimbrians are coming, and instantly the little man toddled across the street and buried his head in her lap; now he broke into a shrill audacious laugh when such nursery tricks were tried on him and he had to be threatened with newer terrors — Now the Germans are coming! That did it.

Yes, the Cimbrians and Teutons had only been one egg that had been loosened from the great ovary of the North; Rome was to be allowed no pause.

But the advanced guard of the Cimbrians ate the bread of captivity and punishment until they died under the far-famed Southern sky.

There was a small second generation — even slaves are permitted to propagate — a smaller third one; the remainder were lost among the heterogeneous bastards of the Roman people. The first unhappy generation of captives wore their chains smooth in the slaves' quarters of many a Roman establishment, till age, affliction and harsh treatment put an end to their sufferings.

Those who had been children when they fell into captivity had to support their misery longest. Of this youngest brood, and perhaps of some descendants of their elders, we hear something thirty-six years later, when the slaves' revolt broke out in Italy and for a time became a very dangerous threat to Rome.

Its leader Spartacus was a Thracian, of a hardy, half-savage race which afterwards gave the Romans a great deal to do; together with a crowd of other gladiators he had broken out of the fighting school at Capua and spread the fire of rebellion among all slaves, so that he had soon collected an army of over a hundred thousand men and beat the Roman troops in several pitched battles. His army was composed of prisoners of war from all quarters of the world; to enumerate them was to draw the map of the Roman empire, every country round the Mediterranean which they had despoiled, men of every tongue and every colour, all under the yoke; and among them it is said that no small part was the remnant of the captive Cimbrians.

Spartacus had the intention of going northward, across the Alps, with his horde, with a sound feeling of getting away from Rome and doing the reverse of what the Cimbrians amongst others had come to grief over; but the elements of his swarm were too dissimilar, they all wanted to go home, which meant to all points of the compass, from which they had been scraped together; his army could not be led towards any definite goal. The Romans exerted all their forces to put down the revolt, and their Consul Crassus, which being interpreted means the fat man, hunted them until he had got them surrounded right down in the toe of Italy's boot.

Here and elsewhere the slave army was beaten and taken prisoner; Spartacus fell.

The Romans submitted his dead body to torture. The right of property in human flesh, beasts of burden born of women, was assured. On the highway between Rome and Capua a horseman might enjoy riding along on an avenue of six thousand crucified slaves.

Among them some of the last of the Cimbrians expired, nailed up in the blazing sun.

Aqua . . . they croaked, like frogs perishing in the dust, *aqua* . . . but they got flies in their mouths instead.

An imposing incident was connected with the servile war. Spartacus and his band at one time took up a position on Vesuvius, which was then extinct and covered with vines to its summit; the crater itself formed their fortress, and the Romans besieged the fissure through which they had reached it.

A fine view they had, over the Mediterranean and beautiful Italy, a promised land; but just as the human skin does not look its best under a magnifying glass, so they found the beauties of the landscape increased by distance; they had climbed as high as they could go, right up the world's chimney, to enjoy a brief rest.

They were starved out. At last, when the Romans thought all was very quiet within, they advanced through the cleft, but were much surprised to find not a soul. The slaves had made ropes of vines and let themselves down the sheer outer wall of the crater on the other side; thus there was a leak in the trap that time.

But the wrath of Vesuvius was roused. For it was no less a person than one of the brothers of Gunung Api himself they had outraged, walking on his hat and making war on his very scalp; he disliked this and broke into eruption, and a century and a half later, for mountains measure time by a bigger scale than men, and burned the vineyards and vermin from his sides, slobbered lava and boiling mud upon the country round, strewed cinders on top, and buried another generation altogether, the great grandchildren of the transgressors; at any rate both Pompeii and Herculaneum were overwhelmed.

It was the end of the world to those who witnessed it. A Græco-Roman author, Dion Cassius, described the eruption in these words:

"Many men of immense size, surpassing all human stature and even our conceptions of giants, appeared now upon the mountain, now in the surrounding country and in the towns, both by day and night, wandering about on the earth and passing to and fro in the air. And afterwards terrible droughts suddenly occurred and mighty earthquakes, so that the whole plain seethed and the mountains leapt; and sounds were heard, as of thunder underground and a roaring above the earth, and the sea roared, and the heavens answered again. And thereupon there was suddenly a fearful crash, as though the mountains were overthrown, and instantly there leapt into the air first stones of immense size, so high that they reached the topmost summits, and then much fire and an infinite mass of smoke, so that the whole atmosphere was overshadowed and the sun completely hidden, as in an eclipse; thus there was night instead of day and darkness instead of light. And some thought that it was the Giants that had risen (for many such gods continued to show themselves through the smoke), but others thought that the whole universe was about to be engulfed in chaos or in fire."

Yes, it was the ancient fire, Gunung Api, also called Lucifer, or Loki, it was his red lads that had left the mountain to play and stride about the sky.

When the eruption was at its height it appeared to those who were never to see another day rather as though fire was bursting out everywhere, from the mountain, from the clouds, the glare of fire came from the sea, fire burst out of the earth, stones and trees became fire, flames formed in the houses' foundations, as though a fire beneath was forcing its way up; tongues of fire ran along the roofs, the air they breathed turned to fire, and in that fire they sank down, gasped and expired, like fire-illumined worms upon the earth.

But it was no more than a brief blaze and a short rumbling; in reality the fire was confined, Vesuvius had only flashed out through the bars. Afterwards he smoked for centuries, to keep his crater clean.

The world did not come to an end; it has to last yet, with its yearnings and its troubles. A couple of towns were destroyed, and the heirs of the dead — oh, they were rummaging for their places before they were in the ground — built towns above them. Later on they were dug up, and eighteen centuries-old moment was brought to light, petrified by an eruption, a resurrection of the Roman and his belongings as though scarcely an interval had elapsed.

A gladiatorial barrack was excavated at Pompeii with everything pertaining to slaughter and punishment, arms, armour, scourges, down to the smallest details, the prisoners' rude drawings on the walls, and they were pretty broad; the smell of their sweaty bodies was not far from being dug up again.

In one of the cells where the slaves were locked in at night a heap of big skeletons was found linked together in the hardened ash, a squad of prisoners that had not been able to get out or that some one had omitted to release; they had huddled together in their chains like dogs, while the cinders rained down from above and closed over them, finally stopping nose and mouth. How the last mouth struggled for the last breath of poisoned air, shaking the ash away once more and opening its lips, a breathing-hole among the ashes, still hoping; but the ashes fell.

There may have been great-grandchildren of the Cimbrians among them, born as captives of captive parents, Romanized by now and perhaps with nothing left but their size to recall the Northman. And that is the last there is to be told of the great, happy, mad boys of Cimberland.

But what of the women?

There was a fair in the slave market in Rome.

It lasted many days, for there was only room for a small part of the female slaves that were to be sold. But there was plenty of time.

After a war, the brief white heat which welds the changes of history and decides in a moment the fate of hundreds of thousands, it is surprising how long the years are, ages can be spared for dividing the spoil.

The number of the captive women was legion, but each one was accurately valued, there was bargaining and haggling, over and over again, about the price per head, before they were all sold and carried off by their new owners.

The goods were all young. The old and useless had been killed, they were not worth transporting; most of them had done it themselves, the Barbarians' terrible female soothsayers and butchers, who had raved both at Aquæ Sextiæ and Vercellæ and fired the other women to murder and suicide, a fearful sort of creatures who as they died had bitten the soldiers' fingers with their toothless gums, as they were taking off their necklets; ugh, the soldiers dried their fingers and shuddered, it was as though a far worse death had sucked at them than that which raged about them in battle. These tortoise-like hags they had stabbed or trampled to death, but besides them there were young priestesses, of very good appearance; these they had taken alive, they would fetch a price.

One of them indeed was noticeable for a kind of barbaric beauty, such heavy tresses had never been seen, nor so fair; the woman's skin too was very white, reminding one even of the chryselephantine Minerva; she was a rarity and would undoubtedly reach a high figure.

It goes without saying that the soldiers offered no violence whatever to the captive girls, however tempting they might be and in spite of the forced abstinence of war-time; for otherwise they would have been unsaleable.

Most of the mothers had killed themselves, or had been dispatched. The children could be sold, those of them that were whole. In any case mothers and children were separated, as were all other relatives, where kinship could be established; for association among slaves was always a thing to be avoided.

Among the Barbarians themselves there was said to have been a difference of rank, some of the young girls appeared to have been of nobler birth than others, a kind of knighthood was spoken of, degrees of birth ranging even to princes, on an uncivilized scale, so there were possibly princesses among the girls; they did not show it, all were alike able-bodied and they were sold as they came. Almost without exception they were fitted for men's work, the handmill, carrying fuel, heavy outdoor and indoor jobs, being big and hardy; but for that matter they might be applied in just as many ways as there were buyers and buyers' tastes.

Intacta! cried the slave auctioneer, getting hoarse as the day went on, over every single female individual who was pushed to the front of the platform on which the sale took place; age, so many years, at a rough guess; and in this they were often out, for compared with the Roman women the Barbarians might be much older than their looks; very muscular, fit for manual labour; hale and sound, no visible blemishes!

The slave-dealer had a wit and added spicy remarks, men laughed, a whinnying chorus passed over the square now and then, like a flock of birds taking wing. And the market had a smell of many warm human beings.

The poor creature was exposed, for they did not sell a pig in a poke, and there she stood twisting her body like the pink worm a human being is, but had no hole to creep into. Rome gazed at her, in silence, a coarse pause which decided her fate; then the slave-dealer threw her garment over her again — the view was not to be a long one, for it was part of what was offered for sale and would become the property of the purchaser.

Most of the buyers were women, the matrons of Rome who had a place for another slave-girl and were carried to the market; their purple-lined litters stood on one side with the slaves sitting on the shafts — perhaps two couples of newly acquired prisoners from the male supply, Teutons or Cimbrians like the females who were being sold, some of them personal acquaintances, it might be; but the new porters showed no sign of sympathy, they looked tired, sitting with bowed heads, and the red pompons with which they had been decorated trailed towards the ground.

A fight started among the porters, origin obscure; they were of many nationalities and in the Babel of voices nobody could make head or tail of their explanations; but it was a Teuton who had flown into a rage over the slave-market and it had taken twenty men to settle him; he had begun it . . . well, the Tiber was very handy, and the corpse was pitched into it.

The Roman matron was noted for economy; the ladies moved about the market-place with their tunics daintily gathered over their feet and examined the slaves, who stood in bunches or lay down on the platforms, a human crust on the pavement with narrow passages between for purchasers to move about and inspect them. The Roman ladies had good eyes, they could spot what they wanted at a distance and pushed along sideways through the crowd, scanned the girl and buried a bejewelled hand in her shoulders to feel if they were firm, examined her breasts, had she had a child? pulled her hair, was it her own? and pursed their lips: far too attractive, these sluts! They resembled each other like ingots of gold, cast in the same mould and bearing the same stamp, all these country wenches, an offensively good-looking breed. Handsome serving-women were by no means desirable in a Roman lady's household; they went for the rougher, more begrimed but useful sort, and these were sold first.

But the rest found buyers too, often after keen bidding by many fanciers, who sent up the price and delighted the slave-dealer. It was men who were bidding, unblushing rakes, whose money-bags, however, made decency superfluous. Nor did they put in an appearance till after dusk, when possible female relations or acquaintances had gone, between theatre time and the bacchanal, perfumed they came, humming a verse of Theocritus; and so they made their choice.

Slowly, one by one, but all in their turn, the young forsaken daughters of Cimberland were sold and crossed off with a chalk mark on the forehead, to be fetched or delivered according to agreement. Could any punishment be too hard for the vainglorious bankrupts who should have protected them?

The defenceless ones passed to thraldom and humiliation in many forms. Not worst of these was the lot of the washerwoman, loaded with burdens and standing to her waist in the waters of the Tiber; nor yet that of chambermaid to one of the rich Roman ladies, who were said not to shrink from stabbing their slaves to death with hairpins when they were in a bad temper; nor grinding flour, head downwards for a life-time, nor weeding and clearing stones on an estate — the company they were condemned to, the world of their fellow-slaves, was worse.

And worst was the fate of the fairest, who attracted the hot attention of sin; the rapid fall, a long step down, and ever down; their path cannot be traced.

But no complaint of theirs has reached posterity. The hardest lot a brutal tyranny, into whose hands they had fallen, could impose on a woman, was not hard enough to make them wince.

Many an inhuman lot has a woman made bearable by her devotion. Nor is every master harsh. Perhaps many of them carried an unspoilt heart into a new, precarious existence, even if no one had a heart for them.

VI

BESIDE THE TIBER

A MAN in a clay-stained cloak, straight from his workshop, but otherwise with the look of a well-to-do Roman, was hurrying anxiously through the streets of the city, paying no heed to his surroundings, like one who has received an urgent message and whose only thought is to arrive in time. But many of those who saw him turned round with a respectful look and nodded to each other: Cheiron the sculptor — and in a hurry!

He was hastening to the slave-market. A strange thing had happened. He held in his hand a letter which he had just received; a hired messenger had brought it to his studio outside the city with no other explanation than that it was to be delivered into his own hands, and without being able to describe from whom it came. It was a folded papyrus, and on it an unskilful hand had traced a drawing which was evidently intended to be a rough plan of Rome. At a spot which could only be the slave-market an object was drawn which after some deciphering proved to be nothing but a beetle . . . and in a flash the meaning was clear to Cheiron: the slave-market and the Northern prisoners of war who were just now being sold . . . the scarab . . . and *Inge!* A powerful memory of old days burst upon his soul . . . the land far, far away where he had once been a prisoner, was he to find it here? Now flushed, now pale, Cheiron hurried through the streets of Rome . . . could it be true? If only he was not too late!

He arrived just as Vedis was led up to the platform to be sold. . . .

Cheiron in the market! All faces turned that way, with a friendly murmur: well, naturally, the sculptor was on the look-out for a model, had evidently come straight from his work for that purpose; and with Roman politeness they made room for him among the bidders. The figures were already high, it was a wonderful woman, but everybody gave way to Cheiron and the slave was knocked down to him on the spot.

He left the market at once with his purchase; they saw him take off his cloak and put it over the slave's shoulders as though to screen her from the eyes of the crowd. She was taller than he, and many a man smiled: how keenly he had been set upon buying that magnificent barbarian woman; he had at once given a gold ring in pledge to clinch the bargain. . . . Oh, the great Cheiron was not so very old yet!

For the first few days she was perfectly dumb, sitting on the floor petrified and lifeless in a dark corner like one who has lost her wits.

She started as though expecting a blow when any one came near her, quivering under the eyes, with patches of white on her cheeks as though she had already been struck; and her hands trembled, she shook all over, big and strong as she was, but all in a state of listlessness, the spasms of a creature quite benumbed.

Food she accepted readily and gladly when it was given her, in her famished condition, but wept at the kindness shown her, wept as she ate and moistened her bread with tears — and her tears got the upper hand, she buried her head in her hair and wept, in long and violent fits; all her sufferings and misfortunes overwhelmed her again, but she checked herself with all her might and tried to stifle her weeping, writhed in her pain and shed rivers of tears, was almost choked and gasped through her hair like a drowning woman; her grief completely crushed her.

And afterwards she sat with wet, blue lips, panting and drawing her breath with difficulty and in hiccups; with long intervals, but again and again, a convulsive sobbing came from her heart.

At last she got over it and sat still, painfully disfigured and swollen, with dimmed eyes, flushed and bathed with tears, looking like a calm after a deluge — all the dripping trees and the heavy sky, exhausted with weeping, which can rain no more.

In a little while she slept; her head drooped and she slept for many hours, rolled in her hair, quivering slightly even in her sleep, with convulsive starts that shot through her bosom.

When she was not sitting shy and bewildered, or weeping, she slept and slept, and Cheiron let her sleep, made a bed for her in her corner and left her in peace.

She was in a miserable, neglected state after many weeks' transport on the roads and detention in prisoners' camps; her hair was a matted mass caked together with dust and rain and tears, her skin streaked all over with dirt, livid blue spots on her limbs from blows and kicks; and she was emaciated, scared out of her wits, completely shattered by terror and despair. And yet neither dirt nor distress could conceal her exquisite features and her youth, the wonderful lines of her tall, sweeping, intensely womanly figure; she remained noble, and with the eagle eye of the sculptor Cheiron detected her form through the outer show.

That it was not Inge, but must be a daughter of hers, Cheiron saw at once, with wonder and the deepest emotion.

In her features she might have been mistaken for her mother: the long face and long, delicate nose, with quivering nostrils full of life like a horse's; but she was still fairer and of bigger build, with an addition of strength from another kin, her father's. It was as though Cheiron's lost devotion of years ago had come to life before his eyes, but transfigured and greater, as a devotion is transfigured by memory. But now she was unhappy, torn out of her existence by the roots like a plant, trembling like a blind girl left alone, with all hope gone, distressed as the only survivor of a world that was destroyed, and lost in a new one.

The scarab hung round her neck; her mother must have given it her, and, though she had lost all else, she still had that. Only a goddess could have guided her destiny as it had been guided; the goddess whose picture was on the scarab, the compassionate Venus.

From whom had the letter come? That she could not have sent it herself was clear from the state she was in. And then Cheiron had given the scarab, many years ago, to the old minstrel in the land of the Cimbrians, expressing the hope that it might come into Inge's hands — it was the night he was to have been sacrificed and had been set free by the minstrel, at the prompting of the lovely May Bride, to whom he had scarcely dared to raise his eyes, and whom he was never again to see. Was it the old minstrel who had sent the letter? Was he then in Rome? Who could understand the workings of the Goddess of Love? Ah, that strange old man . . . . when he had given him his freedom and told him which way to take to reach safety, he had carried his kindness so far as to bestow a fish-hook on him at parting, that he might not suffer want on the journey, and had laid stress on its being a good hook! And in fact Cheiron had fished his way through many an inhospitable country with it.

But now the scarab had come back, and with it a girl who was almost Inge herself! Did it mean that Inge had had a warm feeling for him and now sent her image in her stead? But *she* did not know him, seemed not to see him even. What would happen now? The ways of the Goddess were inscrutable.

After sleeping and weeping, sleeping and weeping, for two days and two nights, Vedis got up. The woman in her conquered, and one morning Cheiron found her changed; she had composed herself and bathed, had washed and combed her hair, a labour of hours, and had put on a simple garment that had been laid out for her, instead of the ragged sackcloth of the slave. She looked up with clear, but impenetrably lonely eyes, when she became aware of her master's presence, dropped them again at once and waited for an order, to be set to her work.

And he set her to work. Oh yes, she was to be a model. She bent her head. As a model she would oblige him by taking her clothes off. She did so. After a pause, during which he was studying her, she heard him give a snort. Then he seized the clay, gave it several hard punches and began to model.

Cheiron lived beside the Tiber above Rome, in a big house which shut out the view of the road beyond; on the other side a garden, enclosed by walls, ran down to the river. The place lay quite by itself, cut off from the outer world, though the turmoil of Rome hummed in the air at no great distance. The spacious house had several courts with arcades and fountains; both it and the garden were full of statues and works of art, and the garden was shady with old and leafy trees. Cheiron worked in the house with his servants and pupils; but when he was modelling Vedis it was always in the garden, under the open sky.

And by degrees, as the work progressed, she began to look about her and come to life; she noticed the trees, the river, and formed ideas of her own, day by day a sense of well-being came over her. It was pleasant in the sunshine, in the caress of the ever-warm air; she raised her eyes to the trees and was as it were renewed by the sight of them, her bosom expanded and remained full, her eyes became so blue, she was like the awakening of a day.

It was her youth asserting itself. Her health had come back, her limbs were rounded, fuller than before, the blood showing through her clear skin; and when she had wholly recovered herself Cheiron felt that the earth had never borne a more beautiful, faultless and radiant female form. She was beauty, she was youth itself.

But Cheiron — he was not so young. His age was double hers, he knew it. And he was not going to hide it from her. The sculptor turned to his model with an old man's manner, added several years to his age, was strict and short with her; she had to work long hours for him, standing in the garden while he struggled with his figure; and he was obstinate, made a long tussle, over and over again till he got it as he wanted it; and then it was not what he had in his mind.

Sometimes he would have a strange wild fit when at work, with a forceful look from the model to the figure and back again, and he walked round it fiercely, breathing only in snorts; at other times he burst into song, was lord of heaven and earth; but it always ended in his throwing up his work, frowning deeply and dragging himself away from the figure like a beaten man, when his day's courage and strength were exhausted.

When they were not at work she never saw him, he left her absolutely alone; she had a room entirely to herself. Others attended to the housework, that was no employment of hers; she had her arduous duties in standing as a model. No one else ever entered the garden.

She still had relapses, hiding herself with her sorrow when it broke out again, and Cheiron heard the sound of inconsolable weeping from an arbour in the garden; so she was thinking of her brothers again, of all the poor warriors she had seen killed or dragged away to captivity; and after a long while she came out with red eyes.

But the flowering of her nature could not be repressed. Her nature was joy, sweetness in the blood, and joy burst out of her like springtime, when the winter of her grief was spent. A warmth was born within her; rosy and sensitive, happy in her solitude, she looked up into the trees of Cheiron's garden, listened contentedly to the river, was ready with a gesture of delight when she saw a bee, played with kittens, was never so happy as when she was alone.

With trees she had a way of her own, an inborn familiarity; she would stand beside them with no other wish than to be near them, they were like sisters together. She decked herself with flowers, without a thought of pleasing, and seemed to play with them, her lips moved as though she were talking to the flowers or to herself, entirely lost in the companionship of green things.

Early in the cool morning she rose and plunged into the Tiber, emerging from it like a nymph and drying herself and her hair in the morning breeze; she walked in the garden among blossoming almond-trees, in dew and perfume, and would lose herself in a tree, standing in its arms, hidden among the white blossoms which shaded into the most delicate pink, herself as white of hue as the blossoms and as rosy as the dawn, her long, rounded limbs like newly grown stems with faultless bark, her hair like a shower of light from heaven; in light and fragrance and colour she vanished in the tree like its soul, the dryad that was there and not there.

She plucked many, many flowers, seized with insatiability, and held them all in her embrace. She gave the rose a kiss, alone with it among the bushes, a big greedy kiss, and blushed with it. She loved the garden and grew brighter and brighter the more she was alone.

But Cheiron was gloomy. He had begun to work on his statue in marble, and it gave him trouble: all his shortcomings were chiselled in the imperishable material.

But he finished it, for everything must have an end, both hopes and failures. And then he walked away from it backwards, when the last polishing strokes had been given and acknowledged to be hopeless, since no one comes up to Nature; — walked from it backwards as it stood shining in the garden, into his house, as though he wished never to see it again.

But it was a good statue. While Vedis had again become human and a woman and had regained her cheerfulness, all the overflowing vigour and carelessness of youth, Cheiron had immortalized her suffering and distress in his everlasting marble.

The image of suffering womanhood was there preserved for ever. It was the strange captive woman, understood by none, as she stands in silent despair, bound and exposed for sale, numb beneath the eyes of the buyer, immersed in a lost world, the doom of a nation which she has witnessed, the death of her whole race, all her kin; a picture of the deepest inward grief which even coarse spectators and the prospect of degradation cannot change to terror, for all her thoughts are turned inward; an expression of the dumb grievance of her sex against the people she belonged to and whose disasters she has seen.

It was the doom of Life, perpetuated in a work of art. To distant generations it would convey the accusation: womanhood outraged and crushed, and the cause of it, the violence of the brutal man of war.

But when Cheiron had gone into his house, and Vedis saw his affliction, as though his work was wasted and he had gained nothing, she went after him and found him in his room, among works of art which depressed his spirits, sitting idly and tired, his tired hands dusty with marble: the statue had refused to come right for him, he thought . . . and the model would not come right for him either. . . .

Then she stretched out her hands to him, in an unconscious, wonderfully beautiful and simple gesture, with anxiety in her face, his trouble reflected in love's mirror, an expression lovelier than he had even seen in any other. And look — now Cheiron smiles, a great light breaks forth, as when a child is given what it has been crying for. And they both laugh, impossible to say which of them laughs first.

It had come, her joy had welled over so that she could no longer bear it alone, and now it had turned naturally to him who had allowed it rest to grow. And he — he was so glad, since, if in Art he could not attain what no one ever attains — Life gave it him instead!

It was the first time she had seen him smile, but it was a smile that had once lured many maidens to a certain smithy in a certain far-off land, where a sooty lad fascinated the natives with his Southern air and his white teeth, in spite of his being only a thrall. And his eyes were radiant now, anything but tired, absent sculptor's eyes; he flashed up with an artist's power of instant transformation and rejuvenation. A moment before it was as though Vedis's sorrow and all the sorrow he had put into his work, the statue's sorrow, the world's sorrow, rested upon him; now Cheiron smiled, a smile which melted and dissolved much loneliness.

Hand in hand they went out and both looked up to the sky, a great day, the day of their happiness; hand in hand they wandered through the garden to a grove where Cheiron had a statue of the Goddess of Love, a piece of the noblest Greek work. A fine thread of smoke rose from the altar before it among the laurels; Cheiron and Vedis offered incense together and poured out wine upon the earth, both holding the same bowl, before the face of the Goddess.

How inscrutably she had confused their paths and guided them for the best! Had not Vedis lost her freedom they would never have met, and she would have remained a vestal all her days and never been human and a woman, as she was now to be. Had not Cheiron been a thrall in exile he would never have raised his eyes to the unattainable and remained in solitude, alone with his dream, until it came to fulfilment.

But to the dead woman who had give both of them life they twined garlands in a silence of deep reverence, and offered them, knowing no better, to the river, watching them silently till the stream carried them out of sight.

Ah, the marbles of the garden recalled Vedis's most sacred memory: her dead mother and the frozen blossoms on her cheeks.

The growth of the garden, great evergreen bushes and trees, looked like the fortunate ancestors of the poor stunted evergreen scrub of the heath that Vedis had played with in winter as a child, and they exhaled the same hidden fire; in a strange way the most elusive scent of her childhood combined and made one with her happiness in a distant Southern land.

And great was their happiness. She expanded in all the heavenly joy of her bright nature, and he enveloped her always with his enraptured gaze, which was so strong that she felt its warmth upon her face, blushing and shielding herself with her hand as though from a scorching fire.

A vanished world, her whole soul imprisoned in regret and growing with her growth, came back to her: childhood, a child of their love, a little Cupid with dark hair, but blue-eyed; and Cheiron modelled the dearest little Eros with sparrow's wings, the life of the past that had come flying to them, doubling as ever its happiness, life repeated and immortalized in an image.

For her first-born Vedis made a song in her own wild language, such as the Cimbrian mothers used to sing over their little ones, as they swung them to sleep in a sheepskin hung to the branch of a tree:

> My leaf, my little tree,
> Grow green, grow close to me!
> Swing him, ye branches,
> Sing him to sleep,
> All little warblers!

The springs around thy foot,
Earth's blood, shall feed thy root.
     Swing him, ye branches,
     Sing him to sleep,
          All little warblers!

The high Gods walk the air,
Waving thy crown of hair.
     Swing him, ye branches,
     Sing him to sleep,
          All little warblers!

Gather both sun and snow,
Take warmth as well as woe!
     Swing him, ye branches,
     Sing him to sleep,
          All little warblers!

Let thy leaf feed the deer
Cheerful his mouth to cheer!
     Swing him, ye branches,
     Sing him to sleep,
          All little warblers!

Eagles, thy heights among,
Shall feed their noisy young.
     Swing him, ye branches,
     Sing him to sleep,
          All little warblers!

Squirrels with timorous glee
Build their green bowers in thee.
     Swing him, ye branches,
     Sing him to sleep,
          All little warblers!

Live on, my stem, increase!
Life comes of growth in peace.
     Swing him, ye branches,
     Sing him to sleep,
          All little warblers!

But make thy seed to fly,
Bounty shall never die!
     Swing him, ye branches,
     Sing him to sleep,
          All little warblers!

> My leaf, my little tree,
> Grow green, grow close to me!
> Swing him, ye branches,
> Sing him to sleep,
> All little warblers!

Another Cupid fluttered into the garden and was petted and modelled, and now Vedis had recovered her world just as when her two little brothers were strutting about the floor and grabbing at everything with little honey hands; but these two little ones were her own, it was she who was the mother, and the world she had got back was wilder and sweeter than the lost world of regrets. Dark they were, her little ones, each bearing a little night upon his head, but they did not live in the depths of a winter house; they were in a garden under the open sky, in everlasting summer.

As Vedis had recognized her childhood's most secret fragrance in the myrtle and oleander of the South, she emerged in an expansion of the soul the great Southern trees of the garden with deeply buried memories of the North, almost forgotten — the sanctuary where, as a child, she had been so powerfully impressed.

She still seemed to hear their moaning over her head, the tall old trees of the sacred grove; the ash with the spring below its roots, the holy water with its border of ochre and a film over it of all the colours of the rainbow; the airy tree-top full of bees and sunshine in the brief summer; the apple-tree with its sacred life-giving apples, the mistletoe high up on a bough of the oak, the holiest of things, the lightning's infant nurtured by the oak; this and a luxuriance of her own, for she herself was like a plant, all this she blended together with the sunny trees of Cheiron's garden, and the Tiber, and the bees, which here again loomed out of the noonday fires, and the columns of the courts, and marble and pictures and music and song; of all this she made a world about her and within her and about those she loved.

After Cheiron had modelled Vedis as a tragic figure he had thoughts of working from her in the free, sublime style, and was in doubt whether it should be a Flora or a Mænad, a Pomona or an Aphrodite, or Demeter, or Minerva; but he ended as time went on in modelling her as all of these.

First as Pomona, since he had seen how she loved trees and flowers: the wild young girl of the woods awaking when for the first time she sees a man and stretches out her hands to him with innocent impetuosity.

As Aphrodite he raised an imperishable memorial to her beautiful, faultless form, nudity transfigured.

And the sweetness in her blood, throbbing to a tempestuous joy of life, he portrayed as a Mænad, with garments in wild disorder, thyrsus in hand.

But more beautiful he made her as the flower-strewing Flora, Spring with her cool, fragrant gifts, her light step, her great open eyes, all her careless newborn wealth.

Demeter — here she was at rest, the ripe reposeful corn, broad, motherly, beautiful growth, the swelling abundance of Summer.

And in a colossal Minerva he set up a monument to her clear, upright, sound good sense. Clay or chisel was never out of his hands.

In Cheiron's garden, that world raised above all other worlds, a secret little Hellas, a Greek island between walls, Norna Gest found his charges, when he came fishing up the Tiber and made fast his little craft to the bank by the happy house.

What a difference in the Tiber above and below Rome! Here the pure water from the mountains; there the outflow of Rome's drains, fish muddy about the gills, and the fish-hook brought up corpses of babies smothered at their birth. The world of Rome bent on achieving its own destruction, but fresh new streams ever on the way to the She-Wolf's city!

And Norna Gest nodded in his wise beard; it was his consolation that the seed which he had helped to sow in this happy garden would prove the forerunner of what later ages possibly might bring to fulfilment: the union of beauty-worship and feeling, the nuptials of Antiquity and the young nations of the North.

Cheiron and Vedis stayed by the Tiber. But Norna Gest would not linger when they bade him, he never stayed long; and one day he took leave of them, he was setting out on a journey; they watched his back as he slowly dipped his paddle and glided with the stream down the Tiber, past Rome and to seaward.

Christopher Columbus

PRELIMINARIES

CHRISTOPHER COLUMBUS CAME FROM GENOA, A LIGURIAN *by birth, but we shall understand the roots of his nature if we regard him as a descendant of the Longobards, of people who had moved from Lombardy to the coast.*

From what we know of Columbus he was of Northern type, fair-haired and freckled, with blue eyes, the stamp familiar in the North among skippers and farmers. The immediately preceding generations of his family were established in the mountains above Genoa, their last stage on the way to the sea; peasants who through handicraft and contact with the port became seafarers. The great Migrations had brought their ancestors from forgotten shores by the Baltic, straight through the countries of the Old World and all the turbulent centuries of the Middle Ages, as far as the Mediterranean — now Columbus was to carry the migration farther. The history of the Longobards, then, is the history of Columbus's past; in his blood, though the origin is forgotten, he inherits profound and powerful promptings from wandering forefathers.

But his spiritual garb is another. Christianity in the literal adaptation of the peasant had replaced the traditions of his race long before he was born, and had become a part of his race's nature. His father, an ordinary craftsman, named him after Saint Christopher, a common thing in those days with pious folk who looked to a patron they could understand, flesh of their flesh, and gladly committed their children to his protection. Everybody was called Christopher, but Colum-

bus when at the summit of his responsibilities felt convinced of his successorship to the carrier of Christ. Therefore the legend of Saint Christopher in its natural interpretation, Christianity accepted in primitive fashion, belongs to the antecedents which went to form Columbus, it contains the taste of the race.

His feeling Columbus derived from early impressions of the Gothic, which is the form under which Northern peoples have adopted the spirit of Christianity. It was an intensity of thought, which was rooted in the Northerner's memories and extended them beyond the finite, that created the pagan-christian myth of God's mother. In its nature the myth is purely Northern; the name is all the Holy Virgin has left of her biblical origin. Christianity demanded soul, adoration, of the pagan, and he gave what he had to give, what to him was sacred, Woman as Virgin and Mother. He centred his religion upon a beautiful ancient devotion to Woman, and in her honour his imagination refashioned his Forest and his Ship into a Cathedral. Columbus was a child of the Gothic; we must seek its genesis if we would know how his nature came about; we must go backward in the youth of the race to the prototype of the myth of God's Mother, the heart of the Gothic. Columbus inherited it in the form of universal longing: the eternal feminine; the Holy Virgin was the woman in his life. Santa Maria was the name of his ship.

Forces which point back to lost elements in his origin, but whose tendency was influenced from elsewhere, directed Columbus onward in search of a world he was never to find.

Deep-lying Northern instincts were crossed and dominated by surface currents from the world that had shaped his con-

sciousness, the Southerner's world, the local stamp, the stamp of his time; he behaved now as an Italian, now as a Spaniard, always as a Christian; an inner illusory world stood between him and Nature, which he still regarded with the prejudiced eyes of his day, several realities one within another, like the heavens of that age, and all of them fairly independent of experience, in conformity with the contemporary imago mundi *— and yet Columbus went clean through all imaginary realities and came out with a new one.*

Pure and monumental was that quality in him which made this possible: courage, a complete dauntlessness which he had received as a heritage from ancestors who were conquerors and colonists and to generations of whom uncertainty and playing for high stakes had become the very form of their existence. Courage and endurance, the sailor's daring, inflexibility of purpose, are the clean line which runs through Columbus's character as a discoverer. He was a sportsman, and he was a man of genius, his motives rose superior to his age; where he regarded his voyage as a mission the elements were at work within him, he pressed on as though the whole of human nature had been pressing upon him.

Personally, on the other hand, as an individual, such as his bringing-up and his circumstances had made him, he gave proof of a mixture of qualities, magnificence and pettiness which are difficult to reconcile, prophetic vision and a weakness in direct judgment, a certain dizziness in his capabilities; in spite of the broad lines of his character he was not always magnanimous, even judged by his own age, but made moan when others stronger than himself treated him unjustly; he was not able to keep his name clear of querulousness. His plans were worthy of a king, but it seemed as if some never-redeemed inheritance held him bound to earth. He had land-hunger and an eye to business, but on a large scale, like the conquerors and freebooters of whose race he came; the Longobard would go far when it was a question of acquiring and retaining possessions. As a born founder of kingdoms Columbus approached the sovereigns in whose service he made his great land-take naturally, as an equal, with an empire in his hand and a dynasty in his head — and what other rank had they but that of being the topshoot of a race that had begun as conquerors and husbandmen? Later, of course, he proved no match for the crowned heads; his ancestry had no long line practised in holding what they had won. Like most sailors Columbus had a rather clumsy gait ashore; he was more himself as the free skipper on his deck than as the decorated Admiral at court. Who was there that could honour him? As colonist on the grand scale he had his own rank, but he submitted to that of others.

Christopher Columbus, as by virtue of his nature and his surroundings he was compelled to develop, may be taken as the type of that flaring up of the faculties and that profound bewilderment which mark the Northerner when he is transferred to the South.

Viewed from the outside as a spectacle Columbus's career is a play which does not resemble any of the current forms of art but has features derived from them all — the romance, the drama, the comedy; it is at once fantastic, tragic and sometimes almost laughable, melodious and discordant at the same time. He begins as an everyday man, the most ordinary of epics, which in fact has remained unwritten; he then takes on prodigious dimensions, painfully true the whole of it and yet on a closer view theatrical, a stage-world of fable and delusion;

and he ends as the disappointed man, with something of the pitiless Nemesis of comedy rattling about his ears. The very action of his great piece develops as a farce; he is let loose as in blindman's buff between two continents and actually blunders into one of them, but has no idea which it is and never finds out. And he dies off the stage, almost like a scene-shifter whose fall nobody notices, while the play goes on without him with new figures and mighty new acts upon the stage. The ill-treatment to which he is subjected belongs to his part as clown of the piece, although he is its author. Everybody is amused, without thinking that even the clown has his feelings; afterwards they reconstruct his sufferings and are severe on his tormentors, martyrdom and halo awarded by the same public; first cruel, then crawling before his name — hasn't the public always been the same? But such as Columbus was, with his fine craving, his failings, we love him as the great lost child he was, our brother.

It was only for posterity that the figure of Columbus rose again and became a myth. No authentic portrait of him has come down to us. The idealized picture that has been formed of the voyager, as we know it from the accepted type of his monuments, hits off some features correctly, a Northern head, but is weaker and more pompous than the essentially popular class he really represents. It is characteristic of Columbus's true portrait that he hides his face from history and is his race; a real description of him must deal with that race.

Only he in whom the past is stowed is freighted for the future. Columbus grows with the bearing of his exploit; we see, however, looking backward, that history passed through his heart. As he stands, he bears a bridge which joins widely separated worlds and epochs. He sets up a boundary between illusion and reality, not by what he thought but by what he was and what his passion gave an impulse to.

In a strange, tragic and grandiose way a magnificent error coincides in his destiny with total disillusionment, which nevertheless proves fruitful; he leads the way through to a new reality though he loses himself. He is the most disappointed man in history:

> *For when he found the saving isle*
> *Gone was his dream.*
> *A world arose to sever him*
> *From the uttermost stream.*
> *Then grew thy heart's great longing,*
> *Conqueror in defeat returning,*
> *And bore, like the billow's burden,*
> *The world's eternal yearning.*

Columbus completes the Northern migration and at the same time renders Christianity impossible as a terrestrial dream. The Kingdom of Heaven he sought was the Bible's mystical abode, Paradise; but then he sought it on earth. He knew not that it was rooted in his nature. He sails for the Indies, means Paradise, and finds the New World — doesn't it look as if the Almighty, or Somebody not so good, was playing a game with him? And yet he makes the discovery!

In the person of Columbus the pagan yearning for Nature unites with Christianity's fata Morgana — and they perish together! It might be said that Columbus, regarded as the hero of a tragedy of destiny in which the elements are too strong for him, is the first modern man, the first god-forsaken figure; he substitutes space and reality for the spiritual prison and the superstition of the Middle Ages. But the modern age is founded upon acquisitions which came after him; other brains with trained qualifications he did not possess shattered the imago he believed in and enlarged the world; he had brought it within range of vision but himself died unenlightened.

We must therefore look on him as a man of his time, such as heredity and experience had made him; we must see what he saw with the eyes he had, as an adventurer, a visionary, a gambler and a victim, with his brief glory and long renown, as skipper of the caravel which bore him with the rest of its medieval cargo — and which stranded upon that coast where he knocked and knocked and was not to be admitted. But his achievement points to the ancestry behind him, and when it passes into other hands, and he is forgotten, it is nevertheless he who is its protagonist.

What remains, however, the real event in his life is the oldest and most universally human of all, what we all sail for and bring home, the loss of hope:

> *Christopher Columbus, thy silver hair,*
> *Frosting thy poll,*
> *Crowns the sea-chilled viking brow*
> *And the wreck of thy soul.*
> *Thou gav'st us back Earth and didst enter*
> *Immortality's murmurous seeming.*
> *Now covers thy mighty shadow*
> *The ne'er-reached goal of thy dreaming.*

The voyages of discovery, which were the work of many, are inevitably connected with Columbus as their central figure. And of all the discoverers he was in fact the one who was governed to the widest extent by the idea of discovery.

When the world had become known in its entirety, more or less, and America had been added as another continent, a conception grew up and spread among seamen, spontaneously and vaguely as is the way of popular legends, of a skipper who might be met with at sea, a phantom in a phantom ship: the Flying Dutchman.

It is as though the old Northern roving impulse, made homeless when all seas had been sailed, and the earth circumnavigated many times, had passed into a myth, a voyage which can never end, the skipper who cannot die. Right in substance but fortuitous in form, the tale of the spectral ship is connected with the name of a Dutch captain, or perhaps we may rather say it hangs in the air — ought it not in reality to be referred to Columbus? It belongs to his myth as its last act. For it is the Santa Maria *that is the phantom ship, Columbus is the restless skipper-soul who is condemned to sail the seas until the Day of Judgment.*

> *Unblest is he whose aching desire*
> *Can never die.*
> *The ocean swell so drear and waste*
> *Goes heaving by.*
> *There stands the fettered skipper, steering*
> *His ship of spectres weary*
> *Under the pallid moonbeams,*
> *In the ocean swell so dreary.*

This spectre is the heavily laden, non-existent but terribly real phantom ship which we call history, the memory of mankind.

Of this ship Columbus is captain. A numerous crew sails with him, lesser and better men than he, seekers and strivers, who are all condemned to continue their lives in an image; as the one who lost most and gained most he is captain of the Dead.

In this vessel we are now to sail.

BOOK ONE: THE CATHEDRAL

I

UNDER YGDRASIL

Some time in the Iron Age it chanced that a hunter lost his way in the forest while pursuing a deer, and reached a tract where he had never been before.

When at last he had brought down the deer and was sitting on it to rest, still angry from the exertion the hunt had cost him, he noticed that the trees here were strikingly bigger and mightier than anywhere he knew — nothing but lofty stems and airy tops, with only a carpet of herbage below, neither brushwood nor swamp as in other places; the spot where they grew stood higher than the surrounding land, like a raised floor, lifting a grove of tall trees up above the roof of the forest like a dome; it seemed a Thing-stead where the giants of the forest had assembled to take counsel together.

The huge slender trunks united their foliage high high up to form a spreading tent of leaves which shut out the sky but not the light; green, cool, resonant halls where sound carried so that the twittering of a single finch made quite a din, as though its tone swelled here of itself. The slightest sound was repeated and multiplied under the leafy vaults: echo, the voice of solitude; here was perfect solitude.

It was many leagues within the forest; from the high place under the big trees you could look over endless silent stretches of wood, dense forest and glades about watercourses and lakes, and again woods and woods, as far as the eye could reach, on three sides; but on the fourth there was a view of a great river which swung in a long bend with one bank against the foot of the rise, as though it had a message to bring; it was a broad, rapid river with a deep bed, which hurried along and raised eddies on its surface as it went; on both banks it was enclosed by virgin forest; only an opening here and there in the sedges showed where the beasts had trampled paths to ancient watering-places along the river. It flowed through the woods from a distant region where blue outlines showed that there were mountains, and it ran on through the lowlands to the horizon on the other side. The hunter's prac- tised eye noted ospreys above the eddies; there were good days to be had with a line, as a change from hunting, if one lived here.

In a cleft on the slope below the trees the weeds grew knee- high, there was a hidden spring; the hunter pressed the back of his hand down into the soaking cushion of moss till it filled with clear water, and slaked his thirst; then he returned to the deer he had brought down, cut his arrows out and began to flay the big, heavy beast, with his knife now in his hand, now in his mouth, working with his knuckles between hide and carcass first on one flank and then, as he took the beast by the horns and turned it over, on the other, till the hide was off. When this was done he quartered the carcass and hung the pieces up on the nearest tree. The frontal bone and antlers he cut out and set up on a bough, for that belonged to the spirits of the place. Then he straightened himself and wiped his greasy hands on the back of his breeches, unrolled a leather pouch and took out a scrap of tinder which he placed on his flint between thumb and forefinger, then drew the steel along the sharp edge of the flint; sparks flew out between his hands, brighter even than the daylight, and at once a glowing spot in the touchwood began to smoke; he knelt and blew gently upon the glow, raking dry leaves together with one hand and bending quite low with his face to the ground; smoke curled up- ward about his head, he made a nest of his hands and nursed it, until at last he rose and at the same instant a flame licked up the heap of leaves. Not long after he had a fire. Then he sharpened a stick with his hunting knife and roasted kidneys on it over the fire, ate and chewed and went to the spring for a sip of water, all in profound silence, which was nothing strange since he was alone.

In a tree close by there was a hole left by a fallen branch, and in it lived a starling; at intervals it came out of its door and flew away, and after a little while it returned with several worms packed together in its beak and flew in a straight line into its hole, like an arrow aimed from a distance at a mark; and when it had disappeared a feeble smothered cheeping could be heard from the hollow in the tree.

Now and then the hunter's eyes wandered as he absently ate, swallowing big lumps at a time; the wood was alive around him and he knew it, he was one with it, saw the squirrel steal into a tree spreading its legs out on the vertical bark with tail erect, now behind the trunk and now back again on a fork higher up; he saw it as the brisk little red creature it was, until it disappeared among the foliage and other things attracted his attention. The forest attended to its affairs, like a great calm business in which everything got done by all concerned, in silence and away from each other. Far off, as though behind many partitions, the wood-pecker was heard beating his tattoo on a sonorous dead branch; high up, from the secret chambers of the sunny tree-tops, from the sweet green light itself, came the thick cooing of the wood-pigeons, a mother full to the throat with happiness. The finch called now and again, making a great noise for such a little crea-ture and rousing echoes in the wood; it had its nest and was as happy as a horse, though it was so small that the least twig could support it. The flies buzzed and excited themselves, spinning wildly in a wheel in the midday fires, and one would fall on a leaf and whiz around on its back, quite dizzy; the sun made the thing bewildered.

The cry of a bird of prey was heard above the tree-tops; down below there was a sniffing under the bushes, and the hunter shrank together as he sat, stopped munching in the middle of a bite: it was the badger come out in the middle of the day with two half-grown young ones, striped in the face and powerful of body; she was out teaching her young to root; she turned the earth with her paw and sniffed, and the young ones turned the earth with their paws and sniffed; but the hunter began to chew again: it was not the time of year, their skins could stay on till another opportunity.

When the hunter had finished his meal he looked up at the sky and guessed what time of day it was — something after midday, ladders of haze leaned steeply down from the tree-tops into the shadow, the wood was very still, with only a busy hum of flies and the cry of a buzzard above the tree-tops. The hunter yawned and worked his jaw, shook his head; he had been on the trail since before sunrise and all the long forenoon, running almost uninterruptedly in a straight line the whole time, so who could tell where he was now? And now he would have to go all that long way back — how long he did not know. But the food and the strong smell of the fire had made him sleepy; he yawned again and shivered and lay down to take a nap on the grass by the side of the fire.

When he awoke it was late. He jumped up.

The wood had filled with dusk which poured in among the roots of the trees and rose nearly to their leaves, but the sunlight still came through. It had come on to blow a little, and the leaves above were in motion and shook blue glimpses of the sky and green and red and yellow patches of light together; in the west a purple glow behind the trunks showed how low the sun had sunk. Other birds than before were heard now, and they had made for the topmost twigs, where they mingled their long, flute-like, questioning notes with the vanishing twilight. Down in the depths of the wood all was dark and still.

The hunter knew that he would have to carry a big load of meat many leagues through pathless forest before reaching human habitations; he had overslept himself, and saw with uneasiness that he would have to spend the night in the open. He quickly decided to stay where he was, rather than halt at some other place down in the dense swampy woods, and while it was yet light he looked about among the big trees for a comfortable fork between two branches where he could ride out the night in safety, even if there was not much chance of sleep. When he had found what he wanted, he laid more fuel on the fire and collected dead wood, getting ready for the night as a man does on such occasions; but he was uneasy. He dragged up big fallen branches so as to have more than enough, sweating and making a noise; he made a sort of attempt to sing, but broke off again. And when he had made ready for the night he kept quite quiet. In the fading sky the moon came out and began to gain power; he dropped his eyes before it, the sky was over him, he could not hide from it.

And gradually as the sun sank, the forest became strangely sombre and stiff, cold blasts from it struck upon the hunter, making him shiver beside the fire, for there was a life in the draught which touched him to the marrow. The air grew thick with all kinds of dumb things that gathered therein. The fire and the darkness augmented each other — the more light the fire gave, the blacker looked the wood. Soon the hunter found himself in a sort of cave of light, where only the nearest tree-trunks stared in the gleam; beyond was thick darkness, the ancient black evil Night.

He looked up, and his soul received a shock, for there were the stars: he was, as it were, in the centre of an immense cave with starry walls, the big familiar constellations stood out over his head — the Great Bear wheeling upon its own length, Orion blustering in the sky, the Pleiads flickering in the wind of eternity, now clearing their stars, now shrouding them in luminous haze, the Milky Way above them all, whose soul is giddiness; radiant and dumb as ever were the stars, with a gaze not to be sustained, the sky full of eyes, all the stars blinking, and between them space with its solemn deep-blue voice; fearful was the starry heaven, and the hunter was abashed before it and bent his neck, shook himself, rubbing his numbed hands together; he was but a poor hunter.

His eyes dropped from one marvel to another, but with this one he was familiar — the world of fire. He looked into his fire and blinked his dazzled eyes, comforted as though by a caress; the fire licked and shot up a flame, it was his friend. And, without giving it a thought, he fetched the entrails of the deer and flung them on the fire. For a moment they almost overcame it: the fire turned black and gasped for breath, the clammy guts and their contents threatened to smother it; but soon the flames grew about them on every side and began to feed upon the entrails as they became charred; the fire puffed strangely and gave off fat worms of smoke, running over the shrivelled skin in many colours before the flame found a place where it could bite and fix itself.

Long and deliciously the fire gave off its fumes, with little cracks, scorching and blistering and feasting itself, and long the hunter sat with dazzled eyes which now saw nothing when he turned them from the fire, sunk in deep thought, fascinated by the fire and what was going on within it, where he divined an infinity before which he humbled himself in his heart.

Then the hunter heard footsteps. He seized his long ash bow, rose and turned a terrible face to the darkness — fear and a mortal challenge together. The footsteps ceased, and then he was aware of a sound of wailing close at hand, the very note of terror; he gave a violent start, and with a roar drew his bow to the arrow-tip;

there was another wail, with more fear in it, and then his eye suddenly fell on a figure that had come into the light of the fire, a vision that had appeared out of nothing, a human figure, a woman; she sat down at once when she knew that he had seen her, and stayed sitting with her feet on the grass. The great arrow with its iron point would have gone clean through an ox at such short range, and she expected it; but then the hunter blew the breath violently from his nostrils, transferred bow and arrow to his left hand and went up to her, relieved of a nameless terror. She rolled over on her back with limbs in the air as he approached, exposed her stomach to ingratiate herself and made painful barking sounds as in a bad dream, whimpering appealingly, unable to defend herself or fly.

It was a woman, quite a young one, who also must have lost her way in the forest and had followed the light of the fire. They were unknown to each other; she belonged to another people and could not say much for herself, but it did not take many words to bring them together; and soon after the strange girl was sitting very confidingly and seriously by the fire, preparing venison for supper.

It was a good thing they had met. When people have lost their way and have to stay out at night it is a misfortune to be alone. Now that they were two the hunter gave the starry sky a casual glance and let fall a remark about its being a clear evening, didn't she think? They turned their backs upon the world, except the hearth and the spit, made a hearty supper and then thought of going to rest, there was nothing to stay up for.

The forest is always the home of the accursed when it is dark, the owl hoots in a lofty tree so that the woods ring again; it goes to one's very marrow even if one knows it is the owl. "Grou, grou," says a beaky noise just above the tree-tops, and a strident beating of wings is heard, rising and dying away again in an instant: wild duck, or something much worse; why else should it give one such creeps down the back?

A ghastly white light begins to haunt the tree-tops; it is the moon, that spectre of the skies. Far away there are shrill cries and answering cries among the slopes from one knows not what horror; a bent bough on a tree near by broods like a black and twisted dragon against the nocturnal sky; every visible shape crouches to become a great monster with horns and snout.

Even the breeze from the dark woods is unbearable upon one's neck, one feels that there are great ringed eyes in the air behind one's back, and now the best thing to do is to hide, a couple of little humans chilled by the dew, who are heavy-hearted and hold each other by the neck; and that is what they did, these two — lay down and pulled the fresh deerskin right up over their heads with the raw side out for all the ghostly things to bite at. They were in their own cosy darkness now and lost themselves in it, while the fire burned down and the moon advanced over the tree-tops out into the floating nocturnal sky, across which it was to travel before day came again.

The finch's call and an airy chorus of rooks in the lofty trees waked them; the light, the day, a lovely sunny spring morning; the great shining trees stretched down green arms to them; she sat up and shook the deerskin from her head, awake at once, and uttered a joyful cry.

But as the hunter opened his eyes he looked straight into a marvel, the sunrise appearing at the roots of the woods between the trees like a mighty rose of light, leaves, sky and sun merged in a radiant ring of green, blue and purple, the world dissolved in colour! As a sea of blood he had seen the sun go down the evening before, on the other side of the forest, a rose of coloured fire as now, all the refracted colours of light in which the sun, the woods and the day were merged and sank — and now this vision! It was to be bound up for ever with an awakening, a dawn in his stern hunter's soul, which understood what a gift the night had given him and at the same time made it inconceivable, a glory in the soul of boundless dreams he had had and could not remember, the reflection of another existence which had been near to him. As though petrified in the middle of a gesture, seized by a thought which made all else stand still within him, he looked out into the dawn; his very breath was checked, so immersed was he in an inner world though without being able to realize it, a lost memory.

They stayed together, the two whom the night had joined. Neither of them ever took the homeward path; they settled on the spot as a free hunter's household in the midst of the kindly woods, and in summer their life was easy. Neither of them was aware of time.

For the winter they made themselves snug in an underground dwelling without ever once feeling the want of human society.

The woods took the place of friends; they loved the grove with its tall friendly trees because there they had found each other. Beyond that she had no world at all but him, and he had his own.

Once in the course of the summer the hunter saw four ships on the river, long black craft with a multitude of oars which all moved together like a loom; slowly they fought their way up stream, in sight for a whole day before they vanished in a bend of the river towards the mountains; long-handled axes were raised with a backward lean along the ships, like vipers stretching their necks to strike, and the regular chunk of the oars against the timber was heard hour after hour as the crews obstinately worked their way against the stream. They had come up from the lower reaches of the river, no doubt from the sea, and whither were they bound? The hunter never saw them return.

Occasionally he saw men over on the other side of the river, people who came out of the woods shading their eyes with their hands from the southern sun; but they could not cross here and withdrew into the forest to find other ways.

With the exception of these signs of an outer world, the hunter and his woman lived undisturbed on the lonely wooded hill by the river.

But as early as the end of the summer there were unmistakable signs that the girl was to become a mother — from eating raspberries, as she supposed in her own mind. They had eaten raspberries together in the woods, and as the new being had made itself felt at the same time it was natural to conclude that that might be the cause; she ate herself quite big, and then it came, and big she remained. She gave birth to the child in the middle of winter and wrapped it in kid's skin against the cold.

It was a warm and wet, pink, naked little thing, which as soon as it was born chirped like a bird and had little closed hands, and nails like buds on trees, tiny little twisted ears and new-born hair like sunshine, eyes like the hazy blue sky and a sorrowful mouth which immediately sought and sought and fell to on Mother's breast.

A nasty storm had swept through the low dwelling in the ground, where the mother had screamed as though some unknown cruel beast had been there, but now all was still, the little boy's babbling sounded like the song of birds on the first warm night of spring, when the great storms that tear the ice from the shore and break the trees of the forest have blown themselves out.

And the first he saw of the world was the spring. She carried him out for the first time when the trees had burst into leaf, and in speechless joy showed his blue eyes to the sky and his hair to the sun and his hands to the new-born leaves on the blessed green beeches.

Without any doubt it was a splendid and wonderful child, a little baby god, a son of the sky and the sun and the woods, that the ecstatically happy mother had brought into the world.

But the hunter who had become a father was enraptured with his partner and his springtime child.

She sat out in the open, now that it was warm, on the slope under the big trees, which flamed like calm green fires in the sun of May, just where they had met a year before; and in her arms she held her son, a thirsty son who gurgled at his work and let the milk run out of his nose in two streams when he could not swallow it all at once. He lay on his mother's knee simply stiff with overnourishment, with his fat, bare feet, each with five rosy toes, pointing in different directions; and when his mouth ran over and he began to choke his mother lifted him with laughter and admiration high in the air and shook him to let the food settle down, so that there might be room for more. Sweet was the scent of the two, and delicious was the fragrance of the still wet leaves on the tall shining beeches. And with the baby in her arms and a dream of happiness on her sweet flushing face the mother followed the starling, that black glistening bird which slipped in and out of the hollow tree with worms in its beak for its nestlings within.

When the hunter was not in the woods or by the river supplying the needs of the family, he was at home, busily building a new, real house. He worked and chipped at the wood and was always beginning again on a grander scale, he had visions of something magnificent and well thought out: a speaking house, he imagined, with images on the posts, which should make manifest his joy and form a precious shrine for the mother and her little god.

Up on the mound among the trees the hunter had a secret, secluded place of prayer which he used to visit alone — nothing but a heap of stones on the ground, on which he made a fire for the Powers when he gave them a share of his quarry; here he cut up the deer and hung them on the trees, and it answered very well;

here he left a bit on one side for the badger who had his hole on the slope and was no ordinary badger — he lived in the ground underneath one, and it was as well to be on good terms with him; and every year at the solstices the hunter made ceremonies for the Powers, quite privately between himself and them. He made burnt offerings for the return and perpetuity of all things, walking cautiously about and mumbling a good deal with his lips — prayers by the look of it, but some part was strong language he had learnt, which he hoped might work upon the Powers and bind them even against their will — for one's position was not altogether a comfortable one in dealing with beings so much stronger than one's self.

But latterly he had got out of the way of appealing to them in the open air; the hunter was more occupied with his house and what it was to shut out, and with the glory and perfection which it was to shelter like a little improved world.

The hunter was becoming more and more of a carpenter. He worked and built all through the summer, and in winter he pondered over his images and shaped them in wood, at times so absent that he might gaze long at his dear ones without seeing them, entirely lost in his visions.

But the two were always about him, giving food for his work; he heard their voices, and he heard the neighbouring spring and the song of birds in the trees as one and the same music, while his thoughts were budding and his hands were shaping. He heard the mother singing, a wordless cooing from the heart which she had learnt from the wood-pigeons; she took the child's feet in her mouth and pretended to eat them, making him laugh so that his little chest clucked; she called him by pet names of her own invention. "My morsel," she would say, with heartfelt emotion, as she played with him; "my sweetest little knucklebone; my darling, darling little dick!" This meant "bird" in the wonder's own language which he was beginning to invent for the wonders about him as he tried to catch them in his hands, stammering expressions for what he wanted, and they were the foundation of an entirely new little language in the forest.

And when his mother had got the wonder dressed she put him out on her knees as on a promontory so that the world might see him, and he it, and made a fortification around his little defenceless body with her sweet, big girlish hands. All the flowers stretched themselves on their stalks among the grass to make a show for him about the place where the two were sitting, the trees shed fragrance upon them, the birds came out on the farthest twigs and chanted a triumphal chorus over this forest picture of childhood. The mother herself sang songs of joy over her miracle, without words, inarticulate hymns of praise that gushed from her throat and woke echoes in the woods as of an enchanted source, a source with the voice of a girl. She was so loving and so full of laughter.

And tender songs of praise and great joy resounded from the hunter's house when at last he got it finished and lodged the two within. It was as though the house, standing by itself in the forest, gave out music; it sang in the midst of the wood, the whole house sang with the happiness concealed within it.

It was built with walls of upright timbers, like a palisade, very firm, which was the first consideration, but with a riot of decoration and with meaning in its plan and all its details. From the lofty gables dragons gaped towards the four quarters of the heavens; above them, still higher up, four more; for upon the roof over the smoke-hole rode a lofty, slender castle, and above it again was a spire which ended skywards in a pole with a vane, and here the cock crowed, always *against* the wind by which it turned; it stood on guard up in the airy regions, and the first gleam of sunrise fell upon its comb. The dragons on the roof were, of course, to keep evil spirits away from the house; besides them the skulls of deer and other game were set up on the sods of the roof, with the double intention of scaring and providing a good hunting memory. Above the door the hunter set up the antlers of the first deer he had brought down in this place; for it was the very entrance to his happiness, the deer had brought him here.

The door was at one end of the house, the plan of which was an oval, and the doorposts rose high above the eaves; they were two whole straight stems; each of them had meant the destruction of an oak, but they had risen again in a higher form, carved all over with the most beautiful sinuosities of oak-leaves and terminating above in a great ornamental acorn.

The door itself was a single oaken plank — an old tree had gone to make it; it had two round panels for the sun and moon, filled with carvings and circles in every conceivable pattern.

The whole exterior of the house was to be a symbol of night, terror and counter terror: the four cornerstones which supported the house were four crouching monsters which were here bound and made to do good much against their will; the dragons explained themselves, they were the personification of Nature's terrors. At a little distance the house really looked like a hideous nest of serpents with the heads of the whole brood raised in rapacity; it was a powerful outside to turn towards the night, for with evil must evil be expelled.

But the inside of the house represented the ash Ygdrasil. Of course, it was a room, and the meaning of all the carvings and embellishments was not apparent at first glance, and yet all the imagery of the forest and the ash Ygdrasil was present. From the middle of the floor rose the great pillar which supported the whole building and the topmost point of which formed the spire; it was a mast, an old fir, perfectly straight but twisted many times about itself in the wood, as though while growing it had turned to follow a heavenly body; it formed the stem, the carvings in the roof and round all the walls were the branches and foliage of the world-tree.

It was like being in a transformed forest, foliage above and below, and in the branching patterns the deer moved with his branching crown intermingled with the crowns of the trees, one could scarcely tell which was tree and which was deer; high up in the top of the world-tree sat the eagle, the far-seeing one, and between its brows a hawk, one bird of prey crowning another; the squirrel hid and appeared downward among the branches like a weaver's shuttle, Ratatosk running with his news up and down the ash Ygdrasil between the eagle and Nidhug, the dragon of Time, who lay under the roots of Ygdrasil devouring them. Ginnungegap was there, below another root of the world-tree, a frozen hole in the earth wherein frost giants brooded with their heads between their knees; Mimi's well was shown, with Odin's eye which he gave as a pledge for a draught of wisdom; Urd's well, and the Norns taking water and mud from the spring to heal the world-tree of the gnawing in its root and top. If you looked up again, there was the rainbow overhead and great constellations, the eternal stars of heaven depicted; and again foliage, great plaited tents where the leaves were birds and the birds leaves. But at the top, in the middle of the roof, where the window was, the light fell in;

you could not see the sky itself but the dim light that came through the smoke-hole, light from above met smoke and the gleam of the fire from below; the daylight above changed with the time of day, paled and took fire again, like a coloured, translucent and veiled halo over the room.

Such was the house of images the hunter-carpenter had raised, that he might give back his soul to what had produced it.

Most of it was still in the rough, not all carried out as he saw it in his mind; far from it, there was work enough for years to come — and already an entirely new plan was dawning in his head, to begin all over again, in a new, wider, still more eloquent style.

Then it chanced that one day the hunter was again pursuing a deer which would not let itself be taken, and which led him farther and farther away, until at last he no longer knew where he was.

The chase and the speed of it excited him so far beyond all bounds that he ceased to be human, he was nothing but passion; in his heat he took no note of anything, and nothing could stop him until he had overtaken the deer and brought it down. He was a hunter who had never suffered any game to beat him, either in endurance, sagacity or strength.

But this was a most extraordinarily powerful stag, it seemed. The hunter was used to finding stags swifter than he was, much swifter of course, to begin with, but not in the long run: their wind was broken before he was exhausted, they spent themselves in one terrified rush after another, while he followed the trail in a steady, persistent trot. The moment was bound to come, even if it took days, when the deer could no longer rise when he came up to it with his hunting-knife. This stag, however, showed not the slightest sign of weariness, it galloped as swiftly every time he started it, and every time it seemed to have grown, to be gliding away ahead of him as though on air, a mighty royal stag with antlers that seemed rather to lift it and bear it than to weigh it down. And as the hunter did not give up — for he had never yet turned back without his quarry — the stag went on soaring ahead with the hunter on its trail, as though he had never done anything but hunt that stag and was never destined to do anything else.

At night he slept on the ground without a fire, with his head in his arms, speechless from fatigue, and every morning he felt less rested, when again he took up the trail and followed it till he had started the stag, to run after it throughout the day.

And as he ran the forest behaved strangely; it was summer when the hunt began, but when he looked about him the trees were bare and he shivered with cold; and then again the woods were green and he was too hot, and this repeated itself he knew not how many times; but he did not let it trouble him.

At last the stag actually did stop. It was at night, for now the hunter was pursuing it in the dark as well as by day; it could not hide, for there was no more forest, they had come out into bare country beyond the inhabited world, a distant, gloomy region where skeletons of dead beasts were seen everywhere upon the ground, great piles of bones; it was evidently the place where all the beasts come when they go away to die. Over this ground the stag soared, and now it could be seen that it did not touch the earth in its flight; but the hunter himself had a sensation as though he was in the air and moved more by the power of his soul than by running.

The plain of the dead beasts ended in an immense cliff which extended on both sides as far as the eye could reach, and below the cliff yawned empty space, sheer black nothingness, the abyss or the place the night comes from; whatever it was, there was no going any farther. The stag stopped on the extreme brink of the abyss and stood against the sky in its full height with its mighty antlers raised, looking like a mountain, with its shoulder exposed. Now an arrow could reach it, and the hunter ground his teeth and shot.

Even while the arrow was in the air he saw the stag rise high above the earth and turn to fire; it galloped to the sky in a flash of flame, and as it mounted higher and higher its light waned and became a group of sparks, revolved once upon itself — and stood still in the firmament!

And then the hunter saw that what he had shot at, believing it to be a stag, was a constellation. He knew it perfectly well, had always known it; seeing it made him feel a child again. But how cold he turned! The starry sky swung above him like a fearful wheel, and a jet of air from eternity struck him to the marrow. He perceived that he was at the world's end, and that it was Time itself he had been hunting. Then the awe of death came upon him.

His hunter's rage had left him, he remembered the mother and the child, turned and began to walk towards home.

A hundred years had passed when at last he came back to the place he had left. Light of foot, with a flying arrow to lead his yearning, he had run from home; he came back staff in hand and swaying like an old old man.

He found the place again where he had had his house, but it was greatly changed. There was the small knoll, but the wood was different, though apparently the same; there were only the rotten stumps left of the trees he had known, or nothing at all, and new ones which before had been young saplings in the undergrowth had become old trees. It was another forest; he was now a stranger in his own home.

The spring had dried up; a depression in the slope showed where it had been, to one who remembered it, but it had no water, it had run out long ago. Of the house with the carved posts in which the couple had had their nest and where fabulous beasts had crowed from the roof-beams, there was not the slightest trace — only a little grassy mound, like an old grave, showed the place. It was so still in the wood; the strange lofty trees raised their branches stiff and bare into the winter mist.

The old man sat down on the grave of his house and gathered dead leaves about him as though for a bed. The nest was cold. He found small fragments of charcoal in the grass, the remains of a vanished hearth-fire; they were covered with rime and seemed to wound his hands. The wood was lifeless, it did not even harbour fear, for what had he more to fear? — only loneliness.

The hunter had grown old, but so great a longing did he feel for those he had lost, so near were they to him, though he was never, never to see them again, that he could not die. The memory of his loss could not die, for that was now the only thing he had left; it was stronger than time, and it craved a form.

He built himself a hut in the forest, and when he had as much shelter as a solitary old man needs he began to model in his mind, trying shapes in the air with his hands and familiarizing himself with visions he had; they were to become an image, he would carve an image, it was to be the two as they lived for ever in his soul. And around them as a centre he began to build a house in his mind for eternity, which was to show forth Life and Time, and the forest and the beasts, and the sun, and the underworld, everything that existed, and all that he had possessed and lost and still possessed in memory. Such was the house his craft would build, and in it the Mother and the Child should dwell, risen again and made immortal in an image.

With them he began, they were to be represented in one, two souls in one shape; he imagined the two as they used to sit under the trees, the mother holding her little son before her on her knee so that the whole forest should see him; and he would show how his hair had borrowed its gold from the sun, and how the old trees bowed down before him with their branches.

Alas! when he had finished there was a block of wood which bore the marks of tools and of much labour; there was indeed a hint of a human image in it, but it was neither the two as he saw them in his mind nor the image of them he had intended. It would have to be made over again, from the very beginning. But until he could accomplish that he set up the image in his hut and fed his soul on it, in the memory of the two never-forgotten ones and in the hope of the real and perfect image, of which this only served as a poor outline.

He often sat before it, as he had sat on the grass before the young mother and her child; he sang to it, while the forest outside roared powerfully above his hut, as he had sung to the two, when the forest roared over them and made them small.

In the spring he moved the image out into the open and played before it on a bark flute; it sounded like new-born babes in the woods. And the beasts, with whom the former hunter had made peace, came sniffing up at the sound and stood quite near the hermit to listen.

On one of these spring days, when he had been playing to his memories under the beeches and was in a rapture, his eyes closed.

The aged easily fall into a doze, and their slumbers are short. But one sleep is as long as another. The old hunter nodded; it might have been only an instant, or it might have been a thousand years. And in an enraptured absence such as this his being passed into Time.

II

THE FERRYMAN

(O)NCE more the oaks grew old after the hunter had dwelt by the river, and then another hermit settled there. Like the hunter he was nameless, but he was to acquire a surname by which he afterwards became known to all the world — Christophorus, the bearer of our Lord. He came from the country of the Goths and left his native land some time during the great Migrations and went out into the world, like so many others who were moving from North to South; but it was his fate to halt and to pursue his calling at a station half-way between the two.

From his birth Christophorus was of unusual stature, big beyond all measure and so strong that he had never reached the limit of his strength. But he was gentle, and that was fortunate, for otherwise he might have wrought mischief. No one had seen him angry; that was out of the question, there could be no occasion for it since nothing could avail to irritate him. Even while he was still serving the franklins he was never in a bad temper, as others might be when the cattle strayed or were unruly; if the oxen got out of hand he simply threw them with his bare hands and held them down till they were quiet again, and if a bull-calf was obstinate and would not be tethered he carried it home in his arms. It was said of him that he was slow, but a man with such mighty limbs cannot be expected to move them so quickly as the small and irascible; he was in no hurry, since anyhow he could get more done than the rest.

At first, when he had just come from the woods, he was perfectly stupid and had to learn everything — how to eat from a bowl and bring the spoon out whole when he had shot the food into his mouth; but he never needed to be shown a thing twice.

He was not deficient in judgment; he thought over his position and had an eye for what suited him. For this reason he did not stay at the farm where he served. The man there, quite a good ordinary franklin, set him to clear waste land, and he pulled up trees by the roots, one in each hand, knocking the mould out of the roots, and went off with stones as big as houses; if he had kept on with it he might have cleared enough land for a whole earldom.

But the giant thought it more and more strange that he should serve a weakling, when it ought rather to have been the other way about. He took an opportunity of finding out whether the man considered any one his superior, and discovered that the good man was ready to bow down to several — people he called his gods, Odin, Thor, and a good many besides, some of whom moreover were females. From other sources also the giant got to know that small or middle-sized people liked to pretend to more strength than they possessed by referring to powerful allies they were supposed to have somewhere or other — beings who, however, as they themselves admitted, were invisible to the naked eye. This kind of thing the giant could not take seriously. He did not believe in spirits, not having met any yet, either by night or by day. Once when something stung him and he thought it might be a spirit, such as the others used to talk about if they felt any pain, he caught it between his finger and thumb, but it turned out to be a sheep-tick. Since nothing in his experience pointed in the opposite direction the giant had come to believe exclusively in his own strength. If therefore he was to serve anybody and to be induced to remain in his service, it would have to be some one even mightier than himself.

Besides his gods the master spoke with reverence of the King, the mightiest of all franklins and an actually living person, not just a doubtful thing in the air; the giant's deliberations therefore led to his taking service with the King. However, he had not been there long before he found out that there were even greater kings than he in other realms; and thus it was that the giant went abroad, since his mind was made up that he would serve no lord but him who did not fear anybody or anything in the world.

Now we know from the legend of Christophorus, which is familiar to the whole of Christendom, that he left the mightiest of all kings because on an occasion this King made the sign of the Cross when the Devil was named. Christophorus asked him why he was writing with his finger in the air, and was told that he feared the Devil; and straightway the giant took his leave and entered the service of the Evil One.

But when one day the Prince of Darkness evinced a fear of the Cross and, when asked by the giant why he went out of his way to avoid what was nothing but two pieces of wood, had to confess that he feared him whose sign was a cross, the giant perceived that the Lord of the Cross was the strongest and went out into the world again to find him. As every one acquainted with the legend knows, he did not find the Kingdom of God immediately in so literal a sense as he was inclined to expect; but he was instructed by a hermit, of whom he sought counsel, how in the meantime his deeds might prove acceptable to the mightiest of all Lords. Ordinary Christian exercises the giant rejected as unfitting for him; he would undertake neither fasting nor watching, and prayers were never on his lips, since he was a man of few words. But he was willing to take upon himself a stout piece of man's work, if our Lord would be pleased with that. And then the hermit had found a suitable occupation for him. It consisted in ferrying wayfarers over a great river which otherwise was difficult to cross: one of the aims of this Lord's rule was to bring people nearer to each other; here was a chance for a strong man. And thus it came about that the giant established himself on the river in question and became a ferryman.

Christophorus had now entered upon a service which was to his liking. Although he could not see the Lord he served nor knew where he was, which he felt to be something lacking, he took the word of the man of God for his existence and appreciation of the work that was carried out in his name. This work was sufficiently heavy and seemed to him useful. He preferred to struggle with the great river rather than, as he had done before, with troops of armed men; for in truth the giant had always loathed war, since by the nature of things he had always been left in peace by his fellow-men and was incapable of comprehending the reason of *their* mutual hostility, except in so far as it could be put down to their frailty. On account of their wickedness it seemed to be necessary for all men to go about with stabbing and cutting implements on them; for his part he preferred to be content with a staff to keep unruly people at a distance when they became numerous; it had never given him any satisfaction to perforate or slice up the bodies even of wicked persons.

To conquer the elements, on the other hand, not on some single famous occasion but every day, unnoticed, merely for the sake of doing it, as fishers and husbandmen contend with the weather, was better suited to his inclination. Just as intangible things, emulation and verbosity, all kinds of wordiness, were foreign to this man's nature, so did he abhor renown. With whom should he seek favour? He travelled when there was a reason, but preferred quiet; it did him good to stay in one place, now that he had found employment, while in return the world passed by him from day to day and from year to year.

The river was always on a journey; it came in a great flowing sweep from the forests and the highlands on one side and swung in a broad and mighty curve into the forests and out of sight towards the lowlands and the sea on the other side. Currents and waves dashed together like a procession of wild bulls; whirlpools and great smooth floors of water, which mirrored the sky and the endless woods, passed silently round points of land; the osprey hung over the eddies and dropped like a plummet upon the salmon which shot like lightning in the depths.

In springtime the river was swollen with the thaw on the distant mountains and flooded the woods, plunging thick and muddy and full of green ice that had fallen from the glaciers about its source, and uprooted trees that floated out from the submerged forest; then it was hard to cross and Christophorus had need of all his strength, both when he waded over with a single traveller on his back and when he had more passengers and had to use the ferry-boat.

It was a clumsy great log-boat or raft, which the giant himself had built, mainly with an eye to durability; an uglier craft was not to be found, it looked as if the giant had used his teeth in building it, and so he had. The pole he used was equally unadorned, a tree whose branches he had scraped off. But both answered their purpose. Christophorus used to push the ferry-boat before him into the current while he himself walked behind on the bottom, and if ice or big trees drifted down upon the ferry he pushed them out of the way with his staff.

But if the teeming river was thus always on a journey — not to mention all the traffic of fishers and traders who went up and down it — there was likewise an endless stream of people travelling across it, for the ferry lay just at that point of its course where it cut the great highways upon which the Migrations had now been moving for centuries on the way from North to South, and on which they continued to pass in ever greater numbers; at first scouts and a few scattered bodies of men in ages long past, now whole tribes and hosts at once. It was like a cross-road of the ages, where the course of nature met that of men, one athwart the other.

The river travelled on, and the people travelled on, but Christophorus stayed on the ferry and carried them over. He came to love the place; if he did not understand the symbol of the Cross, he lived and worked after his fashion in the very midst of it, at a cross of which one arm was actually drawn by the inexhaustible sources of nature and the other by the wandering of mankind.

While he dwelt here in the name of a God unknown to him he assisted half the North across the river, one troop after another of Northern peasants on their journey towards the South. They came in families and clans, often the whole population of a district, who had quitted their homes with household goods and cattle, old and young, women and children, each one having a responsibility within the troop, like the ants; from rude warriors who grunted after a murder as if it was a joke and wiped their bloody swords between two fingers, to little girls carrying in their arms the puppies that had been entrusted to them. They came, one swarm, one tidal wave after another, whatever they might call themselves or come to be called later when they had founded kingdoms in the South and made themselves famous; big ruddy peasants all of them, like Christophorus himself and of the same blood, the same hairy freckled folk with eyes blue as the sea, whether they came from the dense inland forests, from the river countries of the Baltic, from its islands, or from the long harsh shores of the North Sea; and they all travelled with the same object, that which had sent as many more of them by the sea way in ships — *they* came overland, for every road must be tried — to get away from the cold marshes of the homeland, away to the South, to the lands of legend and the sun.

III

KING SNOW

ᗷᴀᴅ harvests it was that had driven these husbandmen from their homes in the North, where they belonged. The winters were always severe, but still they could be endured, otherwise nobody would ever have lived in these countries. It was the winters that had made them what they were; they came of Carl's blood, steeled by adversity, and they could stand much; but even hardy folk will revolt when they think the limit has been reached.

The same Power that had formed the root of their being was still over them, but at a distance; in the farthest North lay the ice-sheet, and at times it seemed again to be stretching a cold arm over the countries where once it had been supreme; then the winters were lengthened and the brief summers were barely able to take the frost out of the ground; icebergs were seen in the North Sea, fog and mist hid the sun for half the year. Already these countries were scarcely dry after the great thawing of the ice, with a net of water, lakes and streams in the lowlands among the damp woods and morasses where the arable land was to be found; the earth held the cold under its surface, great floods from the winter sometimes lay through the whole summer, the corn-field became a lake, or the little corn there was never came to maturity.

But if only one of the brief summers failed, it meant shortage in the winter; the crop did not go very far even in good years, and if several bad years succeeded one another there was famine, no corn at all and but little meat, since the cattle could not be kept alive either if the crops failed; the only thing left was hunting, and for that there were too many. That was it, they were too many, another burden; the homesteads overflowed with children who seemed in a moment to become great, greedy swarms; what was to be done with them in time of famine?

King Snow rules in the countries on both sides of the Cattegat; he comes in a seven days' snowstorm and fills the sky, turns night into a grave, and day into a driving twilight with no bounds between morning and evening; the air is snow, the storm is snow and seems to come from every quarter at once, snow pours out of the sky, and snow stands in vertical showers straight up in the air, the earth is buried, snow begets snow and whirls together into drifts, the whole world is like a white fire, but with a disastrous darkness at bottom, and cold; death is in the air. Men turn pale from looking out into the whirling gloom, an all-powerful breathing can be felt, they think they can see him soaring on limbs of the storm, see how the snow comes from under his wings — Odin, King Snow, is abroad!

And when he has finished his game and sends a calm the lands lie buried under snow, snow half-way up the stems in the woods, the earth everywhere hidden, a single white snowfield as far as the land extends, white shores along the Cattegat, white over in Skoane, on both sides of the Sound, Kullen looking like a headland of snow running out into the sea, the isles like isles of snow; and between all the buried coast-lines the sea open and black, reeking with frost, like gall; until the sounds too are closed with ice a fathom thick and the snow smooths out all the countries in one.

The fisherman who is accustomed to sail has to go on his feet and do miner's work with an axe to get down to his water. In the black nights the ice roars from bank to bank, a vast submarine discharge of force; and men in their beds of skins under the ground and under the snow hear the booming and crawl deeper into their skins; it is the sea arching its back under the floor of ice and lifting it; but the sea is bound, and in the echoes from shore to shore Odin laughs with scorn.

The ice stayed till late in the summer, and it was a rainy summer; sometimes the Sound was still full of old ice-floes when autumn and a fresh frost arrived. In such years there was nothing in the cornfields, the cattle grew lean, and hunger began to drive people out of their villages with long hollow cheeks — there would have to be a change.

On the part of the leaders, the chiefs, the wise men who intervened between the people and the Powers, everything was done to get the bad years to stop. There were sacrifices without stint; first they offered cattle and more than they could spare, and when that did no good they offered men, thralls or prisoners they took and hanged up in the wind for the Wanderer, since he seemed to be gruesome enough to demand it; the summer was just as bad.

In one of the districts they then resolved on an unusual thing; here the king and priest himself was sacrificed, as expiator for all the rest, and at the same time the sacrifice was addressed directly to Odin as the Lord of Fire, for it was in that capacity he failed them. And possibly he had been neglected in this way; latterly people had gradually abandoned the funeral pyre and had been giving their dead to the earth in mounds; perhaps the Lord of Fire had felt aggrieved at being deprived of his due. Now they would try to make amends, and if any one was to be sent to him through the fire, the best ought not to be too good. The king himself raised no objection to the decision.

The sacrifice was appointed for the day of the midwinter solstice, as being the solemnity to which the ancients attributed the most importance, and many old customs that had dropped out of use were dug up again for the occasion, in case there might still be some power in them. The need-fire was kindled with great ceremony after all fires had been extinguished on the hearths, so as to have fresh fire and to give the Powers an example for imitation as concerned the heavenly bodies; many other things were tried which some perhaps only half believed in, but if the world, with the wisdom they possessed, was in danger of collapsing, they could only go back and do over again what the ancients had done to keep the universe going.

The solemnity took place on rising ground within the forest, the oldest sanctified place of sacrifice, whose stones had not been moved since the people took possession of the country, and some of the oldest men with long memories were chosen to perform it. Almost the whole population of the district, all the clans, had collected, women of course excluded; all the men were there, the whole host, for they were all under arms; not that they were summoned to war, but the day was a solemn one. Armed franklins on horseback and on foot were mustered about the sacrificial mound and far into the woods.

The invocation of fire was performed in the dark winter morning before sunrise, at the right moment when the sun might be expected, and it was accompanied by all the proper forms. The initiates made fire by friction, and meanwhile the sacrificial animals were slaughtered. They were not good to look upon, the shaggy, bony beasts they had· the blunt men who led them forward were short-spoken and looked as though they thought the cattle might have been better if certain masters had taken more thought for their grazing. When they had a flame and the new fire began to blaze the whole host set itself in motion at a signal sounded by lurs; the lurs brayed sharply in the cold forest, a harsh and joyless blast, and then came the tramp of the host; levy after levy marched in battle-array up over the mound past the sacrificial pyre, in silence, but as though demanding to be called to witness; the mounted men came up troop after troop on lean horses and dipped their lances to the fire, all in silence; only their tramp could be heard, and the dark troops were seen ascending the mound as though the earth brought them forth, one wave after another.

When all had thus appeared before the fire the king was sacrificed. He came forward of himself into the glare of the fire, swelling with contempt, and offered his forehead; he received the blow in the middle of his wrinkled brow and fell backwards into the fire. At the same instant all the men struck their shields with their drawn swords, in a single clash, and a shout of home rose from the whole army at once, a war-cry from a thousand throats that sounded in the forest like a supernaturally loud roar from some beast of prey.

While the act, which moved them all to wrath, was in progress, silence fell again, and in the stillness, only broken by the beating of the flames from the pyre, the old franklin who presided over the sacrifice stood forth and recited the hymn of the day:

> Now mounts the sun
> with brightest beams,
> and Balder's bane
> goes down in blood.
> Hope has returned
> to sea and sky.
> See and behold!
> Fair is the day!
>
> Allfather promised
> this to our fathers:
> That the lean years
> linger not with us.
> Patient the greybeard

suffers the hardships
of wildest winters —
the sun shall return!

Chary of gold
were the Northern Gods,
but they gave yearly
a new-made sun.
Thus the Preserver
is Lord of the slain;
often the noble
went to the pyre.

Praying, the peasant
sows corn on the land;
chary of seed
ne'er reaped a crop.
Fair wind for mead,
and rain for malt!
Only the fool
gives without getting.

Midwinter's moon
gapes like Hel's mouth.
In a sack of darkness
the sun turns again.
Cheerless sing
the children of earth;
Father of fire,
accept our offering!

But the sun did not show itself. It was a cloudy morning with a
closed sky, the daylight had no power, and it snowed as the
host broke up and returned home. Sacrificial banquet there was
none, nobody had the heart to eat. Before evening the embers
were cold and all traces of the offering were buried beneath deep
snow on the ancient place of sacrifice in the woods.

Through the following summer they waited the result, but
when again it brought no crop they saw that it was useless any
longer to expect the Powers to keep the covenant, and so they
denounced it on their side. The gods of the weather were given
no more offerings, Frey's altars were bare. And when spring
came again and brought no kindness, they denounced the country and its spirits, broke down the posts of their high seats, stamped
out the hearth and sought other shores.

Many had already begun to doubt the power of the Powers — did any such exist at all? As for the sun, it turned whether you played tricks with fire for it or not, but it never came any nearer. You had to go nearer to it. Starved and pretty well godless they turned their backs upon a world that had grown old, ripe now to be filled with a new one.

IV

THE LONGOBARDS

THE COUNTRY was not entirely depopulated, it was only the able-bodied men who left, the younger ones with their women-folk and whatever else they wanted to take; there remained behind the oldest and the youngest, who were not fitted for new and adventurous undertakings. The country became quieter when the host was gone, nothing happened, the homesteads were extinguished; it was as though the men had taken Time with them.

Before the departure there had been disagreements as to who should quit the country. For a while the warriors considered that the best way of remedying the distress was to reduce the surplus population; the aged and infirm might let themselves be buried, and the superfluous children should be exposed; the remainder could then live in the country, even without gods. This counsel was opposed by the aged and the children, supported by their mothers, who advised the younger people to emigrate, and this advice was adopted. The host that emigrated and afterwards became famous was called the Longobards, from the long-handled axes the men carried.

The axe reflected their destiny: originally it was a forester's axe with which they felled trees and cleared land; afterwards it also served as a carpenter's axe, good for shipbuilding and the work of a wheelwright; but first and last it was a weapon, and it became one more and more.

They marched overland to the coast, built themselves ships and became seafarers, went ashore on other coasts and became husbandmen again, built ships once more and committed themselves to the sea; until they landed on the south shore of the Baltic whence the great trade routes ran inland into Europe, and then they pushed towards the South overland, lost their seafaring ways and became a caravan folk that trusted in the rolling wheel. It was not exactly a rapid-whirling wheel, but had its ups and downs, a creaking, laborious wheel, but it carried them on. The journey was a slow one; the young generation that had left home with the thought of reaching the goal next day passed on this goal to a new one and stayed behind in the mounds that marked their track; in the end the journey was inherited through so many generations that its origin was almost forgotten and its purpose no longer remained the same.

Travelling, for an army which becomes a nation on the route, takes time and does not always pass in peaceable fashion; wherever you come there are other people in the world whom you have to make terms with or cut through, a life of difficulties; you have to live, and must stop in every place at least long enough for a crop to ripen, if you have a chance of sowing one; in winter no travelling can be done. Sometimes they stayed on, for a century or so, in some place where the pasture was good and the surrounding people amenable, and a number of them settled there for good, since land was what they came for, becoming absorbed in the population and using the axe again for clearing.

But soon there would be too many of them again; another army was formed which built itself waggons; the long slender axes turned their edge to the South, hope had burst forth again, they were on the march!

And it was while they were thus on the march from one station to another that they struck the ferry where Christophorus lay and were assisted by him across the river.

They announced their coming as so many had done before them; Christophorus knew them a long way off by the din they raised in the quiet woods, a bellowing of cattle and shouts as at a fair, a sound of neighing that dashed along with the horsemen at full gallop; and when the column drew nearer it resolved itself into the roaring and crashing of a thousand throats and many thousand hoofs, while a cloud of dust rose above the tree-tops even before the swarm could be seen; then the first mounted outposts swung out of the wood on the other side of the river, stood still and began to wave and blow their cow's horns lustily to attract the ferryman's attention.

After them the first waggons came in sight — big, clumsily built covered carts in which women and children and whatever else the column carried with it were conveyed; round about them rode the armed warriors. The waggons were regular castles, and when a halt was called they were drawn up in a circle and became a fortress within which the army encamped; on the march they swayed over the trackless turf and creaked loudly with their huge wheels, which were made in one piece like the sun and turned as majestically.

The woods flashed with axes and long spears round the waggons and their stooping horned teams. Behind them came the herd, immense motley crowds of cattle kept together by the thralls; and round about the whole procession swarmed the young people, freckled overgrown striplings who found something to do everywhere, girls who preferred walking to sitting in the waggons; straight, big-limbed young women of seventeen with bare legs under a hempen skirt and honey-yellow hair like sunshine about their shoulders.

In the open fore part of the carts sat the matrons with spindles in their hands, and children big and small with gleaming hair, almost white like that of the aged, looked out over them and beside them, with the world showing in their clear, wide-open, childish eyes. From the back of the waggons projected house-timbers with scarfed ends; they had been taken down at their old home and were to be set up again when they found a new one; the plough, with mould from their old fields still on its board, showed its worn handles sticking out of the cart. But from the hindmost of all came smoke; here sat aged women with their wrinkles full of soot, tending a fire which was not allowed to go out; in the evening when the column camped each housewife fetched a brand from it for her open-air kitchen.

All the waggons were decorated with green boughs, for it was springtime. The woods had just burst into leaf and the travellers had just taken the road; like green woods on wheels the waggons went through the greenwood, like singing waggons, for song came from them, chirping voices of children, like a chorus of birds, and the young girls walked beside them singing, their souls felt so new, the woods were new, the world, the sun was new;

the green young lads sang, with voices as rough and rusty as they could make them, and many a stern warrior leaned back as he sat his horse and sang up to the leaves, the song he had sung as a boy coming back to his throat. The matrons too sang as they span, rocking their heads gently, and their voices could scarcely be heard; the same tones that lured the young into a world they did not know turned them inward and backward to a memory. Here and there an old man, toiling beside the waggon, setting his shoulder to it when it leaned and yelling and struggling with the thick-skulled oxen, had time to join in between the cuts of his whip, a growling hum that exposed blackened teeth, but his face grew brighter for it. It was the song of the wanderers:

> Springtime sweet and green
> Again on earth is seen.
> The sun shoots beams aflare,
> Mild is the air.
> > Southern wind,
> > Roaming mind!
> Take up the staff, bring out the cart!
> Come out, come out and let us start,
> With creaking wheel and glad at heart —
> > To a far country!
>
> The winter, weary jade,
> Within her stall was stayed
> Now she has foaled!
> 'Mid cobwebs by the cold —
> > Foal's foot,
> > Flying foot!
> Up, lusty lads, mount and away!
> Gallop in troop the livelong day,
> As up and down your bodies sway —
> > To a far country!
>
> And wilt thou go with me?
> Till death I'll go with thee!
> My fair young life,
> My roving wife!
> > Girl and boy,
> > Lovers' joy!
> Two together, day and night,
> Double breathing, one delight!
> Behind the dark, before the light —
> > To a far country!

The greenwood's freest glade
Invites us to its shade.
We know not where we go —
Swallows will show.
    Swallow's wing,
    Winds of spring!
Follow the springtime's call so free,
Southward, where the sun we see,
    Follow, no bird so free as we —
    To a far country!

The chorus filled the forest with one great, joyful human cry.
And the children stretched their necks out of the waggons, like
flowers turning their faces to the sun; their young skin caught up
the spring and the breeze from the forest like the first breath of
morning in the world. Never before or after was the day so great
a marvel. As they looked the woods opened out and the river
swung into view as a new almighty wonder, a vast being in motion
which lay about the world in a curve and flowed, bearing suns in
its mirror and mingled with the sky in the distance. But just opposite were the woods again, on the other bank, swelling in their
pride, like another entrance to another new world. Here was the
ferry.

And here was hard work for the grown-ups and for the ferryman, work for many days. The waggons had to be taken across
one by one, then the horses and men, and lastly all the cattle, a
few at a time, as many as the ferry-boat would hold.

But when after much trouble the people had been taken across,
and their leader, the man with the fate of the whole tribe in his
fierce blue eyes, came forward with a pair of scales and a strip of
silver to cut off the ferryman's fee, Christophorus shook his head
and would take no payment.

The chief dropped his hand with the scales. What did he mean
by that?

Christophorus then gave him to understand that he was not a
ferryman on his own account, but had been put there to assist
people over the river for nothing, in God's name.

Oh, that was the way of it. Then *which* god was it that the fare
was due to?

Christophorus pointed with his thumb to the cross he had
planted above his hut, and had to explain to the stranger that he
did men a service in the name of the great King Christ; however,

King Christ did not desire any reward either; out of friendship for men he had appointed people to act thus on his behalf.

The chief, a young man with wild eyes and red hair already tinged with grey, could not make him out. Travelling with his people in a continual state of war and accustomed either to take or to pay for what he required, he had never yet encountered anything but opposition on his way — murder, blood and treachery wherever he went. Here for the first time he came upon a gentler custom, and it startled him; he went on, saving his silver, but could not understand it. And yet he was here at the boundary between the world he had left and the one he was entering. King Christ he would not forget.

Christophorus heard the column receding into the forests as it resumed its journey, the creaking waggons, the cattle and the loud, impetuous voices of the horsemen; they had now got their direction, the Alps awaited them; now they could try to cross them and see what they would find on the other side!

Christophorus shook his head and muttered in his beard: full of joy they travelled now, walking the earth as though they were the first and only men; the difficulties that had driven them out of their homes were forgotten and they saw the whole future in sunshine. But when these same strapping young women one day were reduced to cutting their children's and one another's throats, after their men, the invincible, had been defeated in battle, then it would be a different song; no one who had heard it would lightly forget that howl of a camp when a nation perishes; no, no, and the old man shook his head again and again. Or suppose they were successful, the young warriors whose eyes shone with bloodshed and rapine, then they would become princes, their leader a king and their clans the nobility of the countries they would possess; but still they would have to pay the price in fratricide, in centuries of treachery and violence, for power is dear and devours the soul, as it devours the race; such is the effect of power, but who has ever said "No" when it was offered him? When did one ever hear of husbandmen who stayed on the soil? Christophorus talked to himself as to a whole congregation and admitted the truth of what he said, nodding and nodding again: ay, ay, ay, thus they had chosen their destiny. To travel and get rich, richer than their gaping minds could grasp, make nations subject to themselves, destroy and breed! Women! A kind of

radiance and sweet perfume hung about the ferry after all the
womanhood that had passed over; the old man blew and cleared
his nose suspiciously — phew, new-married people, those Longobards! Couple after couple, hand in hand all of them! Their song
echoed like a single great bridal chorus in a distant wooded valley — behind the dark, before the light! Ah yes, young people
wear madness like a garland of light on their brows so long as
they desire one another; afterwards they call the world to witness their torments in loud, offended birthplaints — ay, ay, ay, thus
Life would live and multiply and die, thought the numbed old
ferryman and saint, shaking his head in his celibate wisdom, cooled
down by much water — but it has to be ferried across.

His own work was not finished; other swarms would come and
want to cross. Christophorus continued to ferry people from the
North over the river on their way to the South until it seemed
that he had emptied all the countries up where he himself had
come from, and sent them down towards the sun and the warmth;
and to all of them he gave the lesson of an unselfish deed performed for the good of all. None of the fresh and vigorous nations he ferried over to the South ever came back.

But when Christophorus had stayed long enough by the river
it was given to him to ferry the Christ Child in the opposite direction, to the North.

For a long long time he had served the strongest of all Lords
without ever seeing him. But hope worked within him and desired
to leave a trace; he began to build, having leisure enough from
his ferrying, and what he built was to be a house for King Christ
to lodge in, if he should ever vouchsafe him a visit. To his own
house Christophorus could not invite him; it was half a hole
in the ground, half a hut of faggots; something more was wanted.
Not unpractised in carrying stones, Christophorus then collected
all he could find and began to pile them one on another into a
building. The ground-plan was a cross, as was befitting, and the
walls took up almost more room than the space they enclosed, for
they were to be durable; the sun and moon shone through, for the
giant was no mason, but the whole bulk held well together, looking
like a little mountain. How the building was to be finished off and
roofed over had not yet been settled, it was not nearly high
enough, Christophorus had thoughts of reaching the stars; at night

when his cyclopean masonry towered up above the trees it seemed to him that the top was already quite near the moon.

The building never got any further, for in the meantime Christophorus really had a visit from his Lord. It happened very differently from his imaginings, as everybody knows from the legend. One evening he heard a child crying by the river and asking to be ferried across, but saw nothing when he went out; and this was repeated three times. The third time he became aware of a little male child standing on the river bank and imploring to be carried over the stream.

Christophorus then carried him over, but now for the first time found a burden which almost exceeded his powers. This little child was a marvellous child, it grew heavier and heavier, and the river swelled beneath him, the darkness closed before him and became doubly dark, it was as though the elements would swallow him. The child weighed him down, never had anything been so heavy. Such is the weight of Life's germ, Life's beginning and the time to come of which we have no knowledge. And yet it seemed that the burden itself sustained him, else he would never have come across without straining himself. When at last he reached the opposite bank it was as though he had carried the whole world upon his shoulders.

The Child looked upon Christophorus with a strange earnestness. "Let it not surprise thee," he said, "that I am so heavy. Know that thou hast not only carried the world upon thy shoulders but even Him who created the world. Behold, I am Christ thy King, whom until this day thou hast served in thy good work. And this shall be a sign unto thee: Strike thy staff into the ground. To-morrow it shall blossom and bear fruit." And when Christophorus awoke early next morning his pilgrim's and ferryman's staff had become a palm. Thus the South came to him.

He himself carried it into the North. But this belongs to another story, how the Kingdom of God penetrated northward and was received in the poor, harsh countries which had thrust out their young men, the stem, and which had only the roots and the young shoots left.

V

OUR LADY

WHEN again the age of an oak had gone by since Christophorus had dwelt by the river, a city stood there.

The forest no longer existed; from the ferry as far as the eye could see was open, cultivated land; the woods began a long way off on either hand and on the other side of the river. The ferry had attracted all kinds of people, fairs had been held there, and then it became a town; the surrounding land was cleared by settlers and came under the plough. On every market-day the peasants now came in from the country with their produce and in exchange received from the town the things brought by vessels from many parts of the world, which found shelter under its walls; thus a city is made, no one remembering that it has ever been otherwise.

The city did not extend far, its height was almost greater than its breadth, it looked like a cake of houses with a thick crust about it, the walls with their roofs and towers running all the way round; on the river side the town wall plunged abruptly into deep water, and on the other sides the river was led into a moat; a hoisted drawbridge gaped like open jaws with a roof of beams on the land side; here he who would reach the city had to swim, and be bitten if he came across. Within the walls the city lay closely packed, with steeply rising houses and many deep and twisting alleys between; the people went about at the bottom of a gutter and lived in many layers above one another.

But in the midst of the city rose the church hill, and on its summit rode the Cathedral, Our Lady's, like a mountain made by hands with peaks and carved-out flanks. It was so big that the shadows of clouds in the sky flecked it like a mountain as they glided over it; it lay here in sunshine and there in shadow with its forest of spires, flying buttresses, garlands of stone, ornamental cornices and thousand figures; at night it rose out of the earth as a mighty body with its foot in the gloom and its airy open towers up in the starry sky irradiated by the moon.

The city beneath it was full of all kinds of everyday life: a bustling in the houses and the alleys, a rumbling on the draw-bridge of peasants' carts when they were allowed to enter, hammer-blows from the cordwainer's shop where sole-leather was being beaten on the stone, little children rolling about, tumbling and getting up again, old women emptying their pails to the pigs in the street, crossbowmen pacing the walls on guard with morions on their heads. The city was a fortress: the beat of drums was heard in its narrow lanes and in the market-place a troop of horsemen paraded disguised in blue-black steel from top to toe, each man a fortress with closed visor, his face concealed by bars and bolts, with spikes and scales all over him. Carronades thundered from the walls on occasion, and the ships lying off the town, with high curving poops, saluted astern with *their* pieces, barking a brief while.

But the Cathedral reduced all to silence when it chose. Throughout the day it slumbered, reposing in its glory and in its proximity to heaven, merely accompanying the hours with a chime of bells, clear melodies like a web of sound, a golden soliloquy of tones high in the air; in the morning it rang for sunrise with rousing, powerfully swelling strokes of the great bell, and at evening the same bell rang down the sun, but then it had a lingering resonance and ended in a single stroke of the clapper, three times in succession, with a pause between, like the last affrighted sigh of the dying day.

But on high festivals or when great matters were to be announced or exorcised, war, fire or pestilence, the Cathedral spoke with all its bells, crying with immense brazen tongues till its towers and walls swayed and resounded to their very foundations, the hill and the whole city resounded, and the sky far and wide and the country and the river winding through it, all this quivered and expanded in music when the Cathedral began to speak. At last it seemed to rise and shake, it opened, not to the day but to Time, the bells swelled as in a tempest and increased in tone, one century after another was revealed, one abyss after another, the Cathedral roared, sweating sound with its whole body; it was the ages rising again and finding a voice, a mighty heart found utterance in it.

On this same spot the hunter had had his dwelling under the lofty trees on the knoll, deep in the forest solitude. On the river bank the otter had had its hiding-places, where afterwards the town walls came down into the water; the badger had had his hole on the hill, where lay the Cathedral crypt.

Instead of the lofty trees the Cathedral soared with its heaven-seeking spires; but at their accustomed height the rooks still flew in and out, filling the upper regions of the church with their resounding cries, in which the spirit of the great trees seemed to live again. Lower down, in cornices and niches behind the statues of holy men, doves brooded and cooed in the sunshine; they too had kept their nests. And at the very top, where the spire stood dizzily against the clouds and seemed to be sailing with them, the falcon lived under the vane, choosing as ever the highest point and the widest view. So old was the church that grass grew on it here and there, high up in some rift where mould had collected, as on a mountain side; the grass too was seeking to return. Up in an angle of the cornice where the wind had swept dust into a little layer of soil, moistened by rain and manured by birds, a rowan shoot grew, a real green tree at a dizzy height on the wall, calling to mind the forest. But from the gutters and galleries all manner of monsters and goblins looked down; they had been turned to stone, and spouted rainwater or made hideous grimaces over the city and the country, impotence perpetuated. They were the dragons from the hunter's house that reappeared in stone, banning night and terror. In the high and gloomy belfry a ticking went on at regular intervals, the pendulum of the church clock measuring time, a tardy ghost of Time that once was young — the woodpecker of the forest.

The hunter's woodland house and his image of Ygdrasil, his heart, the mighty expansion of memory, had passed into the Church; the *Ship* that carried so many yearning men towards the South had become its nave; Christophorus' cyclopean walls exceeding all human measure had passed into it together with his fidelity. He himself stood by the door of the church in everlasting stone, with the Child on his shoulders and a tree in his hand, wading trustfully through the deep; for the old ferryman was the patron saint of the river city.

And on passing through the door one came into a vast and lofty space with subdued light and coloured shadows, apparently boundless, the high, narrow nave of the church, supported by a forest of pillars. They stretched upward like bright and slender stems, one beside and behind the other, losing themselves in the background of pillars and arches and spreading out into vaults of stone ribs and foliage, high up where the air of the interior blended into a strange violet-blue smoke. Here was the rainbow wherever one turned, the high narrow windows through which the light came in every colour, deep blue gleams and sparkling green and red and yellow intermingled as when the sun penetrates the leafy roof of the forest. But there was more than light and colour; on looking closer it was figures not of this world that shone in a celestial eternity, crowned men and calm winged women that had come to rest here, and bright, many-coloured pictures. And at the end of the nave the light was refracted in a mighty checkered rose, a ring of colours that branched into quaint patterns as though all circles and orbits of the universe here ran together and came to rest in one sphere for all time; it was the sun's image depicted in and illumining creation, sunset and sunrise united for eternity.

Up on the piers and in the half-light of alcoves within the walls stood the images of dead princes and warriors and holy men who here continued their existence in stone long after they had become dust in the earth; they spoke in a mute language of the desire to live on in a form, even when the flesh had bowed submissively to mortality. Here they were in their graves, the sarcophagi in the chapels on the top of which princely couples lay at full length in stone, the dead captain with his sword on the coffin lid and old captured banners hanging above in the mist of incense; here they were too in the worn reliefs of tombstones in the floor, paintings black with age but with burning eyes that follow you wherever you go. Everywhere, in the church's pictures and statues, in its stained-glass windows, in its inscriptions and symbols, spoke the voice of a vanished time which is so powerful, the voice of the dead who cannot die.

The beasts of the forest were assembled here and turned to stone that they might not perish: in the carved capitals, amid foliage and from corners murky with the dust of centuries they thrust out their wild visages, wolves and stags together, for here they had finally made peace; they lived in the conventional blazonings of shields and armorial bearings which treasured old hunting joys, spread eagles, wild boars, the raven and the lion rampant in flourishes; fabulous animals here lived in stone a life reality had never seen, the dragon, the hippogriff and the indomitable horse with a long twisted horn in the middle of its forehead. The horrors and spectres of Night, whose existence loses itself in the imagination, could be *seen* here; in the crypt was the Underworld, the bound serpent of Darkness supported the base of its central pillar.

High up in the apse of the choir above the altar, as though on the very wall of heaven, stood solitude and the sign of the Supreme Spirit, the sign one feels behind one's back, but whose sight is death, the Eye suspended in air.

The whole body of the church was like an enchanted forest. At the entrance stood the holy water in an ornamental marble basin; its water came from an ancient well under the foundations of the church, in pagan times a sacred spring.

The hunter was here, now become an obscure legendary figure whose head Time had encircled with the halo of transfiguration; he and the supernatural stag, the speedy, the unattainable, which transported him from the present to eternity.

His soul was in the body of the church, *echo*, the old voice of the forest which rolled among the pillars, in the corners, and haunted the vaulting, that was he. His soul and the soul of all was in the organ, the voice of the church coming from everywhere and nowhere; the very fabric swelled with it, the vaulting, the walls, the piers, the whole stone edifice made music, a soft coloured blast seemed to move within it, a many-coloured roaring, in which could be heard the voice of all the quarters of the heavens, and the deep tramp of the distant sea transmitting itself to the feet as well as to the ear, and the birds twittered in thin high notes, the beasts shrieked, or muttered in the bass, and whole hosts of human voices traversed the vault, clear children's voices, whole solid waves of purest melody, as though invisible flocks of maidens were soaring past in song, and a chorus of darkly brooding men still pondering in the grave over the brevity of life. The forester's long, clamouring night-songs when in fear of the moon, the hermit's simple piping in the first calm light evenings of spring, were here heard again. That which none can put into words, which speaks in the winds and the stars and the seasons and in our blood, that which yearns even when the dead are dead, this reverberated through the building in many tones and united into a single swelling note which was a breath of eternity.

And the fragrance within the smoke that spread, coloured like the Milky Way, as a heaven under the vaulting and dispersed a mist of distance and promise through the air — this was the heaven of all remembrance, the infinite inner world of our memory, the scent of all summers, the perfume of all memories, even memories of things we have never experienced, every secret thing the sun has fostered, from the time when the first fir tree scattered its brew of resin and dropped its cones on the crocodile's back, and the first apple tree blossomed and gave off perfume and hung full of bees in the first garden of the first human pair.

On the altar, just above that spot in the grove where the hunter had his cairn and made fire-offerings to his Powers, in the midst of this marvel of stone, colour, music and fragrance, stood the image of the Mother of God, Our Lady.

She was raised above all corruptibility upon a throne of ivory, for which a hundred elephants had given their tusks, and it was supported by chased and richly gilt clouds; she was robed in the most precious silks, to which hundreds of thousands of silkworms had devoted their blind lives; on her head she wore a great diadem of precious stones, a petrification of the ruttish fires of the South; each stone of them had cost human life and had witnessed lechery, whereby they had become so hard and flashed so immodestly, but upon her head they were the crown of innocence.

In her arms she held the Son of God, from whose childish head three golden rays broke out in the semblance of sunshine; in his hand he played with an apple, the symbol of the origin of all fruit and all spheres. For the rest this Son of God was a boy like other boys, chubby-cheeked, with his fat little limbs in layers from exuberant health. God's Mother smiled upon him, the holy mother-smile that is Nature's most beautiful blooming, the young mother's mute reposing in the marvel that has befallen her.

Before the holy Virgin burned a lamp which had never been extinguished since the church was founded; it was an ancient flame, the cult that kept it alight was older than the Church, it went back to old, forgotten fire-worshippers. Year in and year out it burned: in the daytime it stood in the midst of incense and the coloured twilight from the windows as an admonition of the night, a paled watch-light that had survived into the daytime; at night, when the Cathedral lay empty and still as a vast tomb, it burned like a yellow wheel in the midst of the immense darkness, like a spark left over from the day, a lonely drop of the eternal fire at the bottom of the well of the grave and of darkness.

Terrible was the church at night. Its fathomless space was full of darkness, region behind region of darkness; high up lingered a pale, ghostly, coloured gleam, like a lunar rainbow; and a long spectral ray descended and traced eyes on one of the piers, a hovering blind life in the midst of a world of darkness; but below on the floor of the church the gloom brooded all the blacker, with only the everlasting lamp deep down in its gulf like an eye surrounded by rings of mist. A strange coughing came from distant resonant corners, the body of the church sighing within itself, the night sinking deeper and deeper into itself. The organ was perfectly silent, with redoubled silence; but up under the hanging banners there was a noiseless fanning, and a fanning in the draught under the vaulting, a swiftly fleeting life, the beat of wings, and now and then a little black soul became visible in a moonbeam; bats flitting hither and thither on their little dragon's wings and feeling their way in rapid flight among the pillars and empty spaces of the church.

Far away and high up through many dividing walls and chambers a hooting screech was heard at intervals, the owl in the tower — but it kept outside, it was the church's dismal voice over the city at night. Then the Cathedral beetled above the roofs like a mountain of darkness, clotted together with the night, and from the lofty intricate spaces of the belfry came the hooting of the owl, as though the tower itself was hooting and threatening far and wide with its terror of darkness.

Round the foot of the church brooded crosses and graves and darkness, shunned by all men; and no one who could avoid it would look into the churchyard; no, he shut his eye on that side and spied out his way as well as he could with the other. If any man had been shut up in the church and forced to spend the night there alone he would have died of fright or lost his wits, become a babbling idiot for the rest of his days; nay, the cries of the poor imprisoned maniac would have driven any one mad with terror who chanced to pass by and hear them. The figure of Death, with his bare bones and his horrid grinning teeth, lurked here in the dark corners of the buttresses, among the tombs, behind door gratings; and vaguely connected with the church at nighttime was the idea of the Being of the Abyss, the Evil One, the repulsive male creature with a tail that was thought to be red as glowing iron, stinking of pitch and equipped with all the powerful and loathsome arts that are not to be spoken of.

Only the servants of the church were fortified to visit the Powers of the church by night as by day; these skirted henchmen sang vigils by torchlight in the crypt at midnight; a gleam of fire crept up through openings in the wall level with the ground, and a subterranean chorus was heard; men knew it was the Mass, but thoughts of the underworld haunted them; even such were the cries of those buried alive in Hell, the bloody howls of wolves below, the mad shrieks of distracted souls!

And to such terrors they delivered up their dead. Within the chapels where the dead lay buried, and the alcoves of the walls, gloomy even by day, the gloom condensed at night into the outer darkness; many times buried were the dead here. A sound as of withered leaves arose in the stillness of night and lost itself like trackless footsteps in the draught between the piers, unaccountably; it was a shifting of the bones in a coffin, muffled by boards and walls, one more whispered sign of life and death from what was slowly sinking to pieces through the centuries in the interior of the sarcophagus.

But again the church clothed itself in daylight, in its uplifting power over the eye. Every day it was itself a day above the day. But on Sunday it possessed an added rejuvenation. From early morning Sunday, the Sun's day, could be felt in the air; it set its mark upon everything throughout the day and preserved a greater beauty than all the other days of the week until the evening. The rooks called more clearly and with more of the dawn in their notes on Sunday morning from the roof of the church, the doves cooed and cooed as though there were bursting buds to coo over, and the people came up to the church in crowds as though to a grand migration; for the bells rang with a younger and stronger peal that day, rang out their welcome and the joy of Heaven over town and country, which lay so still and had adorned themselves because it was the day of rest.

Then it was the old world back again: in the church was a song as of waking birds, and the censers before the altar poured out cloud after cloud as they swung to and fro in a dizzy joy: the

birth of the day, the young newborn clouds that the dawn brings
forth and the sun turns red, and a fragrance of eternal summer
spread within the church to its uttermost corners; not a beggar by
the door outside of all but it brought him a message.

Up under the vaulting the smoke lay like the mist of fertility
in a hothouse, and here, high up, could be descried as it were a
web of swallows darting in and out; they had their nests at the
very top among the ribs and scroll-work. But their faint *veet-veet*
was not heard, for the organ rolled, clearer, vaster, fuller in its
tone than on other days; it received the congregation as in an open
embrace of sound. The church stood erect with its pillars and
altars, Heaven was opened.

The organ pealed with full force, a choir of voices filled the
church as though descending from the spheres:

> Torches of the stars eternal
> Burn before thy heart, O Mother,
> Who hast freed the world's repining.
>
> Round thy head the spheres of heaven,
> In thy heart the living waters,
> Wonder-working thou, God's Mother.
>
> Depths of innocence we dream of,
> Girt about with streams of gladness,
> Well of goodness never empty!
>
> Thou the one whose soul reposes
> In itself; the world unheeding
> Thou dost dwell in brightness, smiling.
>
> As a tree from heaven moistened,
> Clothed about with showers of summer,
> Thou hast decked thee, green and gladdened.
>
> Like the tree its dead leaves dropping
> Thou hast bowed in deepest sorrow:
> Dust is every creature's portion.
>
> Thou wert stirring in Life's morning.
> As a rose by dew made fresher
> Breathes Love's spirit from its chalice.
>
> Roses blaze. Their thorns are cruel.
> By the bier of short-lived summer
> Bleeds the berry, with thy weeping.

Trembling dost thou tread, but dauntless,
On Life's pathways, mild and bleeding;
Bounteous art thou, Woman, bounteous!

For in thee has Life his dwelling.
From within thy secret chamber
Comes thy Child's voice, small and tender.

Here thy precious one thou lavest
And with mother-sources stillest,
Lifting, putting down, and tending.

Here when midnight's hour approaches
Softly sounds thy tender prattle
To thy nursling, warm and bonny.

With a song like flowery music
Gently rockst thou him to slumber,
Golden in the light thy tresses.

Newly kindled burn Life's torches!
He is born whom earth's unhappy
Kneel to when the earth is trembling:

Boy who shall the earth inherit,
Seed of man and Godhead's larva,
Hope that shall the future colour!

Wrathful wreaks the world destruction,
Sees itself with fear and loathing —
In thy nest are all things new-made.

Brutish lust would fain betray thee;
Sex's miserable riddle
In thy blood is turned to mercy.

In thy trouble's fiery torment,
When the shock of Nature casts thee
To the dust — then life thou givest!

Full of grace again thou buddest
In a young and lovely daughter,
Horror to sweet smiles transforming.

Miscreant's hand which thought to ruin
Answerst thou with double bounty,
Woman born again in bearing!

This is thy revenge, thou pure one:
Double fruit where first a single
Blushed defenceless 'mid the branches.

As a wave of sunshine chases
Shadows from a golden cornfield,
Even so thou smilest, fair one.

What in all the realm of Nature
Is like beauty, beauteous Maiden,
Eyes' delight, thou shining marvel!

Sunshine's fire and blood's warm billows,
Secret laws of Life pursuing,
Hide within thy maiden bosom.

All Life's sweetness, warmth of gladness,
We may see upon thy visage,
Youth eternal thou, Our lady!

Source of goodness and forgiveness!
Virgin! Mother! Gentle Woman!
Joy with thee to find vouchsafe us!

BOOK TWO: THE CARAVEL

DE MUY PEQUEÑA EDAD ENTRÉ
EN LA MAR NAVEGANDO, É LO HÉ CONTINUADO HASTA HOY.
LA MESMA ARTE INCLINA Á QUIEN LE PROSIGUE Á DESEAR
DE SABER LOS SECRETOS DESTE MUNDE.

I

THE "SANTA MARIA"

ᴸIGHTS were shining at midnight from St. George's Church at Palos, in the south of Spain; a service was being held for the crews of three ships that were to sail at daybreak; it was the third of August 1492.

The little port was as excited as any town could be. The voyage which had been in preparation for the past few months was one that attracted attention, and Palos itself had a vital share in it, for the owners and most of the crews were local men, even if they were not making the voyage entirely of their own free will, both ships and ships' companies having been pressed into it by the Government. The leader, however, was a foreigner, an Italian from God knows where, who gained the ear of the great for his quite obviously insane plans, nothing more nor less than sailing to blazes, down underneath the earth — altogether a fairly eccentric business and one quite calculated to upset Palos, both that part of it which was going to sail and the friends and relations who were staying behind. Not many of the grown-up people went to bed that night; the seamen who were leaving, more or less voluntarily, armed themselves against an uncertain fate as reasonably as they could by fortifying visits to church and to the taverns.

In the church there was great solemnity, the whole of the crews went to confession and communicated; but even later in the course of the night many a sinner dropped in again, when reminded by the bells, to repeat an *Ave* and cool his forehead against the stone pavement, until he felt drawn by the distant irresistible ring of goblets and stole out again. It was a difficult night, and many a worthy fellow swung like a pendulum between this world and the next.

Only one held out steadfastly in church to the last. This was the leader himself, Christopher Columbus. For hour after hour he knelt before the image of the Holy Virgin, with his huge and hairy skipper's hands clasped, himself an image of holy calm and self-communing, silent, with motionless features, weary with watching, absorbed in prayer and meditation. The glare of the candles fell upon the strong head with its reddish-grey mane and the strange blue eyes under eagle brows, which showed quite white against the flaming bright-red skin, weathered by a life in the open air, a picture of weather itself; the unusually tall and powerful frame reposed in itself, strength at rest. If this man was an adventurer he was in any case not one of the windy sort; there was a solidity about him as he knelt, his back and shoulders alone spoke for him, and many a roving eye seeking consolation in the sacred images of the church involuntarily came to rest upon him; it was well to be on good terms with Our Lady, but after all it was he who was to sail the ships! His lips moved like those of a man spelling out syllables, and the others nodded, nodded, mumbling to themselves; if only there might be power in his prayers — for if *he* were not in grace what would become of the rest?

What the Admiral felt, what was working in his soul, could not be read in his face. There was something hot about his eyes; but then it was warm in the church, the air in the confined space was thick with incense and the mawkish smoke of the candles, whose little flames had coloured rings like eyes that had watched overlong. The church was too crowded, the air like a hothouse or a lying-in room, saturated with music and incense; the priests said Mass and rang the altar bell, and the bells in the tower outside made the walls vibrate, the organ blared again and again, the Mass rose as in a wave culminating in loudly enunciated Latin conjurations, the holy images stared as though through a veil — and still Columbus was on his knees before the Virgin Mary's altar. The felted doors at the entrance to the church fell to now and then and let in air as the crews came and went; already a bluish gleam of daylight made its way in each time the door opened, day was breaking; even the priests yawned behind their hands and blinked their red and dried-up eyes. The body of the church stood out of the darkness, as though built up of dust and cobwebs, piers and walls came into being in a light from outside, and the candles grew dim, a wan meeting of day and night. The sailor who had hovered backwards and forwards so often in the course of the night fell asleep in the middle of an *Ave* and a hiccup, and woke again on hitting his forehead against the stone floor, with a groan; well, he would live or die, one or the other!

But a cold breath swept through the dawn outside, and a rich muddy smell arose from the river, hulls and masts came out of the darkness, the three ships lay ready for sea with sails half unfurled; their lights were extinguished, no longer wanted, and the ships' boats pulled to and fro in the stream between ship and shore, taking the last things on board.

In a tavern by the harbour some of the crew were swinging a final tankard and taking a last leave of their friends. Here the brothers Pinzon, who commanded two of the ships, collected a crowd about them and rehearsed once more the whole plan of this more than doubtful expedition. They were conscious of the attention they attracted, but not proud; on the other hand, of course, they had all the information and talked quietly like men who knew, so that every one had to crowd round to hear them; as men of experience and local men they spoke with weight. Martin Alonzo as the elder gave his opinion first, after him Vincente Yannez, who entirely agreed, but could put it in even stronger terms; everything that was obvious was said again and again. There was only one thing on which the brothers would express no opinion but kept their mouths tight-shut, and that was the possible outcome of the voyage. Martin Alonzo held his peace, and Vincente held his, but both were bursting with what was unsaid; and Martin Alonzo, standing in a noble attitude with his weight on one leg and the other advanced, shrugged his shoulders, buried his head in them as though bending to the elements, and showed both his palms — *Quien sabe?* And Vincente arched his back, and he too showed both palms — *Quien sabe?* The brothers wore sea boots reaching to the hips, for they might have a good deal to go through, but the upper part of their bodies was cased in iron, cuirass and helmet, with visor up; but in a little while they clapped it down, and then they were bolted and barred, ready to meet legions of unknown monsters and man-eaters.

It was a great rambling tavern with murky corners, and heads were not very clear; nobody knew exactly what was going on here and there in the background, female voices could be heard amid the clash of tankards, stringed instruments, singing and a rhythmical clapping of all hands in unison like a great raging heart, and above all their heads was a waving, sparkling, bewitching vision — for they had got a girl up on the table, where she was dancing a perilous dance on the very edge; so the Moors hadn't taken away all the dancing with them when they were chased out of Spain the other day, here was a creature as supple as if she had a bow for a backbone, with a stomach like an eel; and there was somebody who knew how to manipulate the flute with few holes and many repetitions. Rather African it was, the dance; the eel wriggled tenaciously on the table, she gave vent to a screech, and keeping her feet on the same spot she let herself go in a presto, the men yelled, *Brava!* and wall and ceiling showed the shadow of the dancer with raised arms and twisting hips, heeling over at the waist; she whinnied like a mare, the guitar-player stormed at his strings, the nasal trills of the flute came quicker and quicker, the audience stamped their feet as well as clapping, the castanets clattered, spurring her on, a teeth-chattering race, no longer an occasional shout but shouting all the time . . . for to-morrow they were to die, but *now, now* they had everything that life could give!

Yes, it had been a wild day in Palos — some of the men were hopping on one leg, the other lamed; others only saw with one eye and had a bloody bandage over its fellow — for this mad evening had begun with *letting the bull loose!* Of course, in a little place like Palos there was no bull-ring, but then they had a town bull and knew how to amuse themselves! Bull loose in the street! Hey! Jesus! Look at the bull, all by himself in the market-place, all powerful, waving his tail — and everybody scampering indoors and upstairs, headlong, on all fours — look at the bull trotting down the middle of the street with horns raised, quite alone, and all the doors are slammed, and a pair of heels vanish over a paling — hey, the whole street swept clean as if by magic, people hanging out of trap-doors and garrets to look on . . . and now the bull-ring is ready, it has arranged itself, out of the houses jump nimble young fellows and begin to tease the bull with their capes, horse-men dash into the street leaning over their mounts as they gallop round a corner, with long lances in rest; collision, crash, a cloud of dust and horses' legs in the air, riders on top of one another, a torrent of blood; the bull has got his horns into the first horse, the street yells, and now it's a mix-up, cracks, falls and hurly-burly, a hunt down the street and back again, till the bull is ready for the death-stroke — then the signal is given and all draw back, except one, a young desperado; he and the bull are left, absolutely alone, face to face in the middle of the street. He has no other weapon but a naked blade, like a spit, with a cloth wrapped round the end he holds. The killing is done in breathless silence. The raging beast, all body and horns, with a bloody gleam in his eye, and the slender, mortally determined man, the lurking spit . . . and then in a moment the street roars and becomes alive with the things people madly fling from windows and cocklofts, hats, clothes, flower-pots, some swing themselves down into the street — for he has done it, the spit lies buried in the bull's shoulder with the point in its heart, it collapses as if struck by lightning!

And now the desperado is sitting here in the tavern on a chair, nodding with his chin on his chest, drunk and sober and drunk again many times that day, sated with honour, worn-out, aged by a generation in a few hours . . . and to-morrow, no, *now, now* he is to sail; outside is the dawn, looking with a grey face upon the desperado and the dancer.

A person nobody paid any particular attention to moved about among the groups in the course of the night, now here, now there, chattering incessantly without any one grasping the connection of what he was saying, not that that mattered; now and then he gave vent to a burst of laughter which made people turn round to see what the joke was; but it was nothing, only that mountebank, the Babuino as they called him, who had once again said something he himself thought intensely amusing.

He was a little swarthy man with a big face, mauve about the mouth, and he looked like an old huckster; he had put in an appearance here to peddle his wares and had in fact done very good business among the seamen who were about to sail and were providing themselves for a long voyage. He was in a mad mood tonight, the Babuino, pretending to be drunk as nobody was sober, declaiming in a loud voice, putting on the airs of a Dionysus, and giving great lurches when he crossed the room; but he was only lame, not a drop of wine had passed his lips. He went up to one or another with his goods, sideways like a crab, with a confidential wagging, all grins and good nature; he stooped down, made himself still smaller than he was, a miserable thing, a dog in every respect, except his eyes, which shone like magic orbs, with a perfectly frank look of impudence, which, however, those present were too thick-skinned or too drunk to notice. When anybody made fun of the Babuino, or tried to shake him off with a threatening gesture, he retreated a step with quivering face, timorous, dazed, and his eyes disappeared altogether; he was then a sufferer, thrust out, infirm and palsied, into a cruel world; but at the same moment his lips drew back from his teeth, it was best to be on guard — only a grimace, and then he grinned again and crept near, fawning, almost lying on the ground, his limbs still quaking with fear, enough to move a stone, and in his forepaw he disclosed something that you had to look at, a brand-new amulet — and then there was a little bargain after all!

When attention flagged the Babuino raised his voice, of astonishing volume and timbre for so small a chest, and became a public crier, in a long and practised recitative, which he accompanied by remarks in a private undertone and emphasized now and then with one of his sudden bursts of laughter:

"Amulets! Amulets! Most excellent Santiago de Compostela! The apostle in silver-gilt, brass or lead, equally powerful, the protector of all seafaring men! Rosaries, imitation olive wood from the Garden of Gethsemane, rosaries that pray by themselves, rosaries! Crucifixes, in ivory or metal, for every passion! Relics, fragments of holy persons, every part of the body! Letters of indulgence, a selection in stock! Images of the Virgin, immaculate! Damaged at reduced price! Remedies! Salves! Rhinoceros-horn for love potions, genuine mummy from Egypt, stolen, with original smell! Prayer books, very effective! Books of magic! Secret books! Ha, ha, ha!"

The Babuino neighed and shook his lame leg; half of what he had uttered was enough to get him burnt alive, if anybody had been listening to his crowing; but all the rest were too busy crowing themselves, so he could play with fire as long as it amused him. The tavern was filled with a general roar, like a fire blazing at its highest.

But at last it burned itself out; after the fire comes the ash. The word went round that the Admiral had left the church at last and was about to take ship; the music died away, an uncanny daylight filled the corners of the tavern, all at once the guests broke up and streamed out to the boats in the river; a cannon shot from the *Santa Maria* announced with a loud boom that the tide was on the turn; it was the signal, the hour of sailing had struck.

Just as Christopher Columbus was stepping into the boat to go off to the ships he was detained a few minutes, though without its attracting much attention; it was only the huckster they called the Babuino who crawled up to the tall skipper's feet and addressed him. Few heard what he said, and nobody understood him, he seemed to be talking Latin. Columbus stood at his full height with a very serious air, still calm and with a cleansed look on his face such as men wear when they come from Communion, and when he had heard all the creature had to say he turned and got into the boat without having uttered a word in answer, nor could any one see what impression the stranger's speech had made on him.

The huckster addressed Columbus in a hurried tone, corrected himself and made light of what he had just been saying, it was all idle words; he made all kinds of absurd gestures, quivering and twitching his face before the tall man as though the sun was in his eyes, but tittering as he wrung his foolish hands in deference — and suddenly all the squirms and grins were smoothed away from his chops, he looked up with the face of a human being, as though through many masks, a strangely old look; still chattering he withdrew, with an empty laugh in his throat, while some incomprehensible reflex action made him take leave of himself; he actually put out one hand and shook it with the other, crouching to the ground in confusion and showing all his teeth, two rows of big molars like millstones, his whole body twitching with a thousand promptings . . . and he was gone! And what was it he had said?

"*Vale* — good wishes for the voyage from an old voyager! Allow me to add: your worship's idea of trying to find the Indies by

sailing to the west, as I hear, when the Indies lie to the east, is not
at all a bad one, since we know by experience that a problem can
be solved by getting away from it in a diametrically opposite direction, he, he, he! A still quicker solution stares you in the face
— why travel so far at all, when short cuts are so much pleasanter?
The only proper voyage of discovery *has* been made, it is always
the same: *a genibus ad genua* . . . and isn't that just where your
worship comes from? Clack!"

He gave his sudden loud laugh, which sounded like the roar of
a beast, but checked it at once and came a step nearer, with gleaming eyes, and dropped his voice confidentially, fleering with his
tongue out:

"The greatest distance mankind can cover, isn't it a marking
time on the same spot? Listen to a piece of advice; save yourself
a costly, doubtful voyage and take up a study at home — this
book that I have, for instance, *Itinerarium Amoris*, written by a
connoisseur, a gynographer, a great rarity even as a volume, I may
say, a unique copy, second century vellum, belonged once to the
Library of Alexandria, from which I removed it, a dishonest thing
to do, but it adds to its value as a curiosity; altogether an in-
estimable volume, isn't it? . . . But I'm talking nonsense, trying
to sell voyages to a man with his foot on the gangway! The sea is
calling! Won't you have an amulet to take with you? Or an innocent idol, a little woman, you're so lonely at sea; look here, no
bigger than the palm of my hand, a bronze of Aphrodite, wonderful patina, the noblest Greek work, smoothed by the hands of
centuries of connoisseurs, but intact in spite of all, Woman herself, in her ripe maiden bloom, ever young . . . no, not that
either! The sea is calling! Well, I must leave too — and who
knows which of us will go farthest, your worship with your big
ships or I with my old seven-leagued boots? Our ways part.
You go to the South, and I am bound for the North. Spain no
longer offers an abiding place for an old wanderer, and he has no
idea of taking the backward road to Africa again with the Arabs.
Ah yes, the earth burns under him here, it's getting too hot for
him, he must seek cooler pastures. If they prepare stake and faggots for the old man, he rises from the ashes like the phœnix, as
everybody knows; but does everybody know what the fire tastes
like . . . sssss! In proof that he can go he shakes the dust of Spain
from his feet, ai, ai, ai!"

He raised first one foot and shook it thoroughly, then the other and shook that too; he looked all round him, hunted, desperate, like a rat in a trap; he sighed, and his distorted features were relaxed, giving way to a human expression, an old man's sorrow, but only for an instant, then he was twitching again, indomitably mocking:

"Well, good-bye! Until we meet again! As I say, your worship goes south and I north, though really it should be the other way. But perhaps we shall meet nevertheless . . ."

He came quite close, put his hand to his mouth and whispered: "Yes, now we're going each in his own direction . . . *but the earth is round!*"

After this stab he hurriedly made off:

"*Vale!*"

At sunrise the field labourers who were up early saw a little man with staff in hand and pedlar's box on his back taking the northern road out of Palos, with halting steps, but covering the ground fast; at the same time they heard the firing of salutes and ringing of all the town's bells, as Columbus sailed with his ships.

The sun lay as a huge red sphere on the horizon as the ships cast off and began to swing down with the tide, saluting with all their pieces. And the bells of Palos kept on: they were but small, those in St. George's Church and a few other chapels; the bells of La Rabida Convent sounded from their height, and in the distance all the bells of Huelva could be heard; all the parish bells out in the country round joined in, it sounded like a regular discussion between a fleet that was sailing and all the churches that stayed behind. It was not like the booming of the great cathedral bells inland in the river cities of Europe, but to make up for it the little bells of the coast went more rapidly, in a fussy tempo, reminding one of swarming bees and people running after them, beating brass mortars and anything that would make a noise, and the meaning seemed to be the same: Will you stop, will you stop! said the bells, chiming and tolling, but the ships would not stop, they fired astern with heavy guns that made the whole hull tremble, shrouded themselves in smoke and warped out of the mouth of the river with the ebb tide under their keels, one big clumsy caravel in front and two smaller and lighter ones behind with their poops towards Palos.

When well out in the bay they all set sail and began to heel over and make way, the Atlantic received them with a swell in which they rose and sank; from the land the three ships were seen nodding in the sea and slowly growing less as though carried away by an undercurrent out into the gently breathing ocean. At last, when they were far out, flags and pennants were seen to be hauled down, a white cloud shot out from the stern of the *Santa Maria* and lay upon the waves, a distant report was heard as though muffled by blankets, the farewell shot.

But those on board saw the Spanish coast unfold itself, turning about its headlands; sunbeams rose fan-like in the direction of Cadiz, the interior of the country extended and came in sight the farther they left it behind, but lost its sharpness; high up in the distance the airy snow-chain of the Sierra Nevada hovered like a cloud among the clouds, the land stretched out its arms to them on both sides of the bay. But as the coast grew vague and began to sink into the sea some of the crew went to the bulwarks and kissed both hands, stretching them out to land in an impassioned gesture, and their eyes moistened, they felt a stab in the breast, the parting was more than they could bear.

Only Columbus paced backwards and forwards on the highest part of the poop, a place he never left thenceforth, backwards and forwards, with his face intently turned in the direction of the ship's course, to the south-west; and, whether he was conscious of it or not, he never once turned to look back toward Spain. At a gesture from him the green wreaths, now withered, with which the ship had been decorated before sailing were thrown over-board. And now those of the crew who had had to be kept below, prisoners and pressed men, were let out; they ran round the deck like dogs, sniffing at the sea and towards the land — a league away — and towards the open sea ahead — *Madre de Dios!* — some of them, old pale-faced men, simply shook their heads, knew that it was all up with them, but the young ones threw themselves on the deck wringing their hands and burst into tears, as though the bottom had been knocked out of their existence and the whole of life was trying to weep itself out at once.

The gulls followed the ships, conversing among themselves in their parsimonious language, with an eye on the wake. With ships they were quite familiar — what? you so often saw an island of peculiar oblong shape break away from the land and drift off on its own account, possibly babies that were born of the land

and went off to visit other shores. They were not the kind of island you settled or nested on, certainly not; there were men on them and it wouldn't do to come too near, but there was this about the islands that not unfrequently something fit to eat dropped off them, the gulls know that. *Meev*, they say to each other as they fly; that means that the day is blue, all is right with sea and sky.

But towards evening the gulls began nevertheless to have misgivings; they were accustomed to see travelling islands keep between coasts that could both be seen at once, at any rate from a height, but these three seemed to be going in a straight line away from all land and out to where there were no more coasts at all. That was too much even for the gulls, and the time came when *they* turned back.

For the first few days not many words were heard from the Admiral on board the *Santa Maria;* he walked the poop with closed lips and dark brows, not to be appeased, even by the fact that now they actually *had* got away, so furious had he been at one delay after another up to the very last.

For they were to have sailed in the spring, everything had been based upon that, a very important thing to have the summer in front of one, of course; now they were leaving when summer was gone and autumn coming on — it was significant of the whole plan, of his whole life. When he was young he was ready with his plan but met with every possible hindrance; now, when at last he was to have the chance of his life, he felt with insuperable bitterness that it was after the time; he had already reached the age when a man looks back. Fourteen years, fourteen long years, from the age of twenty-eight to forty-two, those years of a man's life in which his activity is at its highest, simply to get the vessels fitted out; and now that the voyage was to begin he was stiff and greyheaded, grown grey before his time from vexation at the time that was lost! Impatience, impatience, and nothing to show for it but his years! On then to death, in full sail, if death was all he had to seek!

Once more, for the last time, those fourteen years of adversity passed through his memory; he recalled all his humiliations, and the crew watched the Admiral quicken his pace on the poop, where he walked up and down like a lion; they saw his face swell and turn still redder, and they thought his black looks were meant for them and cast down their eyes, threw themselves eagerly upon some piece of work or other. But it was the years in Portugal that were in the Admiral's mind, the lost years, the insults, the impossibility of moving any one, until some back-handed advantage to themselves occurred to them: the King sending ships out into the Ocean behind Columbus's back, following the course he had laid down — leaving *him* in the lurch as a crazy person and stealing his idea! The great can do such things! That is why they own kingdoms! Of course. But when the King's men had been a couple of days out they got ocean sickness and turned back, reporting that the sea was too vast; they were quite benumbed, in a sort of delirium, and it was some time before they recovered themselves. Ho! A manly idea can always defend itself after all!

The Admiral stood still and raised his lion's head, embraced in a glance the ship below him, an absent glance, above the heads of all the crew; and they shrank from it, did not care to raise their eyes to the poop, any higher than half-way up the ladder. They knew well that they deserved a good deal of contempt, not all had the fear of God in them when they came aboard. It almost seemed that they had a taste for the rope's end, and the rope was busy the first few days; the officers had been catching it from above and passed it on. If Diego thought he was on a yachting cruise he had made a mistake; the chaotic state in which he had joined ship was converted with an iron hand into the strictest discipline. Boatswain and master may have had their own opinion about this fool's trip, but so long as they were at sea all would be ship-shape! Before they reached the Canary Isles Diego was a sober man, obedient, smart, tarry about the hands from stropping aloft and with clean toes from much wholesome swabbing decks before breakfast.

Every fifth man of the crew, as every other man in Spain, was called Diego, that is, James, after the Apostle and Saint; Diego had just as much of his namesake as the name suggested, a distant resemblance worn by time; the rest he made up for by a picture of the holy Santiago stamped on a medal which he wore strung on his bare chest. Ashore Diego was a desperado, a bully for all bulls, as a coast-dweller equally ready for adventure in a mercenary army, as trooper or musketeer, or as a sailor and halberdier on board a galley, the arm was as indifferent to him as the element;

this time it was the sea, half involuntarily, but such was at times the way of Diego's destiny; this adventure looked like being the most incalculable in extent and the most uncertain he had yet *nolens volens* been involved in.

Like a seed that had floated out to sea, with its germ and its possibilities as a plant if it reached land, such was Diego torn away from his Spain and committed to the winds, with what there was in him, to take root — where? — or to die. And many things were concealed within that square Spanish head with its blue-shaven cheeks and its smouldering glance. What had not befallen the Andalusia from which he and his forefathers came? It had its name from the Vandals, a migratory Northern people, who had lost themselves in North Africa after having left their trace here. In return North Africa had pushed up into Spain for some centuries, the Moors with their Arab houses, the horse-shoe over their goings in and out, their cages for women, until they had recently been chased home to Africa again — several of the men on board had seen the banner of Castile hoisted on the towers of the Alhambra — but that did not mean that their ways were altogether driven out of Andalusia. Other foreigners had laid waste here and left their marks behind them, the Goths, the Romans, the Greeks; still farther back the ancient peoples of Africa, old Carthage; in the earliest ages the Phœnicians, those sea-rats from Asia Minor who had their noses everywhere — and Diego had a sprinkling of all of them in his blood, or was marked by their contact as one is by one's neighbours; he had inherited a turbulent destiny from his ancestors, was brave, covetous, blood-thirsty, a destroyer, but had the same godlike contempt of death as those Northern daredevils to whom fear was the only known crime; he was grandiose, with the Spanish bearing that had come down from the Romans together with the toga, the cloak with which to drape one's unwashedness, and he was untrustworthy as is sometimes the way in the Mediterranean countries, he had passion but came short in feeling, in love an Asiatic, violent, above all inconstant — and yet at bottom an Iberian, a primitive Spaniard, for ever reposing in his nature, contradictory and loosely connected as it was; all in all a human creature, very long-suffering, amiable, with a soul full of music — for among his mothers had been the mutest and most beautiful of all the women of earth.

Such was the Diego who was now at sea and who raised his eyes

with a respect none too genuine to the quarter-deck, the holy of
holies, where the Admiral paced his unresting watch — when all
was said and done he was the strongest for the time being (the
cursed Italian), the man whom it was best to look to, if one wanted
to get out of this predicament. The powder-barrels in the *Santa
Maria's* hold were charged with a soul like Diego's, sulphur, charcoal and saltpetre superficially mixed but with a hell imprisoned
within them which could be released by a spark, and the spark was
smouldering in Diego's Kabyle eyes.

The Admiral for his part kept an eye full of reservations on his
crew; when he had walked off the rancour of his thoughts of
Portugal he began to quicken his pace and turned yet more
sharply in his walk up and down the narrow poop as he recalled
what had befallen him in Spain, his nostrils snorted at the thought.
Eight years' empty talk! All the shoes he had worn out in the pursuit of royal personages, in company with suppliants, lackeys and
toadies; the smile that appeared on every silly face when he was
seen or mentioned, Columbus, the eccentric, even the children
hooting in the street when he passed by! The Council at Salamanca that was to test his scheme! Postponements, hopes and disappointments, up and down, poverty, homelessness, the fickleness
and apathy of princes, a long long laborious pilgrimage which had
taught him what beggars have to suffer. Day after day with his
resolution blazing within him, ready for the leap, and day after
day nothing but a fresh insight into human nature, year in, year
out, all through the years! That last weary journey, when aban-
doning all hope he had quitted Cordova with his little boy, intending to leave Spain, and came to the convent by Palos, Santa Maria
la Rabida, and begged bread in the name of God and for the first
time felt with horror that he was an old man — ah, then his luck
had changed, then it was that he was able to get away. But never
could he forget and never would he forgive what he had felt that
time, when with shaking hand he accepted the gift to himself and
his boy — that old people's hands shook in just that way.

Again the Admiral stood still up on the poop, and Diego glancing
up saw that he was terrible, the big, tall grey man was seeing visions
and execrating spirits, how else could he have that frightful look?
And Diego crept behind something, where the evil eye could not
fall on him, crossing himself in great detail, on his forehead and
over his chest, from shoulder to shoulder; *"Madre!"* he whispered,

and turned quite grey in the face. A strong man, the one up there, and who could tell what Powers he was in league with?

But as the days went by before they reached the Canary Isles, where they put in for repairs, most of August and the early part of September, the feeling on board gradually became less strained. After all they were still within the known world, and the crew could not keep up the sense of their misfortune for weeks on end. Diego revived his forgotten songs, and poured out his soul in passionate chest-notes to the winds of heaven; he was full of sweet speech as a wooer, all his thousand bereavements; and at whiles when he had time — and the calm fine weather gave more than enough leisure, the sails stood for days and nights without having to be braced about — he got a game of dice on deck, shook the deceptive cubes out of the box and glared to see how many pips he had thrown, himself with a die for a head and a cinq in his face. They did not play for nothing; what money and valuables there were on board travelled by degrees from one Diego to another and back again, several times; now a man would be the owner of all the movable property in the ship, the object of cringing deference on the part of all the rest, now he would be reduced to beggary again, but whatever happened it stayed in the family. Play was hot, at times not without danger to life and limb, blood boiled up. Diego was stirred to the depths of his soul when luck went against him, he staked everything he possessed, down to his shirt, and his lips could be seen moving as he made secret promises to the Virgin Mary; and when he lost in spite of that he tore his shirt to strips, and included the Mother of God in an oath which cannot be repeated, an exclamation which placed the Holy Virgin in the same class as the unclean creature on whose flesh in a smoked condition the crew lived daily, God's curse on it! At last Diego staked his amulet, and when that too was lost, and he was a naked heathen, he gambled for his hair, his life, his sweetheart, his share of heaven, everything, until at last his luck actually did turn.

Next day Diego might have won back all his possessions and a good deal of the others'. For a change they played cards, those who knew how; higher notions of numbers were required here and the illiterate contented themselves with looking on, a numerous and interested crowd around the few sorcerers who sat in a ring on deck with their naked feet under them, conjuring, each with a fan of the apocalyptically painted leaves in his hand. It was the book of fortune and its reading entailed excitement, the players disagreed and stabbed one another with their eyes, tapped the deck angrily with their fingers, nodded ferociously and shuffled the cards again; they smacked one card after another on to the deck like a blacksmith swinging his hammer: *espadilla, basta, punto*, and the adversary was smashed! They wrinkled their foreheads and thought, threw down all the cards at once and pushed across ducats from one pile to the other, the whole quite incomprehensible to the illiterates who looked on in wonder; how did they manage to keep it all in their heads? With the pictures on the cards they were familiar enough, there were knaves, kings and queens, lovely to look upon, the only ladies they had on board, sad to say; Diego pressed a card to his bosom, clasped it with both his arms in a storm of passion; it was the Queen of Hearts — oh, well, well!

What had come over Diego? He was seen to embrace the water-butt when he came near it, and poured tender words over it; his voice had a queer ring in it, he sang evening hymns and was ready to die of grief, he was gay, fantastic, witty, not exactly decorous, there were few things that didn't prompt his fancy in a particular way, the swelling sails, ho, hey! how they stretched, how they stretched, the mast seemed so straight, slender as a waist, and he had to embrace that too; he kissed his fingers and made declarations of love to the *Niña*, their sister, sailing a little way off; the *Pinta* didn't matter so much, that was a he-ship, but Sister was so sweet, she curtsied so sweetly in the waves, dipped her bow with a girlish air, with foam like a lace collar round her neck, and she had such tight little white sails, hey ho!

Even in the highest quarter there was a change of mood for the better during those sunny days before reaching the Canaries; the Admiral now and then opened his lips, occasionally indeed he came down from the poop and mixed with mortals in the waist of the ship, and Diego had an opportunity of finding out that this man of mystery had a warm and pleasant smile and was in certain respects the most unpretending of all on board.

At other times he was to be seen deeply engaged in his measurements and algebraic arts; every day he hung his astrolabe out in the sun and let it and the elements work upon one another, not without a shiver down Diego's back; properly speaking, no doubt, the magic disc with all its secret signs and the man who used it ought to have been burnt, except that of course the safety of the ship depended on his arts, but it was nasty to look at. At night the Admiral pointed up at the sky with a big pair of compasses straddling between the stars, presumptuously and with a lack of the deference due to one's Creator; necessary, may be, for the navigation of the ship, but Diego didn't like to see it.

And when it was Diego's turn at the helm they were serious hours for him; the actual steering was easy enough, but he could not get used to the presence of the compass, it gave him an uncanny feeling to watch the living, quivering needle in its glass house making for the north all the time with its nose, whichever way the ship was heading; it was what he had to steer by, but it made him uncomfortable all the same, like some kinds of worms and creeping things with feelers. At night Diego's hair was apt to stand on end when he watched the needle nosing about in the gleam of the little lamp; whatever Powers lay behind it, *he* had no compact with them, and Diego crossed himself time and again, he steered and he followed the compass, but beyond that it would have to be on the head of the skipper.

As regards the Admiral, he was calm, with a deep and powerful breathing; at last he had put the years behind him and looked forward to what was to come. He was at sea, and sailing was his nature, he felt more and more at home with every day that passed.

Now they were going as they ought, southward; autumn was advancing, but it grew warmer every day! Ah, age had touched him, they had robbed him of his years, God forgive them, but now, every hour he grew older he was approaching — what was he approaching? Eternal summer, said the sun, the soft air, which every day was softer, the fair wind said it, the waves that leisurely advanced before him like great blue outriders, the stars said it, the stars!

With them Columbus consorted in the long refreshing nights, to them he raised his soul and accompanied them on their sure but inscrutable paths. Abaft the ship's course and high up in the sky stood the lodestars, the two stars in the Little Bear which the seaman steers by, near the North Star, round which in the course of a night they make a half compass, the great clock of heaven whose tilting always tells the seaman what time it is at night. Beneath it the Great Bear, the mighty constellation which takes up more space in the heavens than any other — and yet how immensely greater is the rest of the sky! Orion rises and flaunts himself in the sky like an eagle with spreading wings, the evening star shows its distant gleaming soul, advancing visibly day by day, the moon, that blind one, our friend by night, the beautiful great moon!

Never did he tire of the starry sky, of being under it and watching its movements from evening to morning; Columbus, the sleepless one, fed his soul on the march of time, saw the sun come up and break out of the sea, saw it take its sovereign course over the heavens, till it sank again red and mighty in the sea on the other side, and it was as though time and space left their mark on his inmost sense, he *felt* how long they had sailed and what was his position; an extraordinary cosmic second sight took possession of him, in the calm nights when he was alone on the poop and the stars swung above him it was as though he could hear the music of the seven spheres of heaven, one within the other, shrill but immensely distant; for brief ecstatic instants he caught the feeling of what the reason knows but cannot turn into an image: the heavens and their revolutions with all the heavenly bodies that lie in the same sphere. On rare occasions he thought he heard a crinkling sound, muffled by thousands of miles, and nodded: the axles of the spheres creaking against one another, and the night seemed to him so vast, how mighty was the mill of heaven! Almighty!

And then when he turned his eyes from the shining nails of the vault of heaven the ocean lay beneath him in a ring, colossal, and yet he knew how small a patch it was that could be seen at any time; the ocean stretched to infinity, it made a man dizzy — so enormous, so incomprehensibly wide was the earth!

There was one thing that could be felt. In this very thing Columbus's profoundest experience was wrapped up, an observation summed up through all his life at sea, in itself inconceivable and yet based on direct perception, or a kind of feeling: the earth was round! This had already been declared in ancient writings, though not in the Bible, but a man must have seen it himself, so to speak, to be clear about it. And it was the altitude of the stars, their angle with the horizon, that told it. When one had familiarized one's self with the position of the stars in the sky and had sailed sufficiently far north and south, between Iceland and Guinea, as Columbus had, and when one kept an estimate of distances the whole time, the log, which Columbus carried in his head more than any man had ever done, then one could perceive that the earth was round, nay, in a certain inexpressible sense one could feel how *big* it was.

It was this observation and his inner conviction that had given Columbus his idea of a circumnavigation. For if the earth was round up and down, from north to south, it must also be so from east to west, around the Equator; and if one sailed due west for sufficiently long one must end by going right round the earth. Nobody would believe it; now it should be proved!

Sailing from Spain as far south as the Canary Isles the difference in altitude was already conspicuous to one who was practised in watching it; indeed, to a certain extent the difference could be felt every day; one was conscious of sailing on an immensely extended spherical surface, from north to south, and not for a moment did one lose the sense of how far west one had come.

Now, when he was as far south as he thought of going, the course would be set due west, and then they would see!

In the clear starry nights when Columbus was alone with the universe he could *see* that he was right. How else were the sun and moon and all the fixed stars and planets, the spheres in short, able to swing about the earth, unless it was round and suspended freely in space?

II

ON THE OCEAN

FROM August 9 to September 6, almost a month, they were delayed at the Canary Isles: it was the *Pinta* that had lost her rudder, a sneakish trick of the two men who owned the ship and were taking part in the voyage but wanted to be left behind — treachery and delays to the last, a yet deeper insight into human nature; but the damage was repaired, and with the loss of a month the voyage was resumed, now due west into the Ocean, towards open sea where nobody had ever sailed before.

Tenerife was in eruption that year, and when Columbus sailed past it at night-time the crew of the *Santa Maria* had a vision that took the marrow out of their bones, the whole sky full of blood-red fire, the immense cone in the midst of the sea, illumined from top to bottom by its own flame, smoke and red-hot stones shooting up from the summit which seemed split with veins of fire, lava streams reaching far down the mountain's sides. The deck of the ship was as light as by day, for miles on all sides the night was banished, but stood like a jet-black wall around the horizon. Lightnings came and went amid the smoke, and deep boomings arose as though from below the bottom of the sea. It was a foretaste of the end of the world that the sailors were given; and if the impression afterwards gave place to others it had nevertheless sunk in and did not make them any bolder for the voyage.

Nor had their stay in the Canary Isles been of a kind to harden them; a good deal of softness and self-will that had been fostered ashore on the enchanting islands had to be driven out again by the rope's end before they had a taste for plain seaman's work. Diego, who had come in contact with creatures of a strange native charm, some of the few Guanchos left unmixed in the islands, had added a fresh influence to the many and various ones that had already contributed to form his character; he was out of humour the first few days on board, with something foreign about him, and seemed to be nursing memories that were only half his own, the other half distant; and Diego shaded his eyes with his hand and gazed back at the cone of Tenerife till it floated away in its own veil, like a woman shrouding her face in her hair; he was melancholy, little inclined for talk all day.

But next morning when Tenerife was no longer in sight he surprised his mates by breaking out into new songs, with wild melodies of their own and a text of which he only knew fragments, in a language of which he only understood a few words, the sweetest ones; they often came back to him on the voyage like an echo which made Diego sad; and when the *Niña* aired her white hangings alongside, the only reminder of anything sisterly left on the wide ocean, Diego shook his head bent down between his knees as he sat on deck, he was the poorest man that sailed the sea.

On September 8 they got a stiff north-easterly breeze, just what was wanted, and it held, it had come in earnest. One morning they looked around and could no longer spy a vestige of land, the desolate ring of Ocean all the way round, and they looked at each other: was that the idea? Their hearts sank. Yes, that was the idea; up on the poop walked the Admiral with a face there was no mistaking; he had them in his hand, and he would use them, to the end. They were dazed, their eyes sought help from the other ships which were in sight, now near at hand, now farther off, sailing the same course, due west; and from them no doubt eyes were turned to the *Santa Maria*. There were these three little ships sailing together and keeping each other company, and beyond them nothing but the wide and terrible Ocean. . . .

That first forenoon tears were shed in secret, men came upon each other with red eyes everywhere; deep down in the hold where he had been sent to fetch something a man met a friend in the dark who turned his face away; up aloft where a sail had to be cleared he found a comrade who had climbed up into solitude to weep; the cook in his galley had red eyes. But they could see by the man of iron up aft that there was no turning back. He paced up and down, like a lion, with his eyes on the west, those fathomless eyes, blue as the sea — was he then the sea itself? He was calm, as if he knew the way, as if he was only going home, with his cargo of innocents that he had lured on board — was it Death himself they had shipped with?

The *Santa Maria* pitched in the long, deep Atlantic seas with her curving hull, high fore and aft, like a cradle rocking in the sea, her timbers groaned, her yards and tackle swung, her bows stamped up a collar of green translucent water and foam; she was no good sailer, but now she had a fair wind, and she made headway.

The clumsy caravel — which is a word derived from crab — built half as a fortress, combined in herself the same elements that were found aboard of her. At core she was a viking ship, with a mainmast and a big squaresail, of a hundred tons burthen, like a middle-sized schooner of our days, overcrowded with her crew of fifty-two. In her build she must have been derived from the fleets of the Normans, who made their way into the Mediterranean and left their traces on its shipping, Genoa, Venice — the gondola! — Spain too, where they penetrated up the rivers, the Guadalquivir; but in the Mediterranean they had added to her the lateen sail aft on a mast of its own, and forward she had got another extra mast with a smaller squaresail, and before that on the bowsprit she carried a still smaller squaresail to steady her;

above the main course a topsail was set; she was a ship on the way from one type to another. The castles fore and aft were excrescences based on experience of land warfare, floating towers. The oars of the Norman ship were gone; in place of them she had artillery, little cast cannons, falconets and lombards, she could make a noise and do mischief at long range. Gothic was the style of the rich carvings all over the woodwork. In board she carried the Middle Ages and the Mediterranean, a leader of Northern ancestry, seer, wanderer and ferryman, and a ship's company with the multifarious heritage and the dark fiery blood which the Mediterranean had mingled together from all its shores and all its ages.

And as the caravel was now rocking in the sea, with a rolling, laborious gallop in which she seemed to be pulling herself in, but keeping steadily on, all day long, towards the sunset — a gigantic red sun like a one-eyed cyclops burying himself alone in the lonely ocean and leaving a bloody sky and clotted seas behind — so she rocked on through the brief evening, into the night, heeling over a little with the wind on her quarter; she was a caravel with a mission, she would sail day and night until she reached what she would reach!

Behind her lay the Europe she had left, an ancient world of conflict, countries and peoples mutually involved in relations of conquest and dependence, the Europe of popes, emperors and kings, of proud chivalry and of peasants buried in hovels and obscurity; the all-powerful bishops, the hordes of monks, the burnings of heretics, the commonalty bound hand and foot by the powers above them; the ascending ladder of the feudal nobility; the princes with their arbitrary interchange of kingdoms, their policy of marriages and wars of succession; Europe like a string of great estates, which in fact were soon to be married into one hand, nearly all of them!

But down on the ground it was getting warm, like a fermenting hotbed. A certain Doctor Faust was perambulating Europe with his arts, Satan was abroad! A nine-year-old boy was in Mansfield, having Christian doctrine instilled into him and getting birched, the same year that Columbus sailed from Palos — Martin Luther. Copernicus was nineteen and carried within him the germ of revolutions. The peasants of Europe were meeting in their miserable alehouses and clamouring like dogs; nobody noticed them, and yet more than one great lord, riding by with hawk on hand, would be cudgelled to death in his armour by the swarming mob.

The Europe of that day towered up as though built for eternity, its central pillar was carried down through the earth to the basic rock; but it was after all the shell of an old tortoise they had built upon, and one fine day it moved in its thousand years' sleep and pushed its lizard's head out of the slime. . . .

The *Santa Maria* then had chosen a good time for sailing; Europe's heaven had lasted long enough, it was time to knock a hole in it.

Whatever might be happening at home, *they* were shut out from it, who now felt imprisoned, ringed about by the sea; perhaps they would never see the Old World again. And no word would ever be brought home of what had become of them, they would not even win the fame of the ill-fated like other poor brave men who perish and have a tomb and a great name; they would simply disappear, and soon even their disappearance would be forgotten.

So hard he was, the man aft! They thought they could understand a good deal, those who were with him, but this they could not understand, that he could expose himself to a trackless, inglorious death, for the sake of an exploit the issue of which no man could tell — no, that they could not understand.

A mournful feeling prevailed on board on the second and third days; in the morning they came on deck and saw the ocean's desolate ring, no land either ahead or astern, the loathsome waves, the sun travelling naked and pitiless in the sky, casting a glaring light on their misery, sea and sea and the bare sky right in their faces!

Cheerlessly the sun went down, a faded sea on every side, then darkness; with loud creaking the *Santa Maria* laboured in the waves, plunging and plunging on her way into the uncertain gloom, towards the west.

That night Diego rolled himself up in a corner on deck, too hot to sleep down below. How hot it was getting! What would be the end of it? He shut his eyes tight, clenched his teeth upon his seething inside — impossible to sleep, impossible to lie awake. But a little while after he did fall asleep and twitched his limbs as he slept, with muffled groans from his troubled, racking dreams.

High on the poop a dark waking figure could be seen, the Admiral, with his everlasting rods and circles in his hand, sighting up at the moon, always busy with some celestial tricks — did he never sleep? Night and day he was to be seen on the poop — did he need no sleep at all? He couldn't even be human.

Oh yes, the Admiral slept, a nap now and then, when it could not be avoided, but he never went regularly to bed. He could not do that, for he had the log in his head and dared not lose his estimate of the distance sailed. When he slept it was for a short spell, just such and such a time; he had himself called when the fixed time was up and was thus able to retain his sense of the passing of the hours in conjunction with the headway they were making. And as an old sailor he knew no difference between night and day.

There was another figure moving on the forecastle, the lookout on watch; to-night it was young Pedro Gutierrez; he walked up and down and seemed much engrossed by the moon; he could be heard singing pious songs — evidently a queer fellow.

Young Pedro had joined as a volunteer; he was the son of decent people, but had no means and lent an ear to the siren voices which promised rapid fortunes at sea. On board he had made himself remarked by his innocence and nice behaviour; he would have been an easy butt, if he had not also proved himself a swordsman not to be meddled with. He was very taciturn, his thoughts were fixed on other things than those of the rest, and finally he was allowed to go about unnoticed.

To-night he was singing, standing still by the rail and looking out over the sea where the moon was about to set, thoughtful, with slender, soft features, manly enough but so handsome that it seemed a lovely young girl was buried in them, his mother, who was now so far away. He raised his eyes in the starlight, sighed and sang:

> Now comes the sea's fell darkness,
> The moon sinks fast and hides;
> And coldly blows the porpoise
> Against the ship's thin sides.
> With oily cry a seagull
> Bodes ill for us to-night.
> But I must keep my watch here,
> Until the sun brings light.

The Virgin's starry garment
Is spread across the sky.
We men can be hopeful
And pray to those on high.
We cannot, if we wished it,
Foresee what still shall be —
O vouch, our Lord's sweet Mother,
That land again we see!

With many a tear at parting,
But with courageous mind,
We waved a tender farewell
To those we left behind.
When shall I see my father?
Where is my sweetheart gone?
The ocean's ways affright me.
Am I to die so soon?

Within my father's garden
There grows an apple tree,
A joyful gift from Heaven,
Where many a bird can be.
In springtime when the bee hums
It stands with blossom gay;
And when the birds are silent
It flings its fruit away.

Behind the ancient hedgerow
We used to hide, we two;
'Twas there, my only loved one,
You promised to be true.
Ah, shall I ever see it,
That dear old apple tree?
Will you be there, my darling,
To share its shade with me?

No green leaves here can greet us,
The sea's as salt as tears.
A creature 'midst the billows
Lives lonely with his fears.
Who knows where ocean ceases?
Where shall our voyage end?
In thy hands are we, Mother.
A happy landfall send!

The distant lands of promise,
Where all is made of gold,
They give us dreams of riches,
Until we grow too old.

But what a seaman suffers
I'll tell from what I know —
There's many a time I'm longing
To a dry grave to go.

Beyond the seas and rivers
Lies Paradise, they say —
O merciful God's Mother,
Preserve our souls this day!
To thee in Heaven's glory
We raise our sinful hand —
Give us a peaceful mid-watch,
And bring us back to land!

It was thirty-five days before they sighted land, a long time for men with such crazy nerves as most of the ship's company; to the inflexible leader himself the longest time he had known. As was to be expected, he had great difficulties with his crew.

The deep despondency of the first few days after they had lost sight of land soon gave way to insubordination; there were scowling looks, some trial of strength was felt to be coming, it would have to be seen whether it was safe to treat Spaniards in this fashion; eyes that till now had kept to the deck or never gone higher than the ladder were now fixed with a sinister challenge upon the Admiral. It came to a kind of collision, not open warfare, only a trial, and it fell out in this way.

Among themselves the crew talked of nothing but turning back; they said not a word to the Admiral, but they began to steer badly. It happened more and more frequently that the helmsman was awkward enough to let her come up into the wind, with a northerly course; they were trying it on, those that took the helm, gave the Admiral a stiff look and fell off their course, like naughty children seeing how far they could go. They were corrected and the course was resumed; the Admiral seemed to have no suspicion of what they were up to, or pretended with angelic patience not to see it.

But one morning the game was up on both sides. Contrary to his custom, the Admiral had left the quarter-deck for a short time, and when he came up again, and looked round, the course had been laid as near north as the ship would lie. . . . A couple of seconds later he was at the helm himself, laid his fists over the helmsman's and turned the ship back into a westerly course, turned the tiller with the man and all, and he was no wisp of straw either, a very stalwart man that same helmsman, but his legs trailed under him like a doll's, the Admiral just took a sweep with him and the tiller and the ship herself; she lay right over with the hard helm, heeled around into her new course, and the horizon danced a quarter of the way round. It was just as if the Admiral had lifted the whole vessel and put her down again!

And he was not out of breath after it, hadn't changed colour, was scarcely angry; he only smiled with amusement and a trifle ominously at Sancho Ruiz, the chief mate, who had allowed the thing to happen.

It did not happen again. The helmsman looked at his hands, which were all crumpled, and afterwards soaked them in a bucket of water — they had been badly crushed. The rest of the crew went about their work with pale lips. Had any one imagined that he was so strong! That he was as big as an ox could be seen, but that he was so quick! He was *invisible* for the second it took him to dash to the helm, he leapt like a heavy cat, and those big freckled spades of hands, with their red bristles, why they were blacksmith's tongs and not human hands at all. Unfair!

After that there was nothing wrong with the steering. The dark smouldering eyes the Admiral found turned upon him wherever he went had now a look of suffering, but the spite in them was concealed for the time being. The temper of the ship was dull for a few days, while the open sea still stretched as open before them, and the feeling of how far they were from land grew more and more dismal. And now the sea began to change its character; they still had the finest weather, but somehow the sea was more hollow, it ran in an ugly swell which lifted the *Santa Maria* as high as a house up and down besides making her roll and pitch; it took away the breath of many of them and was an unmistakable warning that they were beginning to sail out of the world and were approaching zones where there was perhaps no world at all. What made the ocean rock in such an abysmal way?

A mast which they saw one day drifting in the sea, a big piece of mast from a ship that must have been bigger than the *Santa Maria*, seemed to answer their anxious question. The ship had been wrecked somewhere in these waters, and if such a big ship could not live, what would become of smaller ones? The Admiral, whom they approached on this serious subject, took a different, cynical view and made light of the whole matter: that a ship had gone down here seemed to him a proof that the sea was just like any other sea — such things happened. Beyond the world there were no ships at all, they might be sure. For that matter nobody could tell how far or from what direction the mast had drifted. With this consolation the crew went to their quarters and wept. The sad piece of wreckage had made them so sorrowful, it had such a mournful look.

It rolled so forsakenly in the sea with its splintered top, green with slime, waterlogged and lying under the surface, always awash, and when the wave sank from it the end of the mast hung with dripping seaweed and studded with barnacles on its under side; and once it had been shaped by human hands, a tree once in the forest, and now the corpse of a mast in the sea's desolate wet churchyard, a thing rocking in the waves, floating with the current, abandoned to a drift unknown, lonely, lonely, travelling out of one horizon into another, a thing without a face and yet like a living creature, it broke one's heart to see it, as the waves carried it away and dashed over it in their sport; as long as it was in sight they gazed after it, and when it could no more be seen they turned away with tearful eyes.

The Admiral observed it too, long and carefully; the rate at which they left it astern was to him a welcome clue for the day's log and for estimating their leeway.

The thirteenth of September was an unlucky day. Not immediately so far as the crew was concerned, they only heard of it afterwards, but that day their fate hung in the balance, as also did several of the heavenly bodies, apparently, racing the compass-needle! Well, a layman forms his own interpretation of matters he is not conversant with but which reach him by way of rumour; perhaps indeed he sees into the heart of things in his own way, even if he is not an astronomer. It was reported that the compass had been deceptive that day, so grossly deceptive that even the man at the helm had noticed it, pointing a good way to one side of north, where it should have been. A serious business, which of course the Admiral tried to hush up, until the sailing master and the mate discovered it for themselves and called the Admiral's attention to it a day or two later. With them, of course, the Admiral could make no secret of what had happened, the magnetic needle *had* deviated considerably from north to west; but was it necessarily the compass that was wrong, might it not be the North Star that had fallen a few degrees out of its orbit?

And it actually appeared that he had succeeded in convincing the other navigators of this, for nothing more came of the affair — they went on sailing as before. Properly speaking, wasn't it a much worse thing that the North Star was toppling? An omen, one would imagine, a clear hint from above. How was it with this foreigner's Christianity if he disregarded such a warning?

More probably, though, it was the compass that pointed wrongly, and that was in reality a terrible thing; it could mean nothing else but that they were nearing the magnet mountain, which, of course, was situated somewhere out here at the world's end; and if once you came within range of its attraction you were lost, the nails and everything of iron would fly out of the ship, going clean through the woodwork, timbers and planks would fall asunder, the ship would part and become a mass of wreckage in the water all in an instant! They had hopes the Admiral would be in full armour when it happened — to see him fly through the air, imagine him smacking against the magnet mountain and sticking to it, rotting against its wall head downwards! Joking apart, was it *justifiable* to keep to the course they were on when the magnetic needle had pointed its silent warning. If so, what did they have this invention of the devil for?

The crew were choking with tears and grievances. But the Admiral continued to pace the poop, calm as ever. Was he though? To tell the truth, this phenomenon of the variation of the compass, now observed for the first time, disturbed him not a little; in reality, he could imagine no explanation — except perhaps just the same as the crew's, that they were approaching some stronger magnetic force, since the needle turned. However, they were out to venture something after all. So long as the nails stayed in the ship they would go on sailing.

But two days after the unlucky Thirteenth something happened which for a while converted the *Santa Maria* into a madhouse, although in itself it was a far less ominous thing than the affair of the compass. A terrible great meteor fell from heaven — in broad daylight, so to speak, towards evening while it was still light. It came straight down from heaven, everybody saw it, like a mighty blazing tail of fire lashing down from on high and disappearing in the sea — with a boiling sound which many thought they had heard, a whistling up in space. The whole ship was one shriek after the fiery portent had gone out. Half the crew lay howling on deck with their hands over their eyes, the rest ran about wailing and wringing their hands; those who kept their senses best fell on their knees and loudly invoked the Virgin Mary, repeating Ave after Ave. One hid himself under the water-butt, another bored his head into a coiled hawser like a worm, wriggling his body and legs outside; even the officers, Juan de la Cosa, Sancho Ruiz, Alonzo de Moguer, the ship's doctor, who ought to have known better, lost their presence of mind and raised an alarm. God's blood! they were all done for. . . .

And then nothing more happened. The mortal terror passed off; but this time the Admiral came right down from his lofty castle and mixed among the crew to calm them and explain the thing. How could they be so terrified of a big shooting star?

Shooting star! Scandalized exclamations, genuine indignation, hands left their faces and weeping eyes were riveted on the Admiral, chests heaving like bellows. What is the blasphemer saying? A portent, a holy portent, that was what it was.

Well, well, a portent if you like — the Admiral was conciliatory and ignored the smack of mutiny in their words — but it had shown itself beneficent, hadn't it? It didn't set fire to the ship but fell quite a long way off. For his part he had seen such falls of fire from heaven before. Perhaps it hurt their feelings to call them shooting stars, but still they were certainly phenomena which were to be explained in the same way, stars or other celestial lights which had come loose from the vault above and dropped down — a very common thing. Naturally there was a meaning in it, as in everything that came from heaven, but to call it a portent. . . .

It *was* a portent! the seamen sobbed. The softer among them obstinately persisted in their grief, weeping and drying their eyes, sniffling inconsolably; but others went about in little knots with clenched teeth, looked at each other, and their eyes grew savage. It was pretty strong what that Italian had the face to offer them! To explain away God's obvious warning written in letters of fire! Had it happened astern of the ship as a warning against turning back? No, ahead, due west — could there be any doubt?

Stars, celestial light — when the fire that fell was bigger than sun, moon and all the stars together! A natural explanation indeed! It was unwholesome to have so many heretics aboard of a ship — that and all the rest!

Scornful and insolent snorts were heard blended with the Admiral's kindly, restraining and reassuring voice. And the discussion was long. Darkness fell, and still they were disputing about the alarming occurrence; several were quite unnerved and spoke in the dying, tearful voice of men stunned by a disaster, while in others hate blazed up again and again. But at last their feelings calmed down. The Admiral talked and talked, and in the end the mere sound of his monotonous voice had a soothing effect.

And meanwhile they were sailing on, since nobody had thought of actually stopping the ship. The wind was fair; they were long past the place where the meteor had fallen. Mentally the Admiral calculated what distance they had covered, making up his log while the talk was going on. And that was until everybody turned in for the night, weary and dull with sorrow, many of them quite sick with emotion; here and there long-drawn sighs and chest-shaking sobs could still be heard from dark corners.

The Admiral went quietly back to his post, took observations and wrote for the rest of the night by the light of a little horn lantern. There was a special piece of work which he preferred to do at night, the log-book, which with provident foresight and knowledge of human nature he kept in two versions: one, the correct one, for his own use, and one to be shown to his officers, who were then free to pass on the information; in this the distances sailed were shortened every day by as many miles as he dared; it was no use scaring the crew by telling them they were farther out in the ocean than was strictly necessary.

In the course of the night there was a milder panic, which however soon subsided: a man screamed out in terror and woke the others; he had happened to look over the side and had seen that they were sailing through nothing but fire, flames and gleaming waves all round the ship! Everybody flocked to the ship's side: wails and lamentations, they were sailing in sheer fire! The Admiral was down among them at once. Hadn't they ever seen phosphorescence before? Weren't they sailors, some of them at any rate? In the Mediterranean it was sometimes just as bright. Oh well, they were sleepy and sore and allowed themselves to be talked round. Some of them *had* seen it before and had only shouted because the others did. But others nodded and nodded, convinced in dead earnest. Of course, it was the fire that had fallen from heaven in the evening and they were sailing straight into it! Then the Admiral could not help laughing. How was it then that it hadn't set fire to the ship long ago? And he had a bucket of water drawn up and asked any one who liked to put his hand in it — it was quite cold. . . .

Well — cold; lukewarm, they would call it. And what was it then that shone down below in the water? That the Admiral could easily explain: it was simply the sunlight which the water had absorbed by day and gave off again at night. This explanation was received with hiccups — they knew what they knew. A reflection from *down below*, Purgatory with the hatches off, may be . . . ! Growling and bitterness; some were not ashamed to turn their backs on the Admiral. Soon after the ship was asleep again.

But from now on the Admiral was more and more often on the main deck. He no longer considered his dignity so strictly, and it was remarkable how this man, hitherto so taciturn, developed eloquence; he would often discuss things with the simplest of the hands for hours at a time, things which he might easily have said were no concern of theirs. It did no harm to the distance which ought to be kept between commander and crew. In one respect he possessed a quality which nothing he said or did could add to or take away from — his size.

Its effect was sure, even if nobody, not even himself, was quite aware of it. But not only did he keep his direct power over the men's minds, he even began to make friends among them. Many of them had not really paid much attention to the Admiral before now, and discovered that this giant, who bore the stamp of courage and indomitable resolution, who at the same time was capable, as he had shown, of unexampled violence, that this man was good-natured at heart. The big head with its reddish-grey mane, and the beard, which was now allowed to grow and was also mottled red and white, would sometimes beam with human feeling, a warmth which reached him from creation in spite of all, and which he gave back again. He had a pleasant smile, which showed two great rows of worn teeth; the blue eyes, usually so distant, might turn with a look of their own upon any one he was talking to, he had quick intelligence and sympathy for everybody. They were curious eyes, quite light and small with white surroundings and pink at the corners, something like what one sees in pigs, rather sore, for he scarcely slept at all. His voice was singular, rather small and weak for such an unusually big man, cautious, penetrated with loneliness and kindness towards men, even those who opposed him.

But it was felt that, whether silent or eloquent, he never disclosed his inmost thought, and to that no one ever succeeded in penetrating.

There was endless talking in the days that followed, on all kinds of subjects. The Admiral was almost always down on deck among the crew, all the time he could spare from his observations. The *Santa Maria* seemed like a sort of floating school, with grown-up boys and a schoolmaster who towered above them all and was regarded with very diverse feelings, who gave lessons all day long, received complaints and gave instruction, over and over again — a providence that was never tired of leading its souls, not the way they would go but the way they should.

III

IN THE TRADE WIND

THE SARGASSO SEA, hundreds of leagues from land; three little ships lost on the boundless ocean, and their crews in despair.

The worst of their fright over this threatening new phenomenon, the masses of seaweed floating mile after mile in the ocean, had subsided; but it had been a hard trial. The first floating island of weed was taken for firm ground, land; it looked like a very low stretch of meadow lying flush with the water, and for a moment the idea that it might be land raised a flicker of hope, which was only to give way to deep disappointment and uneasiness — if it was not land, what could it be?

Soon the islands became so numerous that they formed a continuous carpet of weed over the whole surface of the sea as far as the eye could reach, and the Admiral kept straight ahead, while the crew cried out, in God's holy name, and implored the helms-man to fall off. Too late, they were already in the midst of the green, and look! she could sail through it without losing so very much of her way — for the present. But supposing the masses of weed got denser and they ended by sticking fast in them? That it was a sort of seaweed the Admiral convinced them all by hav-ing some of it fished up; but not any known kind of weed, and how could it grow here, how did it come here, many many leagues from land?

They need not be too sure that they were so very far from land, suggested the Admiral, sanguine of course as usual, and putting on a bold face just when the others looked blackest. But where could this land be? At any rate it was not to be seen for miles ahead or on either side, only a boundless pale-green expanse of tufted water with a false promise of meadows — so deceptive in-deed that many believed in them. Might it not be supposed that sunken countries or submarine realms lay underneath here, from which all this grass had come loose and floated up? In that case it was dangerous; there must be shoals, at any moment they might run aground, and stranding so far from any coast would mean death. The Admiral's only reply to these complaints was to have soundings taken, and the lead ran out for hundreds of fathoms, all the line they had, and no bottom! If the pastures they were talking about lay below, then he must say they were a long way down; and the Admiral was cruel enough to add that *now* nobody would be likely to expect a cow to stick its head out of the sea from the meadows below or to see a church spire jutting out. Loud cries of pain drowned his words; the men were thrown from fright into terror. So deep! Why, there was no bottom at all here! So they *were* outside the world now and over the incon-ceivable abyss of Ocean. They had to prop each other up at the thought, and their eyes nearly dropped out of their heads. To be wrecked here, to sink and sink and sink. . . . But the Admiral asked them rather dryly if it wouldn't be all the same to them how much water they drowned in, a fathom or a mile, if it had to be: a heartless thing to say, and incautious. They roared — one man threw his cap at him. The Admiral turned his back on them, but came again and pointed with a great sweep of the arm out over the sea of weed that shone like gold in the dazzling rays of the sun: if they believed that all this splendour came from impossible submarine islands, then it was *his* belief that it was a presage of real islands, perhaps not so very far off, where the golden fields extended just as far as the seaweed here — floors of gold far and wide! And then they made a fuss like a pack of women over the trouble and risk of getting there — as if the islands wouldn't have been discovered and occupied long ago if there had been no danger in it!

Silence, not a sound; some of them were put to shame, others led into a new train of thought — it sounded wonderful, that about the gold. And the end of it was that they went on sailing; while bandying words they easily did a half-day's run. But the men stuck to their opinion. They passed through the weed right enough, but all the same it was an ominous sign that the sea was getting so thick. What if it thickened still more? They might sail in gruel, but in porridge any man would stick fast. And the Admiral's words had left a sting behind them: if he had more learning, it didn't give him the right to make fun of poor Christian men.

If, however, there were lamentations over the danger of getting stuck in the sea of weed, it was not long before the fact of their slipping so easily through it gave uneasiness. What would be the end of it? This everlasting breeze from the north-east! Why, it held for weeks, they never touched the sails, which stood day and night on the starboard tack, easy sailing, but what about it when they had to go the other way? How would they come home again? What kind of a wind was it anyhow? It had never been reported anywhere else that the wind held so long from one quarter; it could scarcely be interpreted otherwise than that there was a sucking from the opposite quarter, the one they were making for, like the wind that goes over a waterfall; it was from the *Abyss* the sucking came, they were in it now, and it was a desperate thing, it was tempting God and throwing away one's fair wind, which was of the kind the Evil One sends . . . etc., etc.

The Admiral shrugged his shoulders. Truth to tell, he did not understand himself why the wind held so long; it was a new thing in his experience, and every day he scanned the clouds and all other indications a seaman stores in his head and recognizes on later occasions; but these waters were strange to him, and nobody as yet could know how it was with this wind. There was every reason to be grateful for it though, if the crew had not been growing more anxious every day and scarcely to be managed in the long run.

Then it happened one day, the 23rd of September, that the wind changed, they had a head-sea, and the crew could no longer maintain that there were no other winds in these seas but from the north-east; Columbus was saved for another space, and he it was who clasped his hands that evening in deepest gratitude to the All-bountiful, in spite of the fact that they had made no headway that day.

In his private meditations, divided between the Bible and the log-book, he could not help thinking that evening of Moses, who led his refractory people through so many real dangers, but whose most difficult task was to preserve them from their own imagination and instinct of self-destruction.

But all the complaints returned with renewed force when the wind changed again; once more every one could clearly see that all the waves were hurrying to the west, the whole sea was flowing that way, straight into the Abyss!

They now passed out of the Sargasso Sea, out into clear deep waves again, and if lately they had eyed the hated weed with furtive looks of woe, they now cast back inconsolable glances after it. For all the signs of land the Admiral had fabricated with his ready tongue while it was there, were vanished now. That seaweed showed the proximity of a coast had sounded right enough; but now? That crabs which they had found in the weed were a good sign, that birds and fish they had seen, which found food in it, also pointed to the nearness of land, of course — but now it was days ago, and still there was no land!

The men's heads were beginning to get a little addled: they saw sea monsters in every wave that curled, and huddled together in groups at night, afraid of the dark; they wept over the increasing heat, which left no doubt that they were approaching the scorching regions in the immediate neighbourhood of the sun, where nothing can live, except salamanders; they would not escape with being turned as dark as the blackamoors in Africa, they would be completely charred, scorched up like flies, the whole ship would blaze up — in the name of the most merciful God, man, turn about before it is too late!

Other voices made themselves heard, and those of the soberest men on board, the officers themselves. The bottom could be seen of the ship's provisions, in a literal sense; in several places they had gone down through the cargo to the bottom of the ship; if they were to count on food for the same number of days back as they had sailed out, they would have to turn pretty soon. To this Columbus said nothing. In his own mind he looked forward to the hour when they no longer *could* turn back, when their food was exhausted to that extent; then there would be no other way than straight ahead, but he didn't say this.

The other complaints he took up, rather glad to be able to keep them alive, so that they might overshadow thoughts of the provisions; he went through them again with the crew, as often and as long as they liked, talking and talking, hollow-eyed, stiff with fatigue but indefatigable. It ended in a sort of permanent ship's parliament on board, where all, even the ordinary seamen, had a voice, and where the tone grew sharper and sharper. During these discussions all the theoretical side of the voyage was probed deeper and deeper, a kind of cross-examination which the Admiral accepted in good part, and which he spun out with a certain warmth, keeping an inner eye on the log the whole time.

All that Columbus had adduced again and again for fourteen years, before a commission of scholars in Portugal, and before a learned commission at Salamanca, had to come up, and he had to listen to the same arguments against him and refute them again as well as he could. Now how did he think he would reach the Indies by this crazy route which took him farther and farther away from them every day he sailed?

To put it briefly, if the earth was round . . .

Yes, but the earth wasn't round! Everybody knew that, everybody could see it, and it was heresy to assert the contrary, high treason against the Church and against God. Juan de la Cosa, who was the owner of the vessel and accompanied the exposition in that capacity, here acted as spokesman and displayed no mean biblical knowledge. Neither the Pentateuch nor the Prophets nor the Apostles said anything about the earth being a globe; besides, ordinary common sense told you it was an error; take the Deluge, for instance, how would it have been possible if the earth was not flat? all the water would have run off if it had been curved . . .

Storms of applause from the whole crew for Juan de la Cosa, who modestly withdrew into the crowd, and a malicious chorus of yelping at Columbus.

But now the Admiral took to both Latin and Greek against Juan de la Cosa, quoted utterances of St. Augustine and compared them with things Aristotle had said, Strabo, Seneca, Pythagoras, Eratosthenes . . .

Aristotle . . . Juan de la Cosa nodded manfully, he had heard the name before, and knew that it carried weight, but he was not sure of his ground and the Admiral was given a chance of quoting at length all the reasons that had induced the ancients to assume the spherical form of the earth, the shadow it cast on the moon in an eclipse, the weightiest of proofs, which passed over the heads of the crew like the wildest moonshine. Juan de la Cosa, however, had understood it and came forward with an objection:

How was it possible that the earth cast a shadow on the moon, *even* if it was round? In that case the sun would have to pass right round the earth, *under* it so to speak . . .

COLUMBUS: That is just what it does.

JUAN DE LA COSA: Oh, I see. But then the earth must rest upon something, whether it is flat or round, a foundation; how can a heavenly body pass under that?

COLUMBUS: The earth has no foundation; it is a globe hanging freely in space.

Sensation. Suppressed passion here and there. All eyes hung upon Juan de la Cosa, who was quite distressed and looked at the Admiral with genuine sorrow, as he asked in a faltering voice how . . . how . . . the earth, weighing many hundred thousand quintals . . . hang freely in space, how could that be?

What is impossible to Almighty God? answered the Admiral with force. He who has set the spheres in motion and keeps them going, with sun, moon and stars to give light and measure the day, should He not be able to keep the earth suspended in its place in space? *He* alone knows how!

Juan de la Cosa bowed his head and his forefinger went up to his breast, the sign of the cross made itself at the mention of the holy name of God. The crew followed his example, they felt as if they were in church, and the threatening conflict of opinion was resolved in a moment of solemn awe.

But the dispute blazed up again, and Juan de la Cosa obstinately insisted, on behalf of all, that *even* if the earth was round, which it was *not;* nay, even if hung freely in space, by the power of God, whose name be praised, then it was nevertheless an impossible thing they were trying to do. A globe *might* be so big that to us men it would appear to be flat in that part where one was situated, granted, and that must necessarily be the upper part; but if one left it, one would have to proceed along a slope which would get steeper and steeper, vertical at last, and then turn inward on the under side, always supposing that the spherical theory held, which, of course, was sheer nonsense, for how could water hang on a globe all the way round?

Applause. *Bravo! bravo!* they cried to Juan de la Cosa; and he was really brave, he looked the Admiral straight in the face as, with a bow to his superior, he resumed his place in the crowd.

The last question the Admiral left alone and seized on the first, pounced on it like a hawk:

We are sailing *downward* at this moment!

Pause, until his meaning dawned on them, then violent excitement; several men shrieked aloud and ran to the bulwarks to look, some instinctively laid hand on hilt. Juan de la Cosa turned pale, but pulled himself together and asked:

And how did the Admiral think of sailing upward again?

Everybody grasped at once the bearing of Juan de la Cosa's words, pictured the immense curve down which they were engaged in sailing, saw the impossibility of ever coming up it again and stood as though turned to stone . . . .

In the midst of this consternation the Admiral was heard to laugh, a perfectly careless laugh at such a serious moment; he was making fun of them, the hell-hound, the cup was full, they wouldn't listen to him any more . . .

We are sailing *upward* also at this moment, said the Admiral mildly to Juan de la Cosa, and explained his meaning more precisely; if the earth was really round there could be neither up nor down at any given point, except in the direction that passed through the centre of the earth and the zenith . . . But Juan de la Cosa shook his head, gave the Admiral an honest look and shook his head, grieved for him, for his ship and for them all.

The Admiral then changed his tone, laughed with his cavernous eyes, and made as though he accepted the others' view, since they were in the majority; suppose they were right and the earth was flat. But in that case it could not be surrounded by an abyss down which the water plunged, for then the seas would long ago have run off the earth, the Deluge would have been impossible, as Juan de la Cosa very rightly pointed out. If on the other hand the Ocean lay about the earth in a ring, the common conception, it by no means precluded the idea of sailing westward to the Indies, round behind instead of straight ahead, not on a globe but on a circle, half-way round the earth's disc, if they preferred it that way . . .

Chorus of all hands that Juan de la Cosa was right, angry exclamation against the Admiral for evidently trying to obscure the heart of the matter and avoid Juan de la Cosa's direct question: how were you to sail up the curve of the earth again, when once you had had the mad idea of sailing down it? Out with it!

THE ADMIRAL: Now it was *they* who all believed that the earth was round!

Yells and bawling, cries of shame and general howls; and so the lesson came to an end.

In a succeeding one the Admiral had to produce all his reasons and proofs of the existence of land westward in the Ocean, apart from the cosmic ones; an argument they had heard before and that every man in Spain and Portugal had heard before, until they cried for help at the very sight of Columbus; an old trite lesson which he actually repeated for positively the last time, in fluent Spanish but with an accent that betrayed the Italian. In other circumstances than these, where their lives were at stake, they would have taken a wild delight in him, a glorious fool to have on board, all the more glorious as he was so big, so tall and so touched in the upper storey; had they not hated him as they did they might even have pitied him, alone against all, far out at sea, doubly alone as a stranger among strangers, this queer fish who was getting old and made himself a laughing-stock by repeating and repeating, explaining and dogmatizing about the same things over and over again —

Such as: From time immemorial ["Time immemorial . . ." Diego mimicked him, with Italian accent, discreet tone and all; aside, of course, but loud enough to amuse his neighbours] — from time immemorial there had been reports of a vanished land out in the Atlantic Ocean, Plato's Atlantis; opinions were divided as to whether it had been swallowed up by the sea or the way to it had been forgotten; the latter view was supported by rumours repeated through the ages of such lands or islands far to the west of Europe. Many were of the opinion that these were Paradise itself, the Lost Country, from which mankind had once been driven out and had never found the way back; the holy Brandanus had set out in search of them and had actually arrived at a happy isle in the Ocean, the abode of the Blest, as might be read in his legend; but since then the way had been lost again, it was eight hundred years since St. Brandan's voyage. The legend had afterwards been connected with the Canary Isles, wrongly of course; the islands must lie much farther out in the Ocean, at least twice as far as the Azores, which were also out of the question, and presumably more to the southward, possibly in the very direction in which they were now sailing.

Now it was to be remarked that in another, more recent view the legend of these mysterious islands or continents far far to the west might be regarded as obscure but substantially correct reports of the east coast of India, which extended so far around the earth that perhaps there had been contact with it now and then by the other way, straight across the Atlantic. It was known that very large islands lay off the coast of India, like Zipangu, of which Marco Polo had sufficiently trustworthy accounts; these must then be the same as the Antilia or the Island of Brazil which the latest geographers, in anticipation of their discovery, had already marked on their maps, as for example the most learned and famous Toscanelli ["What kind of a fool was he?" from Diego], and as the distance between the west coast of Europe and the extremity of India was more or less known, the width of the Atlantic, that is, the distance to be deducted from the whole circumference of the earth, could be approximately determined; in the Admiral's opinion it was neither more nor less than the distance they had already sailed, so now the islands might appear any day [scornful snorts from Diego and the rest of the audience; how often they had heard this sanguine irresponsible tale!]

Well, well, if the geographical arguments were no more obvious to them than the cosmic, then they had the direct, tangible proofs, the missives to be taken up and felt which from time to time had been brought by the Atlantic and which must point to there being land on the other side. In the first place there were the reports of many people who had *seen* the islands, on very clear days, out in the ocean to the west of the Canary Isles ["Long-sighted people, I must say" — Diego]; that was as it might be. Personal evidence: Columbus himself many years before in Madeira had given shelter to a ship-wrecked man who disclosed to him on his deathbed that he had been driven by a storm twenty-eight days out into the Atlantic on a voyage to England, and had there come upon islands the natives of which went about naked; afterwards he had got a fair wind back to Europe but was so worn out that he died in Madeira, the last of a crew of seventeen ["A nice story that! Why didn't he stay in the islands? Weren't they worth it?"]

There was Pedro Correa ["Oh, *that* fellow"] who was able to tell Columbus about a remarkable piece of driftwood that had come ashore at Porto Santo, a curiously dark wood and, be it noted, carved, though apparently not with iron tools. Still more remarkable: some big reeds had drifted up on the same shore, like a sort of grass on an extraordinarily large scale, almost as though they came from a country where everything was of supernatural size. ["Let's see them!"] Columbus himself might have had a chance of seeing them washed up with his own eyes; he had spent three years in Porto Santo and had himself observed many things there which indirectly pointed to lands in the west, curious cloud formations and appearances of the sky, on which, however, he would not lay stress. The reeds, on the other hand, had been sent to the King of Portugal, and there he had *seen* them. Martin Vincenti, a seaman worthy of credit ["I'd like to have him here" — Diego], had also found carved driftwood far to the west of Cape St. Vincent.

But the most remarkable of all proofs was that reported from the Azores: there after westerly winds they had found boats washed up on the beach, hollowed out of a single trunk, evidently the craft of savages; and on Flores, one of the Azores, two corpses had been washed up, possibly these same savages; they were broad in the face and did not resemble any known race of men. This one might almost call tangible proof of the existence of the Antipodes . . .

The Antipodes . . . here Juan de la Cosa coughed and ventured an observation. To a sober view the finding of the two corpses, if the account was to be relied upon, did not appear to him to convey any information about the Antipodes, since from what one knew about them they must have an entirely different appearance, scarcely confined to such a trifle as greater breadth of face. In the nature of things nothing definite could be known about the Antipodes, but it was obvious that beings who were to inhabit the under side of the earth, where the trees grew downward and the rain fell straight up in the air, must at any rate have suckers on their feet, like certain kinds of lizards, to stay where they were; in other respects also they were doubtless very different from Christians. It was not necessary indeed to go so far as the earth's poles or supports to find monsters; even in the heathen world, towards the outskirts of the earth, there was a great falling-off from the human form, if one might believe travellers and writings whose age entitled them to veneration. Not that he was himself a man of great reading, but still he had heard of the Arimaspians and of the Satyrs and knew that beyond Arabia there were people with only one leg, on which they hopped around, and that very swiftly; that there were Amazons and men without a head but with a face in their stomach was also known. From this it appeared that the farther one travelled from the Christian world, the more men ceased to be created in God's image, and there seemed to be good grounds for supposing that those who dwelt farthest down were created in the image of quite another Person, if indeed one might include the Devil in Creation; in which case they had wings and were to that extent capable of keeping on the under side of the earth. Instead of supposing Paradise to lie in that quarter it was more natural to imagine Hell there, even to an unenlightened view, since there was every reason to presume that the earth rested on fire or had fire in its depths, as could be seen by volcanoes; the fact that it grew hotter and hotter the farther one sailed to the south was an indication in the same direction, as all those present were in a position to confirm. Thus the two corpses at the Azores, in Juan de la Cosa's humble layman's opinion, did not tell them much about the Antipodes. The mention of them, on the other hand, suggested quite other and horrible ideas to the mind.

An uncanny silence fell upon the crew at Juan de la Cosa's rational words. Of course, the Admiral always made it appear to them that the only goal of their desires was to sight land, but it depended a good deal on what awaited them when they did reach land. Speechless resentment against the Admiral was reflected in their features at the thought of what Juan de la Cosa had pictured; they could not find words for their horror and abomination. Was it possible that he intended and had been intending all the time to sail them straight into Hell? Were they to lose their salvation as well as their lives? Had he sold their souls? Then let the Devil take him . . . The oath stuck in their throats, for if he was the foul fiend himself . . .

Ugly pause. Even Jorge, the wholly inarticulate, who sat on deck poking bits of salt pork into his mouth with his knife and audibly pulling the blade out again between his teeth, an old galley slave with scars on his ankles from the shackles and bare places on his scalp like an old horse chafed by the harness — even he gave an *Ouf!* and raised his pock-marked face, shaking a little with age, blinked and cocked his ear: What now, what made the men so quiet? Unwholesome air, he had always found, when abuse died away on men's lips! Could there be worse things in store for him than he had already gone through, in his long, precarious life?

But Jorge was quickly reassured and shoved in another mouthful that had been checked in the air on the point of his knife, for the Admiral was evidently saying things that restored the men's breath and gave them back the use of speech: the Admiral crossed himself so frankly and feelingly for his own part at the mention of the Evil One and his abode that only the most grudging could doubt his piety; assuredly *he* was not in league with the Prince of Fire, far less was he that personage himself, so much would have to be admitted.

A protracted exchange of opinions ensued on difficult theological problems. The Admiral did not hold the view that the Underworld was a place which could be reached by any known route, at any rate not by sea; that was out of the question, since water was an element hostile and opposed to fire; the way thither was inaccessible to man, while alive; for such as died without grace it was easy to find. Paradise, on the other hand, which was commonly placed in Heaven, without more precise indication . . . well, they had no priest on board, but even in the absence of one the holy articles of faith and the revelation of the Scriptures should remain entirely undisturbed; however, even the Scriptures gave nothing that one might call a definite observation of the position of the

Kingdom of Heaven; but as we were told that our first parents were driven from thence it was permissible to suppose that it had lain and still lay somewhere on earth. In contradistinction to the Underworld we had an example in Holy Writ that men might be taken up alive into Heaven, the prophet Elijah; although this happened a long time ago it could not therefore be regarded as absolutely impossible that it might take place again.

Shaking of heads among the Admiral's hearers, divided opinions and an uncomfortable feeling in their insides; as usual, the talk had an inconclusive, unsatisfied ending. To many whose sole unhappy thought was their abandonment in the midst of Ocean, the future appeared in a doubtful, hopeless light; in truth, with all the various prospects suggested by the officers, the cry of *Land* could not come soon enough!

When at last it came, however, it swept aside all other thoughts . . . .

Land, land!

It was from Martin Alonzo Pinzon the blessed cry came. He had just closed the flagship in the *Pinta*, a comparison had been made of logs and charts, apparently of a disquieting nature, when Martin Alonzo noticed something like a low cloud or indication of land ahead to the westward, right in the sunset, a long way off, but with so unmistakably the character of a long, broken coast-line that Martin Alonzo was not in doubt for a moment:

Land! land!

They all saw it, the Admiral saw it and immediately fell on his knees on the quarter-deck and began to thank God with hands raised high. Immense sensation, all troubles forgotten, wild joy all over the ship at the sight of the distant blessed streak of land; the men ran up the masts and down again, fell into each other's arms, were quite beside themselves.

Ay, a mad scene of confusion, until the Admiral in a powerful, solemn voice which penetrated from one end of the ship to the other, ordered all hands to be called on deck for divine service.

A gun was fired, and the *Niña* sailed up; the three ships sailed abreast in the falling darkness, and as the streak of land vanished in the great glow of the sunset, and the afterglow paled away and gave place to the first tiny twinkling stars, the hymn arose from the *Santa Maria*, from the *Pinta* and the *Niña*, three choirs of men's voices which united in one and cried out upon the sea and to the stars:

Salve Regina, Mater misericordiæ, vita, dulcedo, et spes nostra, salve.
   Ad te clamamus exsules, filii Hevæ.
Ad te suspiramus, gementes, et flentes in hoc lacrymarum valle.
Eia ergo advocata nostra, illos tuos misericordes oculos ad nos converte.
Et Jesum benedictum fructum ventris tui, nobis post hoc exsilium ostende.
   O clemens, o pia, o dulcis Virgo Maria.

IV

SAN SALVADOR

NEVER had any night been so long, never any expectation so tense. Course was altered to south-west, the direction in which land had been sighted, and was kept all night in the fresh breeze.

But when the sun rose astern of them it exposed an ocean entirely bare as far as the eye could see; ahead, where the land had been sighted, there was only the sharp line where the distant empty sky met the distant edge of the sea and the waves ran together like snakes, a blue wilderness above and below, on every side!

The disappointment was hardly to be borne. With sinking hearts they realized that what they had taken for land had only been a mirage, a cruel sport with the hopes of poor hard-tried men. Could there be more trials in store?

A voice was heard, after some time of deathlike silence; a man went about among the hopeless ones trying to talk, to talk up his spirits, hopeless himself — the Admiral. Nobody listened to him, he scarcely had the heart to believe his own words, but something had to be said.

Speaking half to himself he explained dejectedly that what they had seen could be nothing else but St. Brandan's Isle, for it was known from his legend to be a movable island, which changed its place in the sea, a wandering isle, so to speak. St. Brandan had sailed after it for days without being able to overtake it; it continued to move on before him in the sea, just like an airy vision;

but he had reached it at last, and in reality it was a mercy they had sighted it, a proof that it existed, and with God's help they too would reach it . . .

They turned from him in disgust, with forlorn looks, turned eyes like blazing coals on him, malice and impotence in one, like captive cats, they looked him up and down, this chattering old map-maker and impostor, Admiral of the Moon, with his Saints and his fine connections and his worn-out shoes; they gazed after him, curling their upper lips and baring their teeth, hating his back, the hair on his neck, his huge size, an advantage which of course the vagabond must have stolen. And the Admiral went up alone to his quarter-deck and stayed there, while the ship beneath him sank into the dull despair of a fasting morning.

It was on the 25th of September that they made the false land-fall; its result was to impair the spirits both of the commander and of the crew. And there was still two weeks' sailing before them.

How did he get them to do it? How was it possible after they had suffered this collapse of all hope? It even repeated itself: once more there was a cry of land, and they believed it; another disappointment. He got them to do it.

The situation on board had changed greatly for the worse; for a time all communication between the poop and the main deck was broken off. The school on deck and the Admiral's long, kindly explanations were things of the past; he stayed aft and paced his watch, night and day, no wonder his shoes were worn out; and down on deck the crew behaved as though there was nobody in command at all, so far as their part of the ship was concerned.

They were still sailing, the westerly course was resumed, but the crew held meetings on their own account, put their heads together in groups here and there, groups which at first were not altogether in agreement, with many opinions and proposals, though none in the Admiral's favour. Diego could be seen, lively and active, with his black head showing up now in one group, now in another, with violent gestures and a programme which he hammered in with bated breath, point by point, one hand striking the other.

It was mutiny that had at last begun to take shape. Diego saw blood and felt the tingling stiffness in his legs that precedes a spring; the Admiral appeared to his imagination like a bull in a cloud of dust, his nerves egged him on to get at it, though he was only a pygmy compared with the monster — to jump over it, literally, right in front of its horns, stick blazing darts into it, tease it by twisting its tail, and finally drive a yard of steel through its shoulder right down to the heart.

Thus it was with Diego, who always wanted the theatrical, a show for the eye; others looked at the matter more soberly. The Admiral was to be got out of the way, without too much exposure or obvious guilt on the part of those who were the means of doing it. Accidents may always happen, man overboard; the Admiral was up at night measuring the stars with his eyes on the sky, right against the low rail; he might lose his footing and go head first into the sea, nobody could tell how, and he himself would never be required to explain it. Then they would sorrowfully return home without an admiral . . .

Here, however, was a point which caused a fairly sharp difference of opinion, the groups nearly came to loggerheads over it: would they be able to find the way home without him? Those passably skilled in seamanship thought there would be no trouble about it, a long beat against the wind, several weeks, months perhaps, tacking to north and south, seeing how badly the ships worked to windward; but how else could the Admiral himself have thought of getting back when the time came? Others wrinkled their foreheads and made no attempt to conceal what could not be concealed, that the Admiral, in spite of all his intolerable idiosyncrasies, undoubtedly possessed remarkable powers, supernatural powers one might even call them; something more than ordinary knowledge of the sea was wanted, he had secrets which he would take with him to the grave, and perhaps it was as well to be wary of getting in one's own way by removing him.

A few men flatly refused to conspire against the Admiral — Pedro Gutierrez, whose hands were too white; Juan de la Cosa too, to the general regret, he would have been a good man to have on their side. But Juan de la Cosa, who had never for an instant believed in the voyage and was now more incredulous than ever, declared that in spite of all he would lay his bones where Columbus laid his; this was such a mad enterprise that life would seem poor to him if he did not see it out — something to be said for that, but it was not a comrade's point of view.

Thus opinions were divided until one of them gained the upper hand and sentence of death was passed.

The explosion came, but it was the Admiral himself who brought it about, just as the plan was ripe. He had long seen what was in the wind, and one day when all hands were on deck, groups and meetings in the greatest excitement, he came down from the poop right amongst them, unarmed, determined to have a talk with them.

Cries of rage greeted him as he came down the ladder; in an instant the deck was in an uproar, every man of one mind, no mercy for him, and if he came of his own accord to meet his death so much the better! A cat-like spring, and a blade caught the light, it was Diego at the head of mob; a scuffle, he and the Admiral hand to hand, a whirlwind nobody could follow . . .

But they saw the upshot. The Admiral had hold of Diego, however he had managed it, held him fast and broke the rapier in his hand, taking the pieces from him; and while holding him with one hand he grasped his forearm with the other and gave him two blows on the ear with his own hand, then swept him aside with his flat palm, with a twitch of the face as when one gets rid of a foul insect. And then Columbus rose and faced the mob . . .

Diego's imagination had not been altogether wrong in regarding him as a bull, for now in his anger there was something bull-like about him, the big head, the snorting nostrils, the attitude; he swelled, the blood went to his head till his eyes showed white against the blue skin, he hunched himself and struck out with his mighty arms as though he would jerk them out of his shoulders, snort after snort came from his nose and all his hair bristled and made him still more terrible, the thunderbolt was in his hand, his voice came in a huge roar. And then he gave them his mind:

Here he was to lead them into kingdoms their eyes had never seen, and by the living God, whether they liked it or not, they should see them! Never should the rabble say of him that he had failed his royal lord and master King Ferdinand of Spain and his Queen Isabella, in whose service he had sailed; never should any force hinder him in his duty! He was a seaman before God and Our Lady, appointed by Heaven to bring grace to the heathen, even if he had to sail to the uttermost sea! So long as there were souls in darkness who had not heard the gospel and received the offer of grace, so long would he sail, to the world's end, a mortal only, but an instrument in the hand of Almighty God for eternity. Who was strong enough to stop him on his way?

He looked around with the eyes of a wild boar among hounds. But not one of them made a sound.

His expression changed to one of sorrow, there was a quiver in his beard, and the giant fell into terrible weeping, turned and hid his face in his arm, staggering like a blind man towards the ladder. A broader target for a crossbow-bolt than his back as he went up to the poop could not have been desired, but now he went scot-free, the hands of all on deck hung limply by their sides. They saw him go into the little cabin aft and close the door after him, like an unhappy man who wished to be alone. And there were some among them whose eyes blinked in their trouble; perhaps after all there had been *too* many of them baiting the giant! Some saw that his hands were bleeding after the encounter with Diego.

Not a word passed among those who stayed on deck. But the men who took their turn at the helm that day steered so carefully, with all their attention fixed on the compass, the course due west.

Those who had noticed the Admiral's worn-out shoes noticed again, in a day or two, that they had been mended. Who could have done it? Was it one of the crew perhaps who had taken upon himself to sew them up early in the morning while the Admiral was asleep? Or had the Admiral done it himself by the little chart-house lantern whose light always shone from his cabin at night?

On they went, in the invariable, mystical wind which seemed to have some mysterious purpose with them; but there was no fair-wind feeling on board, their minds were dark and rankling like the doomed. Signs interpreted as showing the nearness of land came and went, awaking, after their bitter experience, a hope which had no strength and which left traces of a yet deeper affliction in their furrowed faces.

The crew began to lose the fixed notions about the world with which they had set out, they had forgotten Spain, forgotten almost who they were; the world appeared to them in an uncertain light as an enchantment which was already acting upon them, they were in other states of being, would not have been surprised if one day the roc had swooped down and carried off one of the ships in its claws; sea monsters lurked beneath them — that they saw none almost seemed an added unreality.

The quarrel between the crew and the Admiral blazed up again frequently, but was of a barren, disconsolate nature; the crew were too dull to plot together any more and had come to hate each other to an extent that made all common action impossible. It had gone with them as it goes with every collection of men confined in the same place, without women, without a chance of avoiding one another, a repulsion scarcely to be borne. They opened their mouths at each other in loathing, without uttering a word, gaped at each other like sick and sorry beasts of prey, even language was too heavy to lift; they turned their backs on each other as far as might be, got out of each other's way in the narrow ship, climbed out on the bowsprit and enjoyed a few fathoms' distance from the rest and a good long solitary cry, riding astride the spar with their arms round a thin rope; they hid out of sight among the cargo, up on the yard, hanging overboard by a line on the ship's side, like a man hung up for curing — anywhere if they could only escape the sight of one another. Ah, the voyage and the long companionship punished them by letting them see themselves as they were!

All discipline went to pieces, there was just enough of it left for navigating the ship, not that that was much trouble in the fine weather; the ship was like a kennel where you stumbled over meat bones, the men slept where they dropped, scratched themselves where they felt a bite, growled without opening their eyes when they were trodden on. On days when their spirits revived — when birds had been seen or other reminders of a world long ago abandoned and vanished which they had once known, or when the Admiral had been talking about land again like an automaton, the idiot above them, to whom they had grown accustomed as one does to a voice — on such occasions they took omens, a wearisome pastime during which the life ebbed out of them: if a certain cockroach, which they saw sitting still in a certain spot, ran a certain way when it did run, then they would sight land before evening. God help the man who prodded the cockroach and disturbed the divine judgment, or came near it; mad roars scared away any who wanted to approach the group where the trial was taking place; it might last for hours if it was a very sedate cockroach. If at last it ran, why then they would either sight land before evening, which would simply turn out a lie, or it ran the wrong way and all hope was gone, as it was anyhow.

Those of the crew who retained a remnant of humanity retired into themselves and became pious, clutched the crucifix, not now and then but continuously, had it in their hands night and day and moistened it with tears; pictures of the Virgin Mary were kissed as long as they would stand it, pious vows were made. All the pilgrimages they would undertake if they ever saw Spain again! In hair shirt, barefooted! No thought of expense in the matter of candles. Some promised the Virgin a stone of them, a whole stone! Could she hold out against that? Though innocent of any such intention, it gave a pretty good idea of what the giver was worth. But the whole was of no avail.

Away aft the Admiral paced his heavy beat like an ox in its stall, always the same weight, the heavy step that made the planks give under it and was felt all over the ship, a brutish, intolerable endurance. His shoes had burst again under his bull-like tread. The Admiral was all hair and beard, his face more inscrutable than ever before — couldn't he reckon his log by the amount of hair that grew on him?

This was just the sore point, the Admiral's own inner vexation, which of course he concealed from every one: there was something wrong with his calculations of distance. The length of the voyage to India as he had estimated it beforehand and the distance they had covered did not by any means agree, the Atlantic Ocean appeared to be a good deal wider than he had imagined — if it had any end. What was he to believe?

To begin with, the crew had been terrified that they might burst through the sky if they went on sailing, and have the pieces tumbling about them and fall into God knows what calamities outside, a superstition which they no longer entertained — oh no, it did not seem even that there *was* any world's end, it was nothing but sailing and sailing, without any actual catastrophe but at the same time without cessation, till Doomsday perhaps. Who could tell whether they were not already damned and would have to go on sailing, for having presumptuously tampered with the locks of the Ocean; perhaps they were already in eternity and could not die, but would see each other for ever, be shipmates together for all ages, ugh! and sail and sail and sail.

And the flesh would fall from their faces, and they would look upon one another as bare death's-heads but unable to die; and the *Santa Maria* would become an old ship, old as she was already, with splintered deck, sun-bleached sails and frayed ropes like prickly worms, the anchor scaly with rust; but she could not die either, the old tub would plough the infinite to all eternity and rock with her chafed spars and groan in her timbers and gather slimy seaweed at the waterline, and sail, ho, ho, ho, until some day Satan — if not God, who had forgotten her — took pity and opened a vent-hole down in Hell to receive the rotten old wreck!

And yet he pressed on, Columbus, persisted daily in romancing in his cautious voice about the signs of land, until they clasped their hands and begged the monster to stop, begged him to kick them and let them die; still he pottered about with his astrolabes and angles and hushed up to-day what he had expatiated on with criminal optimism yesterday, when it proved to be humbug.

If only they had thrown him overboard that time, when it was not too late and they had it in them to rise! He even grudged them their food now, for all his fatherly talk; they were on rations, the junk was eaten up or gone bad, vermin in what was left; at night the rats ran over them, some day they would have to eat *them*, like heathen dogs, unless it was the other way about; the water was rotten, might he but poison himself with it pretty soon so that they could be rid of his creaking about the deck and be able to lie in peace and close their eyes to the next man's disgusting dirty features, and die.

The heat increased, the heat increased. O dear! O dear!

And then, when they were at their lowest, an asylum in the extremity of moral dissolution, hope began to trickle in, for a long while against their will, for it only came in the shape of the old, hateful, torturing twaddle about signs of land, and the more they had of it the more it worried them. But at last they could not help beginning to see for themselves.

One morning early in October they heard the Admiral singing up on the poop, entirely alone with his God and the sunrise, and they understood that now he was confident, not with a world of hopefulness in his mouth and sick inside, as they had known him so long, for after all they had some sense — his conviction was genuine now. And soon they could do nothing but share it. In the course of that day and the succeeding ones, up to the 11th, the evidences of the proximity of land increased so fast that nobody could be in doubt any longer. They recovered as the sick recover, without any vital strength at first, but rich in the soul; quiet tears ran down their cheeks — no, now there was no doubt!

On the 7th of October the Admiral altered course to the southwest. For several days before they had seen birds, pelicans, but that day they saw great flocks of birds flying from north to southwest. Columbus knew that the Portuguese had found land by sailing after the flight of birds, and he followed their example. His supposition was that they had now passed the islands he expected to find in the Ocean, or had sailed through them without sighting them. He therefore thought he would sail straight on to the mainland; the islands they could always come back to. On the 11th the signs of land were certain: the crew of the *Pinta* fished up a carved log from the water; from the *Niña* they even saw a fresh bough with berries on it in the sea, and were reminded of the dove with the olive leaf in its beak which returned to Noah's Ark after the Deluge; stormy petrels were seen, and that day they sailed in a rising wind and a fairly rough sea, answering to the strength of the conviction that drove them on and the uneasiness which accompanied the thought that very soon, a question of hours, they would see land.

But so late as the day before the Admiral had had to go through a final tussle with his men, impending mutiny, now, now, just as uncertainty was giving way to infallible signs. It was the probability of the approach of land, and nothing else, that raised the crew; they had recovered their strength with surprising rapidity when the world began to be like itself again, and now a flood of misgivings rushed in upon them. Without a doubt they were reaching land, but what sort of land? At the best, if it was India, it would be a gross piece of foolhardiness to fall upon the back-door of the Great Cham's realms with three wretched little ships and scarcely a hundred men; if the Admiral hadn't thought of it before it was time to think of it now and turn back; anyhow the situation had been determined and they could come again with a fleet and an army. They had agreed to join him in the reconnaissance and had borne the indescribable sufferings that pioneers have to undergo in new and unknown seas, but to cut the matter short they would now go home for reinforcements — no question of exposing themselves to be massacred on a hostile shore and wasting the whole voyage if not a single one of them returned to tell of it . . .

Only a hundred men, the Admiral interposed, but *Spaniards* . . .

Proud looks, chests thrown out, the Admiral was courteous, knew how to strike the right note. *But* . . . and then it all came over again, not without hints of who was in the majority and had the power and meant to use it. Shouts, Diego jumping out of the crowd like a leopard out of the jungle, beating the air with all his limbs, a chorus of roars behind him: *thus* far they had sailed the Admiral and made his fortune, now not a mile more!

It ended in the Admiral declaring in so many words that for his part he would continue the voyage until he had found India, according to his plan. He did not get excited this time, did not thunder over their heads; on the other hand, he let them have a taste of his scorn, which had a bitter smack to some at least among the crew; moreover there was a determination in his demeanour which made them see that they would have to cross his dead body ere there was any chance of turning back.

Thus he succeeded once more in dividing them: cries of revenge, threats and much harmless swearing in one quarter, silence and brooding in another: postponement, tension, troubled waves inboard and out, but sailing and good progress all the while. And the next day they were in a different humour. The absolutely certain signs of land carried all with them. The day's work on the 11th of October was a triumphal progress; the sun went down that evening in a waste of water, as it had done for thirty-five evenings before, but with a great red glow of mighty expectation to mark its setting.

The night of the 11th was a dark night; the moon, which was in its last quarter, would rise at eleven. It was about ten o'clock when the Admiral saw from the poop the first direct sign of land, a light ahead in the darkness which moved up and down. Fire was the first sign of welcome that greeted him from the unknown shore, a gleam borne by a man's hand and swaying up and down with his walk. Columbus called Pedro Gutierrez, whom he trusted, up to him and asked if he saw the light, and when he had confirmed it he sent for Rodrigo Sanchez, the King's representative on board, that he might be a witness.

At two o'clock in the morning, when the moon was up, a sailor with good eyes on board the *Pinta* made out the coast-line ahead, Rodrigo de Triana was his name; the *Pinta* fired a gun as a salute, and as the other ships came up they could all distinguish the line of coast, a low-lying land ahead. Sails were taken in, the worn sails, stiff as boards in their clews from standing so long; only a few stitches of canvas were left set, enough to keep the ships moving up and down, more or less where they were; they had only to wait for morning.

What a night! Never before had men's minds been so wrought up by tension, triumph, fear of the unknown, curiosity, the sense of immense and fateful things. And no wonder; the time was now ripe for two worlds to meet here, with all that there was in them, to spread their fires one to the other and brand each other anew; hosts were to be let loose, and men's souls would not remain what they were, therefore the heart pumped so uproariously in every man's breast. All this they could not see, but it was in their veins as a great necessity: jubilation and festival spirit all through the long, sleepless, expectant night.

The night did not pass in idleness, a fever of preparation was everywhere. Some washed themselves in the waning moonlight against going ashore in the morning, others had their hair cut as well as could be managed, even the Admiral himself, whose hair and beard Pedro Gutierrez cropped: it was strange what a comparatively small head he had when his mane was off. The grindstone shrieked under the forecastle, splashing in its trough: the crew were sharpening their swords in expectation of what the morrow might bring, running a sensitive thumb along the edge; they spat between hand and hilt and tried their grip, swung the blade till it whined in the air.

And their tongues went, volubly; loquacity did them good, giving vent to much that was in them; and thoughts were numbed that would have cramped their spirits, after all things had turned out as they should. The Admiral, he was now peerless, the man of the day, and they had shown it too in that mad hour when land was sighted and every one lost his head in a feeling of humanity and gratitude. Some had gone so far as to crawl to his feet along the deck on hands and knees and kiss the hem of his mantle, they had humbled themselves before him as before a deity, as was only fair on the part of those who had been the most impudent in opposing him during the voyage; others kept somewhat in the background, not wishing to recall their existence too prominently. For his own part the Admiral had been greatly moved and had clasped his hands in long speechless gratitude to his Creator, but apart from that it was remarkable how calmly he took his deliverance, really as though he had been quite certain all the time that it must come in this way.

And in this the men had to acknowledge that he was right; the thing was easy enough, nothing startling about it in reality, anybody could have done the same. Straight ahead, straight ahead, that was all, a course drawn with a ruler, with a turn at the end of it, neither storms, rocks, nor winding channels; straight across the ocean, thirty-five days' sail, what do you say to that? From the morrow he *would* actually be Admiral, and Viceroy into the bargain, ts, ts — and when he came out in all his glory it would be seen where *those* were who after all had done the whole of the work on board, built the vessel, so to speak, and trimmed the sails and taken the helm, and had borne all the anxiety on the top of it! For *he* had shown practically no fear at all.

Many were the eyes as the night wore on which were fixed from time to time on the distant indistinct line of coast, rather low-lying, it seemed, not forbidding with lofty mountains or abrupt cliffs, easily mastered . . . now it remained to be seen who lived there. Oh, if they had neither sailed into the Abyss, nor had the sky falling about them, nor been drawn to the Magnet Mountain, nor burnt up by the sun, nor swallowed by sea monsters, it would turn out sure enough that the inhabitants were just ordinary human beings; in that case there would be no concealing the fact that here again the Admiral had solved a problem quite simple from the start.

Among those who gazed landward from the *Santa Maria* was a man with a thick lip; he had been so wanting in tact as to remind a shipmate of all the candles he had promised the Virgin Mary; like a flash he had got one on the mouth. . . . Was *he* the one to claim the candles? Scrimmage, and a black eye for his messmate; and thus it was that one of them gazed at the land with only one eye open.

Diego was singing somewhere in the darkness, up in his highest falsetto, crowing to himself like a lonely cock quail on a spring night. Who would there be for him among the sleepers over there, with her ear hot from dreaming? He would soon find that out; but even now, *now* she was there, sleeping beneath the same moon, longing perhaps, like him, for what was to come — could she but know how near it was!

Up on the poop the Admiral walked with his diminished head and his great new dignity, which on the morrow he would bear ashore in fullest armour, with the banners of Castile. What were his thoughts? A deep surge of emotion filled him at the goodness and mercy of God. Great thoughts, possible and impossible, possessed him as the ship washed up and down, with the waves caressing her bow and her mastheads tracing letters among the stars; each time the ship went about the whole starry sky swung round upon itself; thus in the Admiral's head the world and all his thoughts revolved. What awaited him yonder?

The night was so mild and wonderful, the breeze had dropped and a land-air brought a warm scent out to seaward — many strange, spicy, obscure, powerful odours, of fire, mud, plants, the heavy night-sweat of the tropics that hangs out like a garment from land to sea, the ancient rank and pregnant scent of life.

What a life? The Admiral's head was swimming. For the last few days, which had carried them farther south, there had been a sort of forgotten and yet familiar soul in the air, a growing sense of summer, an atmosphere of rejuvenation, full of vanished summers, childhood's springtime, an eternal May, sky, air and sea reposing as it were perpetually in the Virgin's month . . . *could it be imagined*, was it possible that when day came he would be able to sail with his three ships into Paradise, the land of eternal summer, the land of youth, the abode of the Virgin Mary? *Would he see her?*

His breath failed him, he stood still, pulled himself together. It was not impossible. But it was not to be thought of until it came about, that was not lawful for a man. In the course of the night the thought recurred, but he kept it down, forced himself to think of what was more reasonable and actual, that it was the coast of India he saw there dimly in the moonlight, or the islands off the mainland, probably Antilia, the Spice Islands, from which all precious things came, for the scent wafted out on the night proclaimed it to be an island full of spices and sweet-smelling things; for that matter it might well be the Abode of the Blest. But then surely it would show a greater light than the solitary torch he had seen?

And yet, was the perpetual lamp that burned before the image of the Virgin in the cathedral a great light? Did it not burn as a solitary spark in the midst of an ocean of darkness? How great was the light the shepherds saw shining from the inn that Christmas night when God's Mother wrapped her First-born in swaddling clothes and laid him in a manger? The scent that was now wafted to him on the night airs from the island, the hearths ashore, of perfumed wood, it was the incense, the cathedral, and all it promised! He dared not follow his thoughts, their immensity inflamed him — was the Garden of Eden at hand? With an effort he forced them back into a human train.

By force he held himself to the conviction that it was Antilia he lay off, and thought over all that might be expected, and all that he would have to do.

In passing his thoughts turned back to Spain: the incredulous there, all the crooked smiles he remembered, and his human side came uppermost — down on deck they heard the Admiral snorting, as a horse snorts violently in his bridle — he was getting fiery up there, the Admiral and Viceroy.

But up on the forecastle walked young Pedro Gutierrez, on watch again to-night. He was silent, scanning the moon, scanning the land. The book of fate was dark for him, dark as that night, with only a red initial letter to be seen in it, the blood-red moon. What forebodings had he? Little he knew it, but he was not of those who were to see again the brown Spanish shores. Never more would he look upon the Guadalquivir!

Sunrise on the 12th of October, the long low green island ahead in full daylight, a good league away. Sails hoisted, creaking tackles and joyful chanties from the crew, a festal sailing in!

First the *Pinta*, that dashing sailer, stiff in the breeze and cleaving the waves with a short decided nod. After her the *Niña*, graceful as ever, spreading a fringe of foam about her like the border of a gown, meeting the seas with girlish curtsies. Last of all plunged the *Santa Maria* with her rounded hull like a segment of a wheel, swinging her nose down and ploughing the seas overmuch; but she too kept up, and nothing could be done till she came.

It was a blue day, blue sea, blue sky; in front of the ships flying-fish darted up from the deep clear waves like the vanguard of the sea's wet silvery souls, and between the ships sported a friendly school of porpoises, like mermaids, in a landward gallop, they too on the top of the galloping waves, the whole making a picture, the apotheosis of Ocean and of the fortunate discoverers.

Soon they saw smoke ashore, the mark of human habitation, trees and green plains opened up as the eye slowly took bearings; it was a good, tangible island, with surf about it, veritable, excellent.

The Admiral stood high on the poop, in full dress from early morning, iron all over and a scarlet cloak besides — pretty warm, just think of it, full armour! The crew puffed the sweat from their upper lips and thought they had too much on with a pair of linen hose and a cuirass over their bare skin. Finery was not all clover; one had to suffer for it! Besides being clad in steel, blue plates and scales, with trappings, the Admiral wore a helmet with feathers of a bird called the ostrich, doubtless some salvage from his African voyages. All this finery he had brought with him and laid by till the time arrived, so confident had he been! On his legs he wore brand-new sea-boots of tanned deerskin — imagine it, sea-boots, in his size, a unique pair of boots, each of them fit to hold a sack of flour! And people went abroad in search of curiosities, when they had such strange sights as this at home! Something different from the Admiral's old pointed shoes with the splits in them — what had happened to them, by the way? Ought they not to be preserved, even as cast-offs? they were a sort of relic. To return to the boots, wasn't it a funny thing that all through the voyage the Admiral had gone about in shoes, and now he was to go ashore he put on sea-boots? [Diego's licensed tongue.]

The Admiral heard the laughter and merriment below him on deck but was himself very serious. Was he not *too* serious for so blissful a day, when all the others were singing and the world smiled upon him in his glory?

If any one had observed the Admiral early that morning, when the sun rose and the outline of the island was disclosed beneath its rays, he would have seen as it were a shadow pass over his face; the clearer the view became the darker *he* seemed to grow. And since then he had been serious.

But now they saw him draw himself up and throw out his chest, as he called his officers aft. To them the Admiral announced that the island was to be named before they landed, after the Saviour; it was to be called *San Salvador*.

Juan de la Cosa looked up, in surprise — ought not the first land they sighted be called after the Mother of God, in whose name the voyage had been undertaken? But the Admiral held his peace, which meant that it was to be as he had said.

High on the poop he stood against the blue sky, looking in towards land, blinking his eyes, swollen with sleeplessness; he saw the surf rising against the shore like white figures leaping up from the sea, checking themselves and sinking back again, a noiseless distant play the seaman knows, the spirits of the sea ever seeking the land; the ocean's organ was about him as it had been now for so many weeks, and for most of his life, a note that was a part of himself; the wind plucked its dull harp-chords in ropes and tackle, another part of himself; a roaring, billowing, singing within him and around him, the blue day breathed in its strength, by the bowsprit a bright-coloured soul leaped into the light and vanished again, the rainbow in the flying spray; behind him the morning sun climbed in the sky, and before him lay the day.

And as he stood there under the flying banners and pennants and the ships saluted each other over the surface of the water, fire leaping from the throats of the pieces and the sharp report deadened by sea and wind, the drifting smoke, while the seabirds wavered in their flight and rose high, scared by the shots, and the crews raised a cheer, the ships in chorus — as he stood there looking towards the new land he thrilled and saw his life before him; the life behind him was as nothing, now at last his voyage was to begin!

But it was ended. Many, many things came after — harder years than those he had left behind, petty triumphs and an abyss of toil, the deepest-cut inscription on the tablets of history.

The shadow that had passed across his face that morning would give way to hope, and come again, until hope was driven out and there was nothing left of his face but a mask, the dumb form lent by death.

Labour, a human lot, awaited him, but his achievement as the instrument of the age was concluded. Through the power that was in his heart he had carried the age beyond itself; now it would sweep in his wake, after him and over him; the way was open.

Behind him, in the Europe he had left, it was as though men's souls were pressing each other onward to the coasts; now they would push each other out to sea and over it, the Ferryman had shown the way. The instinct in his fathers' blood had brought them as far as the South; now, he opened up the way to the other side of the world to those who followed after him.

Conquest and settlement were to be the work of others; the theme would be developed without him. For yet a little while he himself pursued the goals of mortals, but from the moment when he saw the light in the night and had thrown a bridge across the Atlantic his being passed over into Time.

V

QUETZALCOATL

THE LIGHT Columbus had seen from out at sea was a burning branch which a man carried aloft on his way from one palm-leaf hut to another on the island.

When one is out so late and alone and the evening is dark, one must carry fire, not exactly to find the way, it is only a short distance through the forest and across open ground, the path is known, but who would dare to walk by himself beyond the abodes of men without fire?

The man was perfectly naked, had always been so; the air, even at night as now, lay about his limbs like a bath at blood-heat, the same heat that he felt in the waters of the lagoon when he plunged into them, the same that surrounded him in his hut and radiated from women and children, natural warmth, the only clothing he and his ancestors had ever known. But he was painted, roughly smeared with greasy ashes and charcoal all over his body in rude figures; in his nose he wore a ring of mussel-shell and an ample string of cachalot teeth about his neck. His hair reached to his shoulders, but had been chafed off between two stones over the forehead and decorated with feathers; in his free hand he carried a spear hardened at the point with fire, and in a cord round his waist was stuck a bamboo-splinter fashioned into a knife.

The fire from the burning branch he held aloft shone upon his eyes, which were black and witless, curiously skewed, like false mirrors; they seemed not so much to see as to give expression to a wild inner imagination; and yet everything, without exception everything that took place around him was brought to his consciousness; with scared eyes he saw every leaf that moved in the forest within the circle of light he carried with him, which continually brought out the trees in front, while behind the darkness closed again upon his heels — parrots dropping noiselessly from the branch they sat on, sweeping down in a curve and up again into another tree, or sitting still and turning an eye towards the light, hopping sideways a step or two along the branch, without meaning to fly off, let's see first . . . he saw the iguana appear as the light suddenly fell upon it, with its thousand scales, its prickly spine, twisted legs, nostrils, little frightened eyes and all — but he was most apt to see what was not there, horrors and forebodings that leaped into life about him at the slightest sound of which he could not guess the cause; he showed the whites of his eyes and clutched the burning branch convulsively, raised it higher above his head and threw the light before him, towards the lofty slumbering Powers, the palms, towards the bamboo thicket, dense and grim, towards the white nocturnal mist, which filled the bushes and was a terrifying thing with a bush in its embrace, until the light made it powerless.

And when he came out of the forest into the open country he went more cautiously, he was a changed man with the different world that here met his senses; nothing but darkness in the air before him where the light ended, grass and stones entering the light as he covered the ground, a wide air here, breezy and open, with a message from afar. Now there fell upon his ears the long, rising thunder that ended in a crash, the seas running upon the reef around the island, just so long between each, he knew them, sensed the island all the way round, caught the sea air, his big, wide-open nostrils worked, the shore was in them, the living smell of coral mud and all that moved within it, the lagoon and all its life was in his nose, his soul was as it were mapped out with all he sniffed up, one with the island, and yet filled with a fear which only the possession of fire could keep under.

A few minutes' walk brought him to a copse and in its depths a hut, like his own, the hut of a friend, a man like himself, who sat on his heels by the fire and received him with a grunt. And all he had come for was to squat on his heels likewise, in company with his friend, and converse with him in a wide-mouthed speech, docked sentences — about what? The fishing, the state of the lagoon, upon which they exchanged opinions, all-wise and marvelling; very good canoe, such and such a one; a misfortune — a man they knew had got a splinter in his foot and was dying, for such a little thing, sorcery without doubt; foreign canoes seen, news from other islands?

In the background of the hut there was a glimpse of a bunch of women and children, asleep; now and then one of them awoke and lay down again with extreme caution . . . oh, if they should happen to disturb the men! Outside the entrance to the hut, in the half-light of the fire, prowled a couple of dogs; a strange kind of dog that had no bark, wise enough about the muzzle and with a wag in the tail, talking with the ears, but with no voice; thin-coated and fat they looked, they were here domestic animals and were fattened up to the right pitch, taking the place of pigs. They showed much attention when the men inside fell to eating: roast crabs, which they opened with a stone implement, and a handful of maize, looking like so many yellow teeth; a part of the crab's fat inside was smeared on the mouth of the god which stood under the roof of palm leaves grinning in coral-rag at the fire; manioc bread, tasting of the women's sweat, took off the edge of their appetite; of all they ate a small portion was offered to the fire and a fire prayer was mumbled between the lips; then big draughts of the calabash and the men had done, after duly belching to get rid of the spirits that might have entered with the food. Their talk naturally ran upon feasting, and their voices sank to a religious whisper: such and such an island, so many suns ago, much man food, good man, fat, big man, num, num!

And then a smoke to the night! Leaves of the good, the best plant were laid on the fire, and the men leaned over the smoke, breathed it in and drank with nose and mouth, coughed and moaned with pleasure, their eyes running and mouths watering, but happy and stifling themselves with smoke, until a god seemed to rise in it above their heads right up to the palm-leaf roof, an almighty being, the sombre narcotic spirit, friend of all poor mortals, whose name is Tobacco. Then they turned dizzy, with a glorious disquiet in their veins, a splendid headache, and they went to rest, laying themselves down where they sat, the guest as much at home here as anywhere else.

And when it was quite certain that they were asleep, shadows stole up to the fire, women and children and the dumb dogs, to share what was left. They were not sorry for it, as with hot whispering they made themselves a lovely late supper in the middle of the night, left off chewing with mouths full to listen — yes, they were asleep — and put fresh things on the fire to brown. The women whispered, loose-lipped and with little pigs' eyes, scarcely able to suppress a giggling gaiety, though most of them were still bleeding or had ugly unhealed wounds from the men's bamboo knives. And at last they came upon a leaf or two of the good weed, flicked the hair from their faces and glanced at the sleeping men; it was as much as their lives were worth, but they laid the leaves on the fire, breathed in the poison and moaned in ecstasy. An infant began to whine and was hurriedly gagged with a breast slung over its mother's shoulder to the inmate of the bag behind. The children quarrelled over the leavings, and the little boys went for the little girls with little bamboo knives, a mimic attack all in the deepest silence, for fear of waking the divinities. Soon the whole hut was grunting in its sleep.

But when all were asleep yet another shadow crept up to the fire, an old mumbling, blind creature, the oldest in the hut, who felt about among the embers and on the floor, eating charcoal and little burnt knuckle-bones and whatever else of a greasy nature it could find, and then stayed sitting by the fire, warming itself at the glow it could not see; its hands came upon the children's bamboo splinters and it scraped its dry bird's skin with them and fell into a reptile reverie: many, many dark ages since *she* had enjoyed man's cruelty! Among the things she found were some charred scraps of tobacco — and she knew well enough which way the good thing ought to go; no smoke for her, no, into the mouth with it; greedily she thrust ashes and tobacco on to her tongue, croaked and found consolation; at last she too crawled to her rest, with the good weed in her mouth.

Smoke from the tobacco fire, that was what had reached Columbus out at sea!

The men barked in their sleep and wriggled their limbs, as though they were all joints: gruesome dreams. Little did they guess that what awaited them next day would surpass even their most frightful and monstrous visions. What a sight they were to see!

face, and all over his skin, almost terrifying to look at in the beginning, and his eyes were pale, like the air; his nose was not natural, flat and open like a human nose, but had its holes underneath and projected from the face like a beak. Strangest of all was
his hair; it was light, like sunshine, and if you looked at him at a
little distance it was as though he wore the sun on his shoulders.
The sun! the sun! they cried when they saw him for the first time,
and fell on their faces; his only difficulty in making friends with
the people he met was that they dared not approach him. His
beard too was light, big and long, not a couple of hairs such as
ordinary men grew and pulled out, but a forest on his face and
down over his chest; it was more white than yellow, he was not
a young man. In the sunlight his head looked like the gold dust they
found in the sands of the rivers, and gold was counted holy because it resembled his sunny head. He was tall of stature; his
strength was never put to the test, nobody entertained such a
thought. He himself brought them no evil, as they found out in
time, and this again made him seem strange. When he stayed
among them and began to show his inherent supernatural powers,
not to the hurt, but, on the contrary, to the profit of all men, why,
then they had him, and they showed him all the honour and solici-
tude that could be lavished upon a man who was the sun in person, came down to live and breathe among the children of earth.

If they asked him whence he came he pointed over the sea to
east and north, the sunrise, and that was what they expected; but
to one who made bold to inquire his name he replied, with a smile
which might mean both that they were not to know it and that it
was true, that he was a guest; later on, when he had left them
again, they owned the truth of what he had said. Men who were
children when he came grew old during the time he stayed, so
long was it, but he himself did not seem to grow older; nor was
it conceivable that he could die. They called him Quetzalcoatl,
which means bird and serpent, referring to the wind and the lightning, over which he was presumed to rule; in the arts of fire he
was more versed than many people cared for, but he never mis-
used his power. They erected a temple to him and a high seat,
and adorned his head with a glory of green feathers, a whole
spacious and beautiful building on his head, the greenest that had
ever been seen, and a splendour reserved for the gods.

Now the man who was thus raised on high was none other than

Norna Gest, who, to his other experiences, had added that of sitting on a divine throne and wearing a crown of birds' feathers on his red hair, no heavy burden and a thing which need not get about, seeing what an out-of-the-way part of the world he was in; when they prayed that he would deign to wear it he had not the heart to refuse. On the other hand he declined offerings that they wished to make to him of a bloody and fearful kind, and would only accept flowers and fruit, which occasioned the institution of a sacrifice till then unknown in the land, and drew a sharp dividing line in their religious ideas; of which more later.

First it must be briefly explained how Norna Gest had come here. A long journey, but not very remarkable in itself for a man who had time at his disposal, and no other business than sailing, like Norna Gest. It was at that period of his life when he had survived his dear ones, and sought them in vain in the most distant countries, the shores of the Dead, which he hoped to find in order if possible to meet them there. For he himself could not die, so long as the candle his mother Gro had given him was not burnt out, but the shores of the Dead he had not yet found. After searching for them in the South, as is related in his Book, he tried in the West, towards the sunset, perhaps a hint that the realm of the Dead lay just there. He could see beforehand that there was no hope of crossing the great ocean beyond Europe in the little single-handed canoe he disposed of; but as an old and tried coaster he had experience of how far one could go if one took time and followed the outline of the land, or went up the rivers, which had taken him all round the known countries of Europe and far into the unknown before; and this form of voyaging he essayed.

First, then, he made for the North, up along the coast of Norway, paddling and fishing his way as was his wont, the life he knew of old, without hurry, staying on for a few years when a place attracted him, and covering long distances at a stretch when there was occasion for it, but keeping the far-off goal of his journey before him the whole time. From the coast of Norway on a clear day he saw islands in the ocean far to the westward, the Shetlands, and risked the passage one summer in calm weather. From there he reached the Faroes, following the flight of birds, and then Iceland; perilous voyages, and black, bitter seas in those parts, a long time to be out of sight of land, but plenty of food for a patient fisherman, broad-jawed cod in the deeps; and he was not lonely, far from it, those waters were populous with great families of whales in the current and thousands upon thousands of seabirds on the rocks ashore. Much delight had the old man in birds' eggs and a fire on a desolate ocean isle, followed by a sleep on the turf and a song to himself in the morning; he rubbed his hands with pleasure and stepped into his boat to feel the sea stirring under him, and to commit himself once more to the waves.

From Iceland he reached Greenland, more by chance than otherwise, and not without distress and loss, since a storm drove him out into the open sea in that direction and ended by casting him on the cold shore. He lay senseless at the bottom of the boat when he reached land; fishing had failed him on the passage, and he happened to get no rain in the bottom of the canoe, his usual drink on long voyages; the seas were tremendous, and eternal night came on, icebergs towered about the hollowed chip with a man in it among the yawning waves. But he rode out the gale in a swoon, and came to himself on Greenland's coast, turned walrus-hunter and clothed himself in the skin of the polar bear, lost himself in endless fjords and wastes, stayed here for ages and worked his way farther and farther north, hibernated in the snow, short of fuel for his solitary fire, nothing but driftwood; but what he got he examined and inferred that there was land to the westward from which it came; and over he went, to the northernmost cold islands on the other side.

So he was across, and then went south along the coast, in and out of fjords, for many ages, on many shores, till he reached milder climes again; still farther down, till he was in the warmth, and then the old man shook his shoulders and let the days go by, living on fish and solitude, among lovely islands; tasted the flying-fish, which came on board of itself, and found it good; and here at last he met with men without avoiding their company.

This was on the mainland, inside the great gulf with all the islands lying beyond it in the ocean; from the coast he came up to the high country where a great nation lived, gathered about the foot of the fiery mountain Popocatepetl, at once the symbol of their origin, their fire-giver and their greatest foe. To them he attached himself; if he had not found the shores of the Dead he had yet found mortals, whose lot in their blindness moved him to stay, if thereby he could alleviate their destinies. And here it fell out that, through no particular merit of his own, he was included among their gods and protected the people, so long as he had their support, against those of their deities who were at any rate worse than himself.

The first thing he did for them was to free them from their dependence on the fiery mountain. For they were still no further advanced than the primitive folk they were descended from, who had dwelt around Gunung Api, in the Lost Country; they knew the use of fire but could not themselves produce it, and had to get it from the mountain, the lightning or the forest fire, if their fire went out. Norna Gest taught them the holy need-fire, produced by drilling, the Ice Folk's greatest acquisition and possession; nothing of an art when you knew it, but to the poor primitive people of an importance scarcely to be measured.

With the difference in intelligence that separated them it was no wonder they connected the stranger with the sky and thought he was son of the Sun, perhaps the Sun himself, the first time they saw him conjure up fire between his hands from two pieces of wood.

It weakened the high, cruel Powers of Fire in whose proximity they dwelt and from whose terrors they had derived the conceptions of their gods — the lightning-god Tezcatlipoca, the bloody war-god Huitzilopochtli, to whom they offered human hearts. Quetzalcoatl showed displeasure when they were named, and utterly refused to accept sacrifices of the kinds that were offered to them. In this way a sort of conflict of gods arose, to which the people were witness, greatly desiring that Quetzalcoatl might have the victory; but as it fell out, the decision was postponed to the future, after the departure of Quetzalcoatl.

Besides the art of fire Norna Gest taught them agriculture. Maize, a very good cereal, grew in these countries, but the natives as yet knew nothing of cultivating it; they only gathered what grew wild, ranging all day for a few handfuls of grain. Norna Gest taught them to plant it, made a hole like a mouth in the ground and put a grain in it, feeding the earth and bidding them see what it would do in return. To be sure, they had a long time to wait, most of them forgot all about it; but when the plant came up, and Norna Gest had made the experiment often enough, the connection actually became clear to some of them; little maize gardens outside the villages came to gladden the eyes of Norna Gest and convince him that now they knew the art of giving in order to get back, before he left them. A proof that the hearts of the poor savages were good at bottom was that they repaid this simple service with boundless gratitude and devotion, and raised his chair on an additional foundation that he might sit more loftily.

By degrees he was raised quite on high, with many steps up. In the working of flint he also taught them things of importance and received their excessive thanks. They had positively superstitious ideas of him as a carpenter. The rudiments of the use of metals too he conveyed to them. On the other hand the country possessed no animals that could be tamed. But he taught them to keep birds for the delight they gave. Nay, so unbounded was the skill they attributed to Quetzalcoatl that many things they themselves produced or developed later were credited to him: architecture, social order, the calendar, the construction of canals, acquirements which came much later, after Quetzalcoatl had departed; all blessings were referred to the White God. Even the children's best games were said to have been learnt from him. Not only the people here but other peoples inland and far down the coast had the same tradition of this teacher and benefactor who had first shown them the way to a better mode of existence and had then gone back to his home in the sun or the morning star. From such a depth did they look up to an ordinary human being.

They did everything for Quetzalcoatl while he was with them, offered him flowers and fruit continually, wove him marvels of robes of humming-bird feathers, made him suns of raw gold in the semblance of his face to adorn his temple, showed him every mark of honour, except blood-offerings, which were distasteful to him. As yet, though, these could not altogether be abolished. Huitzilopochtli demanded his food and got it, but for their wars and human slaughterings Quetzalcoatl showed no sympathy; on the contrary, he turned away or stopped his ears when such things were talked of in his presence.

But in order that no living sacrifice might be left untried, they brought him women, bands of the country's choicest maidens, who would otherwise have been slaughtered and whose hearts would have been given to the god, hot, freshly torn out and still beating, while Huitzilopochtli's priests would have eaten the rest, the young, childishly sweet limbs.

Quetzalcoatl let them come to him, kept them and had them maintained as his property. They should surely not die; oh no, quite the reverse, they should taste of life. He let his eye rest upon them and found them fine and beautiful brown buds, with eyes like the tropical night with a firefly in them, limbs like honey, some of them; they were not to be disdained, a wrong that no woman deserves. But there was something not quite right about their joy at being allowed to live and being given to this sun; they could not be brought to raise their eyes to Grandfather, it was as though they froze in their nakedness amid the warmth of his beams.

So, when he considered them ripe, he gave them to young men of their own year, ho, ho, ho, and it was strange to see how they could shine, now it was they whose faces almost looked like little suns!

And afterwards the young people sent kisses up into the air to Quetzalcoatl, as before they had been wont to send kisses up to the sun; and when he was no longer among them they and their descendants scattered kisses to the winds that they might reach him.

For his part the old man had memories which kept him alone for ever.

The longer he lived among these people, who had so much worship in them, the more layers of their sense of distance did they put under him, more and more steps up to him; soon he was sitting high up in the air at the top of a pyramid, and at last he began to feel rather lonely up there.

The time came when Norna Gest longed for home. Those he bore in his heart and carried with him about the world wherever he went, they were dead, and it would be a long time ere he found the land where they had gone; but at home in northern dales dwelt a people of peasants whose ancestor he was; he wanted to walk beneath rowan trees again and meet blunt young swains upon the roads who would greet an old stranger courteously and in whose features he might see that they had blood in them of her who once, many generations ago, had been so dear to him.

Great was the dismay in Tenochtitlan when Quetzalcoatl announced that he would have to depart, and deep the sorrow of those who accompanied him down to the coast. Yet they understood that he wished to return to his bright abodes in the East beyond the ocean. And he had promised them to come again!

Yes, Quetzalcoatl bade them remember that if he did not come, others of his kind would come; they were not to doubt that, even if, perchance, it might be long.

Thereupon Quetzalcoatl stepped into his old tried canoe, poor enough for a god, but so much the more marvellous since he traversed the seas in it, said farewell to his priesthood and dipped his oar; they saw his back as he paddled out, with long considerate strokes. Ah, kindly even to the waves, thought those who stood ashore with tear-dimmed eyes and were never to see Quetzalcoatl again.

And Norna Gest rowed back the immensely long way in the opposite direction.

But the priesthood of Tenochtitlan raised images to him in stone, wherein he could be seen with his curved nose and his beard, with feathers on his head and surrounded by his symbols as the bringer of Light.

Ages passed, and he became a myth. The worship of Huitzilopochtli overshadowed him again, with all its horror, but stronger and stronger lived the tradition that the White God would come again.

VI

THE WHITE GOD'S RETURN

𝕬 ND thus things stood when Columbus opened up the way from Europe to the new countries in the West, which he believed to be India, but which, without *his* ever finding it out, proved to be an entirely new continent, with yet another ocean beyond separating it from India.

It took a century to make out merely the outline of the immense continent, which was given the name of America, centuries more to penetrate the interior of these countries, which extend for the whole length of the earth, through all the zones from one Pole down towards the other. The islands Columbus found came to be called the West Indies, the natives Indians, to the ineradicable memory of the error which formed the basis of his discovery. In the track of Columbus followed a string of other discoverers, whose luck it was to have the way made easier for them; on their heels came adventurers and conquerors, the Conquistadores; Europe had sprung a leak, its expansion was rapid, by leaps and bounds. But to the natives the whole of this invasion from the East seemed at the outset a movement which could be summed up in one and the same strongly agitated point of view: the return of the White God.

What a difference between the time when Quetzalcoatl left them and when he came again! It was the measure of the change wrought by the intervening centuries in him and his race, the variable ones.

The primitive people themselves were not the same, in many respects they had advanced, and in a very different degree in different parts; but in the main they were still living at the beginning of life, with the same primeval power above them, in the terrible likeness of Popocatepetl, fire and judgment. We are acquainted with their existence down to its details through the accounts preserved by history of their encounters with the Whites, for the most part seen from *their* side and furnishing at the same time the history of the destruction of these American nations as nations; it is best to prepare the meeting of these two widely severed cultures, whose roots were nevertheless in contact, by placing ourselves at the natives' point of view before the meeting took place.

The heart of the native American culture, which the Conquistadores thrust at and pierced wherever they came, lay in Mexico, the ancient empire of the Aztecs, in the interior and towards the centre of the two vast half-continents. The world Columbus found lay outside, a rampart of islands in the ocean fencing the great gulf that leads to Mexico, so far away that the report of Columbus was long in reaching Tenochtitlan, the Aztecs' capital. The tradition of Quetzalcoatl, on the other hand, had penetrated from there to the uttermost islands, so that Columbus was received as the White God as soon as he landed on Guanahani; the great tidings only reached Tenochtitlan in a tangible form with the first reports of the approaching Cortes. The description of the two meetings, different as the two men were, is merged in the same bird's-eye view.

Popocatepetl was in eruption during the years when the Europeans arrived in the new world, like Tenerife in the old world they had left; they seemed to be years of terror on both sides, foreboding great events.

In Tenochtitlan there was great alarm, the Lofty One yawned and sent forth fire, nights of horror with a sooty glow high up among the stars in the region of the mountain-top and a flickering gleam which came and went upon the mud walls of the pueblo. What had come over Popocatepetl, the Reeky, who in the memory of priests and other thinkers had continued peacefully smoking into the sky, from which he had his name? Now he gave off pulsing volumes of smoke by day, flashed lightnings and shrouded himself in fetid airs, and at night he smouldered with bursting bubbles of flame, so that even those down below, huddling in the houses of Tenochtitlan, saw a ghost-like gleam in the holes of the roof and could not sleep. A strange sport was witnessed; the mountain puffed out immense smoke-rings, shaped by his mouth, which rolled up slowly towards the summit of heaven, shining at night, and it looked as though Popocatepetl crowned himself with one halo of fire after another, hovering above his head, and a world of lightnings about his brow; was he angry with the stars? Were fearful fiery visions maturing in his mind? The more simple-minded ventured to suppose that the mountain had fallen out with Iztaccihuatl, Popocatepetl's wife with the white head of snow, the other great volcano of the plateau; that must have been the reason why he girt himself about with storms, thundered continually, rocked in his foundations and gave birth to all kinds of tempests; but the vulgar are ever apt to seek an explanation in their own narrow circle of experience. If they cast their eyes upon the priests they could not help noticing that *they* looked pale and shaken, and the turn given to public worship soon taught them that things were greatly amiss.

At the beginning the priests diligently practised their old and tried art of exorcism and conciliation: they smoked the pipe of peace with the mountain. A simple, an inevitable consistency formed the basis of this holy act, which was almost a legal form; you smoked together, and so long as you smoked quietly and moderately down on earth it was expected that the Great Spirit would smoke quietly and moderately up in Heaven, it was as good as an agreement, a covenant, and in fact the mountain had kept to it hitherto. They went up on high, to the top of the temples, so that he might see it, many men together to remind him of the covenant, the whole priesthood with the high priest at their head; they blew smoke up towards him, held up their stone pipes that he might see them: gentle smoking here, *here* they carried out their obligations! In vain. When the pipe of peace failed they saw that the treaty had been denounced. And then there was nothing for it but great blood-offerings. Popocatepetl blazed and was red, his many hundred altars in Tenochtitlan also blazed and were red.

The temples of the Aztecs were their country and their gods over again, in their very forms they were symbols of the worship; from the holy image the child of nature derives all his conceptions, as does the child. The Mexican dwelt on the roof of an immense temple Nature herself had erected, a plateau raised to the height of a mountain above the surrounding country, a land above the land, with its foot in the tropics and the ladder of the zones with its stages of vegetation climbing its sides; and up on the tableland in the rarefied air, the air of the condor, the home of the cactus and the aloe, mighty volcanoes towered yet higher, mountain crowning mountain, gods set on high, as the simple, wise child of nature thinks, and as he is one with almighty Nature and bows down to her, images leap from his soul and take shape in worship; in this way the Aztec temple had come about.

It was formed as a mound, with no interior, encased in masonry, with many terraces and platforms and steps the whole way up; the way the whole people had once ascended was now followed by the priests as a holy symbol. Above, the pyramid ended in a platform, upon which two towers were raised; within them stood the images of the gods. In front of the towers were two altars with fires that never went out, the eternal fire; more than six hundred of them could be seen burning night and day above the mud roofs of the pueblo of Tenochtitlan, and between them stood the stone of sacrifice. The whole arrangement of the temple an image of the mountain, and worship under the open sky, before the eyes of all, as though it was a worship of the mountain himself, Popocatepetl, the Great One, in an image adapted to human wit, but powerful, as is every likeness.

And now that Popocatepetl was disturbed, the disturbance grew more violent here. Evil portents had occurred before the unearthly terrors of the mountain began; some years previously the great lake in which Tenochtitlan was built had overflowed its banks, without any explicable cause, either tempest or earthquake, and had licked off a large piece of the pueblo; comets had been seen; one of the towers of the biggest temple took fire of itself, the finger of God; and finally, just lately, a heavenly portent had been seen, in the East, as it were a fiery pyramid bedecked with stars; not a doubt but great things were approaching from that quarter, or else the end of the world was at hand. So it was high time to appease the Powers and to sway their minds if possible with appropriate gifts.

No less than seventy thousand victims, prisoners of war and whatever else could be used to stock the pens, where they were kept and fattened up; processions two miles long, advancing slowly, step by step, up towards the temples as the head of the column was eaten off, so many at a time, apart from the daily scores and yearly thousands — such was the human contribution given to the gods. The obsidian knife, of volcanic glass taken from Popocatepetl's flanks and endowed with his nerve, was never at rest, and the priests, clad in red tunics, or with the flayed skin of a newly slaughtered victim drawn over them, grew weary, and so heavy with clotted gore from top to toe that they could scarcely keep going; still a god seemed to hold up their arms for yet another day, fresh strength was ever granted them for the few motions they had to perform; when others had stretched the victim on his back over the convex stone of sacrifice, tight across the stomach, they had only to plunge the flint knife in and tear out the throbbing heart with its roots, show it to the god and fling it into his sacrificial bucket. Then down the steps with the rest to those below, who did the quartering and roasting down in the smoking forecourts, where justice was done to the god's appetite, the holy mimicry — a sacrament, but interpreted so literally by many that they went about in a frenzy of slaughter, with eructations so violent that they nearly threw them down, eruptions which on a small scale were again a mimicry of the mountain. Children were sacrificed . . .

Ugh, no, enough! Things yet more repulsive were done, accounts are not lacking; but it almost seems that the abominations become worse in print, which is of a later day, and belongs to another order of imagination. Those who did the deeds were believers, naïve, when all is said and done there was a certain beauty in their thus devoting themselves to their Powers with blood and death; Nature was so immense, and they were innocent souls. Beautiful was primitive man in his submission to the mountain and the sun, the great marvels at which the enlightened stares in spiritual poverty; Nature was still within his heart, not outside it. Naturally the brute in him also asserted itself — has it even now died out altogether in the enlightened?

Meanwhile, for all their sacrifices and ceremonies, the evil omens did not show any signs of being warded off; and in fact they proved true enough, truer even than had been suspected. And in the presence of so much that presaged ill in Nature, and so much tension among the Aztecs themselves, they tried more and more to fortify themselves in the hope of Quetzalcoatl's return.

Besides the ancient sacred traditions which were kept alive by Quetzalcoatl's priests and by his images and temples — a great but distant tradition — new ones were gradually coming in, without any one knowing exactly where they came from, rumours in the air, such as occur among primitive people who breathe an image from one to another over great distances, short memories, but the rumour lives: Quetzalcoatl *had* been seen!

He was said to be already on the coast, out among the farthest islands, and it was only a question of time when they might expect him on the mainland. Well, well, let him come! Ah yes, all for the best, Huitzilopochtli was hard; even the most zealous in sacrificing to him, Montezuma himself, the high priest and war lord, could but sigh for his own part and feel loathing; he was eating everything up — would that a milder god might come!

It took a score of years before the report of the white man's coming reached the Tenochtitlan, just as the light reaches us from a star which no longer exists. Columbus was dead; and when at last Quetzalcoatl followed his rumour from the islands to the mainland it was not in the person of Columbus but of Cortes that he was received by the Aztecs.

The excitement occasioned by Columbus soon died away, like rings in the water when a stone has been thrown into it; he did not distinguish himself as some of his successors, nor were they the right people he had come in contact with. The first of all, as we have seen, out on the extreme coral islands and skerries facing the ocean, were nothing but poor crab-eaters, without power or possessions, scarcely even capable of great sensations; and yet the meeting was an overwhelming one, so much had they of a culture which was otherwise distant and had its centres on the mainland, that they knew it for the coming of Quetzalcoatl, that day when the strange many-voiced thunder was heard from the sea, lightnings in broad daylight, and the three winged wonders swept in round the north of the island and lay to under the lee of its western shore.

Emotional images, vast and vague, like dazzling mirrors in the soul, arose at once in those who saw anything at all; the majority turned their blind end and dashed headlong into the bush. The women's part was a distant flicker, like everything that happened in the world of men; some disaster, no doubt, this time, perhaps the sea had gone to pieces; what a frightful thing!

But there are those to whom curiosity is the most ungovernable of all forces, it would draw them into the very jaws of death, simply to look down his throat; this sort stayed upon the beach; nay, they even went to meet the god and his attendants when they came ashore. Gradually, as their heads cooled, they began to see properly and experienced the greatest expansion of the soul, as when one infers the unknown from the known and it tallies: why, they were *big canoes* these marvels, mighty huge canoes, too big to be true, but canoes all the same, not to be mistaken! There were trees growing out of them, and they had wings, which they were now folding; they were higher than a man could shoot with a bow, and all at once they had young, a baby marvel that pushed off from the mother and came paddling in to land. Of course, gods who came from the Ocean must live in big canoes, and naturally they carried thunder and lightning with them, for the god in heaven is known by these signs. And now they were to see him!

He seemed to have wings as he stepped ashore, great gloriously coloured things fluttering from his shoulders, and his face was that of Quetzalcoatl, as even the most foolish person could tell, big and fair, with a thick golden beard, not a doubt but it was he! His eyes were like the sky, but he was clothed like the sea, in a shining blue sheath, like a big beetle — God guard our tongues! — but is not the beetle a god too? In his hand he carried a long, long knife, nothing like bamboo, but what was it made of? A flame, a thing of air? The foremost and boldest of the natives was to find out how it felt, for when God held it out to him in greeting he grasped it and cut his fingers.

The great white strangers performed a curious dance; they

knelt on the sand and seemed to address themselves to the heaven they had just come from, lifting up their voices in chorus, slow and powerful notes; and the tallest and whitest among them planted his wings in the sand, delivered a message and caused it to be traced on white tablets, a ceremony of which the savages understood nothing at all — least of all that it meant their own island did not belong to them any more.

Besides the wings, or whatever they were, they raised a tree on the beach, with a man on it hung up to die, only an image but very lifelike; and in the hands of the strangers the savages noticed smaller copies of the same stake bearing a tortured corpse.

?? Shaking of heads . . .

And he who shook his head wore a yellow ring in his nose; that did not escape the attention of the strangers . . .

Thus did they meet, these two whom the ages had parted; the one naked as he was born, still reposing with his child's soul in Nature's bed-chamber, the other clad in iron and bearing about him many deposits which *his* existence had taught him. One side saw in the other the messengers of Heaven and were to have their vision corrected before very long; the other side came with an equipment of factitious dreams which they were to exchange for a reality they did not care for. Such was the traffic that would take place between them, with many, many other consequences.

In all the islands at which Columbus afterwards touched he was taken for the White God, until he, and more particularly his men, took pains to make the natives better informed. Columbus did not treat them harshly, even when as Viceroy and Governor he had to keep order in the colonies he founded, no more than the rights of war according to the ideas of the time; but he had not much luck either. He sold the natives into slavery a little — the morality of the age; and that was not the worst thing, even as certain women prefer rape to missing their destiny — wherever he went he scraped the place clean for gold and reversed the natives' ideas of the yellow metal; it had been prized for its colour, because it reminded them of Quetzalcoatl; now they had a better understanding of its value, since the white men flew at each other's throats to get at it first; one might rather ask how much a red beard was worth in terms of the heavy yellow dust.

Reverence for the messengers of Heaven received a blow, and all the archangels Columbus left behind in a stockaded camp in

Haiti, before returning home from his first voyage, were simply killed off — a lot of galley-slaves and swashbucklers, expert in tearing gold rings out of native ears and capable of surmounting the barrier of dirt, grease and stench which separated them from the natives' women — among them poor young Pedro Gutierrez, who had been put in command. Oh, they were very mortal, the white gods, and reeled just like other men, whether they got it with the bamboo knife, arrows from an ambush, or clubs on the head, twenty natives against one.

When Columbus returned he found them buried here and there, some of them, a nest of carrion full of ants; one of their heads he found in a basket in a native hut. Business was opened.

A trifling incident has been preserved about one of the savages from Guanahani whom Columbus met again later as he was sailing on among the islands and hauled up, for political reasons, in order to cover him with gifts and let him paddle on and make a good impression wherever he landed. He had in his canoe — the inventory is from Columbus's own papers — a piece of native bread as big as a fist, a calabash of water, a piece of red earth powdered and then kneaded into a dough, and some dried leaves, "which must be a thing they set great store by, since they have already brought me some of them as gifts in San Salvador" (tobacco); "and he carried with him a little basket of the native kind, in which he had a chain of small glass beads and two stivers" . . . which showed Columbus that the man came from San Salvador, where he had received these gifts from himself, in exchange for cotton, parrots and spears, which the natives brought of their own accord as offerings to the gods. We can imagine the naked savage in his canoe, far out at sea, paddling for dear life, hastening towards a distant island, where perhaps he has friends to whom before too many suns have set he *must* show his prodigious treasures and tell of the rich god from whose own hand he has received them!

For the untried savages were at first quite staggered with joy at all the wonders that came to them over the sea and of which they had a share. Even now, four hundred years after, our ears may be haunted by a faint tinkle of all the little bells with which Columbus and all the other discoverers after him enticed the natives; the old papers that tell the story of the discoveries simply ring with bells, a huge decoy performance, part of the same trick as the glass beads, red rags and the little mirrors, the backs of which the savages couldn't help clutching the first time they had them in their hands, to get hold of the mystical brother behind.

The little bells which had such a success are always referred to as hawk's bells; they were the kind hunting hawks had on their claws to ring in their flight when they swooped from the sky upon the heron, the primitive joy of the hunter; a bell of this kind is to be seen in Holbein's portrait of a nobleman with a hawk; sleigh-bells are descended from them, and little bells on the reins with which we played at horses as children are the last survivors of them. The medieval predilection for the sound of bells — people once wore them on their clothes — was now discarded to the savages and found a market among them; ah yes, the cannibal, already tricked out to advantage with a bone in his nose and pegs in his ears and nothing else, swaggered about happily with a bell tied in the towzle of his hair. You could lure them to you from a distance with the seductive music, they stood as though rooted to the ground and turned their ear: a little god, a bright thing with a mouth that sang in sweet tones — a smile spread on the face of the cannibal, so that you saw a head full of big, white, greedy teeth; but a hair was enough to bind him when he was moved, his hand came out: if he might but have it, if the little god might be his!

Then they put him to scraping gold dust out of the river sand for fourteen racking days, and he came with his bag, all bent and weighed down on one side from the load, heavy enough to bring a man to his knees, and got his bell, turned his back, went, and his shoulders showed how happy he was. Old hardened caciques with white hair on their legs hobbled long distances to listen to the speech of the bell, it was yet vouchsafed them in the evening of their life to catch a sound so lovely. Youth will always run after a new thing, but here old experience had to admit that it was no delusion, but a real, tangible, divine marvel!

This was the little tinkler; later came the big bell. The time was not far off when from the solid walls of churches it would peal out over coral beach and mangrove, startling birds and filling the sunrise and sunset, as in the old countries.

Ay . . . just as a few centuries before, when the first brave missionaries pressed into the dense forests of Northern Europe and tempted the rude natives in their cowhides with the prayer-bell.

There too it had begun with a little bell and ended with the great doomsday peals of the cathedrals.

Was it then a discarded thing which had now grown too old for Europe and might suitably and with advantage be imposed upon the savages overseas?

In any case the bell which thus ingratiated itself with its lively note meant no harm; it was never the intention of a man like Columbus that the poor creatures who sat in darkness should be won to grace by other than gentle means.

The Conquistadores had other ideas. What did they have cannons for? The souls of the heathen . . . put them in harness first and then the sacrament! Nor were the natives of the mainland so harmless as the happy islanders out in the ocean; the first Whites who had anything to do with them got a taste of their *macquauitl*, a wooden sword with obsidian flakes fixed in both edges, a horrible weapon; the Mexicans were still living in the Stone Age but had not much to learn in the art of making holes in human skin, and they were a numerous, respectable enemy; no cosseting was wasted on them in the course of their conversion to Christianity.

The first news the Mexicans had of the great strangers was when Grijalva appeared off the coast with his ships. The conquest was undertaken from Cuba, where Diego Velasquez was Governor, one of the great family of the Diegos, who now began to get their foot in and spread themselves in the new world. Grijalva had been preceded by another hidalgo, Cordova, who had been in these parts rummaging for slaves, and had put in at Yucatan — which means, "What do you say?" a corruption of the natives' question, *tectetan*, when they did not understand the white men's language, and the country is called so to this day. He saw great permanent buildings there, not palm-leaf huts that would burn in a moment like those in the islands, and the natives were rude, indelicate, able-bodied men, and short of temper. Grijalva's experiences on the coast beyond the gulf came near to martyrdom, he got a dusting, and was chased out to sea again with the remnant of his men.

Among them was Bernal Diaz, who afterwards, when an old man in Guatemala, wrote his reminiscences, an incomparable work, and an incomparable man, eye-witness and participator in the whole conquest of Mexico, brave, simple, without guile, a true, noble Spaniard, and an honourable pen to boot; he it was who even in peace time could not sleep except in armour and on the floor; when he was out of the game a mighty clockwork in him, running down, caused him to write a book bulky as Homer, and as weighty in its contents.

Only the *Iliad* can be compared with the story of the conquest of Mexico, but we are so much nearer to it in time; the action is equally heroic, but the actors are men we almost know. Is that age so far from us? Only thirteen or fourteen generations separate us from it, a living tradition from grandfather to grandson would not have been repeated so very many times, and might have reached us orally, if written authorities had not rendered it superfluous. Here then is the voice of Bernal Diaz across the ages; it is meet to make obeisance to his book, and to refer those to it who would be witnesses of the conquest of Tenochtitlan. Here but a brief attempt will be made to bring out those features which throw light on the meeting between the child of nature and the white man.

The name of the Indian who saw Grijalva's ships and brought the news to Tenochtitlan has come down to us; he was called Pinotl, and was one of Montezuma's tax-gatherers down on the coast. To him came another Indian telling him that he had seen winged towers which moved hither and thither out at sea. Others who were sent as scouts reported that they had seen two such towers at sea, and from one of them a canoe had been put into the water with a kind of men in it; they were white in the face, and had big beards, and were cased in strange bright and shining sheaths. Then Pinotl himself hurried to the coast, and was lucky enough to meet the strangers, even went on board one of the towers, and had a conversation with them; much play of features, we may presume, and an abundance of finger language on the part of the strangers, from which it appeared that the business of the shining beings was to come and visit the great lord in the great city up beyond the mountains of which they had heard . . . he was very rich, wasn't he? how much gold? Arms spread out, and mimic invitations to Pinotl to spread out his arms and show how much gold his master had.

As soon as the towers had flown away to another part of the coast, where, as we have seen, Grijalva was half cut to pieces by the natives' flint swords and afterwards avoided the shore, Pinotl travelled night and day till he reached Tenochtitlan, where he presented himself to Montezuma and the whole Council, and declared that he had seen and talked with gods. Pinotl had caused descriptions of the gods and their sea-palaces to be drawn up on aloe-paper in picture-writing and Mexican hieroglyphics, and these were laid before the Council.

If we had them now! If only they existed as a marginal note to the sanguinary and moving tragedy which was soon to be enacted! They would have been evidence of how the Aztecs conceived and pictured the Spanish knights whom they took for gods; the scale was added by themselves. But no doubt they served with other combustibles to heat the pot in which some Spanish soldier cooked his supper, according to the habit of these descendants of the Vandals. They shared the fate of all the priceless golden works of art from Mexico which went into the melting-pot; the treasures of Peru, which Pizarro laid hands on, vases and wheels of gold, so many that they filled a room twenty-two feet long, and sixteen feet wide, to a height of nine feet from the floor, the ransom of Atahuallpa – which did not save his life – treasures whose value as works of art no European was ever to guess, and which Pizarro ran his bloated swashbuckler's eye over before having them beaten flat, so as not to take up too much room in the heap, and then melted down. The butcher did not know that their value as antiquities was more than their weight in gold, and they rose again in the form of the many four-fold inch-thick gold chains which grace the bull-necks in the portraits of all the sixteenth-century princes and grandees, the *Family*, the end of all estates and all gold: a superfluity of it in Europe and all the corpses, the overthrow of nations in mythical America! But that is the story of Pizarro, the exterminator of the Incas, a chapter by itself and a later one in the red book of the Conquistadores.

Courage is required to pronounce judgment on these terrible men, in whose hands more destiny was laid than Nature had designed captains of condottieri to deal with; for *they* were courageous, perfectly mad fellows as regards life and limb, and one would have to feel equal to a duel with them, even in restrospect, before putting them in their place. They placed themselves where they now stand, men of iron before the eyes of all; we must be content to regard them and leave judgment to self-destructive

Nature, which produced them to the doom of many and to the assurance, in any case, of their own memory. Even bad men they can scarcely be called; when Pizarro as an old man died a violent death, stabbed by Almagro's gang who betrayed him on his own threshold, after fencing like an angel and reviling them entrancingly, he drew a cross of his own blood on the floor with his finger and kissed it before he breathed his last; that man was not solid all through, he had a little space inside in which he kept the image of his God. And with all he brought about Cortes captivates us by a certain extraordinary gaiety, the warrior's and sportsman's superfluous vitality, the propensity to outbursts of joviality among friends, for they were all young, a band of high-spirited boys let loose in a new world; in the face of a cruel death for themselves or for the overwhelming masses of their enemies they could not leave a trooper's jest unspoken or forbear to taste the fruits the country offered. Both Cortes and Pizarro were *Estremeños*, natives of Estremadura, where from of old the population had been a cross between Goths and Moors, without a doubt a very powerful mixture and a clue to the understanding of a character in which chivalry and contempt for human life, pomp and cruelty, imagination and absence of nerves, fortitude, faithlessness, pretty nearly all qualities except weakness, formed a whole of such vitality and frightfulness.

To give Cortes fair play we must in the first place not forget that with an army of six hundred and ten men he entered a country, by nature a fortress, with a population of millions, armies of hundreds of thousands of devils, after having burnt his ships, to conquer it or die. But he had ten cannons and sixteen horses! At his back his own people lay in wait, the Governor of Cuba, with the authority of the Spanish State, who was jealous of his enterprise; at a decisive moment he had to turn against a hostile Spanish army, the Narvaez episode, with all Mexico about his ears; but he beat him and diluted his own band with his men, forcing disasters to his own advantage, and ploughed his bloody way on, in the track of the guns, towards the fable city of Tenochtitlan.

Pinotl's report convinced Montezuma and all other initiates that Quetzalcoatl was in the country. And when in the following year Cortes arrived, he met with the reception due to the White God, though not entirely without reservation; there was a certain hesitation about it, for the interval had already added features to the traditional idea of the god of goodness which were somewhat at variance therewith: first Cortes' relentless war against the Tlascalans, the enemies of the Aztecs, and then his alliance with them, a step unlike Quetzalcoatl and one very dangerous to Tenochtitlan.

But otherwise there could be but little doubt that they were, if not Quetzalcoatl himself, his descendants, in any case *Teules*, supernatural beings. They were associated with fire and thunder, or were themselves thunder gods, that was granted, not rumour and vague talk but actual fact; a sufficient number of people had seen and heard the thunder-engine in their hands and seen the results; the frightful pipe from which fire and smoke leaped, just as from the mouth of Popocatepetl, and with the same deadly effect at a distance as the lightning: trees sent flying in splinters a long, long way from where the thunder was heard, and bloody lanes opened in the native army long before they came near to the ranks of the Teules, men torn to pieces wholesale; Popocatepetl could not have raged more furiously with his showers of stones and lightnings. Occasionally they had even found the thunderbolt lying cold on the ground, but a portent even when dead, heavy, round, of an unknown hardness and with a cold, blue lustre underneath its crust; evidently the same stuff as their thin swords, blue as the air, which gave off lightning while still far away and which they whirled so pitilessly in hand-to-hand fighting; the same stuff as the sheaths were made of which covered them from top to toe, with only little slits for the eyes to look out of, impenetrable to any weapon.

Ah, how poor were the Mexicans' little smoke tricks compared with the Teules'; at the beginning they advanced towards them with their incense-ladles full of smouldering copal, and smoked at them, an idea borrowed from the mountain and of presumed mystical effect, since he whom they smoked was thought, by virtue of similarity and in connection with perfume, to be brought under the influence of their gods. Alas, they needed a favourable wind if the smoke was to reach any one; and there was no heavy, round, murderous body with it to emphasize the enchantment and tear holes in the order of battle. No, they were only human, and the strangers were children of the Sun.

Xicotencatl, the leader of the Tlascalans, finally put the matter to the proof, while his people were still opposed to the Teules; if they were children of the Sun it was to be assumed that they only enjoyed their strength in the daytime when the sun was out; he was therefore advised to attack them at night — but what happened? He found them wide awake and fully aware of the secret plan before the attack took place; they knew everything, useless to strive any more with gods! The authors of the plan had their entrails taken out and pepper put in their place, by way of letting them feel remorse, and Xicotencatl then entered into an alliance with the sons of the Sun as the most sensible alternative, since he had to make a choice.

It was this Xicotencatl's aged blind father, a man of great influence in the country, who begged permission to feel Cortes' countenance, as he could not see him, after peace had been established; and what he felt was perhaps the best characterization of Cortes, if it could have been translated into language; but the old blind Indian took it into the grave with his finger-tips.

Other proofs presented themselves, both to the Tlascalans and to the Aztecs: Cortes sent men up Popocatepetl, and that while it was in full eruption, under the leadership of a certain Ordaz, not without the Christian name of Diego; a demented band who tramped up over Popocatepetl's brow, to the horror and profound distaste of everybody in Mexico, for if they were without fear they ought at least to have had modesty! But it was done, and the mountain allowed it, a fresh proof that they were gods, unpleasant ones, but gods. Cortes was even cool enough to have sulphur brought from Popocatepetl's crater for the production of powder: the identity was obvious, destroyers both!

Not only did they command thunder and lightning but bows with arrows like those of men, cross-bows — the wrath of God in their hands; they had a loud and evil clang, like a hurtling in the air; too late then to jump aside, the bolt was in you, and you had to put your hand behind you to feel it before you fell, it went right through. And these deadly things were tipped with the blue sky-metal, the same kind as the heavy round thunderbolts. Fire would not bite on it; on the contrary it did it good, a ball like this grew bright in the fire, dazzling at last like the very sun, of which of course it was a part; so there again they were face to face with the marvel.

But then the horses! Those who saw a horseman for the first time and naturally thought it was *one* creature, the heavy Spanish tilting chargers, in iron and trappings like their riders, and the trussed and clanking man on top, a single six-limbed, snorting creature charging along — oh, they raised a howl, fell down, crept on all fours to get away, hopelessly, but they couldn't move; they had been struck with a palsy, were like toads inside and out, sick axolotls out of their element; they lightened themselves in their fright, like certain birds when they take wing; the day they saw a horseman for the first time taught them panic. But what when the creature broke in two! For sometimes the man dismounted, and made two terrors out of one! If they had really been reptiles, the luckless ones who saw it, they would certainly have lost their tails; they would have been driven to the extremity of letting their tails go; but they were men and could only shudder until they collapsed, and there they lay.

Cortes took advantage of this, as Bernal Diaz tells us, the terror inspired by the horses at first, to make an impression on an embassy the natives sent to his camp. He had a mare concealed behind the place to which the ambassadors were shown, taking care that it was to windward, and at the right moment had a stallion led forward; it instantly reared and advanced on its hind-legs, with its shoed forefeet in the air, flying mane and fiery eyes, roaring loudly, straight at the spot where the ambassadors stood, while at the same time a cannon was fired! It had the desired moral effect.

If we had had pictorial representations by the Mexicans of their first impression of the horse, or could only realize their conception — a pity we cannot, for *that is how it looks!*

Cortes and his band of young hidalgos and desperadoes had some fun out of that incident! When the place where the messengers had stood was empty, the natives swept away from it as though by a waterspout, they must have burst into their loud peals of laughter. Cortes twirled his moustaches sky-high, one in each hand, and nearly fell backwards with swagger, cocking his legs and strutting. Oh, ho, ho, they knew the tricks! Alvarado, how he laughed! Alvarado, that great tall favourite of fortune, the darling of the expedition, the darling of the chroniclers ever since, and of all his fellows the one the Mexicans observed, feared and admired most; for he was quite fair, a giant with a head made up of gold and sunshine, of pure Gothic blood; they called him *Tonatiuh*, Son of the Sun, and were above all inclined to take him for Quetzalcoatl or his descendant, though he was not the actual leader. He was a mighty soldier and a fountain of mirth, the song-ster of the camp and the one who led the chorus of laughter when wit took fire, and be sure the jesting was of the strongest. Of Alvarado history has left us a long, exciting romance, tearing up and down, now bright-coloured, now clouded, but always heroic and stirring — his women a separate chapter; by his precipitancy he came near upsetting the whole conquest of Mexico, but he shines for all time through the personal bravery he displayed; he afterwards became the conqueror of Guatemala.

After the episode of the stallion, which happened not long after Cortes had landed on the coast, a personage came upon the stage who was to play a decisive part in the conquest of Mexico; a woman, Doña Marina, or, as she was generally called, Malina. She arrived among the Spaniards as one of the female slaves sent by the terrified embassy for the mollification of the strangers, but she was an Aztec by birth and therefore valuable as an interpreter and spy when the Spaniards came up on to the plateau and began to march against Tenochtitlan. She is reported to have been very beautiful and intelligent at the same time, was soon personally attached to Cortes as his secretary and had a son by him, proof that gods and mortals are capable of crossing; soon the country was overrun with demigods.

In contradistinction to other heroic women known to history — Judith, Ildico — who sacrificed themselves for the salvation of their people by delivering themselves into the power of the enemy, she indeed gave herself up, but only to betray the people she belonged to; clearly it was a new world that the strangers had come to.

We shall not judge her; only a woman is permitted to annihilate a whole population — she can produce a new one. Nature mani-fests itself in her deeds — keep her bound! Bound Malina had been, but the worm of chance had eaten through her bonds, and now she was free, let loose between two powers which were approach-ing each other as a lava-stream approaches a tidal wave; let loose indeed, a demon stretching its serpent's belly and throbbing with destruction, naked and drenched with love, in the bare glory of her tropical body, as though made of copper, and one or two par-rot's feathers in her hair, delighting in her soul over slaughter — the obscure, self-destroying soul of her people.

She led Cortes into Tenochtitlan, interpreted to him what her countrymen said — Spanish she had learnt from Cortes' lips —

she mixed among the Aztecs and ferreted out their plans, disclosed them in good time to Cortes and thus gave him all the trumps in his hand. Woman's most astonishing talent, that of listening, of being everywhere with ear and mind and catching all that is in the air, this she had to an astonishing degree. What if she had used it to betray the speech of Cortes and his friends, for the good of those in Tenochtitlan, her own blood, her family and relations among them? No, all there is to be said is that that was not Malina's way, for such was her love of Cortes.

And so she nosed in and out, lovely and deadly, like the reinforced blending of the qualities of serpent and beast of prey which is peculiar to the weasel, the ferret and the ocelot. And every time Cortes clearly manifested the powers of a god by knowing beforehand all the plans of the Aztecs, their thoughts almost; it was she, their own flesh and blood, who was the power within his power! And it was part of her voluptuousness to lay her whole people at his feet, every man of them, torn and bleeding. How she must have loved him! Bernal Diaz says that Cortes was rather knock-kneed. Before setting out on this expedition he decked himself as leader with a plume in his helm and a medal on his breast, anticipated honours; many other things might be dug up to Cortes' disadvantage, but we are constrained to leave them alone and say that he had the love of Malina.

If the Aztecs were thus scared to their very souls by the firearms and horses of the Spaniards, not to mention their divine origin, there were also things on the side of the Mexicans which impressed Cortes. Not their numbers or their hideous war-paint and uncivilized weapons, the fact of being opposed by hosts of a thousand to one, the air full of obsidian-tipped arrows, an enemy that fought with broken glass, and howling, like a tidal wave of shrieking souls washed up from hell — none of these things got on Cortes' nerves. But they were cannibals!

Cortes was genuinely scandalized in his religious feelings. One of the first things that had happened on their march from the coast up into the hills was that a cacique, devout in his own way, had caused some fifty prisoners to be slaughtered, and offered the white gods cakes dipped in their blood; Cortes had been genuinely offended. An unchristian thing, the grossest of all sins, though not mentioned among the deadly sins of Holy Church — its possibility had never been imagined; Cortes positively developed theological skill on the question of anthropophagy and felt that he had an official mission to make an end of this abominable heresy, by all the force of arms if necessary (the symbol of the Host did not occur to him). From a purely personal point of view Cortes was repelled by this form of bloodshed, even to feeling ashamed of humanity; it gave the great strong man emotions he could scarcely control, of a purely nervous nature, like a woman when she sees a spider crawling; he got creeps, huh, huh, talked in falsetto and was a prey to fits of debility which only a refreshing day on the battle-field with stacks of Indians mown down by the guns was able to dispel.

This feeling remained fresh during the whole campaign, nay, it increased in strength the more examples of the Aztecs' gruesome degradation came to his knowledge. In the same proportion the Mexicans lost their awe of the white strangers. The glad tidings that this was the expected coming of Quetzalcoatl nobody could continue to take seriously — superstition that; whether they were Teules or not was doubtful; many had already come to the con-clusion that they were quite ordinary, dirty, rapacious men. The horses that they had feared so much were the first cause of their mortal nature being revealed; they managed to kill a few of them; the Spaniards buried the first ones, lest the truth should come out, but it came out.

Later, things were found on the Aztecs' altars which they had offered to their gods in the first days of the war, amongst them a horseshoe, a Flemish hat and a letter, things which in a strangely living way bring us near to both parties; it was not to remain at that.

But even after Cortes and his men had lost the advantage of be-ing regarded as supernatural, they still had much in reserve, their frightfulness as men.

To Cortes' mission as an apostle of the Faith was added the over-whelming impression he gained of the wealth of Mexico, whereby we do not mean in the first instance its natural resources, but portable property. This came when Montezuma was civil enough to send him presents even as he was marching on the city; trifles scarce worthy of a god's acceptance, as the ambassadors politely expressed it, but in the eyes of the Spaniards fortunes in gold and precious stones, besides works of art, which were ordered to be beaten flat and melted down on the spot. But if *that* was a modest sample — what treasures of Golconda might they not expect to find in the city itself! And they were right.

The Aztecs' fate was sealed.

VII

THE EAGLE AND THE SERPENT

THE MOST ancient symbol of the Aztecs, which was connected with the founding of Tenochtitlan, the place of the cactus rock, was a rock on which just enough mould had collected for the cactus to grow; on the cactus sat an eagle, and in its beak it held a serpent; the natural features of the Mexican plateau summed up in an image.

On the spot where the first Aztecs saw this sign they had built their pueblo. After the arrival of the Spaniards they might have extended this totem to signify their fate, in a dramatic sense, a duel to the death. To this day it is the national standard of Mexico: the Eagle and the Serpent united and combining their forces.

But the epoch of Cortes was typified by the eagle swooping down upon the rattlesnake with beak and claw.

The conquest of Mexico is known to all, in its several data: how Cortes advanced on to the plateau, the conspiracy of Cholula, Malina's service and the massacre, the entrance into Mexico and Montezuma's captivity in his own city, the parenthesis with Narvaez and Alvarado's doubtful conduct in Mexico during the absence of Cortes, the revolt, Montezuma's death and the disastrous retreat from Mexico, the return and the siege, the sacrifice of the Spanish prisoners, the famine among the natives, and finally their surrender. All this we have in lengthy descriptions, losing in rapidity of action the more they are detailed.

With due respect to the true sequence of events, our memory, our inner eye, pictures the conquest of Mexico in foreshortening, a free consideration of the characters as they develop in one place, no matter whether events chanced to come before or after, the law of the drama; we see these protagonists before us, Cortes and Mon-

tezuma, Malina, Alvarado, Sandoval and other heroes, Huitzilopochtli and his repulsive priests, the harrowing night when Spaniards and Mexicans fought together in the gloomy cannibal city
floating on causeways in a salt lake like a Venice of the Underworld — the threescore naked, shivering Europeans who were sacrificed up on Huitzilopochtli's teocalli, in full view of all the survivors — what a panopticon! Burning altars, burning houses, the
whole scene shown up by fire, and in the background Popocatepetl in the burning sky, fire above fire!

And the piece may begin quite chronologically with the conspiracy, with Montezuma in the foreground, in person, not hiding
in the wings, and the scene Tenochtitlan; the massacre we can
lump together with Alvarado's massacre, and assign the butcheries,
multipled by two, to the great spring festival, historically enough
as regards the second; the rest, the great fight in the city, the
storming of the temples, the retreat, the sacrifices, the investment
and starvation, we can present in rapid acts succeeding or jostling
one another.

Well then: the Spring Festival. It was celebrated with remarkable ancient rites, a young Aztec being chosen for his strength and
beauty, proclaimed as a god and married to four of the most beautiful maidens in the country, whereafter the honeymoon was sol-
emnized with all possible luxury and magnificence for twenty
days, a symbol of fertility and of the return of spring with all its
gifts. On the twenty-first day the festival took on a more general
character; all the young men and maidens dressed themselves in
holiday attire, gorgeous cloaks of quetzal-feathers with jewels and
gold on their limbs, spring made visible, and in a great solemn procession, so sacred that no other public act, not even war, might
take place on that day, they accompanied the young family, the
god and his brides, across the great square in the centre of Tenochtitlan and up all the steps to the top of the great temple. Here all
knelt and worshipped the young god, in whose form Tegcatlipoca
himself was presumed to have taken up his abode. Thereupon he
was handed over to the priests, sacrificed and slain; his heart was
thrown into the golden incense-bowl before the image of the god,
and his limbs were delivered to the congregation, to be devoured
amid dancing and song.

But all is not as it should be at this festival, it is destined to be interrupted before it can be brought to a harmonious conclusion. The young caciques marching in the procession, the flower of the Aztec nobility, in precious garments of feathers, and with old hereditary emeralds, do they look as unconcerned and innocent as is fitting at a festival of joy? Put your hand on their hearts and perhaps you will feel something hard; for what purpose do they carry the macquauitl under the very raiment of innocence? Dark is the Mexican by nature, but if you look around in the teeming streets of the pueblo, you will notice perhaps that to-day they are more than usually dark, with lips drawn in and eyes like their own muddy lake.

There is one who reads all these faces like an open book, Cortes; for he knows the cipher, and it is Malina who has given it him. She has been quietly at work, at night, naked as a snake round all the holes and corners of the pueblo, using her ears here, playing the wide-mouthed native woman there, within hearing of a couple of distinguished old caciques; all the disguise she needs is to make herself suitably ugly, not an easy thing for this glaring flame of a woman, but she manages it; in the likeness of a perfectly doltish slave she carries water in and out of the inner sanctuaries of the highest priestly initiates; she is with Montezuma without his suspecting it, a meeting more secret than the abyss; therefore it is that Cortes is so all-knowing, and his lip curls so grimly under the moustache, inscrutable to all . . . what preparations has not *he* been making in the profoundest secrecy!

A notable trio indeed, as they stand there in a mannerly group to watch the spring-time pass in gay and joyous procession — Cortes, Montezuma and Malina. Cortes iron-clad from head to foot in honour of the feast, full dress, with his sweaty soldier's nose sniffing out of his helmet; Montezuma plainly dressed with only a few jewels; as the chief man of the realm he has no need of magnificence, and he is in mourning, for though, of course, he stands here as a free man, the object of the deepest obeisances, he knows he is a prisoner; finally Malina, with feathers on her head and a little apron of humming-bird feathers in open-work. The three can only bestow courtly smiles on one another, gracious and mincing, as they stand there knowing what the other knows; that is to say, Cortes and Malina know what Montezuma knows, and look him in the face when he speaks with an air of frankness — but *he* doesn't know that artillery is posted all round the square, and grimy gunners match in hand, and that cavalry, men in the saddle, drawn swords and all, are waiting behind the doors, which are ready to swing open. . . .

Then it is that the three princely spectators, around whom a courteous distance has hitherto been preserved, seem to become the centre of a circle which draws ever closer, composed as it happens entirely of very tall Aztecs, warlike in appearance, but, of course, unarmed, only in long, voluminous cloaks. . . .

How pleasant on a festal day like this to be able to put away all thoughts of bloodshed and abandon oneself entirely to the confidence one feels in an honourable prince, says Cortes with a bow, as he looks Montezuma in the face, purring through his moustache. He puts his face so close to Montezuma's that the Emperor shrinks back a little as he nods confirming the truth of the remark.

But Cortes comes still closer with his big, sweaty face, and there is a glint of steel in those prominent, audacious blue eyes. He drops his voice and adds another sentence or two, which appear to have a deadly effect upon Montezuma. The life ebbs out of him, his eyes, his features, his frame; he is a dead man, as one is who has betrayed and failed, and is told it to his face by his enemy.

Yes, Cortes tells him in a few dry words that he knows all his schemes, the conspiracy against his life which is ripe for this very moment . . . and by his side Malina crouches, leaning forward so that Montezuma may see her face. He turns yet greyer, for now he knows her, by a gleam she puts into her eyes, so that he remembers her and the night, and how he disclosed all, and in an instant he sees the whole wretchedness of his situation.

Cortes still holds him as though spitted on his gaze, with his face close to his — Eagle and Serpent! — but then he gives over his features entirely to cruelty, draws himself up and throws his gloved hand in the air. A band of disguised Tlascalans, his allies, who have been spread about among the crowd, fall upon certain of the Aztecs, the conspiring caciques and high chieftains, eloquently disclosing the weapons concealed beneath their cloaks — within an hour they are burnt alive at the stake, with a fire of native arrows and spears, a very brisk blaze, under them.

But Cortes' raised hand is a sign for more than that — all at once the cannons thunder from every side, the houses open like yawning mouths, and slowly Alvarado rides out, like a shining tower of steel, man and horse in one, swaying rhythmically up and down, and behind him all the cavalry with closed visors and bright gleaming swords in the air. And now the soldier in Cortes takes fire, now the general is ready for action; with his left hand he closes his helm, and with his right he draws his long singing sword from its sheath, spitting between hand and hilt — *Iago!* A loud, piercing scream is heard at his side, like a leaping ocelot; it is Malina giving vent to her rapacious heart.

Alarum. Volleys of guns and muskets, the twang of cross-bows, cavalry charges, and all the daintily adorned spring procession, the pick of the country's youth, lies swimming in its blood; the god who was to be sacrificed so prettily to himself is knocked down with his flowery wreaths about his head and trodden out of recognition under the horses' hoofs; bloody furrows are ploughed through the tightly packed crowds in the streets, so easily swept from the square; shrieks, curses and death.

And then an ominous pause, a hundred thousand souls hold their breath in horror at what has happened and what there may be to come.

The results: the revolt, the rising of the whole of Mexico, not the nobles this time but the people, whipped up by the priests, the holy war of extermination against this vermin that pretended to be gods and had seized upon the pueblo in order to snatch up all the gold and run away with it. Until now they had put up with all their shamelessness, their desecration of the gods' holy places where they had raised their own torture stake, for no other reason but that Montezuma in his indulgence had taken their part, he whom they had treated like an Indian, and in whose person they had for ever violated the ancient sacred royal house of the Aztecs root and branch, the dignity of the divine king; now there should be an end of that.

The gods were exasperated to the utmost, Huitzilopochtli sweated cold fire at night in his sanctuary, the priests said; he was phosphorescent, and the sacrificial blood on his flanks was alive; Popocatepetl himself, as every one could see, was moved and would soon destroy the world. The omens pointed to the last day being at hand, a three-year-old child which had been sacrificed had babbled prophecies before its death in a language nobody understood; in the stomach of another victim they had found a stone shaped like many-branched lightning; a condor flying from the east had dropped carrion on Huitzilopochtli's teocalli . . . was further evidence required? Mexico's fate was uncertain — but these foreign impostors who had stolen the thunder and in whom everything was false, even to the colour of their skins, should die, even if it cost a thousand Mexicans for every one of the palefaces they made an end of!

The rising came at dawn; notwithstanding all other Powers, they would now have the Sun himself in their company; before sunrise a sound as of cockchafers in a sack arose from Mexico, the ardent whispering of a whole population — and that day, when the sun had reached the zenith, a vast pillar of dust and roaring seemed to rise up towards it, broad as the whole city of Mexico; all the countless hosts of the city attacked the palace, where the few whites had at once barricaded themselves — a rain of stones, obsidian arrows, fire-hardened stakes and spears, bare hands, teeth if they got near enough; thousands dropped before the cannons and the tireless Toledo blades, forming heaps in front of the palace, but other thousands came on, and that with a ceaseless shouting, roaring and howling from a multitude of throats, from the moment the sun rose, without cessation all through the day, calculated to scare the enemy — and it scared them.

The situation of the invested Spanish force, now with Narvaez' troops fully 1200 men, 6000 Tlascalans and 80 horses, was indeed desperate; the whole country rose against them, it was as though the earth opened wherever they looked and gave forth Mexicans, in black waves, host upon host of death-defying savages dressed like devils in the skins of beasts and feathers, rolling on towards the palace, howling, yelling and with a devilish ear-splitting noise behind them of terrifying instruments, drums, an inferno of pipes with four holes which screeched uninterruptedly hour after hour, grooved antelope-horns which were scraped with mussel-shells, a music invented by Satan.

Blood ran that day in rivers through the streets of Mexico. Flaming arrows penetrated the palace and set fire to the woodwork, many Spaniards fell, however many lives they took themselves. The howling and the infernal music exhausted the brain, not every one kept up his heroic spirit; the soldiers of Narvaez sat idly and began to ask why they should die to make Cortes' fortune — disorder even in their own lines.

When the position became untenable Cortes made a sally with

his bravest, — Alvarado, Sandoval, Olid, all sportsmen to whom fighting was an art, — and together they stormed Huitzilopochtli's temple, an impossible thing, seeing that the pyramid was black from top to bottom, on all its hundred and fourteen terraces, with Mexican warriors, who flung down blazing timbers upon the attackers; they *took* the temple, after three hours of acrobatics and slaughter, set fire to the towers on the top, and — then Huitzilopochtli came!

The Mexicans saw him come out of his sanctuary like a toad out of its hole, but in a recumbent position, how now — the Spaniards were behind him, rolling him along; out he came in his square block over the edge of the topmost platform, and down he thundered squarely over all the steps, taking a dozen at a jump, knocking holes in the masonry and a corner off himself, smoking with a breath of thunder, and finally crushing a group of red-jerkined priests who stood howling at the foot of the pyramid!

A mighty exploit, the fall of Mexico underlined — but a piece of bravado; the Mexicans themselves were not dead yet, they came and continued to come, one black wave out of another like the smoke of a conflagration, shooting, stabbing, yelling, not a Spaniard but was wounded; what could be done?

An appeal to the people, through Montezuma himself, was attempted; he had power over them after all, and was induced to go out on the roof and get them to listen to reason. A great moment; the noise actually stopped for a few minutes and gave place to a stillness never known before, when Montezuma showed himself and the crowds saw him they had regarded as the highest and most dignified of all men. He spoke, a single thin human voice was heard amid the ocean of silence, with thousands of lowering eyes directed upon him.

But he had no answer. Stones answered him, arrows and stones; wounded and bleeding, Montezuma staggered and had to be led away.

No, he had no answer. For he was no longer Montezuma. They had torn him out of their hearts. The Council, the ancient power in the land, had met and declared his hereditary rights forfeit; he was a nobody now, and in his stead Guatemozin, the next-of-kin, had been proclaimed God's deputy and leader of the armies.

Then Cortes himself tried to appeal to the people. After the fall of the temple he went up on to the roof with Malina, his interpreter, obtained silence, a silence of death, and spoke to the people; no mild words of peace and conciliation, which was what he desired, but the cold anticipations of the general, designed for moral effect:

Now they could see for themselves, their temple destroyed, their gods reduced to dust, how could they think of resisting him? Amicably, such and such terms; with continued resistance, not one stone left upon another in Mexico!

And these harsh words were translated by Malina into flute-like tones; the ocelot had the ear of the human ocean all to herself, and mewed out the utterances of the man of iron to the thousands of warriors, above whose heads the dust of war hovered in a cloud. She twisted her body charmingly and licked her pink lips, in feathers for the occasion, but with the gleam of her copper limbs shining through like a lavish fire, a willing and voluptuous echo of Cortes' destroying words.

They gave him an answer, some old cacique or other acted as spokesman and spoke very plainly, to the effect that in a short time they would have no more food, that most of them were wounded and patched up — and moreover the bridges on the causeways were broken, they needn't think they could get away!

It was true.

After the pause, drums, pipes, antelope-horn rattles and a hundred thousand howling, yelling Aztecs: the burial chorus started again and would not stop until the funeral was over. And what graves to end in!

Meanwhile Montezuma died. A blow to Cortes, for even if he was now quite out of favour he must have a party and might have been used again. But they could not keep life in him; he tore off his bandages, would not eat, preserved an obstinate silence, with downcast eyes, from the time he was stoned by his own people until his death. The chronicler notes that he refused to kiss the crucifix!

If Columbus was the most disappointed man in history, Montezuma rivalled him in a way; both of them had a great and genuine hope of seeing God, and one of them found a cannibal, the other Cortes.

The night after Montezuma's death Cortes commenced the retreat.

It was the famous night of sorrow, indelicately referred to by Diaz as the night when they were thrown out of Mexico. On this occasion he had an experience he had never known before, and of which he had never imagined the possibility — he was *afraid*. Yes, he mentions the fact with surprise and in remarkable terms, almost as though fear were some kind of horrible creature outside himself with which he here became acquainted. So terrible was the night.

With scattered features and incidents brought together in foreshortening the night appears thus — Popocatepetl in the leading part:

He stands flickering in his heaven, lost in his own glowing dreams, with his own long time, and in one of his instants, when he shoots up fire and lays bare the whole plateau beneath him in the gleam, a land of lava with black shadows, and a salt lake with heavy, sluggish waters, in the lake a city, seemingly caked together with blood and lime — in such an instant it is that they fight and make history down there, Eagle and Serpent, a duel in the air, the bird of prey has the reptile in its claws, and the snake writhes and tries to get at its breast with its poison-fang.

Cortes waited for the darkest hour of midnight, as far as it could be dark in Tenochtitlan with its hundreds of flaming altars, before he set out, with artillery, horses and all, his whole train and all his men, a special detachment to carry the great wooden bridge they had built in all secrecy to lay across the gap in the causeway.

It was this gap of sorrow that separated them from the dry land; here was the fighting, and here they suffered their losses, with the burning city at their back and the Mexicans after them on the causeway, the lake black with their canoes; for they had word of the departure only too soon, and set fire to everything that would burn in the city to show the enemy the way home, came after him with yells and roars and sharp spears, a whole world of splintered glass; and once more the Spaniards had to cut into them and keep them off rank by rank, while everlastingly fresh ranks and more canoes dashed up.

A frightful night. Some got across, then the bridge gave way; a living mush of men struggled in the water, drowned, were slaughtered; the gap was filled up with the guns and the sinking baggage, high enough for a few more to make their way across, last of the rearguard Alvarado, who *jumped* over; impossible, declares the sober Bernal Diaz, but to this day everybody says he did it; over he came.

Yes, down in the muddy bottom of the lake lay all the good guns. The greater part of all Cortes' gold, in chests and boxes, found there a safe deposit for eternity; a terrible pity, the sun and moon in heavy chased gold, as big as wheels, bars enough to build a little house, cast from all the art treasures of Tenochtitlan; precious stones to an untold amount. Only the melancholy songs of the Spanish homeland were capable of giving utterance to such a grief. Yes, they lost all. Yet one long chest was saved of the baggage, it *had* to come through — Cortes had put it in charge of his most trusted porters and given it an escort of his keenest blades; in it Malina was concealed, packed away in feathers like a jewel, a fortune in quetzal-feathers at any rate; we may guess her dreams were warm ones if she slept though the trip.

Malina survived the horrors of the night. Apart from her the Spaniards lost all their slaves, male and female; Montezuma's children, who were with the baggage, were slain. All but twenty of the horses perished. Diaz drops a tear over Alvarado's sorrel mare; she must have been worth it. We hear of one other woman being saved, the only Castilian woman who was ever with the expedition, according to Diaz, by name Maria de Estrada — street? platform? — and a remarkable woman she was, fought like a man on the causeway with a two-handed sword, and came through alive. What a woman! Imagine her experiences!

Seven hundred Spaniards perished that night, drowned or slain, some taken prisoner, nameless most of them, and yet every single one had once been swung up to the ceiling by his mother, a cherub in swaddling-clothes, growing up into a vagabond and soldier of fortune, to end here like chopped straw. But there were also grandees and caballeros among the fallen, Cortes' best friends and supporters, never, never to be forgotten!

The sacrifices: the poor, hapless ones who fell alive into the hands of the Aztecs and were slaughtered to the gods; white men, Christians, ah, their eyes mirrored the greatest horror ever seen, Tenochtitlan's night; they alone of all men knew what it was to go with open eyes, with all their wits about them, straight into Hell!

Their fellows on the causeway saw them being led naked up

all the terraces of the temple, round and round, the whole way up, in a glare bright as daylight from burning altars, burning houses, while distant bursts of flame and lightning flashes from Popocatepetl flickered across the whole sky. Ay, up they had to go, the steep sacred way of the Mexicans, the symbol of the nation's wanderings, from the tropics up the ladder of the zones to the roof of the world, into a rarer air; the doomed white men were forced to pace it, with lash and stab, pinioned like sheep, and from the causeway and the shores of the lake their white bodies could be seen shining among black and red devils, the red priests in their robes of office, sacrificial jerkins, flowing hair — the young white-skinned sons of Spain, with their blue blood, *sangre azul*, showing through the skin like a map of fair rose-pink river-valleys, the skin of their exquisite mothers, milk of their milk — and when they appeared on the platform they were forced to dance before the altar of jasper, Huitzilopochtli's stone sacrifice; he himself was absent for the moment, but represented by his priests!

Face to face with them, the priests of Huitzilopochtli, they were brought, aloft on the top of the pyramid, as though in the air, with night and fire below, night and fire above their heads, the mountain brooding over the world like an evil red eye, and around them a pack of joyful tormentors, in garments as of clotted blood, vultures with befouled drooping wings, their hair matted with blood, long nails, most of them earless, clucking like birds and clinking their obsidian knives together. A clatter of cauldrons, forks and huge ladles down in the forecourt; flutes, antelope-horn rattles — the drum!

The great death-drum! Ay, to-night it sounded, from the top of Huitzilopochtli's temple, the doomsday drum, made of the skins of anacondas and audible for miles over the country as a deep bellowing, a sluggish, fearful pulse in the night, boom — boom! Down in the city the women, alone at home on this night of conflict, came out of doors and smeared blood on the mouth of the serpent totem on the wall of the house, when they heard the snake-drum, conjuring up the oldest, profoundest symbols of Mexico.

To the booming of this voice from the Abyss the doomed Spaniards went to their death. And all the images of death were before their eyes, the place of skulls below the temple lighted up by the fire, the scaffolding of bones, the elaborately built-up mounds of death's-heads, dried mummy heads stuck on stakes, an abyss as though paved with upturned faces, the grinning, naked human form . . . truly this was the Underworld itself!

The young Spanish noble . . . now they had hold of him, came close to him with the bestial warmth of their bodies, forced their way into his soul with their grins, the dogs; now they broke down his bearing, stretched him in a ridiculous posture, now they cut him open — ah well, that only hurt — but then they laid hold of his heart, then they laid hold of his heart!

Boom — boom!

And when his ears rang in the last lulling, when he began to be alone in a friendly darkness — why, then let the drum go on, let the rest be accomplished, hell for hell, let it bustle and boil over down in the priests' kitchens, let the vultures scream from the gods' aviaries, where the great birds fan together darkness and fiery gleam under their wings, let it snarl and hiss from the menageries, where puma and jaguar pad softly up and down and arch their backs, with yellow eyes watching for what their stinking keepers will bring, the ocelot pit like a snake-pen full of cats, marked like the boa and as noiseless, with the same narrow vertical pupil . . .

Splash, splash, sounded in the rattlesnake pit, as the entrails were flung to them, the share of the deadly grey serpent, and in the flickering light which crept in from a reflection in the sky, Popocatepetl's distant fires, a gliding life could be seen, scarcely to be distinguished from the dust underneath the fat, scaly reptiles; they came out of holes and corners, darting a dry tongue from their mouths, tasting the air, with scaly jaws and little enamel eyes, giving a faint rattle in the gloom, the castanets in their tail . . .

Boom — boom!

On the other side of the lake Cortes sat and listened to the ceaseless throbbing of the death-drum, saw the awful scene, recognized his friends in the distance. In the course of the night he had had heads flung at his feet by Aztecs infuriated to madness, the heads of his comrades; he saw them make that terrible progress, saw them die — and then Cortes wept, with a boy's hard, abandoned weeping that hurts the throat and strangles the breath, over the sufferings of his boys and brothers.

A creature stroked her head against him, rubbed her ear on him, Malina, trying to console him, to make up to him for all his loss;

but Cortes flicked her away like a grain of dust that had got into his tears; she could not help him.

No, there was only one thing that could help him, as time would show, that which he swore as he shook his fist at the flaming temples of Mexico — that he would see them razed to the ground, and all their foul butchers rotting corpses in the earth! Was that so strange an oath?

And it came to pass as he had sworn. With murder and man-slaughter he was hunted out of Mexico, with siege and starvation he returned.

Better would it have been if Popocatepetl had buried Mexico and the whole plateau under a layer of ashes than that *that* should be seen which was seen in the streets of Mexico when it was at the last gasp and the mothers took back into themselves that to which they had given life, and Huitzilopochtli's priests in hunger delirium, when the last rattlesnake had been devoured, stole glances at each other — no hope left even if they ate each other, nothing left to eat on them, plucked living corpses of vultures, staggering with the last of their strength to the carrion-heap and falling dead on their faces in it.

To such extremes does one misdeed drive another.

At dawn one more last sacrifice took place up on the platform with the smoking ruins of its towers, after Huitzilopochtli's image, with immense toil, fury and triumph, had been dragged up all the steps, hundreds of men pulling at it, like a swarm of impassioned ants round a caterpillar, and set up in his place again somewhat battered, with a chip knocked out of his forehead and all the precious stones and ornaments broken or shaken out, but still Huitzilopochtli the ancient. They trembled before him, for the insult he had suffered, the revenge he might take — but had they not already avenged him pretty well? Mexico purified, the great and rare offerings he had received — and now he was to receive the last and best, if that was good enough, the white strangers' own god!

Just before sunrise this extraordinary sacrifice took place; the tall life-size crucifix, which the Spaniards had set up in the square before the palace where they had been lodged and from which they had been turned out, was borne in solemn procession round all the steps of the temple the whole way up to the platform.

Here the two gods were confronted with one another. They

were left in each other's company a good while, even the priests withdrawing from the platform to the next step below, and thousands of Mexicans filled the remaining terraces, still mad with the night's orgy of slaughter, silent, glaring like wild cattle.

Well, then the gods had a chance of looking at each other and making some remarks; they might have a good deal to talk about, their passions, their impressions of mankind for a thousand years, and so on. But the gods were dumb.

It was as though they spoke in the language that was spread out before the eyes of all in the dawning, the earth hidden by corpses, half the pueblo fallen in like bakers' ovens after a shower of stones, black smoking logs all that was left of cedarwood timbers, whose perfume was changed to the sour smell of burning; the temple drenched in blood from the top step to the bottom and covered with dead bodies, like a mountain of corpses; the lake stained red far out from the shore, a vast raw scent of blood hanging over the earth as high as the top of the temple.

Underneath the huge drum the drummer lay dead, burst by his own fury, after having danced the whole night long like a devil about his doomsday drum, howling, in a hurricane of his hair, naked, with limbs like glowing copper; now he was cooled down, lying crumpled up on his drumstick like a man of ashes.

Sunrise! Silence! Far and wide the land and mountains stare out into the clear, light air of the plateau, the ring of heaven and earth uniting in the distance. Popocatepetl smokes up into the morning sky, and to-day his smoke is not black but white.

Silence! The gods stand face to face. They do not budge. Huitzilopochtli broad, short in the neck, with a piece chipped out of one eye, nose gone, a good deal knocked about, but still a black; the white god stiff and mute on his cross, in an everlasting agony: Man, after his own handling.

Then they set fire to the crucifix, and as the sun's eye appeared over the horizon it burned, with a pale fire rising straight up into the air.

But Huitzilopochtli was soon to travel down all those steps again, and this time he would be left standing on his head among ruins and rubble, until one day a later generation pulled him out and put him in a museum with a label on him, a piece of monstrous sculpture, for the ecstatic delight of those who recognize their own genius in Negro fetishes, to others only the hideous image of a nightmare from which mankind has awakened. Where his temple was, now stands the Cathedral of Mexico; if fear is no longer to be worked upon there are feelings to answer the purpose.

A gleaming white dome of snow fills the extinct crater of Popocatepetl.

VIII

THE NEW WORLD

We came to Portorico's shore
And fought with cannibals full sore.
　　Chek, chekkelek . . .

　　　　　　　　　　　　(Teeth-chattering, castanets.)

To all our saints we prayed,
And scrap-iron in our gun we laid,
And shot and stabbed and hit around galore.
　　Ha, ha, ha!

　　　　　　　　　　　　(Chorus of howls.)

And then we got an appetite;
A curly maiden came in sight.
　　Chek, chekkelek . . .
The pot's just on the boil,
And in she goes with spice and oil.
Deep water makes you ready for a bite.
　　Ha, ha, ha!

A curly maiden's not so bad,
With skin and hair and all, my lad!
　　Chek, chekkelek . . .
Each epicure his taste —
Give me a cut from near the waist —
There's chops and steaks and brisket to be had!
　　Ha, ha, ha!

Then you can take a lily-white bone
To pick your tooth, the hollow one.
　　Chek, chekkelek . . .
Strike up a dead men's dance,
With skull and crossbones, now's your chance!
Come on, come on, don't let me dance alone!
　　Ha, ha, ha!

Our Eldorado's found, I guess,
Since we've tobacco in our mess.
  Chek, chekkelek . . .
Strike up a firemen's jig,
And puff the smoke about your wig!
Cheers for tobacco, that's the weed we bless!
  Ha, ha, ha!

With whip and loaded gun stand we
And make the slaves work busily —
  Chek, chekkelek . . .
The black man he is black;
He gets the sun right on his back —
And that's what keeps the white man white, you see!
  Ha, ha, ha!

Like stallions we rushed around
And women, lots of them, we found.
  Chek, chekkelek . . .
Old Huitzli we defied —
But strange diseases here betide;
And now some noseless ones are homeward bound.
  Ha, ha, ha!

I've had enough of going to sea,
It's making an old man of me.
  Chek, chekkelek . . .
I'll see my girl again,
She'll meet her boy from off the main —
And she'll have been, let's hope, as true as we . . .
  Ha, ha, ha!

COMPARATIVELY pretty cannibal chanties such as this and others not so nice, in the savages' own gibberish, were sung by the crews of the slave-ships which brought home gold from the West Indies and carried back cargoes of slaves from the Guinea Coast to the islands, to take the place of the native population which was dying out in the mines. Two worlds had begun to infect one another.

Armies of men, whole populations, were ready to force their way over to the other side, now that an escape from Europe had been opened. A great liquidation was going on among prelates, princes and contentious theologians in Europe; the Church was going to pieces and losing its absolute power over men's souls, only to split up into several, equally intolerant; many whips in place of the great scourge. Crowned heads watched their opportunity and raked in estates which the Church could no longer keep hold of since it had become divided against itself. But two or three hundred years elapsed before this liquidation came to an end. And the common people, who found themselves in a tight place whatever happened, who got a Reformation but no reform; the peasants who were bound faster than ever after their flails had struck down one or two nobles and they had burnt a few castles; the surplus of the Middle Ages along the highways, beggars, discharged soldiers, an unthrifty but vigorous rabble — the common people could not wait, the discontented made for the coast and jumped at the bounty money, which men with raw gold on their fingers were offering in every port; the caravels put to sea loaded with men who had not yet become a class; but they were to become one.

Men like Rodrigo de Triana, the seaman who first saw land on board the *Pinta*, but did not get the promised annuity of 10,000 maravedis; he was discontented, furious, and his wrath lasted him his lifetime, however it was with his annuity. The Admiral got the money, he had seen the first light ashore that evening — ho, who was talking about seeing lights, it was land they were looking for! But the Admiral was within his rights, decided his own case, strict justice, first is first! Rodrigo was wild all the rest of the voyage, and beside himself when six months later they came home and dazzled Spain with the mighty news.

While the Admiral was being honoured like a prince in Seville, and invited to attend their majesties' court at Barcelona — now the ex-cartographer was mounting, he was ennobled, had *always* been noble — Rodrigo raged over in his Triana and ran amuck through all the wineshops, from which *he* derived his extraction, banged all their tables and threatened the lives of inoffensive men, without harming a hair of their heads, with a dry sob in his throat, drunken laughter and shaking his head at his glass:

First is first! The great can do these things! Muck to the mucky! Saw a light in the dark — light in my breeches! Puerca Madoña!

Drunk and with drawn knife Rodrigo then reeled through the streets of Seville talking to himself aloud, hiccuping and with many an empty laugh, making way for himself with the edge of his hand, though he had the whole procession to himself — this was when he had heard the rumours of Columbus's triumphal progress through the whole of Spain, the mountebank shows with parrots and gold masks, the dyewoods, and bamboo, and the dozen poor savages with rings in their noses — a nice Spain *they* were shown, the whole of Christendom running after a handful of Indians! — and Columbus himself at the head, propped up aloft on a palfrey, which must have been rigged with a rudder aft so that he could steer it . . . for all this mummery and the honours and Columbus sitting on a chair with their majesties and his newly bought coat-of-arms and the gold chain on his neck and his going hunting with the King, for all this Rodrigo didn't give a blow! Even the wall of the church came in for a share of his contempt!

But when rumours came thick and fast of the Admiral's glory — now he must be eating from the same dish as the King, and be sure they each stirred the soup well to scoop up the dumplings! — then Rodrigo lost all appetite in his native land and emigrated, stormed across to Africa. There he turned Mohammedan; Columbus might take his share of salvation too; a dirty lot of Christians, not another breath would he draw among the dogs!

To the day of his death Rodrigo stayed over in Africa, praising Allah in burnoose and turban, only to be distinguished from other Mussulmans by his wrathful blue eyes. A seaman's calling — Rodrigo spat on it! He broke stones for the rest of his days, and between spitting on his hands and punishing big blocks he shook a clenched fist northward at Europe over the water and gave vent to his feelings in Arabic — might the tongue shrivel up in his throat if his native speech ever crossed *his* lips again!

Such was the wrath of Rodrigo.

It was not America in his particular case, but it was for thousands of others, who without regret turned their backs on Europe for good.

First it was the Conquistadores and all their troop, Cortes and Pizarro, Diego Almagro, who conquered Chile, another man of iron with an uncommon keenness of character which reminds one of the Estremeños, the worst and the best qualities of Arab and Goth united; there were Ojeda, Alvarado; and with them the nameless armies that accompanied them. We may suppose that all Spain could show of old Northern descent, the seed of the Normans, the waggon-folk of the Migrations, the restless ones who at one time had thrust to the South, that these were the first to seize the opportunity of moving on again, now that a Farther-off had been found. It was like a great Magnet Mountain overseas acting at a distance and drawing the nails out of Spain.

But after the discoverers and adventurers came the settlers. This was a slower movement, it was the foundation itself that was transferred; but there was no hurry about it, it is not finished yet.

And this is the great book of the Emigrants. The emigration was divided into two main streams: one from southern Europe which was to settle Latin America, Norman at the top, the Migrations filtered through the South, and Romance at the bottom; but the other later stream came from the North of Europe, the very source of the Migrations, and from it have come the United States.

Once more peasants committed themselves to the waves, nameless unknown bands, once more the emigrant's waggon creaked in new trackless regions, with children's faces looking out ahead from under the awning and long, worn handles of farm implements projecting behind, the plough on its travels again. And once more peasants drew up their waggons in a ring at night, with the cattle inside, a camp-fire and a frugal supper under the open sky, while round about lay the strange and hostile wilderness and a stealthy, powerful and cruel native population: the romance of the Red Indian, with all its bloody and fanatical chapters, the arrow quivering in the awning of the emigrant waggon, the frontiersman's long rifle bringing down the feathered horsemen at impossible ranges, Daniel Boone and the Last of the Mohicans; California — a trumpet-call no longer ago than when our fathers were young! Klondyke — our own fanfares!

A mighty, many-coloured, stirring book! What did they not see, the men who saw the vast young countries, coasts, prairies and mountains, immense rivers, cordilleras, tropical forests, pampas, for the first time! Overwhelmingly the thought forces itself upon us: never, never again will the world be so fresh! Not again will the world renew itself! Childhood lost! Manhood lost!

The poor "prairie schooner" that rocked its way west and made ruts for the first time on untrodden soil, with the elements of a home and of a population within; long-haired, wrinkled, resolute men on horseback surrounding it rifle in hand, and the outline of a mounted Indian far away by a steep pass — well, now the long trains are running there between the Atlantic and Pacific, and from the stern and silent emigrant has come America's robust farmer, the millions who feed millions.

Wide is the shade of Ygdrasil, the Tree of the Migrations, with its root in the North and fresh branches spreading over all the world!

Plants and animals move on and change their places, are given or deprived of a destiny; as though by some unexampled natural catastrophe the North American bison is wiped out from the continent and the ancient domestic cattle of Europe come in. The horse is put ashore, the first ones from the cramped caravels of the discoverers, where they have stood for months in a swinging stall, turning the whites of their eyes upon a desert of waves, kicked and banged at the woodwork, and foaled, long-legged shaggy foals that the waves throw down every time they try to stand up — but at last a gangway is put ashore for them, which the creatures refuse to go down; they throw up their heads and make a great to-do, have to be forced ashore, but then there they are! The prairie! Do they remember that they have been there before? Oh no, that is at least a geological period ago, they remember nothing; but how they shake their heads now that they feel soil under their hoofs, with flying manes, hindquarters in the air and lashing out with pleasure!

Thus they trot into the new world and put their muzzles to its pastures, stamping its soil with the mark of the heart from their feet, from the northernmost North America right round the curve of the globe to the southernmost Patagonia; galloping and neighing and turning back into wild horses, a whole continent bred full from a few pairs; the mustang's swift career, for a time free as the air, but lassoed again and bitted, bucking and kicking but spurred and broken, much ridden, petted and glorious!

The sheep comes over, even with Columbus, and trips ashore with its little hoofs, shakes its tail and drops its marks of habitation on the smallholder's field, has its spring lambs here again and shivers once a year when shorn for man's benefit, chews the cud sideways and stamps its forefoot with frightful peremptoriness when any one comes near its tether, just as in the old world — honour to simplicity! But here the sheep becomes a gregarious and mountain animal again, sharing the soil with the llama and alpaca on more highlands, stony prairies and borderlands than can be numbered.

Wheat comes over, in exchange for maize, which makes its way to Europe with its long straw and fertile cob; all the wheat in

Mexico is said to come from two grains which a Negro found in a sack of rice, as early as the days of Cortes. From some pips Bernal Diaz planted behind a temple are descended all the orange trees of Mexico. Life and nourishment take up but little room and are so ready to replenish the earth, only asking to be lost in the soil and forgotten.

In some remote upland of Chile or Peru, no one has yet discovered where, there grew a nightshade which preserved its life in time of menace by stored-up nutriment in tubers at its root, the *potato!*

Another sallow nightshade, tobacco, acquired a power above all other plants on earth, although it is anything but nourishing, makes a man cowardly and shortens his life; man's inherent craving to multiply his being with poisons and widen his experience, by sickness if need be, holds a protecting hand over it. Chocolate, sweets came in; teeth went out. The barndoor fowl to the new world; the turkey to the old.

But how did things go with the natives? Not well. In countries where a population had spread to the limits it required, and where so many fresh millions came in, somebody had to give way. The natives gave way, they politely died out. Even the Conquistadores could see with their own eyes how places were emptying, and like good economists they replenished them with fresh hands, an island of exiled Africa, which spread and spread beyond the sea.

The weak people of the tropics went out first; they could not share the land with Spaniards, even shook their heads when referred to a life to come, if they were allowed to live here. It is related of a certain Hatuey, a cacique of Cuba, who was burnt alive, that when they wanted to force baptism and grace upon him before his death he inquired whether the Whites also went to Heaven; on hearing that they did he preferred fire to water and went unabsolved to the stake. The Indian farther north withdrew in sinister silence.

The cannibal went out. Of the happy islanders nothing was left but Famine, a lean shadow on the top of a pile of skulls, grinning at *Hope*, which was hanging opposite from a palm tree.

Nor did all the Conquistadores have the same luck; conscience, or Nemesis, struck some of them, or they simply met with a brawler's end; most of them died a violent death.

A sigh of atonement reaches us from the brilliant and admired Alvarado. He met his death on an expedition to California, in an athletic style worthy of him. In scaling a mountain to capture a native stronghold the path was so steep that the horsemen fell from it, and Alvarado got one of them on his head, avoided horse and man but was hit by a piece of rock which they brought down and which broke every bone in his body. He lived for several days, and is said to have wept over all his transgressions, his acts of thoughtlessness and injustice against the natives. One day, when the crushed and contrite man was sighing with more resignation than usual, he replied to a friend who asked him where he felt most pain: *el alma*, in the soul; and in his last will he provided that all the savages he had branded and enslaved should be set free. Thus died Alvarado, in torment, a good lad.

But that did not bring back to life the hundreds of thousands whom other Spaniards in a bestial tropical frenzy had burnt, flayed, infected with Europe, flogged to death in the mines and destroyed.

But the trouble lay deeper than ordinary malignity and callousness; Nature had here brought together creatures incapable of mixing; of the same origin, but at a primitive stage on one side, the other changed beyond all return; they might meet, but could no longer be grafted on one another, one side had to eclipse the other.

Primitive and civilized man had come too far away from each other. The former's state of innocence was doubtful enough, already marked by the beginning of a culture, cruelty conscious and intensified; but how were they to overtake the Whites in the arts of destruction? They, the Christians, had plenty of soul, self-knowledge enough, a noble conception of God — were they the better for it? With the growth of civilization *all* qualities grow, including brutality; even fatuity, callousness and lack of judgment manifest themselves on a grand scale. No, simple savages and the lords of creation, who had parted with their natural disposition, could not understand one another.

Not everywhere was the barrier so insurmountable; in Mexico a crossing took place which has held its own. The incipient culture there! Malina's forces!

But farther north the white man took land for himself and himself alone, claiming latitudes which were his own at home. It was as though Columbus only opened up America at second-hand to those whose instinct had been at work in him, the Northerners;

from a point in his rear these races set out to found the America which is *America*, the States.

Here, on new soil and for a long time unnoticed, liberty grew up, which had become homeless in Europe, the ancient independence of the peasant.

And when it was strong enough it was able to turn back to the old world and show its light there; when the Republic, the pristine national form of the West, was reintroduced in France, the infection came from the young American Union.

The yeomen transplanted, a new root for the race, generation after generation of nameless families hidden here on their sovereign farms, from the hereditary homesteads in the old country to the new free land in the West — that was the true line in Columbus's instinct as Ferryman. What was perverted in him avenged itself in his life and upon his successors.

If it came to the ears of Rodrigo de Triana it must have consoled him that Columbus's glory was so short-lived. For King Ferdinand soon elbowed the "Viceroy" out of all his rights in the newly discovered countries. To follow the course of Nemesis: four hundred years later America drove Spain out of her overseas possessions; Columbus avenged.

But the holy Christophorus, if he could have seen the fate of Columbus and his successors, would assuredly have pointed with his big numbed finger to the dynasty of the discoverer, which died out in a single generation, the race decaying almost at once in the atmosphere of power, pomp and vexation of spirit.

BOOK THREE
THE PHANTOM SHIP

I

PHILIPPA

Bᴜᴛ what of the country Christopher Columbus sought after, unofficially, for his fleets were always fitted out for *India;* but the country that was the source of all his passion, what of that?

Well, it is still to be found; the Admiral wants to get away, he is lying sick in Valladolid and has no time to be sick, he has to go to sea; tries to get up, but can only raise his head from the pillow; he must get up, he fumbles over the bedclothes with his big, feeble hands, has letters to write, looks about him and wipes his ailing eyes, to think that they should be bad again now! The room seems misty to him, he does not know that he is nearly blind. Movement is quite impossible, he is perfectly stiff, the sea salt that has got into his joints; bad luck to have such a poor day just when he has so much to see about. But still he has been worse before, he thinks, that time two years ago in Jamaica when he lay for weeks like a dead man.

Patience; and the Admiral has the Scriptures read to him, dictates with closed eyes, sends for people and has long conferences about what is to be done; though he speaks in a scarcely audible voice he keeps his servants busy, the room is like a highway where everybody is coming and going, very respectful gentlemen who shake their heads as they leave. But the Admiral is busy all day long, lying anchored in his bed with his long frame crippled with rheumatism, snow-white and with deep-sunk eyes, looking like a centenarian though he is still some way off sixty; he is busy all day long, muttering and muttering, the invincible mind flaming incessantly behind the drawn forehead and beneath the closed eyes, over which the brows already yawn with the hollow shadow of death.

Great difficulties at this time, disagreements with the King, always those rights they had taken from him and which he had not yet recovered; opposition, enemies on every hand, infringements of his proprietary rights, and on the top of that delays, delays, hindrances that had to be got rid of before he could come to the real business, a new voyage, God willing, the fifth . . . and when that was successfully accomplished, for now he must succeed, there was the raising of an army and the crusade against Constantinople! The Turk to be driven out of Europe! Christ's sepulchre restored to Christendom! The opening of the Millennium! Much to lay his hand to, when once he had surmounted a mass of worries, and found Eldorado in the meantime, and a vexatious thing to have his old sea trouble tormenting him again when time was so precious.

Thus worked his ever-busy brain, the only part of him spared by four long laborious voyages of discovery, twelve years of toil and disappointment, since the year he had found San Salvador; but had he always kept his brain clear, had he not rambled now and then, seeing how incomprehensible, enigmatical and tantalizing the world persisted in appearing to him?

Ah yes, they were twelve bitter years; it pained him not in his limbs alone to look back on them; years of suffering, full of fatigue, never an affliction was he spared, sleepless, long, hard, anxious, fruitless years! Ever since his first homeward voyage after the discovery, when he had to pay for the easy, untroubled outward passage, and was tossed about in the *Niña* in fearful storms, storms, storms, till all hope of seeing land again was abandoned; the Atlantic in its murky might, the *Niña* riding over mountains of water, from one abyss into another, incredible that the little craft could do it! Yes, there she was pounded and buffeted by the waves, and rolled and flung into such a depth that it seemed as if clouds and seas were flying straight into heaven; there they stood in dripping wet clothes day after day for weeks, watching till they simply could not close their eyes again. . . . Ah, yes, that was the pain he still felt.

Then the second voyage: the beautiful island of Jamaica, *Santa*

Gloria, the airs of Paradise that haunted his nostrils there, the fruit-less hunt for the mainland, the strain, eye trouble, headwinds home, distress and shortage of food in the ships; the failure of the colonies, the King's ill-humour, Spain full of enemies.

Third voyage: still the vain hunt for the passage to India, the private probing of the coasts for the Kingdom of Heaven; a more southerly route this time, Trinidad, the mouths of the Orinoco and the great freak of nature where the mighty freshwater stream meets the Equatorial Current.

This time Columbus was within an ace of it, he got into a whirl-pool with his ships and turned a trifle giddy: here at last was eloquent proof of the proximity of the earthly Paradise, one of the great rivers that run from the source by the Tree of Life, the river from which the Deluge once came! The stars spun a little before his eyes, he felt he was under the sign of the Virgin, and interpreted his whole reckoning as a conjecture bordering on cer-tainty that the earth in these zones must have an immense wart on it, like a sort of supplementary earth; it was round, no doubt, but like a pear, and up at the point of this supplementary earth lay Paradise; that explained why the current was so strong and the volume of water that came from there was so vast, making the sea fresh for miles out, with a smell of vegetation, full of mud and torn-up plants: no question about it, such a stream must come from the Garden of Eden!

Other observations pointed to the proximity of Paradise: in a bay Columbus caught sight at a distance of pink-winged creatures bathing, by all appearance angels. Seamen with undamaged eyes thought they were a kind of long-legged pink birds with long necks and a broken beak, flamingoes; but they did not contradict the Admiral in his hearing.

Columbus thought he had been nearer to Heaven, literally speak-ing, on this voyage than ever before; and his own deluded, rain-bow-coloured letter should be read; a great soul speaks in it in spite of all, we can feel the beating of a heart like the very pulse of the world, the rivers had infected him, he had touched the earth like the Greek hero and had regained his hold of the mar-vellous — hope, hope will never die!

And the heart-breaking letter he wrote to the King after his fourth and last voyage should be read, when he had sailed as a private person and was not even allowed to land in his own colony, which was now administered by others. For he returned from the third voyage as a prisoner, deprived of all his dignities; that was the end of it, and the fetters he had worn were hanging at this moment above his bed. That they had done to him, and never after could he recall the injustice without weeping; that and a life of sleepless nights, salt of the sea and salt tears, that is what made his room seem so misty.

But then on this last voyage he lived to see Bobadilla's death! Yes, there is a God in Heaven. He would not even let Columbus put into harbour, this man who had thrown him into chains; and when Columbus predicted a gale, he knew better, was churlish and sailed out with his ships and his cargo of stolen gold, injustice, cruelty and lies — and was never heard of again! No, God may be long-suffering, but still a noxious beast may goad him into opening a hole in the sea.

Then Columbus felt his way along the coast of Honduras, Nicaragua, Costa Rica, new rich coasts all of them, but no way through; and then the unspeakable sufferings when he was stranded on Jamaica and lay there without ships for many, many months, sick, half-blind, without the slightest hope of rescue, starving, so that he had to juggle with an eclipse of the moon to get food from the savages; then the homeward voyage, against contrary currents and headwinds; a complete wreck when he saw Spain again after a lapse of two and a half years.

Thus the twelve years had gone by, and they had since become fourteen. And now he would be off again. That river mouth was worth attempting. That Paradise lay where the river came from was beyond a doubt, but he had no great hope of being able to sail up against the stream. He would try it. Improved ships, perhaps with oars, nothing was impossible. And then the crusade to Constantinople was urgent, it wouldn't do to lie here any longer, he had to get up. . . .

And the Admiral tries again to raise himself but only gets his head a little way from the pillow, like an insect that has been trodden into the dust and moves a leg now and again, life that will live, when flight is over for ever.

At night the Admiral is alone, and in the long sleepless hours he hears the wind howling in the doorways, a being that finds a voice and calls, the Wanderer; and he sees the waves before him, as he lies there with closed eyes, he is on board his ship listening to the wind's harp, its strings are about him as they have been all his life: I'm coming, I'm coming, is the answer in his soul; and they two, the Wanderer without in the night, the excluded but ever calling, and he within who is anchored down, they blow together, sigh, roar and pass on their way through the long black night, through many nights, many nights and long.

But at last the song has a deeper note and comes from farther away, perhaps the Admiral does not know whether he is dreaming or awake or where he really is, *when* it is; the howling wind awakes a soul within his soul, old forgotten springs burst forth, and with the wind's mournful ballad in his ears, the most mournful of ballads, he sinks in a sea of melancholy:

> The wind is sighing, O hear it wander!
> A lost soul strays through the world out yonder.
> > Oh, ho, huh. . . .

> Like children crying, alone and weary,
> Till early morning — is aught so dreary?
> > Oh, ho, huh. . . .

> As lonely children we wept full often,
> 'Mid howling blasts that a stone would soften.
> > Oh, ho, huh. . . .

> Since then we slept in so many places,
> With sighing bosoms and mournful faces.
> > Oh, ho, huh. . . .

> Then infants filled all our house with crying.
> Now we are left with the midnight sighing.
> > Oh, ho, huh. . . .

> Ah, can it be that we still may hear them,
> In howling wind can we still be near them?
> > Oh, ho, huh. . . .

> Like childbed pangs or like childless mother,
> Like tears of Fate that no time can smother.
> > Oh, ho, huh. . . .

> To pain is turned all our gladness vanished,
> 'Tis gone, but ne'er from our memory banished.
> > Oh, ho, huh. . . .

We hate the cry of a sinful action,
But life unlived is a worse distraction.
        Oh, ho, huh. . . .

The dead are witness in deep graves sleeping
That life has brought them but sighs and weeping.
        Oh, ho, huh. . . .

Beneath the stars is there aught that's lasting?
The wind alone in eternal blasting.
        Oh, ho, huh. . . .

A thousand years shall the wind still wander.
The ancient woe shall return out yonder.
        Oh, ho, huh. . . .

And then it came upon him in his last hour, at last he received his sight when the light from without no longer made impression on his eyes, in a clear inner world he saw that he *had* been there, on the happy isle he had hunted for, the isle of youth, in the days when his children were little.

Philippa!

The far-off days in Lisbon when he was a young man, with a knowledge of the sea from the time when, as a big-limbed lad, he ran away from his father's weaver's workshop and disappeared in one of the ships lying in the port of Genoa, where it had been his boyish delight to hang about, until the sea claimed him; rough years which made a man of him. Then the book which absorbed him more and more, the cosmography that he studied whenever he was ashore, while his companions were out rioting, science and cartography — the convent at Lisbon where the young mate and cartographer entered to kneel and make his devotions among the holy images, surrounded by incense and the tones of the organ and the beautiful choir of women's voices — one voice more lovely than all the rest, which he could single out as a high, clear, silvery ray from earth to heaven amid the hum of sound: Philippa's voice!

Nor was it long before he spied out, eyes and ears helping each other, from whom the voice came, a slender young maiden with narrow cheeks, black and white, the most beautiful black hair and great, dark, warm eyes, looking like a seraph when she opened her throat and with delicate parted lips sent her wonderfully pure notes swelling out into space.

But when he made discreet inquiries and learned that she was nobly born, Philippa Moñez Perestrello, daughter of the distinguished navigator and Governor, a family far, far too high for a plain mate to raise his eyes to — ah, then he was unhappy, without even the boldness to look upon himself as crossed in love; then he was a giant brought low, who might be seen by himself on lonely walks outside the town, weary with thinking, with his eyes on God's birds up in the trees, gently shaking his head; a cartographer who neglected his rolls of paper but with a heavy heart put on his best clothes, striped hose of different colours, as was the mode, combed his hair, and never, never failed to appear in the Convent of All-Hallows when the choir sang there; a man with a fine ear for music and a pair of devout blue eyes turned towards the stalls where the choir were singing.

Could it be possible? . . . passionate incredulity, hope, a resolve to die, violent weeping with cap before the eyes, wooing, days of emotion and disquiet, the dew of love all over him — the unbelievable, that *she, she would have him*, had seen him every day in the church and now told him impossible things of *her* thoughts! Philippa!

Lisbon and the blessed garden where they met and all was well and with a great sigh she gave herself into his hands, content that he was so ruddy and uncouth a giant.

Ah, she was like the damsel sung in every ballad, with a train about her feet, clad in samite and marten, trustful, with smiling eyes and her throat full of song, love all through!

And then came the happy years at Porto Santo, the island remote from the world, framed by the long, thundering, sun-illumined Atlantic rollers, clothed in the hum of solitude and roofed over at night with constellations vaunting in a sky of southern purple, full of great visions and mirages by day over the endless unknown ocean, the heavens a blaze of fire morning and evening when the sun came and went.

Here in a blissful solitude, all in all to each other, their little son was born and they were three, a new little whimper on a desert isle, a helpless life shaded by Philippa's black hair and protected by her long, tender hands.

How is it with man — is it that the greater his happiness, the more he demands from it, a fire that feeds our longing?

For we think that life is long; then looking back on it we see that a few sleeveless errands have devoured the years and that there is no turning back.

An unavoidable expedition to Guinea, to England, his head full of Perestrello's papers and charts, which Columbus had with his wife; plans of discoveries, voyages, the fourteen years of wandering, *all preparatory* — but gone was Porto Santo, Philippa resting eternally with crossed hands in the *Piedad* chapel of Carmelite Convent at Lisbon; Diego, when he saw him one time, a tall, slight boy who was annoyed when given an apple, another time a page at the court of Isabella, already heavy about the eyelids, displeased when his father appeared with his ungainly walk; Diego Columbus, whose name the other pages and their friends underlined with tar.

But never had there been greater happiness than at Porto Santo when the little boy got on his feet and for the first time in high delight ventured a step from his father's arms to his mother's knee. Never had any wound left a deeper scar than when the boy, as they were tramping to Palos, his hand in his father's and said he was hungry, and he had to beg bread for him.

There is a sound in the room as of a dog barking; the blind dying man does not know that it is the heart in his throat.

II

SOUTH OF THE SOUTH

In the winter of 1832–33 a British brig, the *Beagle*, lay off Tierra del Fuego, trying for twenty-four days to round Cape Horn from east to west, but was obliged to give it up and sailed through one of the channels among the islands which now bears the name of the ship.

More than three hundred years before Magellan had found the passage here, a little to the north, the first man to sail from the Atlantic into the Pacific, the passage Columbus sought for in vain, and the first circumnavigation of the globe. Few dreamed that it was necessary to go so far to the south, right down towards the

South Pole, to find a way through, across the Line and down into regions where the climate became raw again as in the North, but with the year turned round, opposite seasons, and with the "South," the warmth and fertility, to the northward; a world on the farther side of hope, new, but a strangely lifeless repetition of the old.

On board the *Beagle* was a young naturalist, Charles Darwin, then twenty-three; the cruise was undertaken with scientific objects and he was the zoologist of the expedition, a tall, rather lanky young gentleman, slow in his movements, beetle-browed, but with genial blue eyes, a bottle-nose which, as he tells us himself, was an annoyance to him and nearly got him rejected for the expedition — and yet it was the keenest nose aboard the *Beagle;* if the ship was the sleuth-hound of the century he was its inmost sense.

The final intellectual conclusion of the voyages of discovery, from Columbus to Cook, was drawn by him. Before becoming acquainted with primitive man, humanity had viewed itself from within in the light of sensibility, God's image; now it was forced to view itself from without, in the light of its origin; Darwin took the backward step. He was hated for it as the one who with a miscreant's hand dragged man down from his height; in reality his thoughts were directed by a profound philanthropy, he drew the despised "savage" up to the breast of civilization as the distant kinsman who stands between the white man and the beast.

When Darwin first had his great idea of the origin of species and their inner mutual kinship as different stages of the same manifestation of life, and what concrete impressions suggested it, he does not tell us, perhaps it was not clear to himself; an impulse of feeling may have been the first point of departure.

It may have come to him in an obscure form, the first subterranean subsidence in his mind, in Tierra del Fuego. Though he himself has nothing about it, his artless description of the Fuegians shows that he was deeply moved; here he was close to the animal and yet pity and sympathy bound him to these outcasts thrust into uttermost misery as to brothers who had fared badly, but still brothers; his heart bled for them, he went as far as he could to meet them, as a zoologist he voluntarily abandoned the old proud charter of humanity and came down into dangerous proximity with the quadruped, well, well, and at last he went the whole length. With his knowledge of apes and after seeing the Fuegians there was nothing else for him to do; they could not come to him, Darwin came to them.

An expansion of feeling and a recognition, the legitimation of mankind's poorest relations, not excluding those farther down either, tail and all, that was the fine step that was taken, from the voyages of discovery to the doctrine of evolution, in itself an evolution, by Darwin, whenever and in whatever connection the idea as an idea may have originated in his brain.

For those four-and-twenty days the *Beagle* lay off Cape Horn sawing backwards and forwards, a zigzag far to the south, till all land was out of sight, and back again towards the foggy, wind-swept promontory, without making way against the ceaselessly raging westerly gales, as it were a barrier of wind raised here to cut off access to the other ocean; during those days there was time for much thought and of many things.

A factor was not wanting to give exercise in humility and candour, a sufficiency of danger, isolation; here they lay in a lonely brig far outside the world's beaten track, totally forgotten by Europe, and who would ever have thought of them again, whom would it have concerned — a surveying vessel lost some time in the thirties — if they had not come home with their momentous cargo of knowledge and a new view of nature?

Nature did its best to wipe them out, fell upon the hard-pressed ship with violent squalls, washed her from stem to stern, broke seas over her on every side and weighed her down, dragged right under water, till every nail in her hull quivered and she only righted herself with the utmost difficulty, shook off the water and lay trembling and motionless like a creature struck to the very marrow by a jet. A world of semi-darkness it was down here, bitterly cold seas, rarely a gleam of sunshine through the ragged flying clouds; and when they were up under the land on their long vain beat there was the prospect of the steep and mournful antarctic coast of Tierra del Fuego, glaciers calving into the straits, wet, misty, sleety forests, foam flying from the breakers far into the inhospitable shore, and hail-showers scourging the barren mountains of the archipelago.

And here dwelt men! Now as in Magellan's time a gleam shone here and there ashore at night, a pillar of smoke in the daytime, man's ancient beacon, which told of the immeasurably rude, inhumanly hardened people who lived here in life's beginning, without hope of ever coming any farther, for they had entered one of Nature's blind alleys, they had come south of the South. Time itself was not the same here, lacking a calendar, the chilly light-forsaken morning of the ages, the glimmering misery we know when we have watched all night and day dawns in a grey, unreal, hope-abandoned twilight.

In such an ebb-tide of the soul, half-light within and without, it befell the little company on board the *Beagle* to meet the Flying Dutchman.

Unhistorical this, no written accounts of it, either from the hand of Captain Fitz Roy or Darwin or any one else on board; such things are not even talked about, they are hushed up, or one doesn't trust one's own senses after the event, putting it down to fatigue, hallucination perhaps, after days and nights of sleeplessness and hard work.

But even regarding it as improbable, a lie if you will, it gives one a cold shiver down the back to imagine the encounter. It is in the grey dawn, doubly gloomy in these latitudes which are always gloomy, and only the white foam on the crests of the waves shines with a cold light like phosphorus in a cellar. The *Beagle* is close-hauled with the wind on her starboard bow, heeling hard over, reefed almost to the yards, thumping in the seas as though lashed to her course, the Horn looming ahead through the mist like a hoary head from which thin white hairs are flying in the westerly gale; a good deal of leeway again to-day, storm and current seem to keep the ship in the same spot in spite of all the distance sailed — then it is that they sight a ship astern to leeward, the first they have seen for many weeks; suddenly she appears within the narrow horizon which lies like a grey ring in the sea — but what's that? she's sailing *against* the wind!

In a few moments the ship had passed them, for an instant a collision seemed inevitable; the strange ship came sweeping along under full sail against the wind, like a thunderstorm, rocking from side to side like a ship running free and climbing up and down over the waves; she seemed to be sailing in her own gale, directly contrary to the one that was blowing; not a very big vessel when she came nearer, a kind of barque-rigged schooner — but what kind of a schooner, what a way for a ship to behave, what sort of a rig was that?

Rapidly the vessel came near in the grey, poor light, strangely clear though the air was within the ring of leaden water; her hull was clearly seen, a curiously short hull, high fore and aft like a swing, and she moved in the water like a segment of a wheel, rolling her bow down and ploughing up the sea in a collar round it as though trying to stand on her head, checking her way and rolling up again, advancing a little on her stern with the masts pointing aft and flapping sails, sticking her nose into it again, but on she came; and before the silent crew of the *Beagle* had time to recover themselves, before any one exchanged a word, they saw the sailer run past with her broadside towards them, two or three little open gun-ports, richly carved stanchions and rails around the lofty castles fore and aft; near and yet strangely indistinct, as though the sea showed through the whole vessel, she swept by, rocking her high and narrow stern, with its carvings and little windows whose panes were like flies' eyes, a great unlighted polygonal lantern high up aft; in flying foam, up and down between the hollow waves, she was now visible, now lost again, till she ran beyond the narrow horizon on the other side up in the eye of the wind. The storm raised a squall, lashing salt drops from below and a scourge of hail from above; behind this curtain the stranger vanished, and nobody asked his companion whether it was a vision they had seen or a real vessel, whether they were living men or dead they had made out behind the taffrail of the rolling mist-grey vessel, or who was the tall man who stood on the poop with his great white head held high amid the squall. Nobody spoke of what he had seen, and afterwards it was buried in the secret chambers of the soul as a thing he kept to himself and could not communicate.

But the captain wore his ship round, gave up his obstinate attempt to force a passage south of Cape Horn, whether he had privately accepted the omen, or came to see that it was impossible.

Meeting the Phantom Ship is supposed to mean shipwreck, this did not hold good here in a literal sense; on the other hand it meant that the fatal hour had struck for the whole fundamental view of life on which the mental edifice of Europe rested.

But the *Santa Maria* continued her ghostly voyage south of Cape Horn, round the Cape of Good Hope, across the oceans, round the world, into every remote channel, past every island, as she must so long as the yearning lasts which once fitted her out to sail for the Lost Country.

A strange ship, more powerful as a memory than she ever was in reality. Of the old tub, built for trade, which was taken by chance for that memorable voyage, there may possibly be left even to-day some timbers or nails deeply buried in coral-rag on the West Indian coast where she stranded on Christmas night 1492 and broke up at once, incapable of sustaining her own weight without the water to hold her together; the coral grew about the wreck, Time's layer upon layer, and there the mortal remains of the *Santa Maria* are nobly preserved; but neither iron nor any other solid is imperishable as is the ship that passed into the ages.

A spacious ship, in all respects the image of a caravel but without bounds when seen from within, capacious and airy as our memories, our dreams, the yearning of the dead which reaches us, and our yearning which can never let them go.

And there they are, all the yearners and discoverers who craved to see the earth, the great names — nothing but vocal sounds, like an organ pealing in the soul, but true music — *Columbus, Vasco da Gama, Bartolomeu Diaz, Cabral, Balboa, Cabot, Magellan, Frobisher, Hudson, Cook!*

Storms, seas, vast new continents, mountain ranges, rivers and channels which they opened up have for ever become one with their names; the discovery of America, the sea route to India, the circumnavigation of Africa, the discovery of Brazil, the Pacific seen for the first time by the eyes of a man and named, Labrador, the whole northern passage opened; the first circumnavigation of the globe, to the everlasting memory of the unswerving, indomitable Portuguese; the thrusts up north into Arctic waters locked by ice; the navigation of the South Seas and Australia.

There they are, all the later travellers, pioneers and map-makers who gave their names to rivers and mountains, the bridegrooms of the Mississippi, the Amazon, the revealer of Chimborazo, the man who saw Ruwenzori for the first time as a cloud in the sky and who scattered the darkness of Africa, Stanley, white-haired and worn-out before his time, a man without an equal; the scent and expanse of the earth, all the trees and beasts, the varied babble of colour, all the breath of the open air surrounds you when you live their lives over again in their company.

And there are the first nameless subduers of Nature, before the days of history, who began to pry about in their surroundings and to ponder over means of making themselves their masters, the first unknown leaders on mankind's long journey out of primeval darkness; the man who tamed fire and made movement possible, the inventor of the boat and the car, the first horseman; here are those who tamed beasts and sowed corn in the earth; here are the ravenous seafarers who opened up the world with their sharp sword, the Vikings on their sea-steeds; here they are, all the seekers and strivers.

The wind, *anima*, that first conception of the soul, the earliest of impulses, from the time the air first enters the lungs of the new-born babe with a scream till he gives up the ghost in a sigh: to taste the breeze of many lands between birth and death, that was their soul, that was the rhythm of their lives.

III

AT HOME

Bᴜᴛ now, is the phantom sailor, the flying skipper, never to find peace? Is there not some condition that sets him free, if he can see it and fulfil it?

There is. The condition provides that if he can acknowledge when he is himself, he shall be redeemed. Impossible, no man can do that. That is why he has already sailed for centuries, with the prospect of being at sea till Doomsday.

But supposing the terms are that if only he is able *afterwards*, when he has sailed for such and such a time and had occasion to look back and reflect, to recognize at what moment of his life and in what respect he came nearest to realizing himself as a man — even if during all the rest of his life his desires and conduct were other than properly accorded with his nature — he shall find peace. This comes about at the moment when he returns wholly and in truth to his own nature.

And when this acknowledgment comes to him, these things shall be seen, as it were a recurrence in his soul:

The storm, which the phantom skipper always carries along

with him and always sails in, shall subside, a calm shall follow, clear weather, and with dazzled eyes the skipper shall find his altitude, the correct one at last; and then the old sea-worn vessel of eternity beneath him will spread out and become an island, securely moored in the sea, the deck will turn green and become a cool Northern plain giving off a scent of mould and grassy sweetness and covered with flowers, a cool and humble show, but here the nights are light and bees and flowers consort in the mild honeyed air of noon. Broad is the land, no mean island after all, a mighty continent, more than room enough; if the old salt-stained ocean-farer has had the elements for his world within his narrow hull, he will have room to expand and stretch himself on the firm land to which it is now transformed.

But the sails swell and become great domed clouds in the sky, roofing the summer day like a cool tent and casting slow-moving shadows upon the earth, smiling pastures, forests and lakes blended together.

The masts burst into leaf, from every knot a branch shoots out, the top expands like a banner of fresh foliage, yards and spars change into trees, there is a murmur as of a breeze of spring, a blaze of pale green and a fresh leafy scent, the wood is fully out and trembles in its cool bright garment beneath swelling white clouds and blue patches of sky, sun and shade blending like a refreshing draught among the slender Northern trees.

And behold, all the carvings and ornaments of the old ship have come to life, the stag steps out of his convolutions and stretches his legs, casts off his larva of artistry and wanders easily among the trees with rocking antlers, his muzzle nibbling at the sweet dewy leaves. The squirrel leaps out of his scroll-work, straightens his twisted limbs and flies into the colour of life, the reddest of reds, and up he darts like a flame, clutching the trunk with all his paws, rearing his lively tail and vanishing in the top of a birch. Out of the woodwork, from holes and corners of the carving, fly the birds, the hawk sailing in slow flight above the tree-tops and circling on the wing, the owl shunning the light and flapping noiselessly as a moth among the branches, losing itself in a shadow; song-birds whirring out and distributing themselves upon the hanging leafy twigs, puffing out their feathered throats in song.

But now comes the greatest marvel, the *Santa Maria's* figurehead, the Mother of God with the Child, comes to life and seats once a single ferryboat splashed across from forest to forest; of the forest nothing left but a reconstruction in the form of parks — and from the whole monster a heavy grating rumble, the interminable note of the city, rising up towards heaven.

She above hears it and looks down, wondering, clutches at her heart; and not one of those below has an inkling of the sympathy felt for them in eternity, of the pain and deep pity with which a loving heart, unable to help, follows their doings.

Who is she? The rolling Earth, what is it? Why? What is this phantom ship in eternity, abandoned entirely to itself among spheres it cannot reach, with a terrible amount of lore about them, but no help from that, just as much alone; what is it carrying, why, whither? At the very moment when the chemist is busy with his tubes and his mysterious rays, the inmost life of matter, Negroes are lying in wait for each other behind anthills with long assegais; what is their object, what is working in them both, how did it all begin, and how will it end?

Schoolboys ask questions; the rest go about their business and multiply, build or pull down, and die.

But the cosmic Being that appears over the earth as a Woman to those who can see her, she is Life, the stem of Life beyond the æther, from which the germs have come to earth; true Life, the source of Love, of which we can know no more than longing teaches us.

Have the creatures of Earth, through a long process of life and change — approximate, faulty, abandoned and taken up again — been seeking a form for an eternal, intrinsic, unknown type existing on other stars?

Ave Stella!

A NOTE ON THE TYPE

This book was set on the Linotype in Janson, a recutting made direct from the type cast from matrices (now in possession of the Stempel foundry, Frankfurt am Main) made by Anton Janson some time between 1660 and 1687.

Of Janson's origin nothing is known. He may have been a relative of Justus Janson, a printer of Danish birth who practised in Leipzig from 1614 to 1635. Some time between 1657 and 1668 Anton Janson, a punch-cutter and type-founder, bought from the Leipzig printer Johann Erich Hahn the type-foundry which had formerly been a part of the printing house of M. Friedrich Lankisch. Janson's types were first shown in a specimen sheet issued at Leipzig about 1675. Janson's successor, and perhaps his son-in-law, Johann Karl Edling, issued a specimen sheet of Janson types in 1689. His heirs sold the Janson matrices in Holland to Wolffgang Dietrich Erhardt.

The book was composed, printed, and bound by The Plimpton Press, Norwood, Massachusetts. Typography by W. A. Dwiggins.